Vitamins and Coenzymes

Vitamins and Coenzymes

By Arthur F. Wagner, *Ph.D.*

Merck Sharp & Dohme Research Laboratories
Division of Merck & Co., Inc.
Rahway, New Jersey

and

*Karl Folkers,** *Ph.D., D.Sc.*

Merck Sharp & Dohme Research Laboratories
Division of Merck & Co., Inc.
Rahway, New Jersey

* *Presently at* Stanford Research Institute, Menlo Park, California

Interscience Publishers

a division of John Wiley & Sons, New York · London · Sydney

Library of Congress Catalog Card Number: 63-22568
Printed in the United States of America

Preface

When Alfred Burger of the University of Virginia was planning the second edition of *Medicinal Chemistry*, an invitation was extended to revise or to rewrite the chapter on vitamins which was published in his first edition of 1951. This task was begun with the realization that about ten years of new literature had to be included. We finally decided that the original chapter should be completely rewritten, and managed to do so—thanks to Professor Burger's patience.

On the occasion of our visit to the offices of Interscience Publishers, Inc., Mr. Maurits Dekker and Dr. Eric S. Proskauer commented that our manuscript was almost extensive enough for a single book. We were invited to consider a modest expansion of the manuscript and particularly an updating of any timely sections for publication as a separate book. It was evident that Mr. Dekker was very interested in publishing a new book on vitamins, which he believed would have utility in several disciplines of chemistry, biology, and medicine. We agreed, although with some concern, to expand and revise the manuscript for the chapter into one for such a book.

We were admittedly concerned about the propriety of a book that would be largely based on our already published chapter in Dr. Burger's book, *Medicinal Chemistry*. However, a policy was defined which was considered equitable to all parties. As is common to the preparation of manuscripts for most books, the rapid pace of new literature and a continuing struggle to cope with new publications along with one's normal responsibilities made it necessary to so considerably update and revise the original manuscript that there could be no conflict of interest. Further, the difference in publication times would be in the order of three years or longer.

As each new vitamin was discovered and isolated, the organic chemist, as well as the biochemist and biologist, quickly lost interest in the details of these original studies because these phases are only the means to the useful end of biological activity and application in animal and human medicine. Nevertheless, students and research workers in new fields can, on occasion, greatly benefit from past knowledge of successful discoveries and isolations.

Consequently, we have felt that appropriate sections on discovery and isolation of the known vitamins and other factors should be included in this book to provide summarized and useful information for research workers studying new topics.

The organic chemistry of a structural elucidation of a vitamin is likewise of less interest as the biological aspects advance even though the structural chemistry may have some remarkable unique features. One notable exception to this declining interest in the technique and the reactions of a structural elucidation is the use of such knowledge in the study of enzymic transformations of the molecule or its metabolic degradation. Knowledge of the structural chemistry of the molecule is also helpful for research studies on biosynthesis, especially for work on the chemistry of various radioactive forms.

Summaries and commentaries on the various syntheses used to produce vitamins, coenzymes, and their structural modifications are of never-ending interest. Perhaps this continuing interest reflects the creative and productive aspects of organic synthesis.

Those, such as the authors, who have labored in several stages of vitamin research from discovery and on to isolation, structural elucidation, organic synthesis, biosynthesis, and biological role are understandably interested in summarizing the earlier phases of vitamin research to a greater extent than is found in many books. If the labor expended to include these earlier phases is really useful to research workers and students, the authors will be pleased that this effort made a contribution.

During the last few years, increasing research brought forth extensive new knowledge on the molecular structure and metabolic reactions of the coenzyme forms corresponding to several vitamins. Because of the greater chemical complexity and frequently the greater lability of the coenzymes, more arduous effort and time was required for these elucidations. The close correlations between the organic structures of the coenzyme forms and their biological activities naturally focus current organic and biochemical attention on the coenzyme structure in its complete electronic detail. Consequently, we felt it imperative to include up-to-date information on the chemistry of the coenzymes in the text for the several disciplines of readers. On this basis, our title for this book, *Vitamins and Coenzymes*, readily became apparent.

Attention should be drawn to certain aspects of this manuscript which differ considerably from our chapter in the second edition of *Medicinal Chemistry*. The chapter describing the evolution of the vitamin and coenzyme concepts and that presenting a survey on nomenclature are new. The chapter on the coenzyme Q or ubiquinone group is also new. The elucidation of coenzyme Q was in the early stages during the preparation of our manuscript for the chapter in the second edition of *Medicinal Chemistry*. Although the benzoquinone derivatives comprising the coenzyme Q group are not considered as vitamins *per se* at this time, their role in enzymic reactions easily justifies the inclusion of this new and rapidly expanding field of biochemistry in this text. The most extensive revisions and additions are found in the chapters on the water-soluble or B-complex vitamins, especially in the sections devoted to coenzyme forms and metabolic studies. A notable addition is the section on cobamide-containing coenzymes; these vitamin B_{12} coenzymes were unknown at the time our chapter appeared in the second edition of *Medicinal Chemistry*.

The arduous task of preparing this manuscript was lightened considerably by Professor Alfred Burger's permission to use our chapter in his second edition of *Medicinal Chemistry* as our starting point and with the provision of typing services by the Merck Sharp & Dohme Research Laboratories. We are grateful to both for their contribution.

Omission of material has been deliberate in some instances and undoubtedly inadvertent in others. The authors hope that their choice of material for the text is reasonable and that it will be accepted with an understanding of the problems of preparing such a text in addition to one's normal responsibilities to position and family.

Arthur F. Wagner
Karl Folkers

Rahway, New Jersey
September, 1962

Contents

CHAPTER I

Evolution of the Vitamin Theory

"No general or widespread belief in the view that an adequate diet must contain indispensable constituents other than adequate calories, a minimum of protein, and a proper mineral supply, could be said to exist till the years 1911–12."

Sir Frederick Gowland Hopkins
1929

In early times man demonstrated a belief that his food was a source of attributes in addition to those of energy and substance. At the most primitive level, he believed that strength and courage were endowed to those who ate the flesh of an especially brave animal; extension of this belief to a heroic fallen foe allegedly started the practice of cannibalism. Records of medical science from antiquity attesting to man's association of certain foods with either the cause or prevention of disease and infirmity could be considered the nebulous beginnings of a concept of essential nutrients; however, even at the beginning of the twentieth century the value of food in human nutrition was expressed solely in terms of its ability to provide the energy and basic building units necessary for life. Consequently, the nutritive value of food was defined in terms of its carbohydrate, fat, and protein content, and since these components together with water and minerals accounted for almost one hundred per cent of the mass of most foods, it was assumed that they constituted all that was necessary for normal nutrition.

The slow sequence of events leading to the "vitamine hypothesis" can be divided into three distinct chronological phases: The first phase covered empirical cures of certain diseases by dietary means; the second phase began with the discovery of experimental avitaminosis in animals, and the third was characterized by the use of synthetic diets in the quest for knowledge of the essential constituents of food. When the results of these investigations were examined collectively, the vitamin theory was advanced, and the intensive research which followed continues unabated to this day.

The first phase leading to the "vitamine hypothesis" began several hundred years ago and was characterized by the gradual recognition that the cause of diseases such as night blindness, scurvy, beriberi, and rickets, could be traced to the diet. Although the true cause, nutritional deficiency, was not suspected, these results marked the first uncertainty in the germ and infection theories of origin for these diseases. A very old example of nutritional therapy stems from the writings of ancient Greek, Roman, and Arab physicians who knew the therapeutic value of animal liver for the prevention or cure of night blindness; in most seafaring communities the value of a liver diet for the prevention of night blindness was also common knowledge. Records dealing with the prevention of scurvy go back as far as the middle of the sixteenth century when an extract of spruce needles was used to cure the disease. During the seventeenth century the East India Company successfully eliminated scurvy among its crews by providing regular adequate supplies of oranges and lemons in the diet. As early as 1720, the Austrian physician Kramer recorded that three to four ounces of orange or lime juice sufficed to cure this dreadful disease. The English physician Lind, who is also regarded as the father of modern naval hygiene, published a treatise on scurvy in 1753 which clearly demonstrated the nutritional origin of this disease, and by the beginning of the nineteenth century, the consumption of lemon juice for the prevention of scurvy was compulsory in the British Navy. Toward the end of the nineteenth century, the Japanese physician Takaki recognized the cause of beriberi in the Japanese Navy as stemming from an unbalanced rice diet, and virtually eliminated this disease by increasing the consumption of vegetables, fish, and meat and by substituting barley for rice in the diet. During this same period the use of cod liver oil for the cure and prevention of rickets was being established. In spite of this apparent preponderance of evidence for the nutritional origin of certain diseases, general acceptance of the concept was lacking.

The second phase leading to the development of the "vitamine hypothesis" began just prior to the close of the nineteenth century. This period was characterized by the discovery of diseases of nutritional origin in animals which opened the way for controlled experimental studies of nutritional causes and cures for such diseases as were common to both man and the lower animals. In 1890 Eijkman, a Dutch physician, found that fowl fed almost exclusively on polished rice developed polyneuritic symptoms bearing a marked resemblance to those of beriberi in man.

During 1890–1897 he was able to show that the disease disappeared when unmilled rice or a combination of milled rice and its bran were substituted for milled rice in the diet. Later he found that the curative agent could be extracted from the rice millings and concluded, at first, that he had isolated an antidote for a toxin present in rice. By 1907, however, both Eijkman and his collaborator Grijns abandoned the toxin theory and announced that the curative factor for beriberi was in effect different from protein, fat, or salt and yet was a substance essential for health. They further postulated that the absence of this substance from the diet was the sole cause of beriberi. In 1907 the Norwegian investigators Holst and Frölich announced the production of nutritionally induced scurvy in guinea pigs. Subsequent studies by these and other investigators revealed the identity of foods containing the antiscurvy factor.

During the third phase, investigators were searching for the essential constituents of food by using synthetic or highly refined diets in a study of animal nutrition. In 1881 the Swiss biochemist Lunin reported that animals did not survive on synthetic diets composed solely of purified fat, protein, carbohydrate, salts, and water. As a result of his observations, Lunin proposed that natural foods such as milk contain small quantities of as yet unknown substances essential to life. These results were confirmed by other workers in the ensuing years, and by 1905 the Dutch physiologist Pekelharing specifically proved that these unknown essential substances were effective in very minute quantities. By 1909 Stepp in Germany reached the same conclusion by extracting natural foods such as bread and milk. Animals fed on the extracted residues failed to survive, whereas those fed the residues fortified with the extract survived.

The year 1912 was noteworthy since the "vitamine theory," as propounded by Funk, was published, and the classic paper by Sir Frederick Gowland Hopkins on "accessory growth factors" appeared.

Casimir Funk, a young Polish biochemist, while working on the isolation of the antiberiberi factor, reviewed the existing knowledge of diseases traced to faulty nutrition. As a result of his literature survey, Funk proposed that beriberi, pellagra, rickets, and scurvy were diseases of nutritional origin which could be prevented or cured by protective factors present in natural food. He proposed the existence of four such factors: an antiberiberi factor, an antipellagra factor, an antirickets factor, and an antiscurvy factor. Since he believed that each factor was distinct and probably nitrogenous, the name "*vitamine*" was coined for them. This expression is derived from the Latin word for life, *vita*, and the chemical term *amine*. Later, when it became evident that not all "vitamines" contained nitrogen, the term became *vitamin*.

The Nobel Prize in Medicine in 1929 was awarded jointly to Christian Eijkman

"For his discovery of the antineuritic vitamin"

and to Sir Frederick Gowland Hopkins

"For his discovery of the growth-stimulating vitamins."

Eijkman's discovery that polished rice was the cause of polyneuritis in birds and beriberi in humans led to the eventual isolation of thiamine. Hopkins' experimental investigations at Cambridge were conducted with rats being grown on purified dietary mixtures to which he added test supplements of milk. Culminating publications by Hopkins in 1912 reported that milk contains substances, in extremely small quantities, which make growth possible.

Scientists in general now began to seriously consider the new class of essential nutrients. It has been said that Hopkins' papers succeeded in an area where earlier papers had failed because his experiments were carefully planned and executed, and the results were quantitatively evaluated. For the first time, it was proved that

(a) Rats consuming an amount of purified food considered more than adequate for normal growth failed to survive;

(b) Cessation of growth on purified diets occurred long before there was an effect on appetite;

(c) Compared with the amount of food necessary to produce a given weight increase on a pure basal diet, the less-pure basal diets were at least twice as effective; and

(d) "Astonishingly small amounts of the accessory factors" were sufficient to sustain growth.

The combined impact of Hopkins' "accessory growth factors" and Funk's "vitamine theory" supplied the stimulation necessary to make progress inevitable.

The integration of the "accessory factor" and "vitamine" concepts was well under way by 1915. McCollum and Davis at Wisconsin found that the rat required at least two essential growth factors, a "fat-soluble A" factor and a "water-soluble B" factor. In addition to being required as factors for normal growth, the "fat-soluble A" factor was found to cure xerophthalmia; the "water-soluble B" factor cured beriberi. A common point in the two theories was reached when the identity of the "water-soluble B" accessory factor and the "antiberiberi vitamine" was established. To emphasize this identity of the activities and to symbolize the merger of the two theories, a nomenclature was devised using elements from both theories. The "antiberiberi factor" became "vitamine B"; the "fat-soluble A" factor became "vitamine A." When it was found that the "fat-soluble A" factor did not contain an amino group, the term "vitamine" was changed to the generic term vitamin, as suggested by Drummond in 1920. At this time the antixerophthalmic factor was designated vitamin A, the antiberiberi factor vitamin B, and the antiscorbutic factor vitamin C. The adoption of this alphabetical system was popular, and as new factors were studied, successive letters of the alphabet were assigned for their designation. Some confusion was generated, however, when letters were assigned out of order so that the letter could signify an activity of the factor or an area affected by a deficiency of the factor. For example, the letter K was assigned to the blood coagulation factor by using the first letter of the Scandinavian word *koagulation*. The designation of an antidermatitis factor as vitamin H was from the German word for skin, *Haut*, and the designation of vitamin L was from the word lactation. The letters of the alphabet were also used indiscriminately to designate "unidentified factors," and it was not long before most letters of the alphabet had been used. Nomenclature was further complicated by the fact that factors originally designated as a single vitamin were in effect a mixture of vitamins. The most celebrated example is the vitamin B-complex. The antiberiberi factor, designated vitamin B, was later found to contain both a heat labile antiberiberi factor and a thermostable growth factor. The term vitamin B was abandoned, and the terms vitamin B_1 and vitamin B_2 were assigned to the antiberiberi factor and the thermostable factor, respectively. The latter also proved to be a mixture and in later literature the term vitamin B_2-complex appeared. In time the components of this mixture were isolated and designated as B-vitamins by using successive numerical subscripts.

The activities assigned to each of the fat-soluble vitamins A and K were later found to be shared by several other closely related compounds. Here too, subscripts were assigned to the letter to designate the different compounds. In such cases the letter denotes the activity or vitamin family, and the subscript designates the specific compound. With vitamin E, the term tocopherol was assigned as the generic expression, and the letters α, β, γ, . . . etc., were used to designate the specific compounds.

Many elements of the nomenclature system described above are in use today. It is becoming increasingly popular, however, to designate the physiological activity of a vitamin with an alphabetical character and to describe the vitamin itself with a generic or trivial name. In the United States for example, antiberiberi activity is often described as vitamin B_1 activity, whereas the vitamin is designated thiamine. Likewise, antipernicious anemia activity is called vitamin B_{12} activity; cyanocobalamin and aquocobalamin are generic designations of compounds possessing such activity.

From time to time since the adoption of the generic designation vitamin, other terms have been advanced to describe this class of compounds. Among the terms suggested were such names as advitant, biocatalyst, catalin, ergin, ergon, exogenous hormone, and nutrilite. Of all those suggested, only the terms vitamin, biocatalyst, and nutrilite are being used in current literature.

The term vitamin is generally used to designate *an organic compound which*

(a) *is a component of natural food but distinct from carbohydrate, fat, or protein;*

(b) *is present in normal food in extremely small concentrations;*

(c) *is essential for normal health and growth;*

(d) *when absent from the diet or not properly absorbed from the diet causes a specific deficiency disease; and*

(e) *cannot be synthesized by the host and must therefore be obtained exclusively from the diet.*

This last characteristic is the one used to distinguish a vitamin from a hormone; however, it is possible that the same compound is a vitamin in one species and a hormone in another. For example, ascorbic acid is a vitamin for man, other primates, and the guinea pig; since all other animals are able to biosynthesize the compound, it is also a hormone. On the other hand, compounds such as *meso*-inositol and *p*-aminobenzoic acid are vitamins for certain microorganisms and animals but apparently not for man. In practice, therefore, the term vitamin is applied to a compound only if the definition holds with respect to higher animals. A second term, *nutrilite*, is applied to compounds when the definition is fulfilled solely with respect to microorganisms.

The early investigators had little time to concentrate on the mechanism of vitamin activity; they did, however, assume that vitamins acted as biological catalysts. This assumption was based solely on the small concentration of vitamins necessary to produce profound biological effects. Soon an intuitive association of vitamin activity and enzyme action developed. This relationship was considered even more seriously after 1926 when the first crystalline vitamin, thiamine, and the first crystalline enzyme, urease, were isolated. These intuitive assumptions were realized in 1935 with the identification of riboflavine as an essential component of Warburg's yellow enzyme; in this same year nicotinamide, not to be discovered as a vitamin until 1937, was identified as a component essential for an enzymic conversion of glucose. In 1937 a phosphorylated derivative of thiamine was found to be essential for the enzymic decarboxylation of pyruvic acid.

Soon it became evident that vitamins participate in many of the enzyme systems fundamentally important in the chemistry of living organisms. By 1948 *meso*-inositol, pantothenic acid, and pyridoxal were identified as constituents of enzymes participating in fat, carbohydrate, or protein metabolism, and the vitamins *p*-aminobenzoic acid, biotin, cyanocobalamin, and pteroylmonoglutamic acid were known to be essential constituents for one or more enzymic reactions.

Enzymes are biological catalysts that facilitate the controlled chemical and energy transformations required for metabolism. Examples of enzymic reactions include hydrogenation and dehydrogenation, ester hydrolysis, peptide hydrolysis, cleavage of carbon-carbon bonds, synthesis of carbon-carbon bonds, and oxidation. This catalytic activity is appreciated even more when one considers the narrow temperature ranges, moderate oxidation-reduction potentials, restricted and almost neutral pH's, and high dilutions of these metabolic reactions which take place *in vivo*. Among the many properties of enzymes, however, the most striking is their specificity.

Enzymes are usually described in terms of at least two components, a protein portion and a cofactor portion. The cofactor in the simplest case is a divalent ion such as Ca^{2+}, Mg^{2+}, Zn^{2+}, Co^{2+}, or Mn^{2+}; it may also be an organic molecule, such as a vitamin derivative. The more complex enzymes contain both an inorganic and an organic cofactor. An important step in the characterization of an enzyme is its cleavage to inactive components and the subsequent recombination of these components to regenerate the original enzyme. The intact enzyme is usually referred to as the *holoenzyme*; the term enzyme is also used in some cases. The inactive protein portion is designated as the *apoenzyme*, whereas the smaller essential portion is referred to as coenzyme, prosthetic group, or activator. It has been suggested that the term *coenzyme* be reserved for the organic fragment normally not isolated with the apoenzyme, *prosthetic group* for a coenzyme moiety which is firmly attached to the apoenzyme, and *activator* for the metal ion. Vitamin derivatives known to function as cofactors include not only simple derivatives such as phosphorylated thiamine, riboflavine, and pyridoxal, but also complex derivatives such as the flavine-adenine dinucleotide from riboflavine and the di- and triphosphopyridine nucleotides from nicotinamide.

Although the role of vitamins and their fundamental enzyme systems is becoming increasingly clear, many fundamental enzyme systems remain to be identified or discovered. Consequently, a complete knowledge of the role of vitamins in the maintenance of health belongs to the future. Today vitamin deficiency disease is usually attributed to one of two basic causes. Diseases caused by *primary* or *dietary deficiency* result solely from inadequate quantities of the vitamin in the diet. Such diseases are alleviated rapidly and sometimes dramatically by improved diets or supplementary vitamin therapy. To ensure the prevention of primary vitamin deficiency, considerable effort has been spent determining the minimum daily dietary requirements for most vitamins. In the United States, a Food and Nutrition Board was appointed in 1940 to study the available evidence concerning the various dietary essentials and to formulate the dietary allowances necessary for the maintenance of good nutrition in healthy persons. The first publication of this Board appeared in 1943 under the title *Recommended Dietary Allowances*. This report has been re-evaluated periodically and revisions have appeared in 1945, 1948, 1953, and 1958. Other countries have adopted a similar policy with subtle differences leading to different recommendations. For example, the recommended allowances of the United States report are broad enough to provide for the maintenance of good nutrition in all normal persons, whereas the Canadian recommendations consider the minimum requirements and establish a base line below which the maintenance of health cannot be assured. The British, on the other hand, project a standard aimed at the nutrition of the average person.

There are vitamin deficiencies, however, even under conditions where the diet would normally be considered adequate by most standards. Such deficiencies, usually referred to as *secondary* or *conditioned deficiencies*, arise from metabolic stress or organic disease. The increased metabolic demands during pregnancy is a prime example of a metabolic stress state requiring extra vitamin therapy. The stress placed on carbohydrate metabolism in the alcoholic is another example of a condition requiring more than normal daily vitamin consumption. The usual treatment in such stress states requires the administration of large or therapeutic concentrations of vitamins. Another important cause of conditioned deficiency results from organic disease. In these cases an organic defect in the host results in decreased absorption of the vitamin from the diet. Pernicious anemia is considered a conditioned vitamin B_{12} deficiency because a lack of gastric intrinsic factor severely limits the absorption of the vitamin from the gastrointestinal tract. Another example of this type is the vitamin K deficiency caused by inadequate supplies of bile. Vitamin therapy in such cases is usually in the form of parenteral or intravenous injection.

Large doses of certain vitamins have also been shown to have pharmacologic effects which have not been explained on the basis of nutrition.

These results have led to successful therapy in a variety of cases of unknown etiology. In effect, we are at the threshold of knowledge concerning vitamin function and the effects of vitamin therapy. Much research is needed before the story is complete. Today there are three distinct areas of nutritional interest which may be conveniently classified as (a) the nutrition of the normal individual; (b) the nutrition of the diseased individual; and (c) the nutrition of the individual under physiologic stress.

Timely research fields include vitamins and nutrition in relation to infection and immunity, in relation to dental caries, and in relation to the aged.

Have all the vitamins been discovered? From all indications in the extensive recent and current publications in the scientific literature dealing with the purification and effects of "unidentified factors," the answer appears to be "no." It is from such studies that new vitamins may be recognized and characterized.

Sources and Recommended Reading

1. L. J. Harris, *Vitamins in Theory and Practice*, University Press, Cambridge, England, 1955.
2. L. J. Harris, *Vitamins, A Digest of Current Knowledge*, Churchill, London, 1951.
3. E. V. McCollum, *A History of Nutrition*, Houghton Mifflin, Boston, 1957.
4. J. Needham, *Hopkins and Biochemistry*, Heffer and Sons, Cambridge, England, 1949.
5. J. B. Nielands and P. K. Stumpf, *Outlines of Enzyme Chemistry*, Wiley, N.Y., 1955.
6. R. J. Williams, R. E. Eakin, E. Beerstecher, Jr., and W. Shive, *The Biochemistry of B Vitamins*, Reinhold, N.Y., 1950.
7. Food and Nutrition Board, *Recommended Dietary Allowances*, Revised 1958, Natl. Acad. Sci. Natl. Res. Council Publication No. 589.

CHAPTER II

Compilation of Vitamin Activities and Nomenclature

In the preceding chapter it was shown that the classification and nomenclature of vitamins were conveniently developed along the lines of activity or function, rather than on the basis of chemical structure. Increasing effort in the field and the concomitant participation of several specialized scientific disciplines made it increasingly evident that a precise classification and nomenclature system be adopted. Although not universally accepted, a vitamin is presently defined in terms of both its activity and its chemical structure. The nomenclature used in this and succeeding chapters is in accord with the definitive rules for the nomenclature of vitamins which are recorded in the IUPAC Rules of 1957.(1) The following list of activities and factors derived from Cheldelin's classification(2) affords a useful summary of accepted, duplicate, premature, and obsolete designations of vitamins and vitamin activities encountered to date.

Vitamin A	An activity preventing xerophthalmia, nyctalopia, and hemeralopia. Also essential for the maintenance of normal epithelial tissue and for growth. The most common compounds are retinol, retinal, retinoic acid, and 3-dehydroretinol. The activity is also shared by a group of closely related carotenoids. Obsolete designations include vitamin A_1, vitamin A_2, retinene, fat-soluble A, biosterol, and ophthalamin.
p-Aminobenzoic Acid	An essential microbial growth factor. Reported at one time to promote chick growth and prevent achromotrichia in the rat.

1. IUPAC Commission on the Nomenclature of Biological Chemistry, *J. Am. Chem. Soc.*, *82*, 5581 (1960).
2. V. H. Cheldelin, *Nutr. Revs.*, *9*, 289 (1951).

Vitamin B	Original antiberiberi activity. Now known as a mixture of activities and designated vitamin-B complex.
Vitamin B_1	Antiberiberi or antineuritic activity. The compound is designated thiamine in the United States and aneurine in Great Britain. Obsolete designations include polyneuramin, oryzamin, and vitamin F.
Vitamin B_2	An activity that stimulates growth and prevents certain ocular and orogenital irregularities. The compound is designated riboflavine. Obsolete designations include vitamin G, lactoflavin, ovoflavin, hepatoflavin, uroflavin, and lyochrome.
Vitamin B_3	A pellagra-preventive activity in the chick and a growth-promoting factor in the pigeon. Identical with pantothenic acid.
Vitamin B_4	An activity preventing muscular weakness in rats and chicks and believed to be a mixture of arginine and glycine or riboflavine and pyridoxol.
Vitamin B_5	A growth-stimulating activity in pigeons and probably identical with nicotinic acid.
Vitamin B_6	An activity promoting growth and preventing acrodynia, anemia, and epileptiform convulsions in animals. A deficiency is related to atherosclerosis and dental caries in the monkey. The deficiency syndrome in man is characterized by skin lesions and a mild but definite lymphocytopenia. It has also been administered for the suppression of dental caries and for the alleviation of nausea and vomiting in pregnant humans. The term pyridoxine designates the group of naturally occurring pyridine derivatives with vitamin B_6 activity. This activity is shared by the structurally related compounds, pyridoxol,

	pyridoxal, and pyridoxamine. Obsolete designations include yeast eluate factor, factor I, factor Y, vitamin H, and adermin.
Vitamin B_7	An activity said to prevent digestive disturbances in the pigeon. Probably is a mixture. Also is known as vitamin I.
Vitamin B_8	Adenylic acid which is no longer classified as a vitamin.
Vitamin B_9	Designation was apparently never used.
Vitamin B_{10}	An activity promoting growth and feathering in the chick; probably is a mixture of pteroylmonoglutamic acid and cyanocobalamin.
Vitamin B_{11}	An activity promoting growth and feathering in the chick; probably is a mixture of pteroylmonoglutamic acid and cyanocobalamin.
Vitamin B_{12}	An activity preventing pernicious anemia in man and promoting growth in animals. The activity is shared by the structurally related compounds cyanocobalamin and aquocobalamin. Obsolete designations include animal protein factor, factor X, zoopherin, and erythrotin.
Vitamin B_{12a}	Aquocobalamin.
Vitamin B_{12b}	Aquocobalamin.
Vitamin B_{12c}	Nitritocobalamin.
Vitamin B_{12d}	Aquocobalamin.
Vitamin B_{13}	Unconfirmed.
Vitamin B_{14}	Unconfirmed.
Vitamin B_{15}	Unconfirmed.
Vitamin B_c	An activity preventing nutritional anemia in the chick; now known to be pteroylmonoglutamic acid.

Vitamin B_p	An activity preventing perosis in the chick; can be replaced by choline and manganese.
Vitamin B_t	An activity promoting insect growth. The active component was identified as carnitine.
Vitamin B_x	An activity associated with both pantothenic acid and *p*-aminobenzoic acid.
Biotin	A compound preventing "egg white injury" in the rat. A microbial growth factor. Obsolete designations include bios IIB, vitamin H, factor X, and coenzyme R.
Vitamin C	An activity preventing scurvy. The compound is designated ascorbic acid. Obsolete designations include hexuronic acid, antiscorbutic vitamin, and cevitamic acid.
Vitamin C_2	An antipneumonia activity which was also designated vitamin J.
Choline	A compound participating in biochemical transmethylation.
Citrovorum Factor	N^5-Formyl-5,6,7,8-tetrahydropteroylmonoglutamic acid. A naturally occurring but metabolically unimportant coenzyme form of pteroylmonoglutamic acid. The synthetically derived compound was designated folinic acid-SF or leucovorin.
Vitamin D	An activity preventing rickets in man. The activity is shared by a group of about eight structurally related 9,10-*seco* steroids which are designated as calciferols. Most common compounds are ergocalciferol and cholecalciferol. Obsolete designations include vitamin D_2, vitamin D_3, rachitamin, rachitasterol, and antirachitic vitamin.
Vitamin E	An activity preventing nutritional muscular dystrophy in animals and sterility in the

	rat. The activity is shared by eight chromanols, commonly referred to as tocopherols. Most common compounds are α-, β-, and γ-tocopherols. Obsolete designations include factor X and antisterility vitamin.
Vitamin F	Designates the activity of the essential fatty acids, especially as reflected in preventing atherosclerosis in animals. The term is especially popular in Europe. It is also an abandoned term for thiamine activity.
Folic Acid	Designates pteroylmonoglutamic acid and a group of closely related derivatives that promote growth in animals and produce a hematological response in man.
Vitamin G	An obsolete designation for riboflavine activity.
Vitamin H	An obsolete term for biotin activity.
Vitamin I	A mixture; also designated vitamin B_7.
Vitamin J	A postulated antipneumonia principle which was also designated vitamin C_2.
Vitamin K	An activity preventing hypoprothrombinemic hemorrhage. The activity is shared by a group of closely related naphthoquinones; the most widely known are vitamin $K_{1(20)}$ (phylloquinone), vitamin $K_{2(35)}$, vitamin $K_{2(30)}$ (farnoquinone), phthiocol, and menadione. Obsolete designations include vitamin K_1, vitamin K_2, prothrombin factor, *koagulations vitamin*, and antihemorrhagic vitamin.
Vitamin L_1	A liver filtrate activity believed to be necessary for lactation. The compound is probably related to anthranilic acid.
Vitamin L_2	A yeast filtrate activity believed to be necessary for lactation. The compound is probably related to adenosine.

Lipoic Acid	Participates in enzymic oxidative decarboxylation at a stage between thiamine pyrophosphate and coenzyme A mediation. Also referred to as α-lipoic acid and 6-thioctic acid. Obsolete designations include acetate-replacing factor and POF.
Vitamin M	An activity preventing nutritional anemia and leucopenia in the monkey. The compound is pteroylmonoglutamic acid.
Vitamin N	An obsolete term for a mixture believed to inhibit cancer.
Nicotinic Acid	The pellagra preventive factor. Obsolete designations include niacin, PP factor, vitamin PP, and pellagramine.
Nicotinamide	The pellagra-preventive factor. Obsolete designations include niacinamide and vitamin PP.
Vitamin P	An activity believed necessary to reduce capillary fragility. The activity is related to Citrin which is no longer considered a vitamin.
Pantothenic Acid	A compound preventing achromotrichia in the rat and dermatitis in the chick. Also referred to as vitamin B_3. Obsolete designations include chick A.P. factor, liver filtrate factor, and yeast filtrate factor.
Pteroylmonoglutamic Acid	A compound producing a hematological response in man and stimulating growth in animals. Related compounds are pteroyltriglutamic acid and pteroylheptaglutamic acid. Obsolete designations include Norit eluate factor, liver *Lactobacillus casei* factor, vitamin M, factor U, and vitamin B_c. The triglutamate was formerly designated fermentation *L. casei* factor and the heptaglutamate, vitamin B_c conjugate.

Coenzyme Q	An activity related to electron transport and shared by a group of related 2,3-dimethoxy-5-methyl-6-polyisoprenoid-1,4-benzoquinones. The five compounds in the series are indicated as Q_6–Q_{10} where the subscript designates the number of isoprenoid units in the 6-substituent. The compounds are also referred to as ubiquinones with a parenthetical numerical designation indicating the total number of carbon atoms in the 6-substituent as in ubiquinone (30) and ubiquinone (50).
Vitamin R	An activity promoting bacterial growth and apparently related to folic acid activity.
Vitamin S	A chick growth activity related to the peptide streptogenin. The term was also applied to a bacterial growth activity probably due to biotin.
Vitamin T	A group of activities isolated from termites, yeasts, or molds and reported to improve protein assimilation in the rat.
Vitamin U	An activity from cabbage which reportedly cures ulcers. It was also applied to tissue preparations which promote bacterial growth. The latter effect is probably due to the presence of one of the folic acid activities.
Vitamin V	An activity from tissue which promotes bacterial growth. The activity is probably due to the nicotinic acid-containing coenzyme, diphosphopyridine nucleotide.

CHAPTER III

Thiamine and Cocarboxylase

1. Introduction

Recognition of vitamin B_1 activity dates back to 1890 when it was observed that hens fed exclusively on polished rice developed polyneuritic symptoms suggestive of those common to beriberi patients. Studies during the period 1890–1897 showed that the paralysis that was induced by feeding polished rice could be cured by adding rice bran to the diet. At first it was assumed that milling removed a protective factor necessary for the neutralization of a toxin in polished rice, but this concept was abandoned and nutritional deficiency became suspect as the cause of the disease.

In the ensuing years, efforts were made to isolate the active principle from rice bran, and by 1906 active concentrates of the factor were obtained by extracting rice bran with water or aqueous alcohol. The extract was effective in curing beriberi, and the thermolabile nature of the active principle was demonstrated. A low-order molecular weight was predicted for the active factor by virtue of its ready diffusion through membranes, and it was shown that the substance was distinct from protein, fat, carbohydrate, and minerals. From these observations, it appeared that the curative factor for beriberi was a new essential dietary factor.

2. Isolation

The 1920's were marked by many attempts to isolate this important factor. Although several workers succeeded in obtaining highly active concentrates, it was not until 1926 that the isolation of a crystalline hydrochloride of the active principle was reported.[(1)] The sensitivity of this procedure to minor variations coupled with the lability of the vitamin was such that several years elapsed before the substance was isolated in other laboratories. This initial success has been attributed to the application of fuller's earth adsorption of the factor from concentrates and the development of a rapid reliable assay for the determination of antineuritic activity.

1. B. C. P. Jansen and W. F. Donath, *Proc. K. Akad. Wetensch., Amsterdam, 29*, 1390 (1926); *Chem. Weekblad., 23*, 201 (1926).

Using small rice birds, the antineuritic activity of a given fraction was determined in a ten-day period.

The vitamin was later isolated from yeast, wheat germ, and rice bran by other workers. Several improvements in the method of isolation were necessary, however, before a sufficient quantity of the vitamin could be made available for structure elucidation. By 1934 an improved process was reported for the isolation of thiamine from rice bran which yielded 5 g. of thiamine hydrochloride from each ton of rice bran processed.[2] The process had been developed to a remarkable efficiency; the yield was about 25%.

This method, like earlier ones, employed aqueous extraction to separate the active principle from rice polishings and fuller's earth adsorption to remove the factor from the aqueous extract. The vitamin was eluted from the adsorbent more efficiently by substituting aqueous quinine sulfate for barium hydroxide in the elution step. Many accompanying impurities were then benzoylated and removed by extraction and filtration. At this stage, the vitamin was precipitated from aqueous solution as a phosphotungstate; the phosphotungstate was decomposed, and the vitamin was reprecipitated as a gold trichloride complex. After decomposition of the complex by molecular silver, the vitamin was extracted with water and was precipitated from aqueous ethanol as a hydrochloride.

3. Structure Determination

The structure of thiamine, elucidated in the mid-thirties, was established as 3-(4-amino-2-methyl-5-pyrimidinylmethyl)-5-(β-hydroxyethyl)-4-methylthiazolium chloride hydrochloride (**1**).[3] The key reaction in the structure determination (Fig. 1) is the unique and quantitative cleavage of thiamine to the pyrimidine (**2**) and the thiazole (**3**) in neutral sodium sulfite solution at room temperature.

The 4-amino-2-methyl-5-pyrimidinylmethylene moiety of thiamine was established as follows. Acid hydrolysis of the pyrimidine (**2**) yielded ammonia and the hydroxypyrimidine (**4**). The presence of a sulfonic acid group in both the pyrimidine (**2**) and (**4**) was demonstrated by the formation of sulfuric acid after treating each with water at 200° and by the formation of sulfurous acid after treating each with alkali. The elemental analysis and ultraviolet absorption spectrum of both (**2**) and (**4**) suggested

2. R. R. Williams, R. E. Waterman, and J. C. Keresztesy, *J. Am. Chem. Soc.*, *56*, 1187 (1934).
3. R. R. Williams and T. D. Spies, *Vitamin B_1*, Macmillan, N.Y., 1938.

that each contained a pyrimidine nucleus. Treatment of the pyrimidine (**2**) with sodium in liquid ammonia gave 4-amino-2,5-dimethylpyrimidine (**5**); the structure of this degradation product and that of the hydroxypyrimidine (4) were proved by synthesis. On the basis of these data, the structure of the first cleavage product (**2**) of thiamine was shown to be 4-amino-2-methylpyrimidinyl-5-methanesulfonic acid.

The structure of the thiazole moiety of thiamine was established as 5-(β-hydroxyethyl)-4-methylthiazole. It was apparent that the thiazole (**3**) contained a hydroxyl group since acylation of the compound yielded a derivative that retained the basic properties of a thiazole; in addition,

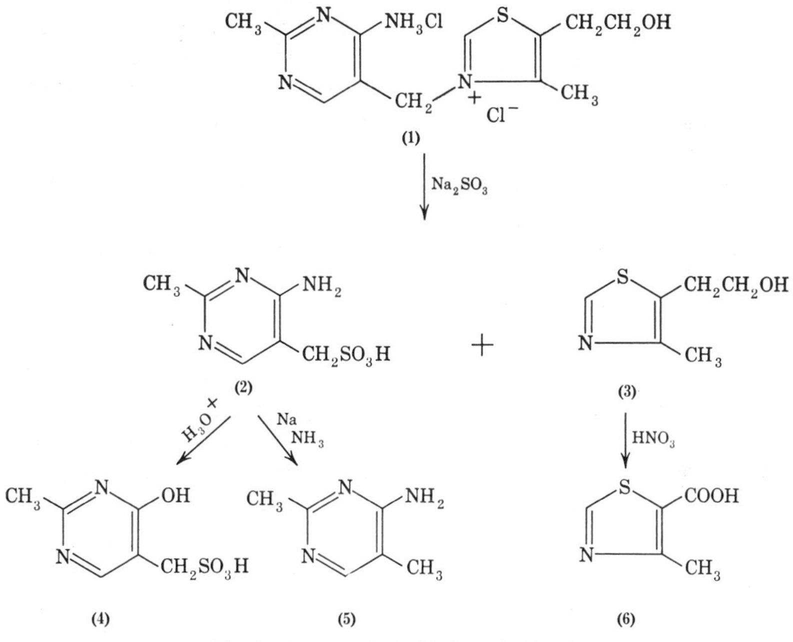

Fig. 1. Structural elucidation of thiamine.

treatment of the thiazole (**3**) with hydrochloric acid at 150° resulted in the displacement of hydroxyl by halogen. Oxidation of the thiazole (**3**) with nitric acid resulted in the loss of one carbon atom and yielded the known compound 4-methylthiazole-5-carboxylic acid (**6**). On the basis of these observations, the thiazole (**3**) contained either an α- or β-hydroxyethyl substituent at the 5-position. A β-hydroxyethyl substituent was formulated on the basis of (a) a negative iodoform test with the thiazole (**3**) and (b) the optical inactivity of thiamine.

Attachment of the thiazole to the 5-methylene group of the pyrimidine moiety was established from the position of the sulfonic acid group in the pyrimidine (**2**). The linkage of the 5-pyrimidinylmethylene moiety to the nitrogen atom of the thiazole ring was established by the then-unusual behavior of both thiamine hydrochloride and 5-(β-hydroxyethyl)-4-methyl-thiazole methiodide on titration with alkali. This behavior common to both compounds was attributed to a quaternary nitrogen atom in the thiazole ring and led to the formulation of thiamine as the quaternary ammonium salt (**1**).

4. Synthesis

Thiamine has been synthesized in two basic ways. In one method each moiety is synthesized separately and then the two nuclei are condensed; in the second method one moiety is synthesized with an appropriate side chain conducive to the formation of the remaining structure. Although the final product is usually obtained as the chloride hydrochloride in either case, the mononitrate of thiamine is reportedly more stable and is especially recommended for food enrichment.[4,5]

The first synthesis (Fig. 2) of thiamine to be reported demonstrates the two-nuclei approach[6] and is the basis of a method used today for the commercial manufacture of this vitamin.

The pyrimidine portion of the molecule was synthesized starting with condensation between acetamidine (**7**) and the sodio derivative of ethyl β-ethoxy-α-formylpropionate (**8**).[6] The hydroxyl group of the resulting pyrimidine (**9**) was displaced by halogen yielding the 4-chloropyrimidine (**10**) which was converted to the 4-aminopyrimidine (**11**). The ethoxyl group of (**11**) was cleaved with hydrobromic acid to yield the hydrobromide of 4-amino-5-bromomethyl-2-methylpyrimidine (**12**).

The thiazole moiety was synthesized starting with the condensation of ethyl acetoacetate and ethylene oxide.[7] The resulting α-acetyl-γ-butyro-lactone (**13**) was chlorinated to α-acetyl-α-chloro-γ-butyrolactone (**14**) which in turn was hydrolyzed and decarboxylated to yield 3-acetyl-3-chloropropanol (**15**). Condensation of the acetylchloropropanol (**15**) with thioformamide gave 5-(β-hydroxyethyl)-4-methylthiazole (**3**).

The third and final stage of the synthesis was accomplished by heating a mixture of equivalent amounts of 4-amino-5-bromomethyl-2-methylpyrim-idine hydrobromide (**12**) and 5-(β-hydroxyethyl)-4-methylthiazole (**3**).

4. T. J. Macek, B. A. Feller, and E. J. Hanus, *J. Am. Pharm. Assoc.*, *39*, 365 (1950).
5. C. M. Hollenbeck and H. G. Obermeyer, *Cereal Chem.*, *29*, 82 (1952).
6. R. R. Williams and J. K. Cline, *J. Am. Chem. Soc.*, *58*, 1504 (1936).
7. E. R. Buchman, *J. Am. Chem. Soc.*, *58*, 1803 (1936).

a. The Pyrimidine Fragment.[6]

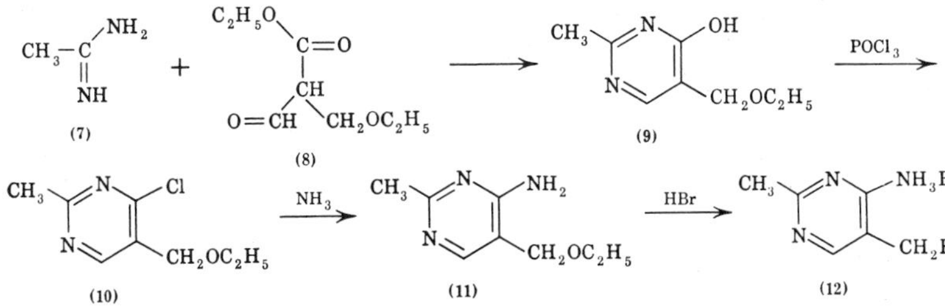

$CH_3-C(=NH)NH_2$ (7) + $C_2H_5O-C(=O)-CH(CH=O)CH_2OC_2H_5$ (8) → CH_3, N, OH, N, $CH_2OC_2H_5$ (9) $\xrightarrow{POCl_3}$

CH_3, N, Cl, N, $CH_2OC_2H_5$ (10) $\xrightarrow{NH_3}$ CH_3, N, NH_2, N, $CH_2OC_2H_5$ (11) $\xrightarrow{HBr}$ CH_3, N, NH_3Br, N, CH_2Br (12)

b. The Thiazole Fragment.[7]

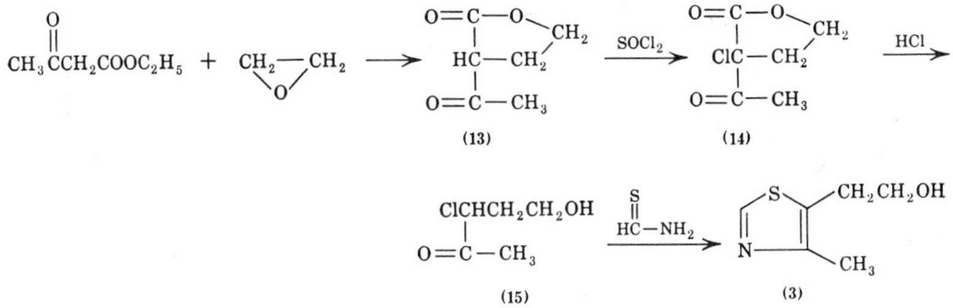

$CH_3\overset{O}{\overset{\|}{C}}CH_2COOC_2H_5$ + CH_2—CH_2 (O) → $O=C-O-CH_2$, $HC-CH_2$, $O=C-CH_3$ (13) $\xrightarrow{SOCl_2}$ $O=C-O-CH_2$, $ClC-CH_2$, $O=C-CH_3$ (14) $\xrightarrow{HCl}$

$ClCHCH_2CH_2OH$, $O=C-CH_3$ (15) $\xrightarrow{HC(=S)-NH_2}$ S, CH_2CH_2OH, N, CH_3 (3)

c. Thiamine.

(12) + (3) $\xrightarrow{\Delta}$ CH_3, N, NH_3Br, N, CH_2, S, CH_2CH_2OH, $\overset{+}{N}$, CH_3, Br^- (16) $\xrightarrow{AgCl}$ Thiamine (1)

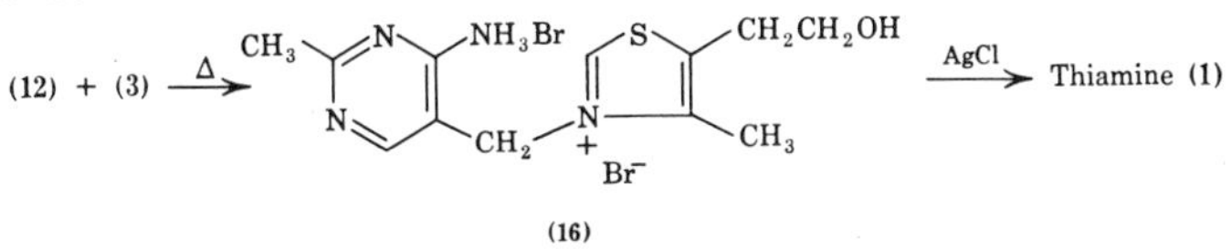

Fig. 2. Synthesis of thiamine by the condensation of its moieties.[6]

The resulting thiamine bromide hydrobromide (**16**) was converted to thiamine chloride hydrochloride (**1**) by treating an aqueous solution of (**16**) with silver chloride.

A synthesis of thiamine demonstrating the second approach (Fig. 3) begins with the condensation of ethyl α-ethoxymethylene-α-cyanoacetate

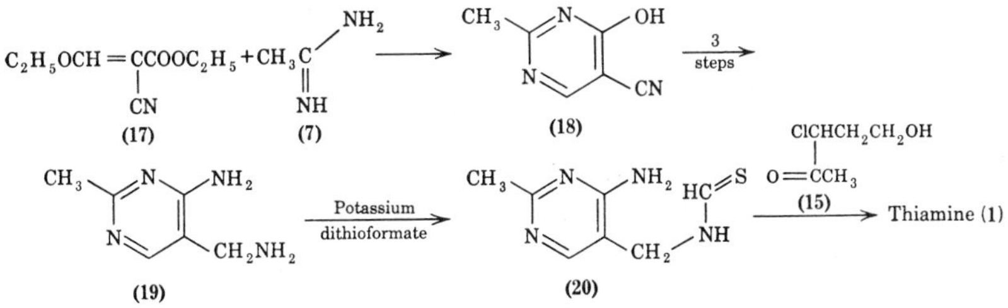

$C_2H_5OCH=C(CN)COOC_2H_5$ (17) + $CH_3C(=NH)NH_2$ (7) → CH_3, N, OH, N, CN (18) $\xrightarrow{3\ steps}$

CH_3, N, NH_2, N, CH_2NH_2 (19) $\xrightarrow{\text{Potassium dithioformate}}$ CH_3, N, NH_2, N, CH_2, $HC(=S)-NH$ (20) $\xrightarrow{ClCHCH_2CH_2OH,\ O=CCH_3\ (15)}$ Thiamine (1)

Fig. 3. Synthesis of thiamine from a pyrimidine containing a thiazole-precursor substituent.[8]

(**17**) and acetamidine (**7**).[8] The resulting 5-cyano-4-hydroxy-2-methylpyrimidine (**18**) was converted in three steps to 4-amino-5-aminomethyl-2-methylpyrimidine (**19**), which after treatment with potassium dithioformate yielded 4-amino-2-methyl-5-thioformamidomethylpyrimidine (**20**). The formamido substituent at the 5-position of (**20**) is the thiazole ring precursor. Condensation of the 5-thioformamidomethylpyrimidine (**20**) with 3-acetyl-3-chloropropanol (**15**) completed the formation of the thiazole moiety yielding thiamine (**1**).

5. Reactions

The reactions of thiamine with alkali (Fig. 4), studied extensively since 1935,[9–15] were recently reviewed and reexamined experimentally.[16] When thiamine, depicted in this instance as the cation (**21**), reacts slowly with alkali (e.g., titration) it forms the *pseudo*-base (**22**); the latter is never present in high concentration in thiamine solutions because the thiazole ring is easily opened yielding the colorless thiol form (**23**). Oxidation of this thiol form gives the corresponding dimer, thiamine disulfide.

If thiamine is added to media at a pH of 11 or higher, it is converted to the yellow thiol form (**25**) which has been isolated and characterized as the sodium salt. The color of this compound fades rapidly in aqueous media and is only stable for an hour or so in methanol solution; decay is attributed to the conversion of the yellow form (**25**) to the colorless thiol form (**23**). The reaction of thiamine with alkali giving the yellow thiol (**25**) is completely and rapidly reversible and requires the participation of two protons.

A form of thiamine intermediate between the cation (**21**) and the yellow thiol form (**25**) has also been isolated from methanol solutions of thiamine hydrochloride treated with two equivalents of sodium ethoxide. This form, isolated as a white crystalline compound, has been characterized

8. A. R. Todd and F. Bergel, *J. Chem. Soc.*, 364 (1937).
9. G. Barger, F. Bergel, and A. R. Todd, *Ber.*, *68*, 2257 (1935).
10. R. Kuhn, T. Wagner-Jauregg, F. W. Van Klaveren, and H. Vetter, *Z. Physiol. Chem.*, *234*, 196 (1935).
11. R. R. Williams and A. E. Ruehle, *J. Am. Chem. Soc.*, *57*, 1856 (1935).
12. E. R. Buchman, R. R. Williams, and J. C. Keresztesy, *J. Am. Chem. Soc.*, *57*, 1849 (1935).
13. J. G. Baxter and C. D. Robeson, *J. Am. Chem. Soc.*, *64*, 2407 (1942).
14. O. Zima and R. R. Williams, *Ber.*, *73*, 941 (1950).
15. P. Sykes and A. R. Todd, *J. Chem. Soc.*, 534 (1951).
16. G. D. Maier and D. E. Metzler, *J. Am. Chem. Soc.*, *79*, 4386 (1957).

as the cyclic compound (**24**). When this cyclic form is dissolved in water, it disproportionates completely, but does so only partially in methanol giving a mixture of the cation (**21**) and yellow (**25**) forms.

Both the cyclic form (**24**) and the yellow form (**25**) of thiamine are oxidized to thiochrome (**26**), a compound exhibiting an intense blue

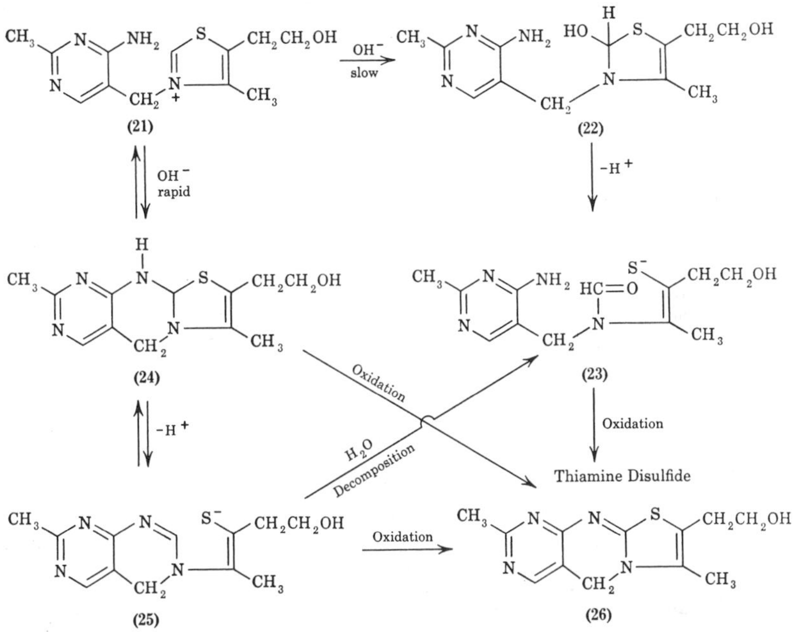

Fig. 4. Structures of thiamine in alkali.[16]

fluorescence; this property observed in early studies of thiamine oxidation[9,10] serves as the basis for the chemical assay for thiamine. In more recent studies, it was shown that thiochrome is not formed if alkaline thiamine solutions are allowed to stand long enough for the yellow form of thiamine to disappear before the oxidizing agent is added.[16] This observation supports an earlier view that the yellow thiol form of thiamine is the thiochrome precursor.[15]

6. Metabolic Role

A. Cocarboxylase

1. DISCOVERY AND ISOLATION. Prior to 1911 all known decarboxylations in biological systems were attributed to the action of putrefactive bacteria. In that year, however, a new era in biological chemistry began with the discovery of a purely enzymic cleavage of a carbon-carbon bond in the

decarboxylation of pyruvic acid to acetaldehyde by yeast.[17] The responsible component in yeast was designated carboxylase, and by 1914 the enzymic decarboxylation of an α-keto acid to the corresponding aldehyde proved to be a general reaction for a large number of α-keto acid substrates.[18,19] Twenty years later this holoenzyme was partially characterized by demonstrating its dependence for activity on divalent magnesium and by liberating a thermostable coenzyme on treatment with an aqueous alkaline phosphate solution.[20–22] The coenzyme was designated cocarboxylase. In 1937 pure crystalline cocarboxylase was isolated using the reactivation of carboxylase apoenzyme as an assay to follow purification.[23]

2. STRUCTURE DETERMINATION. Cocarboxylase was characterized as thiamine pyrophosphate (**27**) from the following reactions.[23] Enzymic

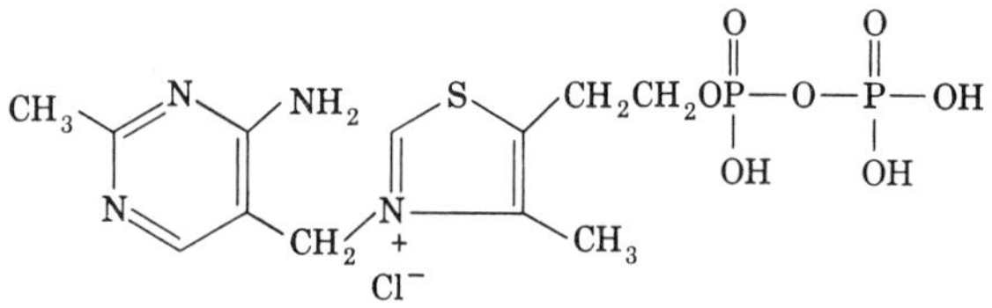

(27)

cleavage of cocarboxylase by a phosphatase yielded two equivalents of phosphoric acid and one equivalent of thiamine. The exact nature of the diphospho function was established as pyrophosphate by titration and hydrolysis; titration of cocarboxylase with alkali showed that the molecule contained one strongly acidic group with an approximate pKa of 3.5 and two weakly acidic groups with ionization constants ranging between 3.5 and 8.5. If the basic nature of both the thiazolium nitrogen atom and the pyrimidine moiety are taken into account, a di-phosphoric acid derivative of thiamine would presumably contain one strongly acidic and three weakly acidic groups. A pyrophosphoric acid ester would have only one strongly acidic group and two weakly acidic groups, and since this interpretation reflected the actual titration data, the phospho function was assumed to be pyrophosphate. This assumption was confirmed by the rate of acid hydrolysis of cocarboxylase and by the identification of inorganic pyrophosphate after alkaline hydrolysis.

The pyrophosphate function was shown to be in the thiazole moiety since

17. C. Neuberg and L. Karczag, *Biochem. Z.*, *36*, 68, 76 (1911).
18. C. Neuberg and L. Karczag, *Biochem. Z.*, *37*, 170 (1911).
19. C. Neuberg and W. Peterson, *Biochem. Z.*, *67*, 32 (1914).
20. E. Auhagen, *Z. Physiol. Chem.*, *204*, 149 (1932).
21. E. Auhagen, *Z. Physiol. Chem.*, *209*, 20 (1932).
22. E. Auhagen, *Biochem. Z.*, *258*, 330 (1933).
23. K. Lohmann and P. Schuster, *Biochem. Z.*, *294*, 188 (1937).

sodium sulfite cleavage of the coenzyme yielded a phosphorus-free pyrimidine and a diphosphothiazole.

The structure of the coenzyme was confirmed by demonstrating cocarboxylase activity in reaction mixtures obtained after treating thiamine with two molar equivalents of phosphorus oxychloride.[24]

3. SYNTHESIS. The first synthesis of the pure cofactor was detailed.[25] Thiamine was phosphorylated with sodium pyrophosphate in orthophosphoric acid solution, and the product was isolated as the chloride **(27)**. In the course of converting the phosphorylated product to the chloride, however, a considerable portion of the pyrophosphate ester was hydrolyzed to the monophosphate. The reaction mixture, therefore, required purification by precipitation of the product first as the silver salt and then as the phosphotungstate. A subsequent modification of this process[26] resulted in improved yields when precipitation of the chloride was avoided and the coenzyme was isolated as the thiazolium phosphate.

An improved synthesis consists in treating the 5-(β-bromoethyl) analog of thiamine bromide **(28)** with silver pyrophosphate in phosphoric acid

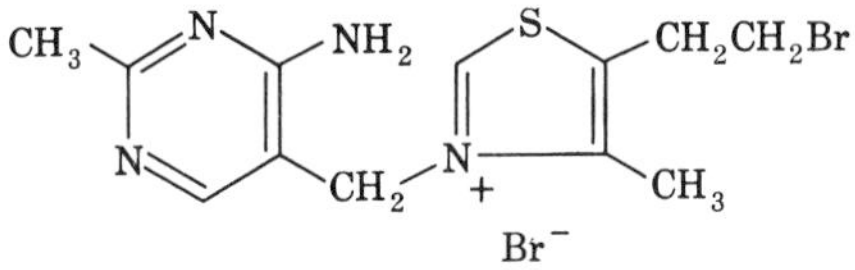

(28)

solution at 100°.[27] Pure cocarboxylase was obtained after precipitation of the product as the silver salt and then as the phosphotungstate.

4. HOLOENZYME. The holoenzyme carboxylase was shown to contain one gram atom of divalent magnesium and one mole of thiamine for each 75,000 g. of protein.[28,29] The apoenzyme was reactivated by Mg^{2+} and thiamine pyrophosphate, but not by thiamine or monophosphothiamine. Other divalent ions such as Cd^{2+}, Co^{2+}, Fe^{2+}, Mn^{2+}, and Zn^{2+} can replace Mg^{2+} as activators. The inhibition of apoenzyme activation by molecules containing a pyrophosphate group has been interpreted as an indication that the coenzyme is at least partially bound to the apoenzyme through the pyrophosphate group.[27,30]

24. K. G. Stern and J. W. Hofer, *Science*, *85*, 483 (1937).
25. J. Weijlard and H. Tauber, *J. Am. Chem. Soc.*, *60*, 2263 (1938).
26. P. Karrer and M. Viscontini, *Helv. Chim. Acta*, *29*, 711 (1946).
27. H. Weil-Malherbe, *Biochem. J.*, *33*, 1997 (1939).
28. F. Kubowitz and W. Luttgens, *Biochem. Z.*, *307*, 170 (1941).
29. D. E. Green, D. Herbert, and V. Subrahmanyan, *J. Biol. Chem.*, *138*, 327 (1941).
30. E. R. Buchman, E. Heegaard, and J. Bonner, *Proc. Natl. Acad. Sci.(U.S.)*, *26*, 561 (1940).

B. Role in Mammalian Metabolism

1. EARLY EVIDENCE. The discovery of thiamine pyrophosphate resulted directly from studies with microorganisms, but evidence obtained during the same period indicated a similar role for thiamine in mammalian metabolism. It was shown that the cocarboxylase which was isolated from yeast was the same as that found in animal tissue.[22] The tissue concentration of cocarboxylase in thiamine deficient rats was found to be less than normal,[31] and ample evidence was presented showing a thiamine requirement for tissue respiration and carbohydrate metabolism in pigeons.[32] In the same experiments it was apparent that pyruvate accumulation was a primary result of thiamine deficiency in pigeons and that thiamine was required for normal carbohydrate metabolism, and more specifically for pyruvate utilization in animal tissue. Soon after, thiamine pyrophosphate was shown to be the active form of thiamine in all cells and a coenzyme for all enzymic decarboxylations of α-keto acids.

2. ROLE IN ACYL TRANSFER. Thiamine pyrophosphate is recognized as one of the essential cofactors for the enzymic transfer of acyl groups from substrates such as α-keto acids, dicarbonyl compounds, and ketose phosphates. Diverse reactions such as the following, all require thiamine pyrophosphate at some stage of the process:[33–35]

(a) the decarboxylation of α-keto acids to aldehydes;

(b) the conversion of α-keto acids to acyloins;

(c) the oxidative decarboxylation of α-keto acids to carboxylic acids or transformation to dicarbonyl compounds; and

(d) the conversion of α-keto acids to acyl phosphates and formate.

Although all these reactions appear to differ significantly, they may be conveniently classified into three groups according to the final oxidation state of the original acyl radical and carboxyl group. When this is done, thiamine pyrophosphate is recognized as one of the coenzymes necessary for the direct nonoxidative decarboxylation, the oxidative decarboxylation, or the phosphoroclastic cleavage of α-keto acids. The term phosphoroclastic indicates cleavage of a phosphate ester bond at some stage of the reaction.

a. Nonoxidative Decarboxylation. The first group of enzymic reactions dependent upon thiamine pyrophosphate are those which generate

31. P. E. Simola, *Biochem. Z.*, *254*, 229 (1932).
32. R. A. Peters, *Lancet*, *230*, 1161 (1936).
33. S. Ochoa, *Physiol. Revs.*, *31*, 56 (1951).
34. L. J. Reed, *Physiol. Revs.*, *33*, 544 (1953).
35. I. C. Gunsalus, *Nutritional Symposium Series*, *13*, The National Vitamin Foundation, Inc., N.Y., 1956, p. 6.

aldehyde or its oxidation equivalent (e.g., acyloins) from α-keto acids. Among the examples[33] of such reactions are (a) the formation of acetaldehyde from pyruvic acid by carboxylase; (b) the formation of acetoin (**32**) from two equivalents of pyruvate by cell-free extracts of *Aerobacter aerogenes*, *Bacillus subtilis*, or *Serratia marcescens*; and (c) the formation of acetoin from one equivalent of pyruvic acid and one equivalent of acetaldehyde by certain preparations from yeast or *Escherichia coli*.

Enzymic reactions of this type may be regarded (Fig. 5) as proceeding by direct decarboxylation of the α-keto acid to an acyl carbanion (**29**) or a stabilized equivalent. The carbanion may then either react with a proton

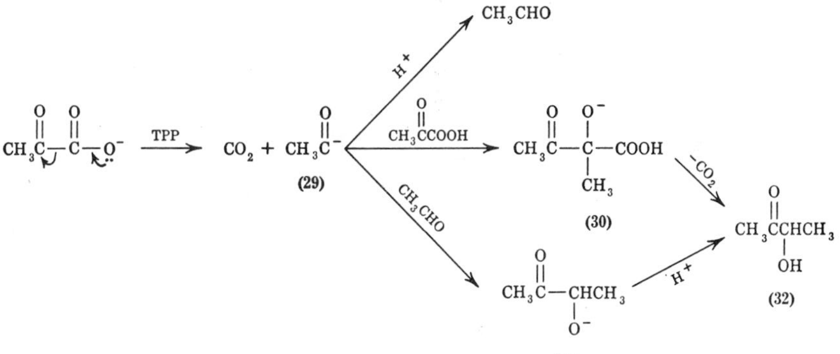

Fig. 5. Enzymic synthesis of aldehyde or its oxidation equivalent by direct decarboxylation of α-keto acids.

yielding an aldehyde or with an acceptor such as pyruvic acid or acetaldehyde to give a second anion (**30** or **31**, respectively). Decarboxylation of the anion (**30**) or reaction of the anion (**31**) with an acceptor proton yields acetoin (**32**).

Direct enzymic decarboxylation of α-keto acids is rare in mammalian metabolism. Simple enzymic decarboxylation of pyruvate to *free* acetaldehyde is restricted to microorganisms and never occurs in mammalian metabolism. The synthesis of acyloins from *free* acetaldehyde is also unimportant in mammalian metabolism, but it has been suggested that the acetoin reaction might serve as an "accidental" metabolic pathway for the elimination of acetaldehyde accumulating in an individual during an abnormal alcohol-load.[36]

b. Oxidative Decarboxylation. The second group of enzymic reactions dependent on thiamine pyrophosphate are those which generate acetate or its oxidation equivalent (e.g., diacetyl) from α-keto acids.[33,34] These

36. P. Handler, *Federation Proc.*, *17*, *Suppl. 2*, 33 (1958).

reactions, which are especially important in animal tissue and bacteria, may be regarded (Fig. 6) as proceeding by decarboxylation of the α-keto acid to yield a bound stabilized equivalent of the acyl carbanion (**29**). This stage of the reaction sequence is dependent on thiamine pyrophosphate, and the coenzyme-bound carbanion equivalent is usually designated as an

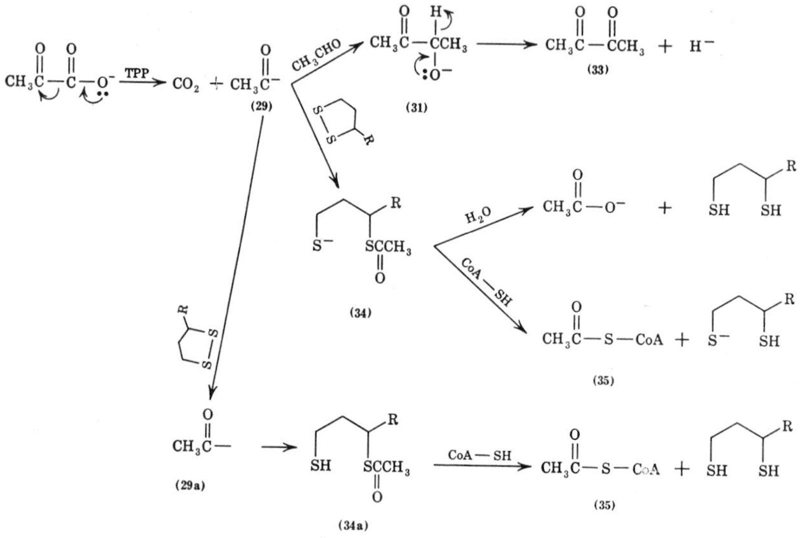

Fig. 6. Enzymic synthesis of acetate or its oxidation equivalent by oxidative decarboxylation of α-keto acids.

"active aldehyde." On the basis of studies with cell-free extracts of *E. coli* and *Streptococcus faecalis*, it is known that lipoic acid (Chapter XI) participates at the next stage of the oxidative decarboxylation sequence in which the stabilized acyl carbanion is oxidized to an active acyl group. This stage may proceed by the transfer of the stabilized acyl carbanion from thiamine pyrophosphate to lipoic acid with concomitant oxidation or by oxidation of the "aldehyde-thiamine pyrophosphate" complex to an acylthiamine pyrophosphate, followed by acyl transfer to dihydrolipoic acid. The mechanism has not been established, but recent data indicate that acylthiamine pyrophosphate derivatives participate in the oxidative decarboxylation sequence.

If the "aldehyde-thiamine pyrophosphate" complex is not oxidized to the corresponding acylthiamine derivative, the stabilized anion (**29**) may react with an acceptor such as an aldehyde giving the anion (**31**), which in the presence of the proper electron acceptor may liberate a hydride ion and be oxidized to the dicarbonyl compound (**33**). This reaction has little or no role in mammalian metabolism. Of greater significance, the bound stabilized acyl carbanion (**29**) may react with lipoic acid under the same conditions to yield the 8-thio-anion (**34**) of the corresponding 6-*S*-acyldihydrolipoic acid. According to this mechanism the stabilized acyl carbanion is transferred oxidatively from the thiamine pyrophosphate complex to lipoic acid; as a result, the acyl carbanion is oxidized and lipoic acid is reductively acylated.

According to an alternative mechanism the bound stabilized acyl carbanion may be oxidized to a bound active acyl group prior to its transfer from the thiamine pyrophosphate complex. For example, the thiamine-bound anion (**29**) may be oxidized to the correspondingly-bound acyl group (**29a**) by lipoic acid; the acyl group may then be transferred to a dihydrolipoic acid intermediate that was generated during the oxidation of the acyl carbanion to yield the corresponding 6-*S*-acyldihydrolipoic acid (**34a**).

In the final stage of the oxidative decarboxylation sequence, the *S*-acyldihydrolipoic acid derivative (**34**) or (**34a**) transfers its acyl group to coenzyme A giving the corresponding acyl coenzyme A (**35**). The latter contributes its "active acyl" to the Krebs citric acid cycle or to fatty acid metabolism. These reactions are discussed in the section on pantothenic acid (Chapter VI).

In mammalian metabolism, two enzymic oxidative decarboxylations occur in the Krebs cycle. A key reaction of this tricarboxylic acid cycle is the condensation of "active acetyl" with oxaloacetate. Pyruvic acid, an end product of carbohydrate metabolism, is the source of "active acetyl" for this cycle and is introduced in the system after oxidative decarboxylation to "active acetyl" through the participation of thiamine pyrophosphate, lipoic acid, and coenzyme A. A later stage in the cycle requires the oxidative decarboxylation of α-ketoglutaric acid. As in the first stage of the cycle, thiamine pyrophosphate participates through the generation of an "active aldehyde"; α-ketoglutarate is decarboxylated initially to "active succinyl semialdehyde," which is oxidized and transferred to give succinyldihydrolipoic acid. Transfer of this acyl group to coenzyme A gives succinyl coenzyme A, an important intermediate in mammalian metabolism.

Another reaction involving an "aldehyde-thiamine pyrophosphate" intermediate is the transketolase reaction. This reaction is important in mammalian metabolism for the enzymic cleavage of ribulose 5-phosphate in the "direct oxidative pathway" of glucose catabolism.[36] Triose phosphate was identified as one product in the cleavage of a ketopentose phosphate by purified preparations of transketolase from liver, spinach,

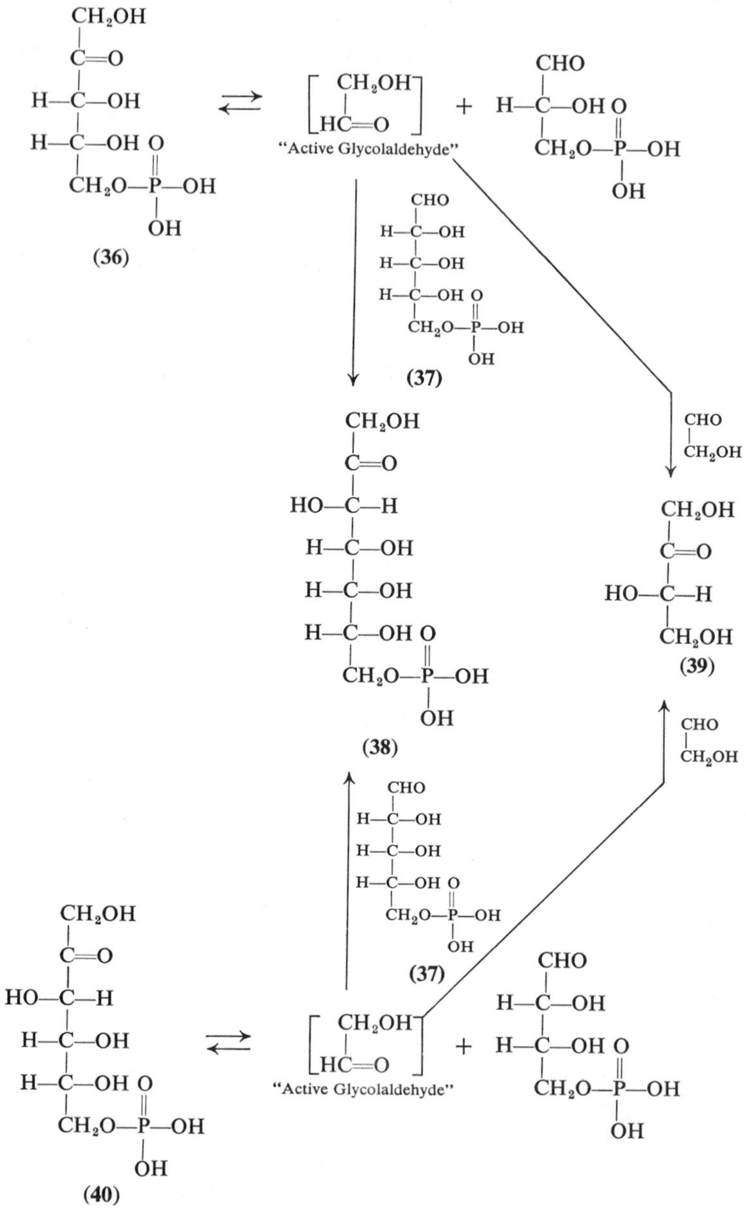

CH_2OH
C=O
H—C—OH
H—C—OH O
CH_2O—P—OH
OH

(36)

⇄ [CH_2OH / HC=O] + CHO / H—C—OH O / CH_2O—P—OH / OH

"Active Glycolaldehyde"

CHO
H—C—OH
H—C—OH
H—C—OH O
CH_2O—P—OH
OH

(37)

CH_2OH
C=O
HO—C—H
H—C—OH
H—C—OH
H—C—OH O
CH_2O—P—OH
OH

(38)

CHO
CH_2OH

CH_2OH
C=O
HO—C—H
CH_2OH

(39)

CHO
CH_2OH

CHO
H—C—OH
H—C—OH
H—C—OH O
CH_2O—P—OH
OH

(37)

CH_2OH
C=O
HO—C—H
H—C—OH
H—C—OH O
CH_2O—P—OH
OH

(40)

⇄ [CH_2OH / HC=O] + CHO / H—C—OH / H—C—OH O / CH_2O—P—OH / OH

"Active Glycolaldehyde"

and yeast,[37,38] but the expected two-carbon fragment, glycolaldehyde, was not detected in these early studies. The dependence of the enzyme on thiamine pyrophosphate was demonstrated,[37,38] and crystalline transketolase was isolated from baker's yeast.[38] In studies with the crystalline enzyme, the cleavage of *D*-ribulose 5-phosphate occurred only in the presence of an "acceptor aldose" to yield *D*-glyceraldehyde 3-phosphate and a 2-ketose phosphate containing two more carbon atoms than the original "acceptor aldose." The reaction is visualized as proceeding by the cleavage of *D*-ribulose 5-phosphate (**36**) to "active glycolaldehyde" and *D*-glyceraldehyde 3-phosphate.[38] When *D*-ribose 5-phosphate (**37**) is the "acceptor aldose," the active two-carbon intermediate is condensed with it to yield sedoheptulose 7-phosphate (**38**); when glycolaldehyde is the acceptor, the condensation product is *L*-erythrulose (**39**).

The first evidence for the participation of a glycolaldehyde-enzyme intermediate in the transketolase reaction was obtained from studies of isotope exchange between C^{14}-glycolaldehyde and *D*-fructose 6-phosphate (**40**) in the presence of transketolase.[39] The same investigators also isolated the glycolaldehyde-enzyme intermediate in the enzymic cleavage of *D*-fructose 6-phosphate (**40**) by transketolase.[39] The presence of bound glycolaldehyde in the intermediate was demonstrated by (a) the transfer of the ketol group to "acceptor aldoses" such as *D*-ribose 5-phosphate and glycolaldehyde, and (b) the formation of glycolaldehyde on denaturation of the intermediate. The enzyme complex is very stable, and glycolaldehyde is liberated so slowly that it serves as an "acceptor aldose" to yield erythrulose. This observation accounts for the fact that glycolaldehyde is not detected in the cleavage of 2-ketose phosphates by transketolase.

c. Phosphoroclastic Cleavage. The third class of α-keto acid cleavages dependent on thiamine pyrophosphate are phosphoroclastic (Fig. 7). In these reactions the acyl group of the α-keto acid is converted to acyl phosphate (**41**) presumably by way of acyl coenzyme A, and the carboxyl group is converted to either formate or hydrogen and carbon dioxide, depending upon the enzyme used. The mechanism of such reactions is still obscure.

C. *Mechanism of Coenzyme Action*

Most reaction mechanisms considered for systems that are dependent on thiamine pyrophosphate have one stage in common; they all assume

37. B. L. Horecker and P. Z. Smyrniotis, *J. Am. Chem. Soc.*, *75*, 1009 (1953).
38. E. Racker, G. de la Haba, and I. G. Leder, *J. Am. Chem. Soc.*, *75*, 1010 (1953).
39. A. G. Datta and E. Racker, *Arch. Biochem. Biophys.*, *82*, 489 (1959); *J. Biol. Chem.*, *236*, 624 (1961).

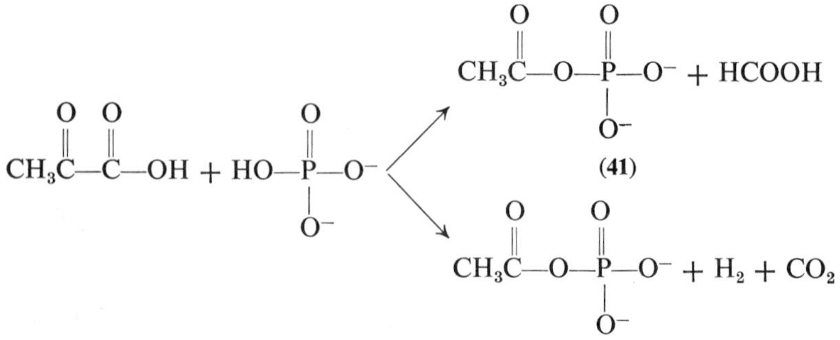

$$CH_3\overset{O}{\overset{\|}{C}}-\overset{O}{\overset{\|}{C}}-OH + HO-\underset{O^-}{\underset{|}{\overset{O}{\overset{\|}{P}}}}-O^- \nearrow CH_3\overset{O}{\overset{\|}{C}}-O-\underset{O^-}{\underset{|}{\overset{O}{\overset{\|}{P}}}}-O^- + HCOOH \quad \textbf{(41)}$$

$$\searrow CH_3\overset{O}{\overset{\|}{C}}-O-\underset{O^-}{\underset{|}{\overset{O}{\overset{\|}{P}}}}-O^- + H_2 + CO_2 \quad \textbf{(41)}$$

Fig. 7. Enzymic synthesis of acetate and formate by phosphoroclastic cleavage of α-keto acids.

the initial formation of an intermediate acyl carbanion or a stabilized equivalent usually referred to as "active aldehyde." How does thiamine participate in the generation of the acyl carbanion? What is the nature of the bonding between the acyl carbanion and the coenzyme? Do acylthiamine pyrophosphate derivatives participate in the oxidative degradation sequence? These topics have been an object of research for the last two decades; some still receive critical attention.

Mechanisms for thiamine participation in enzymic decarboxylation are based primarily on model systems. No progress was made, however, until systems were developed in which the activity of thiamine could be studied in the absence of enzyme specificity. The first proposed mechanism for such reactions of thiamine required the formation of a Schiff base.[40] As a

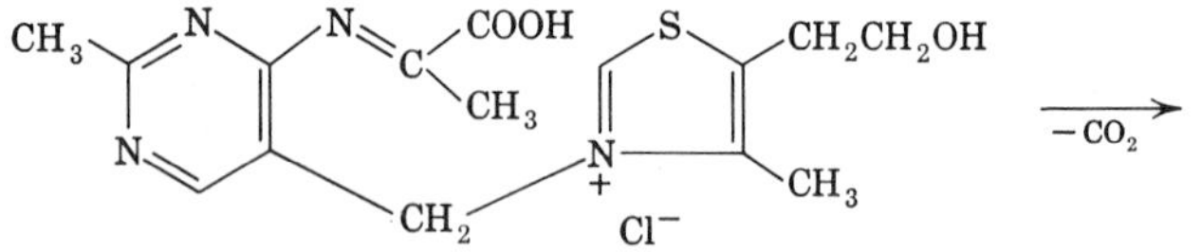

CH_3 N N=C(COOH)(CH_3) S CH_2CH_2OH N $\overset{+}{N}$ CH_3 CH_2 Cl^-

(42)

$\xrightarrow{-CO_2}$

CH_3 N N=C(H)(CH_3) S CH_2CH_2OH N $\overset{+}{N}$ CH_3 CH_2 Cl^-

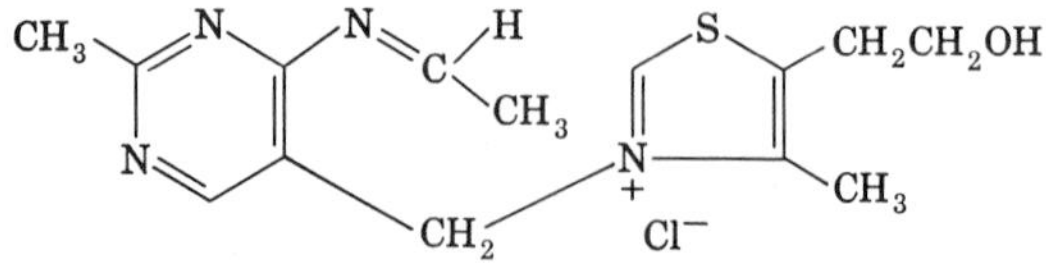

(43)

40. W. Langenback, *Die Organischen Katalysatoren*, Springer, Berlin, 1935, p. 55ff.

result of studies with a model system in which various amines catalyzed the decarboxylation of pyruvic acid, it was assumed that thiamine would react with pyruvic acid through its amino function to give the Schiff base (**42**), which would then eliminate carbon dioxide to give the Schiff base (**43**). There were two objections to this formulation. Firstly, the resonance contribution (**44**) ↔ (**45**) deactivates the amino group of thiamine preventing Schiff base formation. Secondly, the mechanism overlooks the most

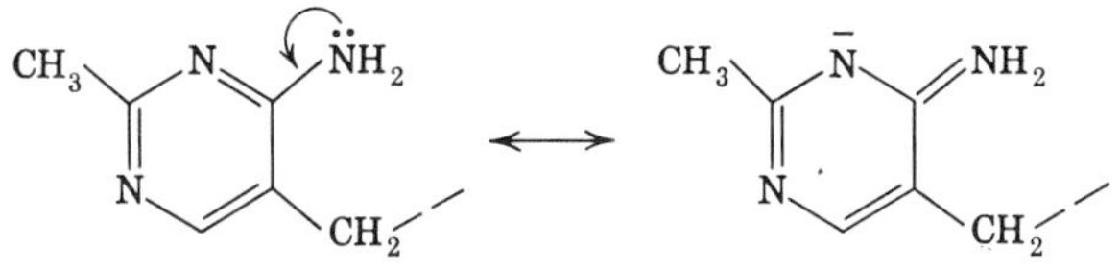

(**44**) (**45**)

novel feature of the molecule, its thiazole ring. This scheme was no longer contemplated after the system was shown to be a poor model when thiamine itself was ineffective under these conditions.[41]

A new mechanism depicting a Schiff base was suggested in which the intermediate (**42**) is visualized as tautomerizing to an *ylid* of type (**46**)

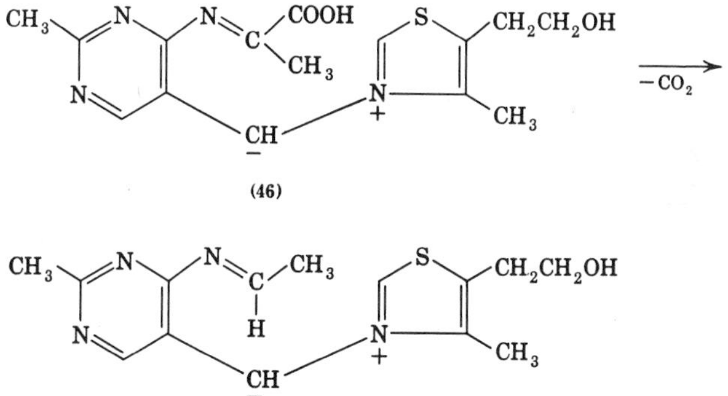

(**46**) $\xrightarrow{-CO_2}$

(**47**)

which eliminates carbon dioxide giving the *ylid* (**47**).[42] The intermediate was then assumed to transfer its "active acetyl" through lipoic acid to coenzyme A as shown in the zwitterion (**48**). Although this mechanism suggests a stabilizing role for the thiazole moiety of the molecule, it too requires participation of a relatively unreactive amino group.

41. K. Stern and J. Melnick, *J. Biol. Chem.*, *131*, 597 (1939).
42. K. Wiesner and Z. Valenta, *Experientia*, *12*, 190 (1956).

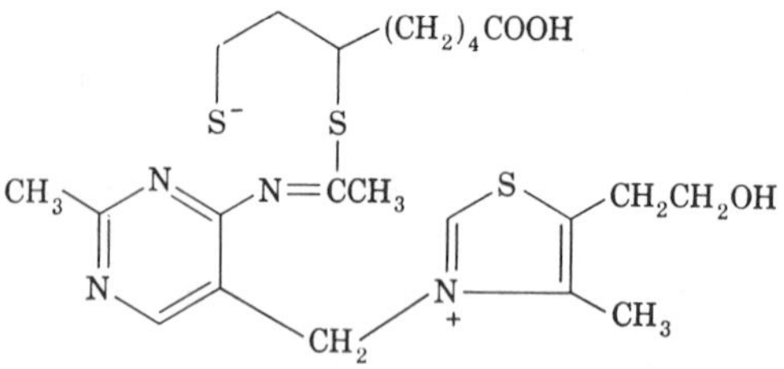

$(CH_2)_4COOH$
S^- S
CH_3 N $N{=}CCH_3$ S CH_2CH_2OH
N N^+ CH_3
CH_2

(48)

A mechanism requiring the generation of a sulfhydryl group from the thiazole ring was suggested earlier; in this mechanism the reactive form is depicted as the formylaminothiol (**49**) obtained by opening the thiazole

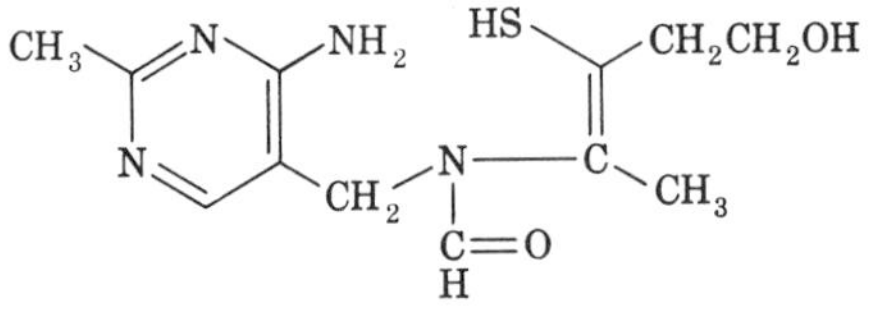

CH_3 N NH_2 HS CH_2CH_2OH
N CH_2 N—C CH_3
C=O
H

(49)

moiety of the coenzyme.[43] This formulation, though compatible with the known chemical reactions of thiamine, has received no further biochemical support.

The first substantial progress in this field came with the discovery of a benzoin condensation catalyzed by a thiazolium halide.[44] Subsequent modification of the conditions of this reaction allowed all the known enzymic cleavages of pyruvate promoted by thiamine to occur in the absence of enzymes;[45] consequently, the first nonenzymic model system was available for the study of thiamine activity. Study of a nonenzymic acyloin condensation in this system using several different catalysts showed that the most effective catalysts contained an activated *N*-methylene group. Therefore, an activated methylene moiety was assumed to be essential for catalysis, and thiamine participation in enzymic and nonenzymic reactions was depicted through the *ylid* form (**50**).[46] The first step toward "active

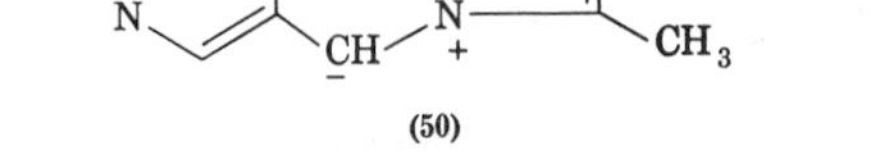

CH_3 N NH_2 S CH_2CH_2OH
N $\underline{C}H$ N^+ CH_3

(50)

43. P. Karrer, *Bull. Soc. Chim. France*, 149, (1947).
44. T. Ugai, S. Tanaka, and S. Dokawa, *J. Pharm. Soc. Japan*, *63*, 269 (1943).
45. S. Mizuhara, R. Tamura, and S. Tsubokawa, *Proc. Japan Acad.*, *27*, 302 (1951).
46. R. Breslow, *Chem. & Ind.* (*London*), R28 (1956).

aldehyde" in this sequence would be condensation of pyruvic acid on the *N*-methylene group of the catalyst.

The mechanism requiring the *ylid* (**50**) was abandoned when it was proved that the *ylid* form of thiamine was not present in alkaline solution. This was demonstrated through deuterium incorporation studies which showed nonionization of the hydrogen atoms of the methylene bridge of thiamine during thiamine-catalyzed decarboxylation of pyruvate.[47,48] It was also established by using benzyl-(α-d_2)-thiazolium bromide as a catalyst for the furoin condensation.[49] Since deuterium was not lost in this reaction, it was considered that the *N*-methylene group of the thiazole does not participate. Further confirmation for these conclusions was derived from a study of the decarboxylation of pyruvate by carboxylase in tritiated water.[50] After reaction, the coenzyme was liberated from protein and was cleaved to the pyrimidinylmethanesulfonic acid (**2**). Since the sulfonic acid (**2**) was not tritium-enriched, the experiment confirmed the inactivity of the hydrogen atoms of the methylene group bridging the pyrimidine and thiazole moieties of the coenzyme and eliminated the possibility of participation by the *ylid* form (**50**) of the protein-bound coenzyme during catalysis.

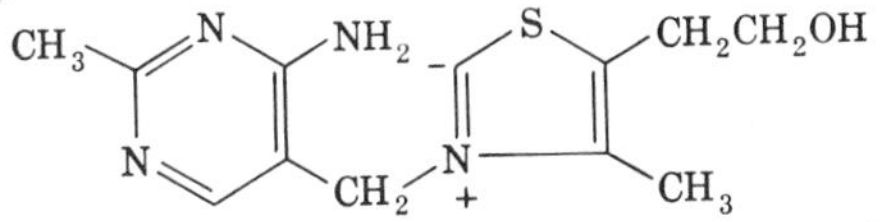

CH3 N NH2 S CH2CH2OH N CH2 N + CH3

(**51**)

The thiazolium zwitterion (**51**) is now regarded as the active form of thiamine.[49,51] The initial conception was based upon the fact that thiazolium salts are in equilibrium with their C-2 anionic forms under mild conditions and upon a structural similarity between cyanide ion and the thiazolium zwitterion (**51**).[49,51] Cyanide is a familiar catalyst in the benzoin condensation and its role has been depicted in the now-classic Lapworth mechanism. The mechanism of the thiamine-catalyzed acyloin condensation has also been presented (Fig. 8) in an analogous fashion.[49] The aldehyde is depicted as condensing with the zwitterionic form of thiamine (**51**) to yield the compound (**52**) which liberates a proton generating a new zwitterion (**53**). This species contains a stabilized acyl

47. K. Fry, L. L. Ingraham, and F. H. Westheimer, *J. Am. Chem. Soc.*, *79*, 5225 (1957).
48. L. L. Ingraham and F. H. Westheimer, *Chem. & Ind.* (*London*), 846, (1956).
49. R. Breslow, *J. Am. Chem. Soc.*, *80*, 3719 (1958).
50. D. F. De Tar and F. H. Westheimer, *J. Am. Chem. Soc.*, *81*, 175 (1959).
51. R. Breslow, *J. Am. Chem. Soc.*, *79*, 1762 (1957).

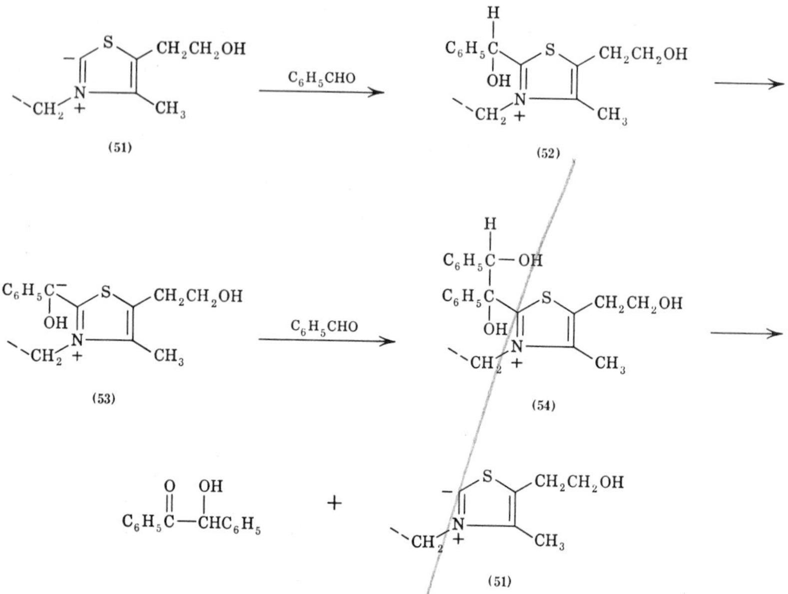

Fig. 8. Mechanism for thiamine catalysis of an acyloin condensation.[49]

carbanion and represents the so-called "active aldehyde" of thiamine catalyzed reactions. The "active aldehyde" (**53**), stabilized by resonance with the form (**55**), reacts with benzaldehyde, now in the role of an "acceptor aldehyde," giving the compound (**54**) which generates benzoin and the original zwitterionic form of the vitamin.

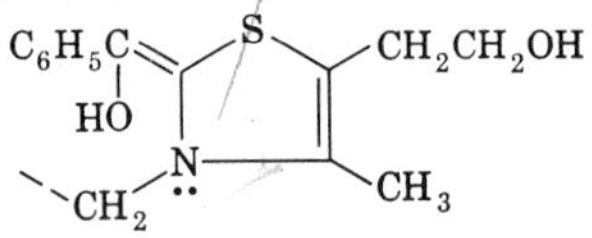

Evidence for this mechanism was derived from a study of the effectiveness of various analogs in model catalytic reactions. For example, thiazolium salts with a hydrogen atom at carbon-2 are active in the benzoin condensation, but those substituted in the 2-position are inactive. Also, a 3-isopropylthiazolium salt was inactive, a fact readily acceptable on the basis of steric hindrance at the 2-position. The known equilibrium behavior of thiazolium salts provides additional support for this mechanism. Low pH's should repress the zwitterion concentration and consequently decrease catalysis; equally important, high pH's should promote the formation of the conjugate *pseudo* bases (**56**), (**57**), and (**58**) at the expense of the zwitterion and also decrease catalysis. The relatively narrow pH range observed for optimum catalysis is in accord with these predictions

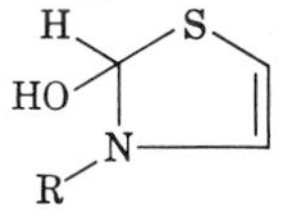

(56) 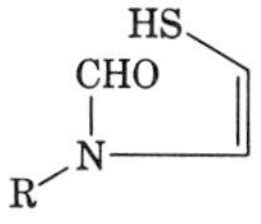 (57) 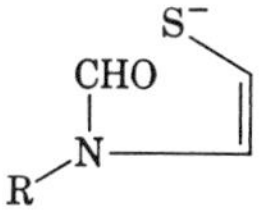 (58)

and the proposed mechanism. Furthermore, compounds known to exist preferentially in either *pseudo* base or open forms are poor catalysts for the benzoin condensation. The failure of oxythiamine to catalyze the acetoin condensation is also compatible with the mechanism. Under the conditions of the reaction, this analog is expected to ionize yielding the oxyanion **(59)** which in turn prevents zwitterion formation by condensing at the 2-position of the thiazole ring to give the corresponding tricyclic compound.

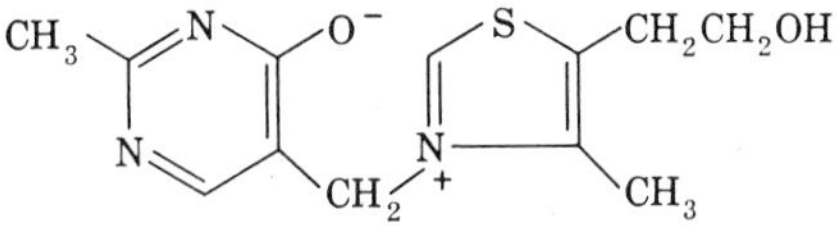

(59)

Additional support for the mechanism was derived by the synthesis of suggested thiazolium intermediates which were more effective catalysts than the simple thiazolium salts.[52] The conclusions drawn from this study designate the thiazole moiety of thiamine as the primary site of activity; aromatic substituents such as the pyrimidine moiety are depicted as enhancing activity by inductive electron withdrawal. Results demonstrating the kinetic lability of 2-acylthiazolium salts on solvolysis[53,54] are also in accord with the mechanism since it is implicit that 2-acetylthiamine would be yet another form of "active acetate."

Further proof for this mechanism was provided by the synthesis of "active aldehyde" in the form of *DL* 3-[(2-methyl-4-amino-5-pyrimidinyl)-methyl]-2-(1-hydroxyethyl)-4-methyl-5-(2-hydroxyethyl)thiazolium chloride hydrochloride **(62)**.[55] 2-(α-Benzoyloxyethyl)-5-(β-hydroxyethyl)-4-methylthiazole **(60)** was synthesized from α-(benzoyloxy)-thiopropionamide and 3-acetyl-3-chloro-1-propanol; treatment of the intermediate **(60)**

52. R. Breslow and E. McNelis, *J. Am. Chem. Soc.*, *81*, 3080 (1959).
53. R. Breslow and E. McNelis, *J. Am. Chem. Soc.*, *82*, 2394 (1960).
54. F. G. White and L. L. Ingraham, *J. Am. Chem. Soc.*, *82*, 4114 (1960).
55. L. O. Krampitz, G. Gruell, C. S. Miller, J. B. Bicking, H. R. Skeggs, and J. M. Sprague, *J. Am. Chem. Soc.*, *80*, 5893 (1958).

with potassium hydroxide in methanol gave 2-(α-hydroxyethyl)-5-(β-hydroxyethyl)-4-methylthiazole (**61**). Condensation of this intermediate with 2-methyl-4-amino-5-bromomethylpyrimidine hydrobromide in dimethylformamide solution yielded the factor as a bromide hydrobromide which was converted to the chloride hydrochloride (**62**) and purified by

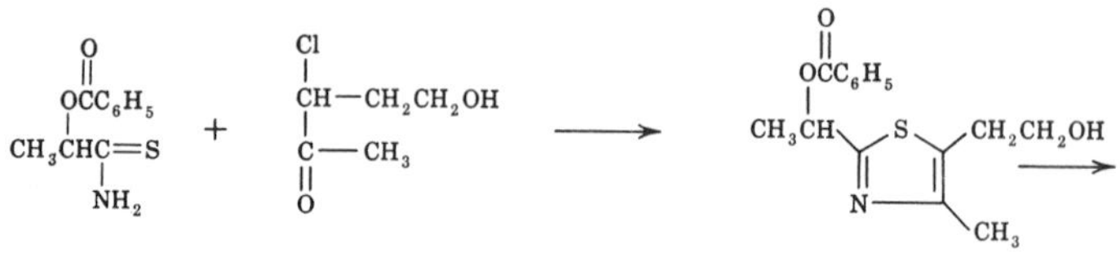

(60)

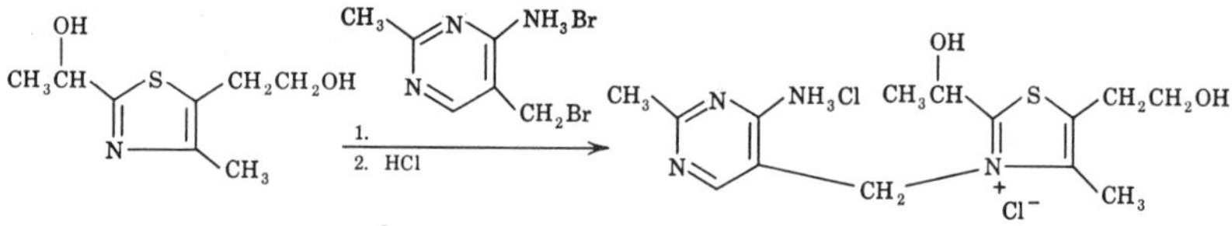

1.
2. HCl

(61)

(62)

paper chromatography. The activity of synthetic "active aldehyde" (**62**) was demonstrated by the reactivation of carboxylase and in growth-promoting assays with *L. fermenti* or *L. veridescens.*

Until recently the evidence supporting this mechanism was derived from nonenzymic model systems. Its validity in an enzyme system was demonstrated with the isolation and characterization of two intermediates during the decarboxylation of pyruvate by a pyruvate decarboxylase from brewer's yeast or a pyruvate oxidase from baker's yeast.[56,56a] Incubation of C^{14}-labeled pyruvate in the pyruvate decarboxylase system yielded two intermediates designated "activated acetaldehyde" and "activated pyruvic acid." Using 1-C^{14}-pyruvic acid, only "activated pyruvic acid" is labeled; if 2-C^{14}-pyruvic acid is used, both "activated acetaldehyde" and "activated pyruvic acid" are labeled.

Sulfite cleavage of the labeled "activated acetaldehyde" yielded a pyrimidine and a radioactive fluorescent thiazole. The thiazole compound gave a positive test for phosphate and accounted for the total radioactivity in the original "activated aldehyde." Treatment of the thiazole derivative with hydrogen iodide gave a low yield of propionic acid. On the basis of these data and the assumption that a 2-(1-hydroxyethyl)thiazole would behave as an imido-thioester of lactic acid on reductive cleavage with

56. H. Holzer and K. Beaucamp, *Angew. Chem.*, *71*, 776 (1959); *Biochim. et Biophys. Acta*, *46*, 225 (1961).
56a. H. Holzer, *Angew. Chem.*, *73*, 721 (1961).

hydrogen iodide, the "activated acetaldehyde" compound was assigned the structure (**63**) corresponding to the 2-(1-hydroxyethyl)thiazole analog of thiamine pyrophosphate.

The structure of "activated pyruvic acid" is visualized as the 2-(1-carboxy-1-hydroxyethyl)thiazole analog of thiamine pyrophosphate (**64**). This conclusion is based on the observation that "activated acetaldehyde" and "activated pyruvic acid" are closely related in structure, but only

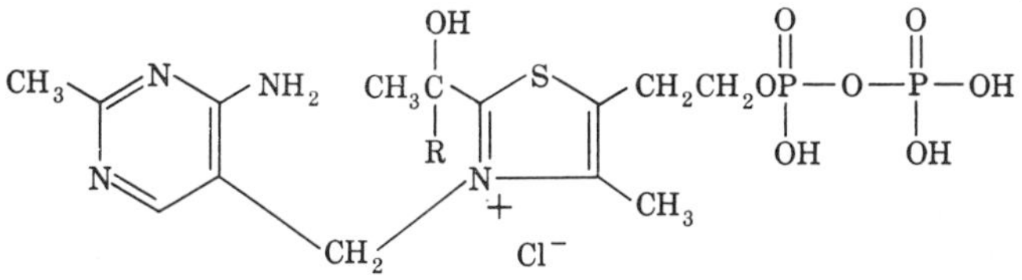

(**63**): R = H
(**64**): R = COOH

"activated pyruvic acid" is labeled when 1-C^{14}-pyruvic acid is used for the enzymic synthesis of the two compounds.

On the basis of analogy "activated glycolaldehyde," the intermediate in the enzymic cleavage of 2-ketose phosphates by transketolase, was formulated as the 2-(1,2-dihydroxyethyl)thiazole analog of thiamine pyrophosphate.[39] This conclusion appears to be substantiated on the basis of preliminary studies with the "active glycolaldehyde" isolated from an incubation mixture of transketolase, C^{14}-fructose 6-phosphate, and thiamine pyrophosphate.[56a,56b] Chromatographic purification of the reaction product yielded a C^{14}-labeled enzymic derivative of thiamine pyrophosphate which reacted with glycolaldehyde in the presence of transketolase to yield C^{14}-erythrulose.

Confirmatory evidence for the formulation of "activated glycolaldehyde" as the 2-(1,2-dihydroxyethyl)thiazole analog of thiamine pyrophosphate was obtained by degradation.[56c] Labeled "activated glycolaldehyde," prepared from 3-C^{14}-hydroxypyruvic acid, was dephosphorylated with a phosphatase and then cleaved with sodium sulfite. This reaction yielded a nonlabeled pyrimidine and a radioactive thiazole derivative. Treatment of the labeled thiazole derivative with hydroxylamine yielded labeled 2,3-dihydroxypropionohydroxamic acid. Since a 2-(1,2-dihydroxyethyl)thiazole would react as a thioimide of 2,3-dihydroxypropionic acid on treatment with hydroxylamine to yield

56b. H. Holzer, R. Kattermann, and D. Busch, *Biochem. Biophys. Res. Commun.* 7, 167 (1962).
56c. K. W. Bock, L. Jaenicke, and H. Holzer, *Biochem. Biophys Res. Commun.*, 9, 472 (1962).

2,3-dihydroxypropionohydroxamic acid, this sequence of degradation reactions confirmed the presence of a 2-(1,2-dihydroxyethyl)thiazole moiety in "activated glycolaldehyde."

The actual mechanism for the generation of an "active acyl" group from an "active aldehyde" complex during oxidative decarboxylation is an object of current research. On the basis of studies with a ferricyanide-linked enzymic oxidative decarboxylation of pyruvate to acetate in which neither bound lipoic acid nor flavine-adenine dinucleotide are required, it was suggested that 2-acyl derivatives of thiamine pyrophosphate are intermediates on the pathway for biological oxidative decarboxylation.[56d] This conclusion is in accord with earlier observations on the kinetic instability of 2-acylthiazolium salts.[53,54] In the biological systems that require enzyme-bound lipoic acid, the reaction is visualized as proceeding with the oxidation of the "aldehyde-thiamine pyrophosphate" intermediate by lipoic acid;[56d] the products of the reaction are the corresponding 2-acylthiamine pyrophosphate and an enzyme-bound dihydrolipoic acid derivative. Next the 2-acylthiamine pyrophosphate transfers its acyl group to the dihydrolipoic acid intermediate to yield a 6-*S*-acyldihydrolipoic acid.

7. Biosynthesis

Studies with a series of thiamine-requiring *Neurospora* mutants showed that the biosynthesis of thiamine proceeds by the condensation of a pyrimidine and a thiazole.[57,58] Early evidence regarding the nature of these precursors was derived from studies with extracts of baker's yeast.[59] In the enzyme system from yeast, thiamine was synthesized from ATP, 4-amino-5-hydroxymethyl-2-methylpyrimidine, and 5-(β-hydroxyethyl)-4-methylthiazole; ATP was not required if the synthetic monophosphate ester of 4-amino-5-hydroxymethyl-2-methylpyrimidine was used in this system. On additional purification of the enzyme system, it was shown that ATP was required for maximum biosynthesis of thiamine even from the pyrimidine monophosphate.[60] Since pre-incubation of either the precursor thiazole or the pyrimidine with ATP enhanced the initial rate of thiamine biosynthesis,[61] it was concluded that the phosphorylation of both precursors precedes their condensation in the biosynthesis of thiamine.

56d. M. L. Das, M. Koike, and L. J. Reed, *Proc. Natl. Acad. Sci.* (*U.S.*), *47*, 753 (1961).
57. E. L. Tatum and T. T. Bell, *Am. J. Botany*, *33*, 15 (1946).
58. D. L. Harris, *Arch. Biochem. Biophys.*, *41*, 293 (1952); *57*, 240 (1955); *60*, 35 (1956).
59. D. L. Harris and J. Yavit, *Federation Proc.*, *16*, 192 (1957).
60. I. G. Leder, *Federation Proc.*, *18*, 270 (1959).
61. Y. Nose, K. Ueda, and T. Kawasaki, *Biochem. et Biophys. Acta*, *34*, 277 (1959).

Comparison of the effect of various phosphorylated intermediates on the rate of thiamine biosynthesis indicates that the pyrophosphate of the precursor hydroxymethylpyrimidine and the monophosphate of the precursor thiazole are the most probable intermediates. The participation of the thiazole monophosphate was indicated when the first product of the condensation between the pyrimidine monophosphate and the non-phosphorylated thiazole was identified as thiamine monophosphate.[62] Since the addition of the thiazole monophosphate had no effect on either the yield or the ATP requirement for the incorporation of the pyrimidine monophosphate, it was concluded that a pyrophosphate of the precursor pyrimidine was required for condensation with the thiazole monophosphate in thiamine biosynthesis. This conclusion was supported by the enzymic conversion of the pyrimidine pyrophosphate (**65**) and the thiazole monophosphate (**66**) to thiamine monophosphate in the absence of ATP.

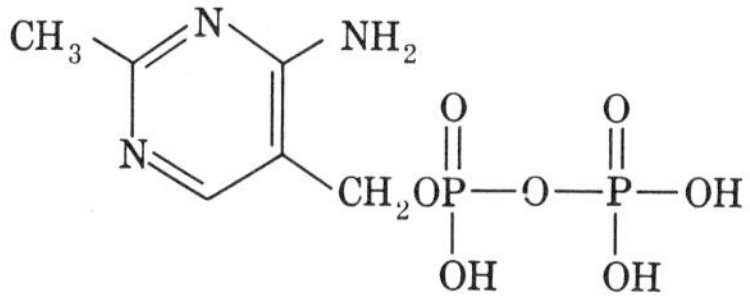

(65) 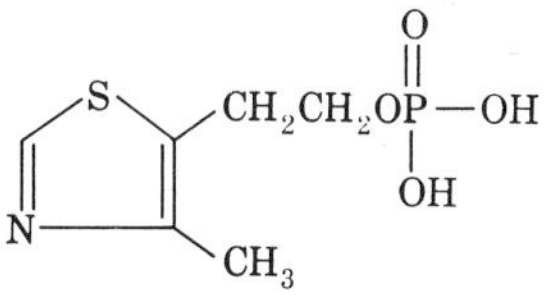 (66)

The monophosphate esters of the precursor pyrimidine and the thiazole were isolated from enzymic thiamine-producing reactions, and the pyrophosphate ester of the precursor pyrimidine was detected in the incubation mixture.[63] Whether the pyrimidine monophosphate ester is a precursor or a degradation product of the pyrophosphate was not established.

On the basis of these data, the biosynthesis of thiamine and thiamine pyrophosphate in yeast systems is visualized as proceeding from the compound tentatively identified as the pyrimidine pyrophosphate (**65**). The initial condensation product, thiamine monophosphate, is dephosphorylated prior to conversion to the coenzyme form.

a. "Hydroxymethylpyrimidine" + ATP $\xrightarrow[\text{Pyrimidine Kinase}]{Mg^{2+}}$ "Pyrimidine Pyrophosphate"

b. "Thiazole" + ATP $\xrightarrow[\text{Thiazole Kinase}]{Mg^{2+}}$ "Thiazole Monophosphate"

62. I. G. Leder, *Biochem. Biophys. Res. Commun.*, *1*, 63 (1959).
63. G. W. Camiener and G. M. Brown, *J. Am. Chem. Soc.*, *81*, 3800 (1959); *J. Biol. Chem.*, *235*, 2404, 2411 (1960).

c. "Pyrimidine Pyrophosphate" + "Thiazole Monophosphate"

$$\xrightarrow[\text{Thiamine-P Synthase}]{Mg^{2+}} \text{Thiamine Monophosphate}$$

d. Thiamine Monophosphate $\xrightarrow[\text{Thiamine-P Phosphatase}]{}$ Thiamine

e. Thiamine + ATP $\xrightarrow[\text{Thiamine Pyrophosphokinase}]{Mg^{2+}}$ Thiamine Pyrophosphate

8. Nutritional and Therapeutic Role

Thiamine is an essential nutrient for all mammalian species studied and functions in its coenzyme form, thiamine pyrophosphate. The vitamin is transported in the host as either thiamine or its monophosphate; the metabolically reactive form, thiamine pyrophosphate, is synthesized at the site of catalysis.

A. In Animals

The clinical manifestations of thiamine deficiency in animals are associated with the cardiovascular and central nervous systems and are the same for most species studied. Thiamine, concerned almost exclusively with carbohydrate metabolism, has been shown to be an essential nutrient for all animal species studied including the rat,[64] chick,[65] pigeon,[66] guinea pig,[67] pig,[68] calf,[69] cat,[70] and monkey.[71] When foxes are maintained on diets containing more than 10% uncooked fresh water fish, they develop a peculiar disease called Chastek paralysis. This condition can be cured or prevented by providing thiamine in the diet.[72] The source of disease was ultimately traced to the presence in raw fish of the enzyme thiaminase, which depletes the thiamine store of the host by rapid cleavage of the vitamin between its pyrimidine and thiazole moieties.[73–75]

Among the earliest signs of thiamine deficiency in animals are loss of

64. E. V. McCollum and M. Davis, *J. Biol. Chem.*, *23*, 181 (1915).
65. C. Eijkman, *Arch. Pathol. Anat. Physiol.*, *148*, 523 (1897).
66. H. W. Kinnersley and R. A. Peters, *Biochem. J.*, *22*, 419 (1928).
67. B. Carlstrom and G. Jonsson, *Skand. Vet.*, *29*, 181 (1939); Abstr. in *Nutr. Abstr. Rev.*, *9*, 71 (1939).
68. M. M. Wintrobe, H. J. Stein, M. H. Miller, R. H. Follis, V. Najjar, and S. Humphreys, *Bull. Johns Hopkins Hosp.*, *71*, 141 (1942).
69. B. C. Johnson, T. S. Hamilton, W. B. Nevens, and L. E. Boley, *J. Nutr.* *35*, 137 (1948).
70. G. M. Everett, *Am. J. Physiol.*, *141*, 439 (1944).
71. H. A. Waisman and K. B. McCall, *Arch. Biochem.*, *4*, 265 (1944).
72. R. G. Green, W. E. Carlson, and C. A. Evans, *J. Nutr.* *21*, 243 (1941); *23*, 165 (1942).
73. D. W. Woolley, *J. Biol. Chem.*, *141*, 997 (1941).
74. E. H. Spitzer, A. J. Combes, C. A. Elvehjem, and W. Wisnickey, *Proc. Soc. Exptl. Biol. Med.*, *48*, 376 (1941).
75. L. O. Krampitz and D. W. Woolley, *J. Biol. Chem.*, *152*, 9 (1944).

appetite and a concomitant steady loss of weight. Eventually neurological disturbances, loss of muscle tone, bradycardia, and cardiac enlargement develop. The fat stores of the body usually decrease rapidly and the body temperature is lowered. Decreased ability for energy output, also a manifestation of thiamine deficiency, was demonstrated in lowered work performance by the swimming rat.(76) Most of these manifestations are dramatically reversed by the administration of thiamine.

A study of the thiamine requirement of animals has shown that the carbohydrate content of the diet is a determining factor. When animals are fed diets rich in carbohydrate, they have a higher thiamine requirement than those maintained on fat- or protein-rich diets.(77–79) Thiamine deficiency symptoms were related to an inability of the host to metabolize dietary carbohydrate in the absence of thiamine,(80) and it was shown that rats consuming diets containing as little as 9% sucrose or glucose did not survive in the absence of thiamine.(81) Sorbitol has been reported to spare thiamine.(82) When rats were fed thiamine-free diets containing up to 20% sorbitol, they survived for thirty weeks and gained weight. Addition of sorbitol to thiamine-free diets containing up to 40% glucose also produced a growth response. If the sorbitol was replaced by glucose, the rats developed the usual deficiency symptoms and died in five to ten weeks. From these data it was suggested that sorbitol might produce a change in intestinal flora allowing biosynthesis of thiamine in the rat. Under such a condition the rat could be independent of exogenous sources of the vitamin. When coprophagy was prevented, however, a thiamine-sparing action by sorbitol was not observed.(83,84) Consequently, the extra thiamine arising from intestinal biosynthesis is available to the animal only through its feces. Furthermore, a sorbitol-induced thiamine-sparing action could not be demonstrated in man.(84)

B. In the Human

The classical pathological syndrome of thiamine avitaminosis in the human is called beriberi. This disease, rarely seen in the Western World

76. M. Kniazuk and H. Molitor, *J. Pharmacol. and Exptl. Therap.*, *80*, 362 (1944).
77. A. Arnold and C. A. Elvehjem, *J. Nutr.*, *15*, 429 (1938).
78. H. M. Evans and S. Lepkovsky, *Science*, *68*, 298 (1928).
79. G. G. Banerji, *Biochem. J.*, *34*, 1329 (1940); *35*, 1354 (1941).
80. G. G. Banerji and J. Yudkin, *Biochem. J.*, *36*, 530 (1942).
81. J. Yudkin, *Biochem. J.*, *48*, 608 (1951).
82. T. B. Morgan and J. Yudkin, *Nature*, *180*, 543 (1957).
83. T. B. Morgan and J. Yudkin, *Nature*, *184*, 909 (1959).
84. H. D. Cremer, *Intern. Rev. Vitamin Res.*, *30*, 376 (1959), *Nutr. Revs.*, *18*, 63 (1960).

because of food enrichment, is prevalent in areas of the Orient where rice constitutes the basic dietary staple. Fatigue, weight loss, and anorexia are among the early symptoms of this disease. As the deficiency develops, gastrointestinal complaints and neurological manifestations appear; the most advanced neuropathies appear in the peripheral nerves, particularly in the lower extremities. Circulatory and cardiac involvement usually result in an enlarged dilated heart and generally lead to edema and irregular cardiac rhythm. Except in cases of extreme organic impairment, thiamine therapy produced dramatic recoveries.

Beriberi as observed in adults and older children has been classified as (a) chronic, dry, and atrophic; (b) mild and subacute; or (c) acute fulminating.[85] The most prevalent type by far is mild and subacute. The chronic, dry, and atrophic type is generally found only in the older adult. It is characterized by the absence of biochemical changes usually associated with the acute types of beriberi and is extremely resistant to physiotherapy or dietary treatment. The most frequent manifestations of the mild subacute form of beriberi are polyneuropathies in the peripheral regions. In its mildest forms it is characterized by calf muscle tenderness, difficulty in rising from a squatting position, burning feet, and muscle cramps; the later stages are characterized by edema and mild cardiovascular complaints such as breathlessness and palpitation. Cardiac enlargement has also been established in many cases. The acute fulminating type of beriberi is relatively uncommon and until 1936 invariably resulted in death. Ironically, such a patient slowly develops nerve lesions and as a consequence of his not being forced to rest during the early stages of the disease, there is an apparent violent manifestation of symptoms dominated by cardiovascular insufficiency and an enlarged liver. This fulminating type almost never occurs in adults and older children.

The problem of infantile beriberi is serious, and its importance in infant mortality has apparently never been adequately assessed.[86] The disease, common to rice-eating countries, is associated frequently with children of mothers with beriberi. The disease occurs during the first year of life but is rather uncommon in a child under one month of age. The more severe grades of deficiency which may occur between the first and fourth month of life are generally regarded as most dangerous and may run a rapid and fulminating course. After the fourth month of life the syndrome tends to be subacute and chronic. The disease is usually characterized by either a dry or wet type of beriberi. In the dry type the infant superficially

85. B. S. Platt, *Federation Proc.*, *17*, 8 (1958).
86. R. C. Burgess, *Federation Proc.*, *17*, 39 (1958).

appears well nourished; in the wet type considerable edema and malnutrition is evident. A striking feature of infantile beriberi is an aphonia symptom that has been described as the "visible cry"; the child apparently cries but no sound is heard. This aphonia has been attributed to either a paralysis of the laryngeal nerve or to edema of the vocal chords.[87]

Secondary or conditioned thiamine deficiencies are also in evidence throughout the world. Among the more common forms are alcoholic polyneuritis caused by a combination of high caloric intake and defective thiamine absorption and the polyneuritis of pregnancy caused by the increased metabolic demands of the fetus.

In the treatment of beriberi and the polyneuritides which result from thiamine deficiencies, thiamine hydrochloride is administered in 20–100 mg. daily doses orally or 20–50 mg. parenterally for two weeks and is then continued orally on a maintenance basis. The recovery is rapid and the vitamin is generally regarded as nontoxic.

For adults with ordinary caloric intake the recommended daily thiamine requirement is 0.5 mg. for every 1000 calories consumed up to a total of 3000 calories and 0.3 mg. for each 1000 calories over 3000.[88] The richest sources of thiamine among natural foods are pork, mammalian livers, yeast, whole cereals, and fresh green vegetables. The thiamine content of most foods is essentially unaffected by freezing, but considerable losses are sustained during the milling of rice and flour and during cooking. For this reason some processed foods are now enriched regularly with thiamine.

87. V. Ramalingaswami, *Federation Proc.*, *17*, 43 (1948).
88. L. S. Goodman and A. Gilman, *The Pharmacological Basis of Therapeutics*, 2nd. ed., Macmillan, N.Y., 1955, p. 1695.

CHAPTER IV

Riboflavine, Flavine Mononucleotide, and Flavine-Adenine Dinucleotide

1. Introduction

Shortly after the isolation of thiamine from yeast concentrates, the presence of a second nutritional factor in such materials was suggested.[1] This second "factor," in contrast to thiamine, appeared to be a thermostable growth-promoting substance. In time this second "factor" was also reported to have a pellagra-preventive activity since it alleviated a deficiency-induced dermatitis in rats.[2] It was designated "vitamin B_2" in Great Britain and "vitamin G" in the United States.[3] The mistaken concept that the thermostable "factor" was a single entity related to a single deficiency disease led to confusion and delay in the isolation of certain members of the vitamin B complex.

In 1926 a statement was made concerning "the remote possibility of more than one thermostable factor in yeast concentrates which further study may succeed in differentiating."[2] In retrospect this statement was reasonable and even conservative. Recognition of the complex nature of the thermostable "factor" and progress toward the isolation of given components were delayed by the failure to realize that not all animal species respond similarly to a given nutritional factor. Since animal assays were used almost exclusively to guide fractionation of the thermostable "factor" at the early stages, apparent loss of activity was indicated occasionally with purified fractions because a noncorrelating animal assay was being used for that particular active compound. For example, little headway was made toward the isolation of vitamin B_2 on the basis of pellagra prevention in the rat, but prompt progress was reported after its identification with rat-growth activity. After variation in species response to a given nutritional factor was recognized, the complex nature of the thermostable "factor" was demonstrated, and the so-called "vitamin B_2 complex" was found to consist of riboflavine (a rat growth-promoting

1. A. D. Emmett and G. O. Luros, *J. Biol. Chem.*, *43*, 265 (1920).
2. J. Goldberger and R. D. Lillie, *Public Health Repts.* (*U.S.*), *41*, 297 (1926).
3. B. Sure, *J. Am. Med. Assoc.*, *99*, 26 (1932).

factor), pyridoxol (a rat pellagra-preventing factor), pantothenic acid (a chick antidermatitis factor), and nicotinic acid (a human pellagra-preventing factor).

The first substantial progress in the isolation and characterization of riboflavine was made after the recognition of its growth-promoting activity.[4,5] When young rats were maintained on a synthetic deficient diet that was supplemented with thiamine, the weight response curve flattened-out or showed a decline. After the addition of thiamine-free milk concentrates, whey, or crude thiamine-free extracts of yeast, liver, or rice bran, normal growth was restored. The assays based on rat-growth required a period of three to four weeks, so progress was necessarily slow. Fortunately, a yellow-green fluorescence was observed in the active concentrates, and the fluorescence became more intense as the activity of the concentrates increased. This identification of activity with color facilitated the assay and led to a rapid final isolation of riboflavine.

Before these studies were completed an anomaly was encountered. Up to a stage the fluorescence of the solution could be correlated with growth activity, but then biological activity began to diminish as the fluorescence increased. If the rats' diets were also supplemented with fluorescence-free yeast extracts, the growth-promoting activity of the highly purified fluorescent fractions was restored. This information was construed as experimental evidence for the removal of a second essential component of the thermostable component during the purification of riboflavine, and the purification studies were continued using the fluorescence assay. After the isolation of crystalline riboflavine, the synthetic diets were supplemented with thiamine and riboflavine, but the rats failed to maintain a normal growth rate; the further addition of a colorless flavine-free yeast eluate restored growth. The eluate factor, inactive in this assay in the absence of riboflavine, later proved to be pyridoxol and substantiated, in part, the concept of a thermostable "vitamin B_2 complex."

Using the increase in yellow-green fluorescence of the various fractions as a measure of increased rat-growth activity, a small amount of the active factor was isolated from egg white,[4] and the compound was designated "ovoflavin." When whey was substituted as a source material in the same isolation procedure, the factor was designated "lactoflavin." Shortly thereafter, the presence of similar substances was reported in milk, liver, kidney, muscle, and yeast.[6] The term "lyochrome" was rejected, and the

4. R. Kuhn, P. György, and T. Wagner-Jauregg, *Ber.*, *66*, 317, 576 (1933).
5. P. György, *Nutr. Revs.*, *12*, 97 (1954).
6. P. Ellinger and W. Koschara, *Ber.*, *66*, 315 (1933).

designation "flavin" was adopted for these growth-promoting water-soluble pigments. During the early studies a prefix was usually added to the term "flavin" to designate the origin of the compound. Accordingly, the terms "ovoflavin," "lactoflavin," and "hepatoflavin" described the product isolated from egg white, milk, and liver, respectively. The name riboflavine was adopted after it was known that the factor contained a ribose moiety attached to an isoalloxazine nucleus. Since this vitamin is the first member isolated from the "vitamin B_2 complex," it is also referred to as vitamin B_2; the term should not be confused with the earlier designation of a pellagra-preventive activity as "vitamin B_2 or G."

2. Isolation

Riboflavine occurs in nature as free riboflavine, the monophosphate (flavine mononucleotide), and the pyrophosphate (flavine-adenine dinucleotide). Free riboflavine is found only in whey, urine, and the retina; in all other living cells it is found either as flavine mononucleotide or flavine-adenine dinucleotide.

A general scheme for the isolation of free riboflavine may be summarized as follows.[7] Riboflavine is liberated from protein-bound forms by extracting macerated tissue with solvents such as alcohols, acetone, water, or aqueous acids. Lipid impurities are usually removed by ether extraction, and other impurities are eliminated either by fractional precipitation from aqueous solvents or by precipitation with specific reagents such as picric acid, silver nitrate, or mercuric sulfate. Extracts containing free riboflavine are partially purified by the precipitation of accompanying protein with ammonium sulfate. Such partially purified extracts may be treated with fuller's earth if the solution is acidic or with Florisil or Frankonit if the solutions are neutral. Bases such as pyridine, ammonia, triethanolamine, or $0.1N$ sodium hydroxide are used for elution. Riboflavine is usually crystallized from aqueous acetone-petroleum ether mixtures.

The isolation procedure using egg white as the source material will serve as a specific illustration.[4] The yellow-green component of egg albumin was extracted by methanol, leaving behind most accompanying protein. After acidification, the active principle was adsorbed on fuller's earth and eluted with dilute aqueous pyridine; the addition of alcohol or acetone to the pyridine eluate precipitated many impurities. The purified active principle, now in neutral solution, was adsorbed on fuller's earth and

7. T. Wagner-Jauregg, in W. H. Sebrell, Jr. and R. S. Harris, eds., *The Vitamins: Chemistry, Physiology, and Pathology*, Vol. III, Academic, N.Y., 1954, p. 303.

eluted. The vitamin was precipitated from solution with silver nitrate and then liberated with sulfuric acid. Crystallization of the purified product from $2N$ acetic acid yielded pure crystalline riboflavine. By this procedure, 30 kg. of dried egg albumin, corresponding to about 10,000 eggs, yielded 30 mg. of pure riboflavine.

3. Structure Determination

The structure of riboflavine was established as 6,7-dimethyl-9-(1′-*D*-ribityl)isoalloxazine (**1**).

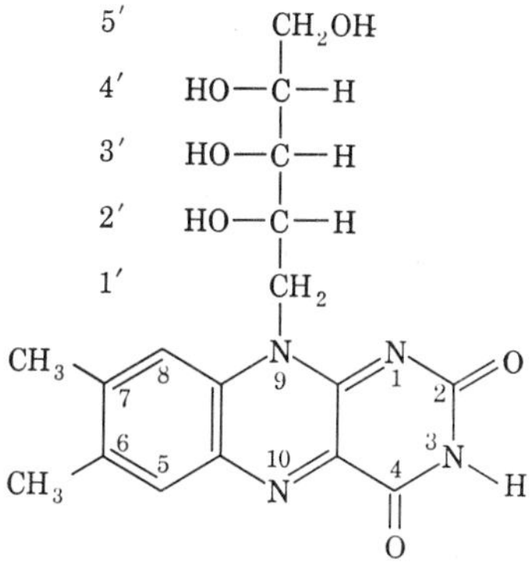

(1)

The structure of the isoalloxazine moiety was deduced from the following series of reactions.[8–10] Riboflavine was reversibly reduced by mild reducing agents to a leuco compound which was reoxidized to riboflavine on exposure to air. The factor was stable to some oxidizing agents; however, chromic acid oxidation of the compound yielded ammonia, carbon dioxide, and an unidentified compound. Hydrolysis with barium hydroxide gave urea. Photolysis in alkaline solution yielded a new compound, lumiflavine (**2**), which contained the isoalloxazine moiety.

Lumiflavine under alkaline conditions reacted with two molecules of water and gave urea and a new carboxylic acid (**3**). Since hydrolysis required two molecules of water, it was assumed that the reaction resulted in a ring cleavage. The keto acid (**3**) was thermally decarboxylated to the cyclic amide (**4**), which was degraded with alkali to 4-amino-1,2-dimethyl-5-methylaminobenzene (**5**). From these data, 6,7,9-trimethylisoalloxazine was proposed as the structure for lumiflavine. The synthesis of lumiflavine

8. P. Ellinger and W. Koschara, *Ber.*, *66*, 1411 (1933).
9. R. Kuhn and H. Rudy, *Ber.*, *67*, 892, 1298 (1934).
10. R. Kuhn and T. Wagner-Jauregg, *Ber.*, *66*, 1577 (1933).

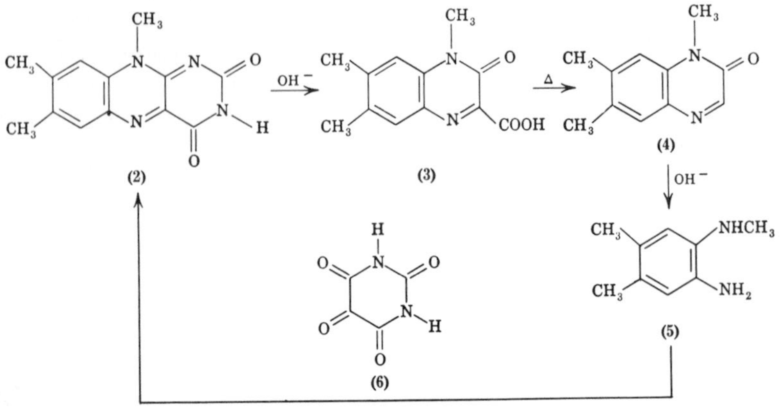

(2) (3) (4) (5) (6)

by the condensation of 4-amino-1,2-dimethyl-5-methylaminobenzene with alloxan (**6**) confirmed the assigned structure.[11]

Since lumiflavine was derived from riboflavine by the loss of a hydroxylated side chain and since it was known that riboflavine did not contain an *N*-methyl group, the nitrogen-containing moiety of riboflavine was formulated as the 6,7-dimethyl-9-isoalloxazyl group (**7**).

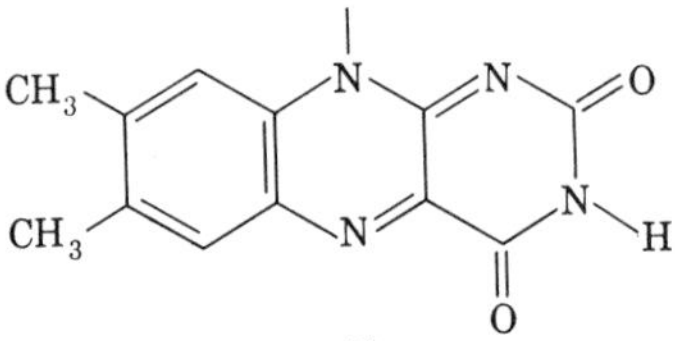

(7)

The 9-ribityl side chain was deduced as follows. Acetylation of riboflavine gave a tetraacetate and treatment with acetone gave a bis-isopropylidene derivative. Oxidation of riboflavine with lead tetraacetate gave one equivalent of formaldehyde. At this stage the data were consistent with a side chain containing four hydroxyl groups of which only one was primary and therefore, terminal. Since the irradiation of riboflavine resulted both in the loss of the elements $C_4H_4(OH)_4$ and the formation of an *N*-methylisoalloxazine, it was concluded that the side chain is an unbranched five-carbon skeleton with hydroxyl groups on four consecutive atoms; the deoxy-carbon atom presumably served to link the carbohydrate moiety to the isoalloxazine as in (**8**). The configuration of the side chain was established as *D*-ribityl by synthesis.

$$—CH_2CH(OH)CH(OH)CH(OH)CH_2OH$$

(**8**)

11. R. Kuhn, K. Reinemund, and F. Weygand, *Ber.*, *67*, 1460 (1934).

4. Synthesis

The confirmatory synthesis began with the reductive condensation of 4-amino-5-carbethoxyamino-1,2-dimethylbenzene (**9**) with *D*-ribose (**10**) which yielded 4-amino-1,2-dimethyl-5-*D*-ribitylaminobenzene (**11**); condensation of (**11**) with alloxan (**6**) gave riboflavine.[12]

(9) + (10) → (11) —(6)→ Riboflavine (1)

Early commercial syntheses of riboflavine required the condensation of a suitably substituted *D*-ribitylaminobenzene with alloxan and suffered the disadvantage of using *D*-ribose at some stage of the process. Since ribose was a relatively difficult compound to obtain in good yield, the over-all yields of such processes were low. Since that time many syntheses have appeared which avoid the direct use of *D*-ribose at any stage of the process. The following synthesis exemplifies a process using *D*-arabonic acid as the ribityl precursor, and also demonstrates the application of condensation between *o*-amino-diazo compounds and barbituric acid to the synthesis of isoalloxazines.[13,14] *D*-Arabonic acid (**12**), a compound readily prepared from *D*-glucose, was epimerized to *D*-ribonic acid. The latter was converted by way of the corresponding amide to tetraacetyl-*D*-ribonitrile (**13**). The reductive condensation between tetraacetyl-*D*-ribonitrile and 3,4-dimethylaniline (**14**) yielded 1,2-dimethyl-4-tetraacetyl-*D*-ribitylaminobenzene (**15**). Condensation of this product with *p*-nitrophenyldiazonium chloride yielded 1,2-dimethyl-4-*p*-nitrophenyldiazo-5-tetraacetyl-*D*-ribitylaminobenzene (**16**), which after condensation with barbituric acid (**17**) gave riboflavine.

Currently a large proportion of the commercial riboflavine for animal feeds is produced by fermentation. Among the organisms used in the

12. P. Karrer, K. Schöpp, and F. Benz, *Helv. Chim. Acta*, *18*, 426 (1935).
13. M. Tishler, J. W. Wellman, and K. Ladenburg, *J. Am. Chem. Soc.*, *67*, 2165 (1945).
14. M. Tishler, K. Pfister, R. B. Babson, K. Ladenburg, and A. J. Fleming, *J. Am. Chem. Soc.*, *69*, 1487 (1947).

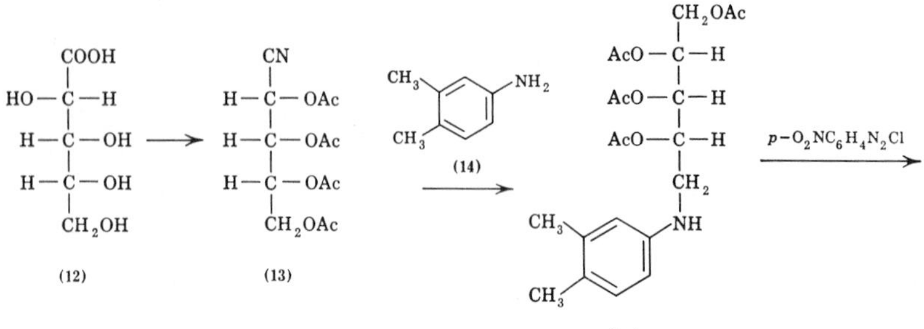

(12) → (13) + (14) → (15) $\xrightarrow{p\text{-}O_2NC_6H_4N_2Cl}$ (16) $\xrightarrow{(17)}$ Riboflavine (1)

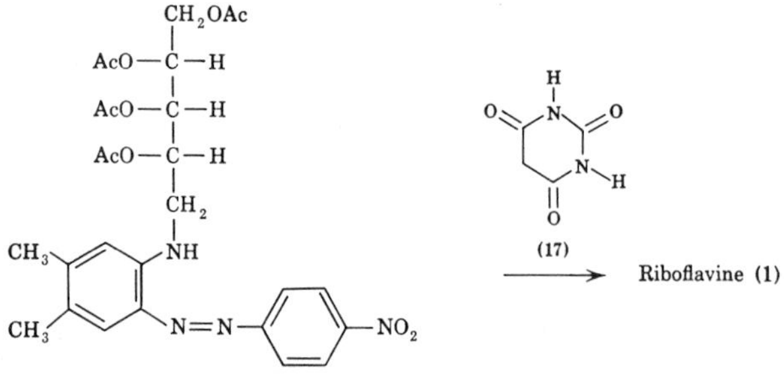

commercial biosynthesis of this vitamin are the bacteria, *Clostridium* spp.; the yeasts, *Candida* spp.; and the fungi, *Eremothecium ashbyii* and *Ashbya gossypii.*

5. Reactions

Two distinctive features of the chemistry of riboflavine are its cleavage on irradiation and its behavior on reduction. Irradiation of riboflavine in alkaline solution gives the isoalloxazine, lumiflavine (**2**);[15] in acid solution the alloxazine, lumichrome (**18**), is obtained.[16]

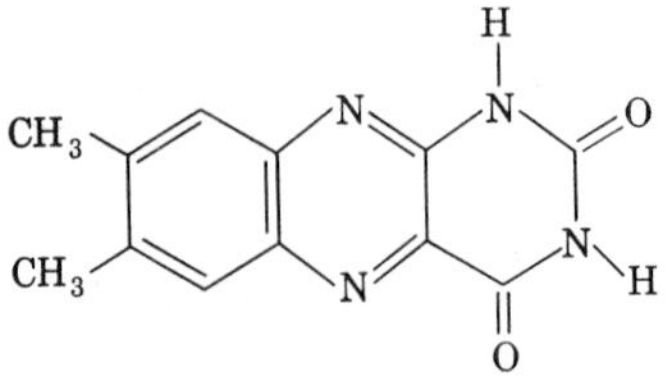

(18)

15. R. Kuhn, H. Rudy, and T. Wagner-Jauregg, *Ber.*, *66*, 1950 (1933).
16. P. Karrer, H. Salomon, K. Schöpp, E. Schlittler, and H. Fritzsche, *Helv. Chim. Acta*, *17*, 1010 (1934).

Riboflavine is reversibly reduced to the leuco compound dihydroriboflavine (**19**).[15] If the reduction of riboflavine is carried out in a stepwise

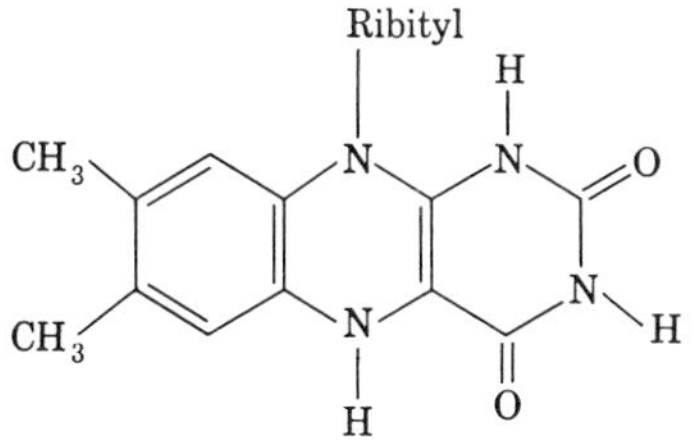

(19)

fashion, intermediate semiquinoid forms of the molecule are detected in solution.[17,18] In some cases a series of highly colored molecular compounds comprised of flavine, leucoflavine, and intermediate forms have been isolated and characterized. Three such molecular compounds which are formed during the partial reduction of araboflavine were isolated.[17] Since the differences in solubility between these compounds were far greater than those between corresponding compounds from riboflavine, they were good model compounds. This research resulted in the isolation of a bronze-green complex (verdoflavine) composed of one equivalent of flavine and one equivalent of monohydroflavine, a grass-green quinhydrone (chloroflavine) that contained one equivalent of flavine and one equivalent of leucoflavine, and a red compound (rhodoflavine) composed of the hydrochlorides of monohydroflavine and leucoflavine.

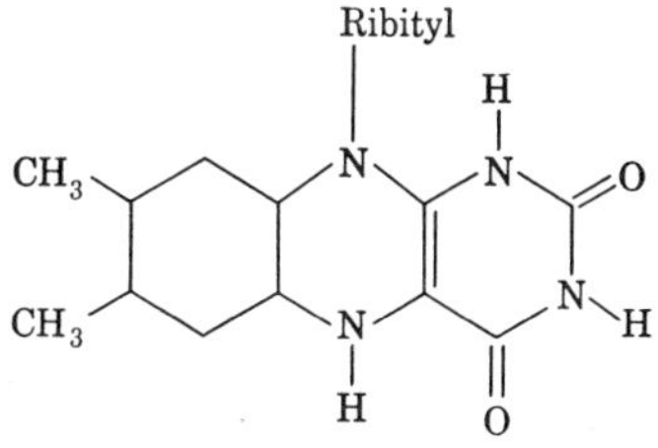

(20) 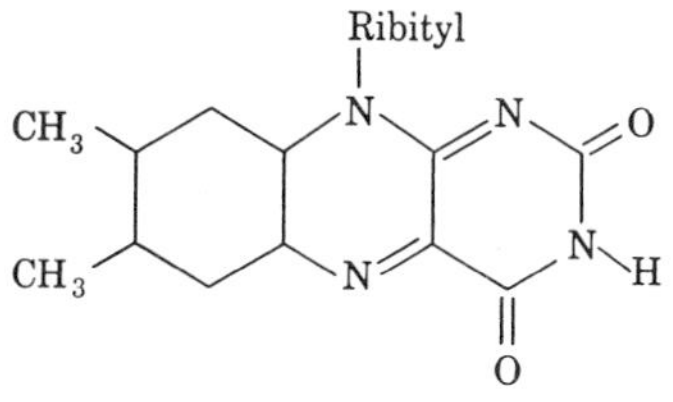 (21)

Rigorous catalytic hydrogenation of riboflavine yielded octahydroriboflavine (**20**) which was partially oxidized in alkaline solution to yield hexahydroriboflavine (**21**).[19]

17. R. Kuhn and R. Strobele, *Ber.*, *70*, 753 (1937).
18. L. Michaelis, M. P. Schubert, and C. V. Smythe, *J. Biol. Chem.*, *116*, 587 (1936).
19. P. Karrer and R. Ostwald, *Rec. Trav. Chim.*, *57*, 500 (1938).

6. Metabolic Role

A. Coenzyme Forms

The two coenzyme forms of riboflavine are known as flavine mononucleotide and flavine-adenine dinucleotide. They are found in a large number of systems which function in carbohydrate metabolism and serve as agents for the transfer of hydrogen between the nicotinic acid-containing coenzymes I and II and the iron-porphyrin cytochromes. These flavine enzymes actually constitute only part of a complex enzyme system that effects the cascade of hydrogen from a substrate to molecular oxygen forming water.

The simpler coenzyme form is riboflavine 5′-phosphate (**22**). It is usually referred to as flavine mononucleotide although by strict nomenclature it is not a nucleotide, but rather a glycityl- or, specifically, a 5-phosphoribityl derivative. Its structure was deduced from the observation that

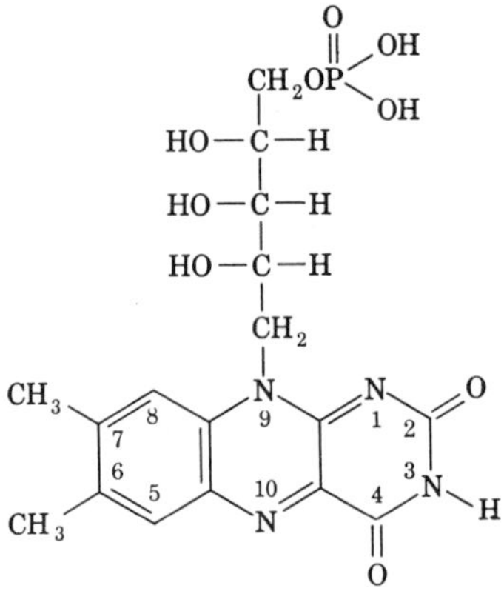

(22)

treatment of riboflavine with phosphorus oxychloride yielded a product with the same activity as "cytoflav" isolated from heart muscle.[20] Structural conclusions based on this reaction were verified by the following unambiguous synthesis of the coenzyme.[21] Treatment of riboflavine with triphenylchloromethane in pyridine solution yielded 5′-tritylriboflavine. After this compound was triacetylated, the trityl group was removed, and the 5′-position was phosphorylated with phosphorus oxychloride in pyridine solution. The product was then deacetylated by mild treatment with dilute sodium hydroxide, and the coenzyme was isolated as either the sodium or calcium salt.

20. R. Kuhn and H. Rudy, *Ber.*, *69*, 1974, 2034 (1936).
21. R. Kuhn, H. Rudy, and F. Weygand, *Ber.*, *69*, 1543 (1936).

Flavine enzymes containing riboflavine 5′-phosphate include Warburg's yellow enzyme[22] and cytochrome c reductase;[23] both systems participate in the enzymic oxidation of hexose monophosphate to phosphohexonic acids. *L*-Amino acid oxidase (*L*-hydroxy acid oxidase), which participates in enzyme systems that oxidize *L*-α-amino acids and *L*-α-hydroxy acids to α-keto acids, also contains flavine mononucleotide.[24]

The second coenzyme form, flavine-adenine dinucleotide (**23**), is found in a group of enzymes known as diaphorases. This coenzyme was deduced to be P^1-adenosine-5′ P^2-riboflavine-5′ pyrophosphate on the basis of degradation and synthesis. The structure determination was based on its cleavage to riboflavine 5′-phosphate and adenosine 5′-phosphate[25] and on the absence of formaldehyde after treatment with periodic acid.[26] Synthesis of the coenzyme from 2′,3′-*O*-isopropylideneadenosine 5′-benzylphosphorochloridate (**24**) and the monothallous or disilver salt of riboflavine 5′-phosphate (**25**) confirmed the existence of a pyrophosphate link in this molecule.[27]

Enzymes that contain flavine-adenine dinucleotide include xanthine oxidase, *D*-amino acid oxidase, glycine oxidase, fumaric hydrogenase, glucose oxidase, and histaminase (diamine oxidase).[28] This group of flavoproteins participates in biochemical oxidations by mediation in the transfer of hydrogen between the nicotinamide-adenine dinucleotides and the cytochrome system.

B. Coenzyme Role

The mechanism of riboflavine participation in enzymic hydrogen transfer is a topic of current interest. Among the problems being studied are the nature of intermediate forms of riboflavine that participate at various stages of the hydrogen transfer process, the mode of bonding between flavine coenzyme and apoenzyme, the role of metal ions in these processes, and finally the structural relationship between metal ion, flavine, and protein in these enzymes.

1. FREE RADICAL FORMS. Riboflavine participates in enzymic reactions through the formation of stabilized intermediate free radical forms. The

22. O. Warburg and W. Christian, *Biochem. Z.*, *254*, 438 (1932); *266*, 377 (1933).
23. E. Haas, B. L. Horecker, and T. Hogness, *J. Biol. Chem.*, *136*, 747 (1940).
24. M. Blanchard, D. E. Green, V. Nociti-Carroll, and S. Ratner, *J. Biol. Chem.*, *161*, 583 (1945); *163*, 137 (1946).
25. E. P. Abraham, *Biochem. J.*, *33*, 543 (1939).
26. P. Karrer and H. Frank, *Helv. Chim. Acta*, *23*, 948 (1940).
27. S. M. H. Christie, G. W. Kenner, and A. R. Todd, *J. Chem. Soc.*, 46 (1954).
28. M. K. Horwitt, in W. H. Sebrell, Jr. and R. S. Harris, eds., *The Vitamins: Chemistry, Physiology, and Pathology*, Vol. III, Academic, N.Y., 1954, p. 334.

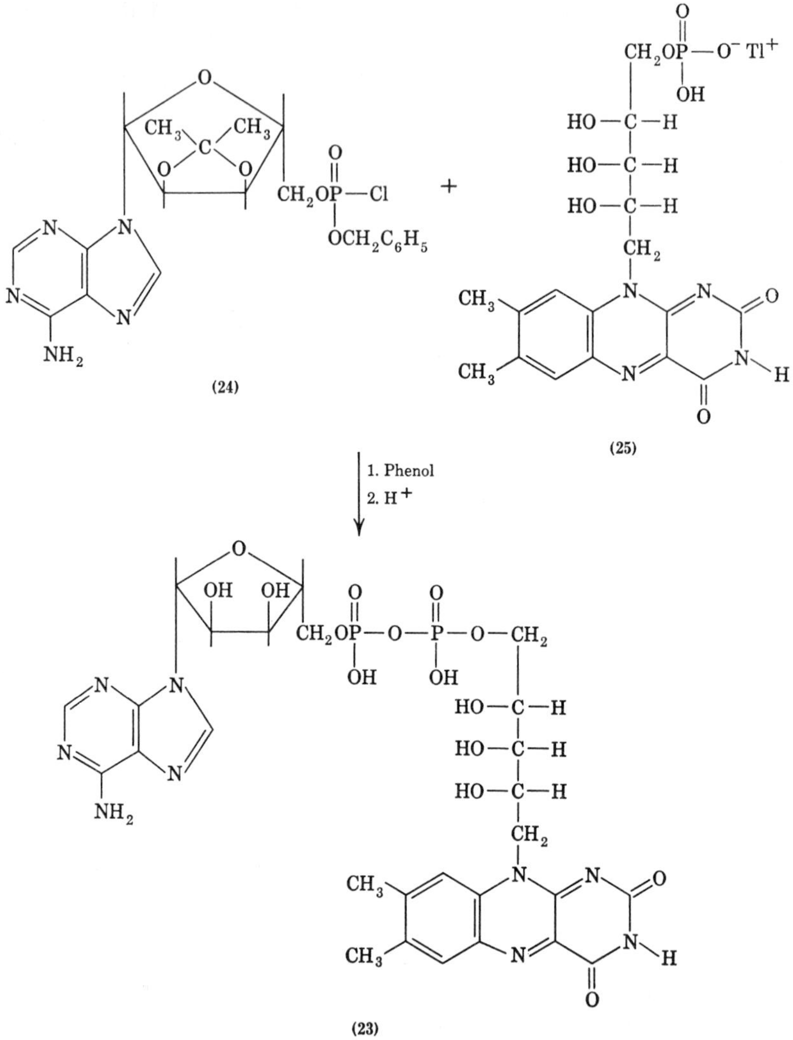

O
CH$_3$ C CH$_3$
O O
O
CH_2OP—Cl
$OCH_2C_6H_5$
N N
N N
NH_2

(24)

+

O
CH_2OP—O^- Tl^+
OH
HO—C—H
HO—C—H
HO—C—H
CH_2
CH_3 N N O
CH_3 N N H
O

(25)

1. Phenol
2. H^+

O
OH OH
O O
CH_2OP—O—P—O—CH_2
OH OH
N N
N N
NH_2
HO—C—H
HO—C—H
HO—C—H
CH_2
CH_3 N N O
CH_3 N N H
O

(23)

formation of red solutions was observed during the partial reduction of riboflavine in 10% hydrochloric acid solution.[29] Strong absorption by these solutions at 490 mμ and reversible re-oxidation of the red intermediate to the original flavine was also demonstrated. By analogy to the pyocyanines, it was suggested that partial reduction of riboflavine in strongly acidic solution produced an equilibrium concentration of a

29. R. Kuhn and T. Wagner-Jauregg, *Ber.*, *67*, 361 (1934).

monohydro semiquinoid form of the flavine. A detailed study of this reaction confirmed the existence of a red semiquinone form of the monohydroflavine at $\text{pH} < 0$.[18] In the pH range 2–12, however, different ionization states of the intermediate monohydroflavine produced green rather than red solutions. The green solutions could also be re-oxidized to

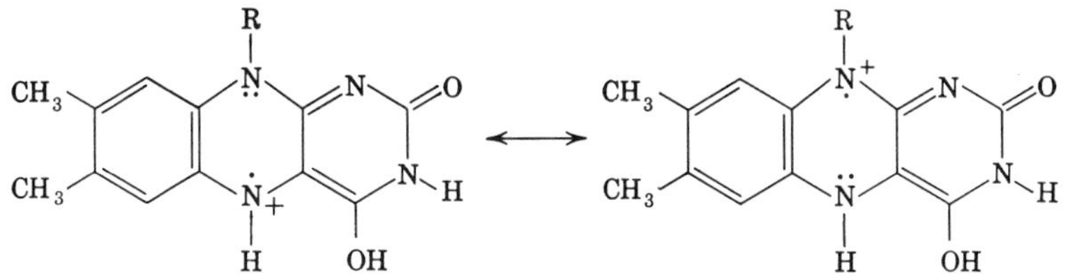

(26)

the original flavine. Analysis of the response of normal potential to pH in the dihydroflavine-semiquinone, flavine-semiquinone, and dihydroflavine-flavine systems led to the formulation of the red monohydroflavine as the resonance system (**26**), the green monohydroflavine as the resonance

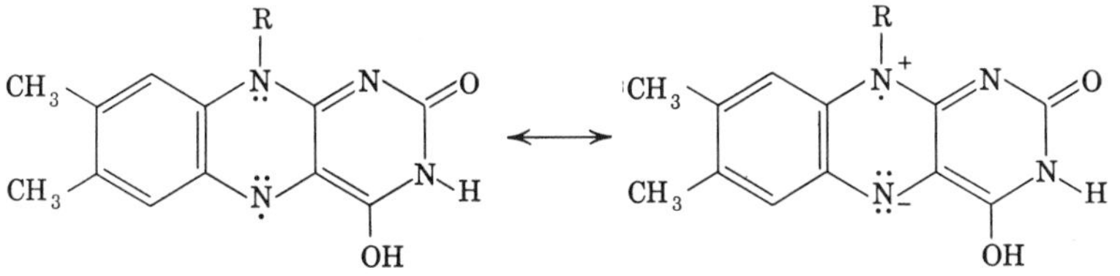

(27)

system (**27**), and the dihydroflavine as (**28**) up to pH 6 or the anion (**29**) above pH 6.

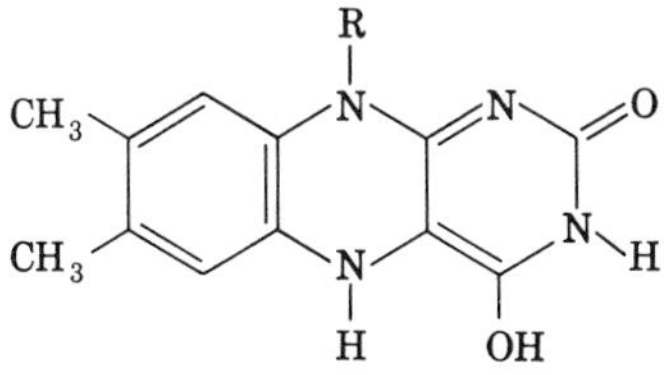

(28)

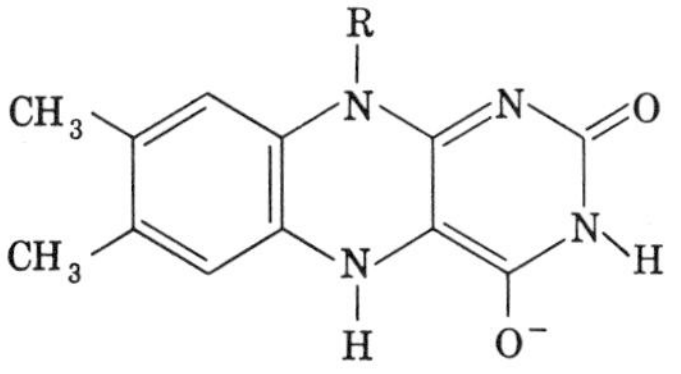

(29)

When Warburg's "old yellow enzyme" was partially reduced with sodium dithionate in the presence of excess triphosphopyridine nucleotide, a transitory red color corresponding to a shift in the ultraviolet absorption spectrum from 465 mμ to 475 mμ appeared.[30] On the basis of spectral

30. E. Haas, *Biochem. Z.*, *290*, 291 (1937).

changes that were noted in the partial reduction of flavine dyes, this observation was construed as evidence for the participation of free radicals in flavoprotein catalyzed oxidation-reduction reactions. Furthermore, the red color of the intermediate was cited as evidence for the existence of the semiquinone form (**26**) of the bound coenzyme even in neutral solution.[18,31]

After several years during which no further effort was devoted to the study of the reduction of riboflavine to its semiquinoid forms, the spectral properties of the semiquinoid form of riboflavine were reported and the occurrence of free radicals during flavoprotein catalysis was reinvestigated.[32,33] The conditions of one experiment were such that a red complex was not observed with flavine-containing enzymes in oxidation-reduction systems; the only change noted was the appearance of a broad absorption band at 565 mμ in the ultraviolet absorption spectra of these systems. When a ten- to fifteen-fold excess of reduced triphosphopyridine nucleotide was used in the partial reduction of the "old yellow enzyme," the original observation of a red intermediate was confirmed.[34] After ultracentrifugation of the reaction mixture, the complex was established as a compound containing the "old yellow enzyme" and triphosphopyridine nucleotide. A spectrophotometric assay of uncombined reduced triphosphopyridine nucleotide in the supernatant indicated that the enzyme bound two moles of triphosphopyridine nucleotide for each mole of flavine mononucleotide. The stability of the red complex was demonstrated by dialysis. The presence of free radicals in the reaction mixture was established by paramagnetic resonance absorption, and the free radical concentration was estimated to be about 15%. It was emphasized, however, that the absence of kinetic data prevented identification of these free radicals with the actual intermediates of the enzymic reaction.

It has been reported that flavine mononucleotide, flavine-adenine dinucleotide, and the flavoprotein enzymes readily form free radicals on exposure to ordinary intensities of visible light.[35] These light-induced free radicals appear to be identical with those formed during oxidation-reduction processes. In neutral solution, the characteristic green verdoflavine color appears; in acid solution the red intermediate rhodoflavine is obtained. The effective light intensities were of an order suggesting that

31. L. Michaelis, in J. B. Sumner and K. Myrbäck, eds., *The Enzymes: Chemistry and Mechanism of Action*, Vol. II, Part 1, Academic, N.Y., 1951, p. 49.
32. H. Beinert, *J. Am. Chem. Soc.*, *78*, 5323 (1956).
33. H. Beinert, *Biochim. et Biophys. Acta*, *20*, 588 (1956); *J. Biol. Chem.*, *225*, 465 (1957).
34. A. Ehrenberg and G. D. Ludwig, *Science*, *127*, 1177 (1958).
35. B. Commoner and B. B. Lippincott, *Proc. Natl. Acad. Sci.* (*U.S.*), *44*, 1110 (1958).

the preparation of a flavoprotein enzyme in ordinary light would alter the "natural" free radical content and consequent behavior of the enzyme.

In view of these data, the mediation of hydrogen transfer by a flavine coenzyme is regarded as proceeding through a reversible system stepwise, by the acceptance of one hydrogen atom at a time. In the course of reaction, the coenzyme progresses through the sequence, flavine $\rightleftarrows$ semiquinone $\rightleftarrows$ dihydroflavine.

2. COENZYME-APOENZYME BONDING. Another problem of immediate concern is the nature of the bond between flavine coenzyme and apoenzyme. The evidence supports the view that the phosphate group of flavine mononucleotide plays an important role in binding FMN to the protein component of Warburg's "yellow enzyme."[36–40] A similar situation is assumed to exist in other FMN-protein systems, and it has been suggested that at physiological pH's, the negatively charged phosphate group is bound to a positively charged amino group of the protein.[39,40]

There is also interaction between the isoalloxazine moiety of the coenzyme and the protein. For example, free- and protein-bound FMN differ in absorption spectra, fluorescence spectra, and oxidation-reduction potentials. Furthermore, combination of riboflavine with the "old yellow apoenzyme" quenches the fluorescence of riboflavine.[36,39] The failure of 3-substituted flavines to form enzyme systems also supports the concept of isoalloxazine participation in binding coenzyme to protein.[36] Actually, the early suggestion of a hydrogen bond between the protein of the apoenzyme and the imino group in the 3-position of the isoalloxazine ring[36,41] has become increasingly popular during the years. Kinetic data from reactions of native and iodinated "old yellow enzyme" provide evidence for hydrogen bonding between protein and isoalloxazine.[39,40] One such link is visualized as a hydrogen bond between the imino group in the 3-position of the isoalloxazine and the hydroxyl function of a tyrosine component of protein. There is also evidence for the participation of the nitrogen atom in the 10-position of the isoalloxazine moiety in binding coenzyme to protein.[42]

Alternatively, molecular charge transfer has been suggested as a more important factor in coenzyme-protein binding than hydrogen bonding.[43]

36. R. Kuhn and H. Rudy, *Ber.*, *69*, 2257 (1936).
37. H. Thorell, *Biochem. Z.*, *278*, 263 (1935).
38. H. Thorell, *Biochem. Z.*, *290*, 293 (1937).
39. H. Thorell and A. P. Nygaard, *Acta Chem. Scand.*, *8*, 1649 (1954).
40. A. P. Nygaard and H. Thorell, *Acta Chem. Scand.*, *9*, 1587 (1955).
41. R. Kuhn and P. Boulanger, *Ber.*, *69*, 1557 (1936).
42. T. A. Geissman, *Quart. Rev. Biol.*, *24*, 309 (1949).
43. H. A. Harbury and K. A. Foley, *Proc. Natl. Acad. Sci.* (*U.S.*), *44*, 662 (1958).

This suggestion is based on a series of spectrophotometrically determined disassociation constants for complexes formed between isoalloxazine derivatives and several conjugated molecules. Where hydrogen bonding is possible, the relative values of the apparent disassociation constants bore little relation to values predicted on the basis of interaction by hydrogen bond formation. Also, 3-methylriboflavine, which is incapable of hydrogen bonding through the 3-position, was as reactive as riboflavine or flavine mononucleotide. Bonding by charge transfer between protein and riboflavine is also indicated by a study of free radical formation in riboflavine complexes.(44) The production and stabilization of a semiquinoid form of riboflavine was observed after the addition of either tryptophan or proteins containing tryptophan to solutions of riboflavine 5′-phosphate. In addition, a shoulder at 490 mμ in the absorption spectrum of the "old yellow enzyme" was interpreted as absorption due to a semiquinone form of riboflavine 5′-phosphate stabilized by the tryptophan of protein. It is conceded that hydrogen bonding may account for additional linkages within the cell itself. If charge transfer between protein and riboflavine does occur, it has been suggested that electron transport could be visualized as proceeding through the protein molecule, rather than on the surface of the protein molecule.(44)

3. ROLE OF CATIONS. The dependence of enzymes on metal-ion activators has been established for a variety of biological oxidation systems, and a series of metallo-flavoproteins has been isolated in which firmly bound flavine, protein, and metal ion function as an entity rather than a loosely bound aggregate. Seven such metallo-flavoproteins, containing copper, iron, or molybdenum, have been characterized. Among these complexes are the cuproflavoprotein, butyryl-CoA dehydrogenase;(45) the molybdoflavoprotein, xanthine oxidase;(46) the iron-containing flavoprotein, DPNH cytochrome reductase;(47) and the molybdoflavoprotein, aldehyde oxidase.(48) The properties and structural aspects of these metalloflavoproteins have been summarized, and a mechanism of action has been proposed.(49,50)

The apoenzyme of a given system requires a particular metal ion and usually cannot be activated by any other cation. The degree of affinity between protein and ion varies. Copper ion, which is perhaps the most

44. I. Isenberg and A. Szent-Györgi, *Proc. Natl. Acad. Sci.* (*U.S.*), *44*, 857 (1958).
45. H. R. Mahler, *J. Am. Chem. Soc.*, *75*, 3288 (1953); *J. Biol. Chem.*, *206*, 13 (1954).
46. B. Mackler, H. R. Mahler, and D. E. Green, *J. Biol. Chem.*, *210*, 149 (1954).
47. H. R. Mahler and D. G. Elowe, *J. Biol. Chem.*, *210*, 165 (1954).
48. H. R. Mahler, B. Mackler, and D. E. Green, *J. Biol. Chem.*, *210*, 465 (1954).
49. H. R. Mahler and D. E. Green, *Science*, *120*, 7 (1954).
50. H. R. Mahler, A. S. Fairhurst, and B. Mackler, *J. Am. Chem. Soc.*, *77*, 1514 (1955).

firmly bound, usually requires dialysis against cyanide ion to liberate it from the apoenzyme. Molybdenum ion is easily detached, and repeated precipitation of the enzyme with ammonium sulfate or dialysis against dilute ammonia liberates this ion. The affinity of iron for the protein is intermediate between that of copper and molybdenum. Once the ion is liberated, the concentration of metal ion required for complete reactivation exceeds the original concentration by factors up to 5000. This behavior is typical of conjugated enzymes since the ion can no longer be as firmly bound as it was by the unmodified protein.

Metal ion is not required for the reaction of reduced flavoprotein with two-electron acceptors such as organic redox dyes, quinones, or molecular oxygen. It is essential, however, for the reaction of reduced enzyme with one-electron acceptors such as cytochrome *c* or ferricyanide. The most profound effects of metal ion are observed in its influence on the oxidation-reduction potentials of flavine enzymes and on the reaction characteristics of the flavine with which it is associated. The observed changes in reaction velocity of any one reduced flavoprotein with a series of quinone acceptors, both in the presence and absence of "bound ion," clearly demonstrated the profound effect of the cation on the active site of the enzyme.[(50)]

To account for these observations, the "native enzyme" is visualized as a single resonance-stabilized entity comprised of metal ion, flavine coenzyme, and the amino acid moieties at the attachment sites on the apoenzyme. The enhanced mobility of π electrons in this system adds considerably to the stability of the semiquinoid forms of the coenzyme which are implicitly regarded as the intermediates in enzymic hydrogen transport. Facilitation of electron transport to the acceptor substrate during actual catalysis is envisioned by expanding the resonance hybrid to also include the acceptor molecule. The substrate, metal ion, flavine coenzyme, and protein are all part of one resonance system and electron transfer is intra- rather than intermolecular. Therefore, certain cations participate in flavoprotein catalysis by binding coenzyme to protein and stabilizing the active semiquinoid forms of the reduced coenzyme. These cations are essential for the reaction of flavoprotein with one-electron acceptor substrates, and participate by binding the acceptor to the flavoprotein system to facilitate rapid and efficient intramolecular transport of electrons from coenzyme to substrate.

4. RIBOFLAVINE-METAL CHELATES. Additional evidence for metal-ion participation in binding coenzyme to protein may be derived by comparing the pH stabilities of synthetic riboflavine chelates with those of native flavine enzymes. In view of the relative pH instability of certain synthetic chelates, it is suggested that the locus of stability or metal-ion affinity of

the intact enzyme is not confined to the prosthetic group but distributed between the coenzyme and protein moieties.

Early potentiometric studies of the behavior of riboflavine toward metal ions indicated the existence in solution of 1:1 chelates. By analogy to the behavior of 8-hydroxyquinoline, it was assumed that the cation was bound to N-10 and the adjacent enol at C-4 of riboflavine.[51] Insoluble complexes of riboflavine containing two gram atoms of Fe^{2+}, Co^{2+}, Cu^{2+}, Mn^{2+}, Ni^{2+}, or Zn^{2+} for each mole of flavine have also been reported.[52] In view of newer results, the composition and structure of riboflavine chelates is a subject for further investigation.

According to the most recent reports, model compounds with certain structural similarities to riboflavine form chelates containing either one or two molecules of the ligand for each metal ion.[53–55] The composition of the chelate is dependent upon pH, and the stability of the complex is dependent upon the steric or electronic effects of substituent groups near the site of metal-ion bonding. As the structures of the model compounds approximate that of riboflavine more and more, their ability to bind metal ion in a stable chelate form becomes less and less.

As a result of these studies with model compounds, certain observations have been recorded with respect to two highly probable structures for the riboflavine moiety in "native flavine enzymes." One such form is the

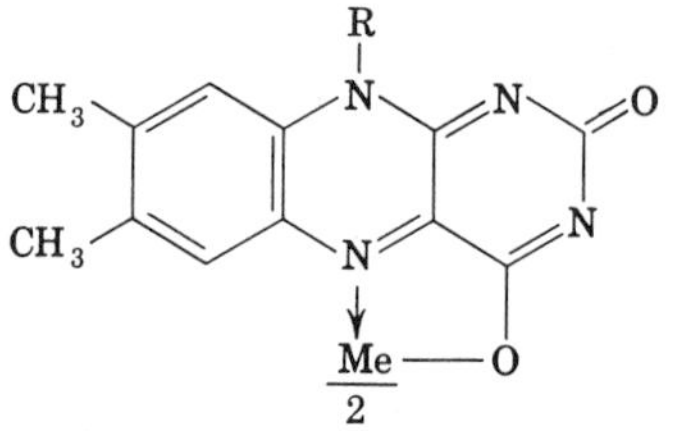

(30)

"8-hydroxyquinolate-like" moiety (**30**). With model bicyclic compounds containing the structural elements depicted in (**31**), highly insoluble chelates containing two molecules of ligand and one atom of Cu^{2+} were isolated at low pH. When mixtures of the model compound and Cu^{2+} were titrated with alkali, titration curves corresponding to the formation of 1:1

51. A. Albert, *Biochem. J.*, *47*, 27 (1950); *54*, 646 (1953).
52. W. O. Foye and W. E. Lange, *J. Am. Chem. Soc.*, *76*, 2199 (1954).
53. P. Hemmerich and S. Fallab, *Helv. Chim. Acta*, *41*, 498 (1958).
54. P. Hemmerich, B. Prijs, and H. Erlenmeyer, *Helv. Chim. Acta*, *43*, 372 (1960).
55. P. Bamberg, P. Hemmerich, and H. Erlenmeyer, *Helv. Chim. Acta*, *43*, 395 (1960).

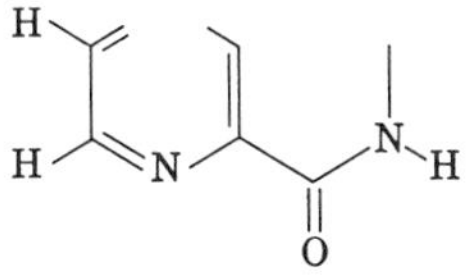

(31) 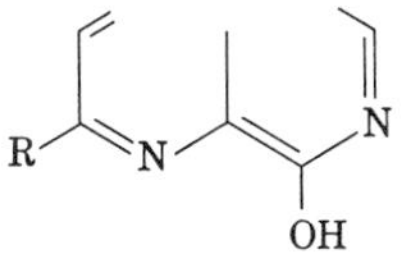 (32) 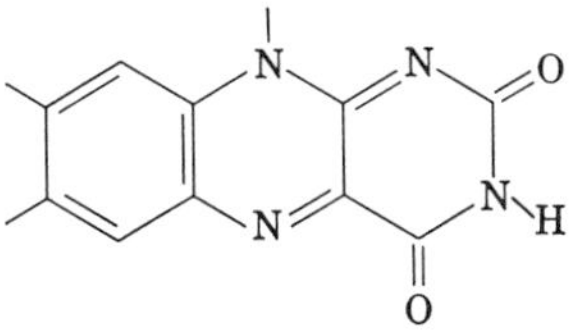 (33)

chelates were obtained. On the other hand, if solutions of bicyclic compounds containing the structural elements of (**32**) or tricyclic models of type (**33**) and Cu^{2+} were titrated with alkali, the data were interpreted to indicate the preliminary formation of $Cu(OH)^+$, and $CuO \cdot H_2O$ was eventually precipitated. A similar behavior was reported for riboflavine itself, and it was suggested that the riboflavine content reported for insoluble products might be due to adsorbed flavine. From these data, it was concluded that the stability of the "8-hydroxyquinolate-type" chelate is highly dependent upon the steric nature of the substituent at the position

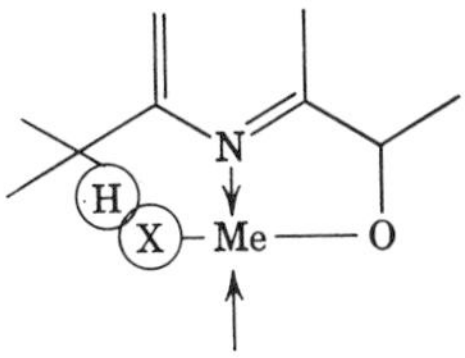

(34)

ortho to the participating nitrogen atom (cf. (**34**)). Consequently, an "8-hydroxyquinolate-like" moiety in a stable flavine enzyme is considered unlikely.[53] Further evidence for the exclusion of this moiety has been derived from the synthesis[54] and demonstrated instability[55] of the

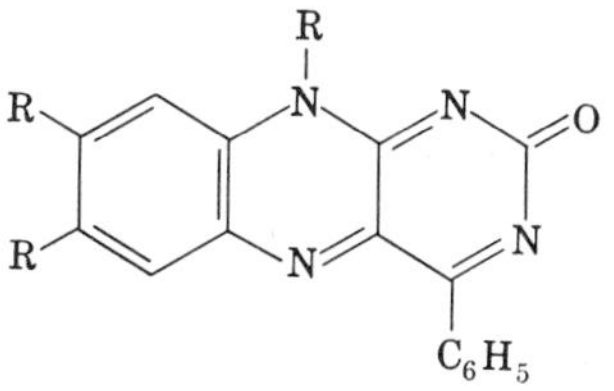

(35)

semiquinoid forms of 4-phenyl-4-deoxyisoalloxazines (**35**). The reaction of these radicals with oxygen, unlike those of true flavine semiquinones, is irreversible and results in the cleavage of the phenyl group and the formation of the corresponding isoalloxazines.

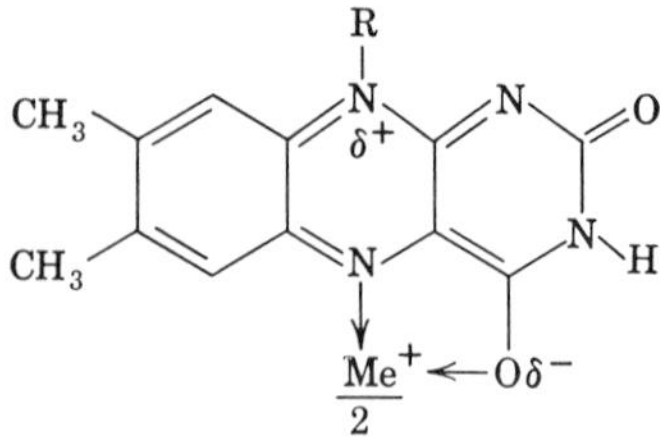

(36)

A more probable structure of the riboflavine moiety in flavine enzymes is the ion-dipole formulation (**36**). Model compounds most likely to yield such complexes were chosen from a series of acyl pyridines (**37**) containing no active hydrogen atoms. The simplest member of this series, 2-formylpyridine, forms the stable chelate (**40**) containing 2 molecules of ligand and 1 metal ion at pH 4–6; above pH 7 the stable 1:1 chelate (**41**) is formed.

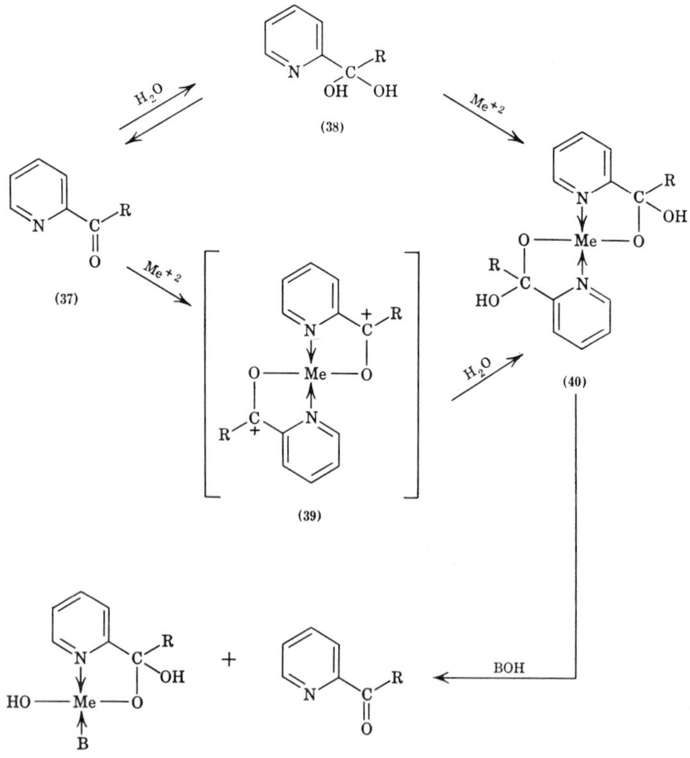

(38)

(37)

(39)

(40)

(41)

Other model compounds yielded similar complexes, but they were less stable. With the exception of 2-formylpyridine, which probably reacts in the acetal form (**38**), the reactions may be visualized as proceeding through the ionic intermediate (**39**).

Since the 1:1 chelate complexes (**41**) are equivalent in composition to the reactive species of flavoprotein in hydrogen transport, the affinity of the model compounds (**37**) for metal ion in the presence of hydroxyl ion was studied to establish the stability of an ion-dipole moiety. The stability of such a moiety is dependent upon both the steric and electronic influences of the substituent group in the 2-position and decreases progressively in the series: R = H, CH_3, OCH_3, C_6H_5, and $N(C_2H_5)_2$. With pyridine-2-(*N*,*N*-diethylcarboxamide), the stability of the ion-dipole moiety (**42**) is

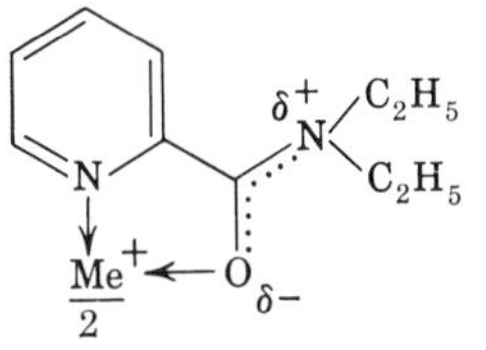

(**42**)

decreased to the extent that copper oxide is precipitated at pH 6–7. Since the arrangement of atoms adjacent to the binding sites in this model is closely related to that in riboflavine, an ion-dipole moiety cannot be considered likely in the flavine enzyme unless the protein participates in binding the cation and adds to the stability of such a moiety in native enzyme preparations.

7. Biosynthesis

The biosynthesis of riboflavine by growing cultures of *A. gossypii* has been studied extensively by using radioactive precursors and following the distribution of radioactivity in the riboflavine synthesized by the organism.[56–59] Part of the biogenetic pathway for this synthesis has been uncovered, but the results depicted in (**43**) fail to disclose the origin of the dimethylbenzo- or ribityl moieties. However, they do show a close metabolic relationship between purine biosynthesis and the biogenesis of rings B and C in riboflavine.

56. G. W. E. Plaut, *J. Biol. Chem.*, *211*, 111 (1954).
57. G. W. E. Plaut, *J. Biol. Chem.*, *208*, 513 (1954).
58. G. W. E. Plaut and P. L. Broberg, *J. Biol. Chem.*, *219*, 131 (1956).
59. G. W. E. Plaut, *Nutrition Symposium Series*, *13*, The National Vitamin Foundation, Inc., N.Y., 1956, p. 20.

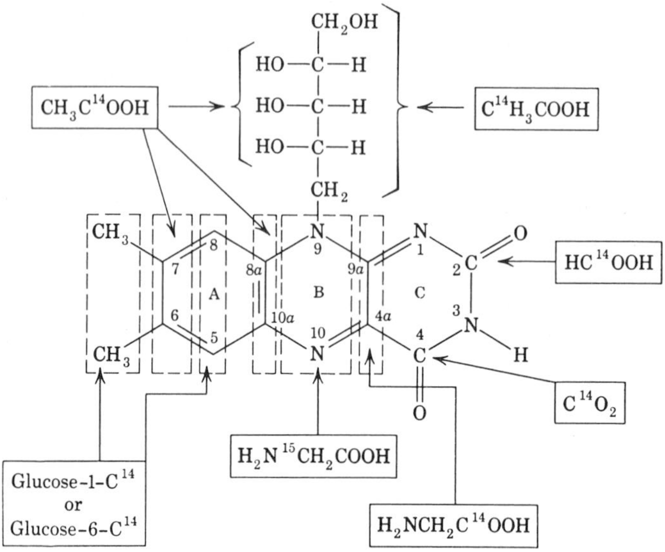

(43)

A study of the incorporation of labeled acetate and glucose by *A. gossypii* into the dimethylbenzo moiety showed that with either glucose-1-C^{14} or glucose-6-C^{14}, principal incorporation of radioactivity was in the 6- and 7-methyl groups and in carbon atoms 5 and 8.[56] With $C^{14}H_3COOH$, the distribution of radioactivity was more or less random but still predominantly in the 6- and 7-methyl groups and the carbon atoms 5 and 8. With $CH_3C^{14}OOH$, most of the isotope was in the carbon atom pairs 6 + 7 and 8a + 10a. Prior to these data, a demonstrated stimulation of biosynthesis by threonine[60] led to the proposal that the dimethylbenzo moiety could arise from the condensation of two molecules of threonine (**45**). If this were the case, it was predicted that the incorporation of threonine that was biosynthesized from $CH_3C^{14}OOH$ by way of aspartate (**44**) would give radioactivity predominantly in the 6- and 7-methyl groups and in the carbon atom pair 8a + 10a of (**46**).[59] Since isotope incorporation was observed in the carbon atom pairs 6 + 7 and 8a + 10a and not in the 6- and 7-methyl groups, the data do not support the earlier proposal on the biogenesis of ring A.

Another view on the biosynthesis of ring A was based on its possible derivation from 4,5-dimethyl-*o*-phenylenediamine in a manner analogous to cyanocobalamin biosynthesis. This compound and several of its

60. T. W. Goodwin and S. Pendlington, *Biochem. J.*, *57*, 631 (1954).

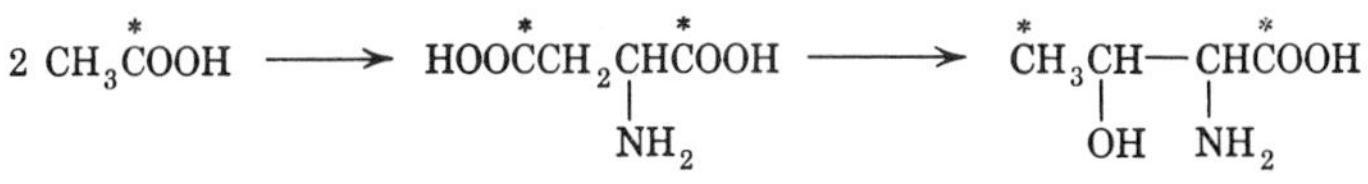

$$2\ CH_3\overset{*}{C}OOH \longrightarrow HOO\overset{*}{C}CH_2\underset{\displaystyle NH_2}{\overset{*}{C}H}COOH \longrightarrow \underset{\displaystyle OH}{\overset{*}{C}H_3CH}{-}\underset{\displaystyle NH_2}{\overset{*}{C}H}COOH$$

(44) (45)

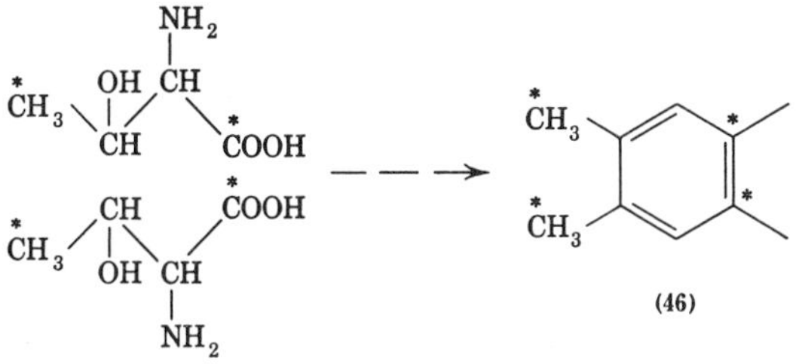

NH$_2$ | $\overset{*}{C}H_3$ OH CH CH $\overset{*}{C}OOH$; $\overset{*}{C}H_3$ CH OH CH $\overset{*}{C}OOH$ | NH$_2$ $\dashrightarrow$ $\overset{*}{C}H_3$, $\overset{*}{C}H_3$ (46)

derivatives, however, failed to stimulate the synthesis of riboflavine by *E. ashbyii* or *A. gossypii*.[59]

The pattern of C^{14} incorporation in rings B and C of riboflavine is remarkably similar to that observed for purine biosynthesis[57] and lends support to the purine pathway proposed earlier.[61] Labeled formate was incorporated at the 2-position and both $C^{14}O_2$ and $CH_3C^{14}OOH$ were incorporated at the 4-position. With either of the C^{14}-labeled glycine molecules, radioactivity was found in positions 9a + 4a. Stimulation by threonine, formerly associated with ring A biogenesis, can now be related[62,63] to incorporation at positions 9a + 4a. The threonine molecule is first cleaved to glycine and acetaldehyde by threonine aldolase. Consequently, only C-1 and C-2 of the threonine molecule are incorporated, and in a manner identical to glycine incorporation.

With N^{15}-glycine, the nitrogen atoms in position 9 and 10 contained thirty times as much N^{15} as found in the nitrogen atoms 1 and 3.

Purine-induced stimulation of riboflavine synthesis in *E. ashbyii* was also suggested by the observation that xanthine, adenine, or adenosine were effective riboflavine precursors.[60] A direct precursor relationship between purines and riboflavine in *E. ashbyii* was demonstrated,[64] and it was shown that adenine (**47**) incorporation proceeds with the pyrimidine ring intact. The biosynthetic incorporation of the entire purine system exclusive of the 8-position is suggested by the fact that little isotope enrichment was observed after addition of adenine-8-C^{14}, whereas significant

61. J. A. MacLaren, *J. Bacteriol.*, *63*, 233 (1952).
62. T. W. Goodwin and A. A. Horton, *Biochem. J.*, *73*, 13*P* (1959).
63. T. W. Goodwin and A. A. Horton, *Biochem. J.*, *75*, 53 (1960).
64. W. S. McNutt, *J. Biol. Chem.*, *210*, 511 (1954); *219*, 365 (1956).

radioactivity was found in riboflavine following the addition of randomly C^{14}-labeled adenine. This biosynthetic introduction of an intact pyrimidine ring into riboflavine by *E. ashbyii* was confirmed[65] since radioactive riboflavine was obtained using guanine-2-C^{14} but not with guanine-8-C^{14}. Consequently, the carbon atom in the 8-position of purine precursors is lost at

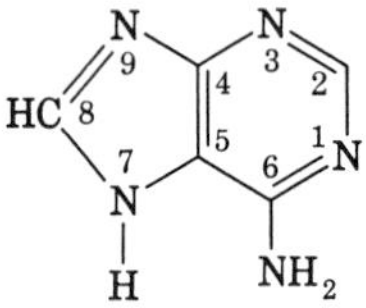

(47) 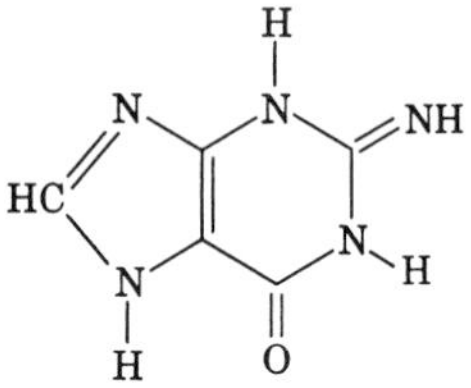 **(48)** 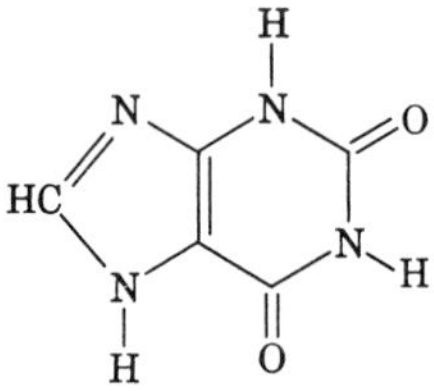 **(49)**

the oxidation stage of a guanine (**48**) or xanthine (**49**) derivative during riboflavine biosynthesis. As yet, intermediate steps between the purine and flavine are unknown. Diaminopyrimidines had been considered as likely intermediates, but their addition to growth media of the organism failed to stimulate biosynthesis.[66] The failure of uracil or thymine to stimulate riboflavine biosynthesis in *E. ashbyii*[67] and the lack of isotope enrichment in riboflavine that was synthesized by *A. gossypii* in the presence of orotic acid-6-C^{14} also suggest that pyrimidines *per se* are not riboflavine precursors.[68]

The role of pteridines in riboflavine biosynthesis is a topic of current interest. The isolation of 6,7-dimethyl-8-ribityllumazine (**50**) and riboflavine from cultures of *E. ashbyii*[69] and *A. gossypii*[70] suggested that pteridines such as (**50**) are intermediates in the biosynthesis of riboflavine. Studies on the incorporation of 2-C^{14}-6,7-dimethyl-8-ribityllumazine confirmed this precursor relationship.[70] Later studies indicated that two or more molecules of the lumazine derivative were required for the biosynthesis of each molecule of riboflavine by the enzyme system.[71,72]

65. U. al-Khalidi, *Federation Proc.*, *17*, 180 (1958).
66. E. G. Brown, T. W. Goodwin, and S. Pendlington, *Biochem. J.*, *61*, 37 (1955).
67. J. A. MacLaren, *J. Bacteriol.*, *63*, 233 (1952).
68. P. L. Broberg, *Thesis University of Wisconsin* (1954); through G. W. E. Plaut, *Nutritional Symposium Series*, *13*, The National Vitamin Foundation, Inc., N.Y., 1956, p. 21.
69. T. Masuda, *Pharm. Bull.* (*Japan*), *4*, 71, 375 (1956); *5*, 28, 136 (1957).
70. G. F. Maley and G. W. E. Plaut, *J. Biol. Chem.*, *234*, 641 (1959); *J. Am. Chem. Soc.*, *81*, 2025 (1959).
71. G. W. E. Plaut, *Federation Proc.*, *19*, 312 (1960); *J. Biol. Chem.*, *235*, PC41 (1960).
72. T. W. Goodwin and A. A. Horton, *Nature*, *191*, 772 (1961).

This reaction has now been demonstrated under nonenzymic conditions.[73] The reaction is visualized as proceeding by the cleavage of the pyrazine moiety of the lumazine derivative (**50**) to yield the intermediate (**51**). Aldol condensation between two molecules of (**51**) yields the dimer (**52**) which cyclizes with the loss of one diaminopyrimidine moiety to yield riboflavine.

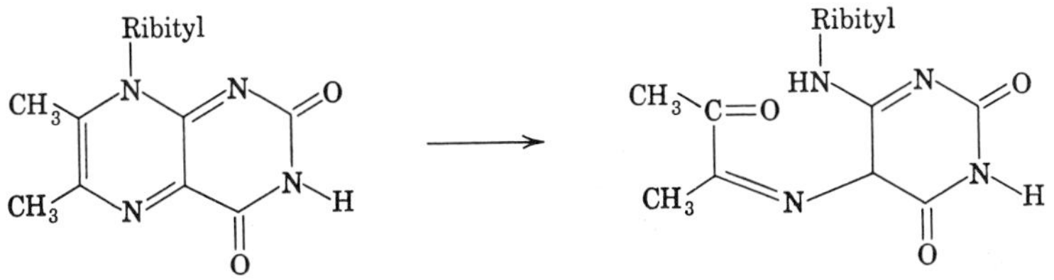

(50) (51)

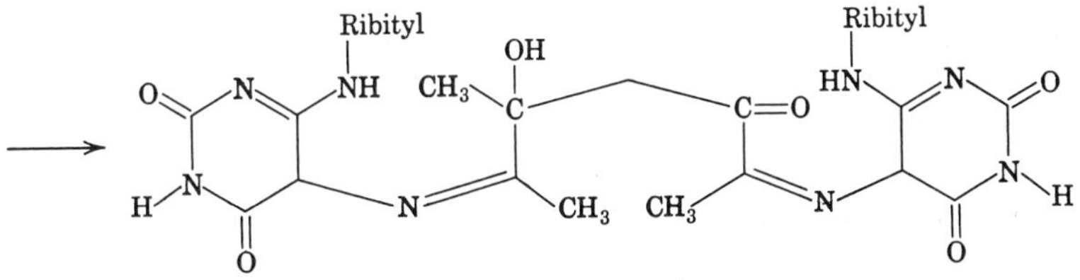

(52)

⟶ Riboflavine

Experiments on the incorporation of radioactivity in the ribityl side chain were essentially negative with labeled formate, carbon dioxide, or glycine.[58] With $C^{14}H_3COOH$, incorporation of C^{14} was mainly at position 5′ and with $CH_3C^{14}OOH$, positions 2′, 3′, and 4′ were the only sites of incorporation of radioactive carbon. With glucose-6-C^{14}, radioactive carbon was incorporated predominantly in the 5′-position and with glucose-2-C^{14}, C^{14} was introduced at the 1′-position. These facts suggest an oxidative pathway by way of a hexose monophosphate as one mechanism for the biogenesis of the ribityl moiety. The importance of a metabolic pathway by a transketolase-aldolase for the introduction of the ribityl group is evident from the labeling pattern with glucose-1-C^{14}.

73. T. Rowan and H. C. S. Wood, *Proc. Chem. Soc.*, 21 (1963).

8. Nutritional and Therapeutic Role

A. In Animals

Riboflavine is essential for growth and tissue repair in all animals.[74] In rats the ariboflavinosis syndrome is characterized by poor growth,[5] ocular abnormalities,[75–77] and dermatitis.[78,79] Ocular manifestations of ariboflavinosis in the rat include conjunctivitis, opacity of the cornea, and corneal vascularization. The dermatitis consists of an eczematous condition of the skin about the nostrils and eyes. Anestrus is also observed in rats deprived of riboflavine; the damage is irreparable if riboflavine is not restored to the diet within ten weeks after the first symptoms appear.[80] Congenital skeletal malformations have been observed in the litters of riboflavine-deficient mothers in some cases[81] but not in others.[82]

Ariboflavinosis in the dog results in weight loss, fatty infiltration of the liver ("yellow liver"), muscular weakness, opacity of the cornea, and coma.[83,84] In the pig the deficiency syndrome is characterized by retarded growth, corneal opacity, dermatitis, and terminal collapse.[85]

Riboflavine is essential for the growth of fowl.[86–88] It is also necessary in growing chicks for the normal function and maintenance of the nervous system, particularly the main peripheral nerve trunks. The rapid onset of an acute paralysis and the slowly developing form of paralysis known as "curled-toe paralysis" are manifestations of chick ariboflavinosis.[89]

The diets of young calves must include riboflavine until the rumen

74. M. K. Horwitt, O. W. Hills, C. C. Harvey, E. Liebert, and D. L. Steinberg, *J. Nutr.*, *39*, 357 (1949).
75. H. Chick, T. F. MacRae, and A. N. Worden, *Biochem. J.*, *34*, 580 (1940).
76. H. R. Street, G. R. Cowgill and H. M. Zimmerman, *J. Nutr.* *22*, 7 (1941).
77. B. Sure, *J. Nutr.*, *22*, 295 (1941).
78. S. B. Wolbach, *J. Am. Med. Assoc.*, *108*, 7 (1937).
79. S. B. Wolbach and O. A. Bessey, *Science*, *91*, 599 (1940).
80. K. H. Coward, B. G. E. Morgan, and L. Waller, *J. Physiol.*, *100*, 423 (1942).
81. J. Warkany and R. C. Nelson, *Science*, *92*, 383 (1940).
82. M. M. Nelson, E. Sulon, H. Becks, and H. M. Evans, *Proc. Soc. Exptl. Biol. Med.*, *66*, 631 (1947).
83. W. H. Sebrell, *Natl. Insts. Health Bull.*, *162*, Part 3, 23 (1933).
84. W. H. Sebrell, *Public Health Repts.* (*U.S.*), *44*, 2697 (1929).
85. A. J. Patek, Jr., J. Post, and J. Victor, *Am. J. Physiol.* *133*, 47 (1941).
86. R. M. Bethke and P. R. Record, *Poultry Sci.*, *21*, 147 (1942).
87. D. M. Hegsted and R. L. Perry, *J. Nutr.*, *35*, 411 (1948).
88. T. H. Jukes, E. L. R. Stokstad, and M. Belt, *J. Nutr.*, *33*, 1 (1947).
89. P. H. Phillips and R. W. Engel, *J. Nutr.* *16*, 451 (1938).

develops.[90] Once the rumen has reached functional capacity, animals such as cattle and sheep can supply their need for the vitamin B complex by intestinal synthesis.

B. In the Human

Symptoms of human ariboflavinosis resemble those observed with animals and include the orogenital syndrome characterized by angular stomatitis, glossitis, and cheilosis together with ocular manifestations such as photophobia, indistinct vision, and corneal vascularization. The clinical manifestations of deficiency, however, are usually less clearly defined than those associated with other B-vitamin deficiencies. The formation of characteristic lip lesions and a seborrheic dermatitis about the nose, ears, and eyelids were the first characteristics of the avitaminosis syndrome to be described.[91] Angular stomatitis, seborrheic dermatitis, scrotal skin lesions, and loss of ability to perceive flicker were also recorded as typical manifestations of riboflavine deficiency.[74] The ocular manifestations occur in a large percentage but not in all cases. Riboflavine therapy produces a response after several days of administration; photophobia and related symptoms are relieved in one or two days, but oral lesions require several weeks for complete resolution.

The riboflavine requirement is not related to caloric intake or muscular activity but rather to body weight. The minimum daily allowances for riboflavine has been set at 0.5–0.8 mg. for infants, 1.0–2.5 mg. for children and adolescents (1–20 years), 1.5–2.5 mg. for women, and 1.8 mg. for men. Additional allowances are set during pregnancy and lactation and for above-average-weight subjects.[92] Among the best dietary sources of riboflavine are heart, liver, kidney, eggs, milk, yeast, green vegetables, and germinated seeds. The vitamin is routinely incorporated in enriched bread, enriched flour, and in animal rations. Most of the riboflavine produced for supplementing animal rations is used for poultry and swine. Supplementation for cattle and sheep is unnecessary because of bacterial synthesis of the vitamin in the rumen.

90. A. C. Wiese, B. C. Johnson, H. H. Mitchell, and W. B. Nevens, *J. Nutr.*, *33*, 263 (1947).
91. W. H. Sebrell, Jr. and R. E. Butler, *Publ. Health Repts.* (*U.S.*), *53*, 2282 (1935).
92. *Recommended Dietary Allowances*, Natl. Acad. Sci., Natl. Res. Council Publ. 589, Washington, D.C., 1958, p. 12.

CHAPTER V

Nicotinic Acid and Nicotinamide, Diphosphopyridine Nucleotide and Triphosphopyridine Nucleotide

1. Introduction

The pattern of events associated with the discovery and identification of certain vitamins was reversed in the case of nicotinic acid. The compound was prepared in the organic laboratory as early as 1867 by the oxidation of nicotine with nitric acid.[1] Later nicotinic acid was isolated coincidentally from natural sources such as yeast[2] and rice bran[3] during the search for the antiberiberi factor, thiamine. Since nicotinic acid had no effect on beriberi, it was of no biological interest in nutrition for many years. Finally nicotinamide was isolated from the hydrogen-transporting coenzymes I and II,[4,5] and a year later its nutritional significance was recognized.

The history of pellagra, its recognition as a nutritional disorder, and the discovery of its prevention by nicotinic acid and nicotinamide have been reviewed.[6] Pellagra was medically recognized sometime during the early 1700's. Later the incidence of pellagra was associated with the widespread use of corn in the diet, and in areas where highly refined maize was the principal cereal of the diet, pellagra epidemics were common. Critical and noteworthy contributions to the recognition of nicotinic acid and nicotinamide as the human pellagra-preventive factors were the recognition of pellagra as a nutritional disorder, and the discovery of a nutritional relationship between the cause of canine blacktongue and the cause of human pellagra.

1. C. Huber, *Ann.*, *141*, 271 (1867); *Ber.*, *3*, 849 (1870).
2. C. Funk, *J. Physiol.* (*London*), *43*, 395 (1911); *J. State Med.* (*London*), *20*, 341 (1912).
3. U. Suzuki, T. Shamimura, and S. Okade, *Biochem. Z.*, *43*, 89, 99 (1912).
4. O. Warburg and W. Christian, *Biochem. Z.*, *287*, 291 (1936).
5. H. von Euler, H. Albers, and F. Schlenk, *Z. Physiol. Chem.*, *237*, 1801 (1935); *240*, 113 (1936).
6. V. P. Sydenstricker, *Am. J. Clin. Nutr.*, *6*, 409 (1958).

In 1912 it was suggested that pellagra resulted from the absence of a "vitamine" in maize.[2] By 1914 knowledge of the requirements for cysteine, lysine, and tryptophan in nutrition led to the suggestion of an amino acid deficiency in zein diets as the cause of the disease.[7] In retrospect, each suggestion was formally correct on the basis of the recently discovered tryptophan-nicotinic acid relationship in mammalian metabolism.

In the United States alone, it was estimated that at one time up to 100,000 persons were afflicted with pellagra, and the annual death toll was of the order of 10,000. Consequently, several groups were commissioned to study the etiology of the disease. During the period 1912–1916, extensive animal tests proved the impossibility of contracting the disease by infection. By 1916 investigators in the United States Public Health Service were convinced that the disease was of dietary origin. In public institutions where the disease was rampant, cures were effected and recurrences were prevented by adding liberal amounts of milk and eggs to the diet, and pellagra was induced in healthy subjects by sustaining them on diets usually associated with pellagra. From these observations it was written, "Pellagra may be prevented completely by a suitable diet without intervention of any other factor, hygenic or sanitary. There is no sound evidence that the disease is controllable in any other way."[8] Further confirmation of this dietary concept was provided by the observation that therapy with the amino acids cysteine and tryptophan was also effective in controlling the disease.[9]

With a dietary origin established, effort was focused on the isolation of an essential factor. The choice of a valid assay was especially confusing since it was not recognized that "pellagrous-like" conditions in experimental animals had more than one nutritional origin and that not all such conditions were related to human pellagra. Studies with rats and chicks failed to reveal the human pellagra-preventive factor; a rat antidermatitis factor proved to be pyridoxol, and a chick dermatitis-preventive factor was identified as pantothenic acid. A reliable assay for the elusive pellagra-preventive factor for humans was not available until the nutritional origin of human pellagra was related to the cause of a disease in dogs referred to as canine blacktongue. Only after this discovery was significant progress made in identifying the human pellagra-preventive factor.

In 1922 the disease canine blacktongue was produced by feeding dogs

7. T. B. Osborne and L. B. Mendel, *J. Biol. Chem.*, *12*, 473 (1912); *17*, 325 (1914).
8. J. Goldberger, *J. Am. Med. Assoc.*, *66*, 471 (1916).
9. J. Goldberger and W. F. Tanner, *Public Health Repts.* (*U.S.*), *37*, 462 (1921); *J. Am. Med. Assoc.*, *79*, 2132 (1922).

diets that were essentially the same as those associated with human pellagra.[10] Yeast, which cured canine blacktongue, also produced dramatic recoveries in pellagrous patients.[11] In the period 1926–1927, the analogy between canine blacktongue and pellagra was emphasized, and it was suggested that both occurred owing to a deficiency of the same pellagra-preventive factor.[12] Wheat germ and liver were also found to be equally good sources of the pellagra-preventive factor and were effective in curing canine blacktongue and pellagra.[13] By 1928 the curative factor was established as a thermostable activity that could be adsorbed on fuller's earth and eluted. Such eluates were active in the cure and prevention of canine blacktongue.[14]

In the early 1930's several groups of investigators succeeded in concentrating the pellagra-preventive factor using the canine blacktongue assay. The active substance, referred to as filtrate factor, was separated from yeast and liver and was found to differ from thiamine, pyridoxol, and riboflavine.[15–17] By 1937 nicotinamide was isolated from liver extracts that had high antiblacktongue activity, and the effectiveness of both nicotinamide and nicotinic acid in curing canine blacktongue was demonstrated.[17] Later in the same year the curative effect of nicotinic acid in human pellagra was established.[18–20]

The recovery of pellagrins after the administration of nicotinic acid or nicotinamide has been described as dramatic. With the discovery in 1945 of a precursor relationship between the amino acid tryptophan and nicotinic acid in mammalian metabolism, the role of maize in causing pellagra became even clearer. Diets low in protein and containing large

10. G. A. Wheeler, J. Goldberger, and V. Blackstock, *Public Health Repts.* (*U.S.*), *37*, 1063 (1922).
11. J. Goldberger, G. A. Wheeler, and W. F. Tanner, *Public Health Repts.* (*U.S.*), *40*, 927 (1925).
12. J. Goldberger, G. A. Wheeler, R. D. Lillie, and L. M. Rogers, *Public Health Repts.* (*U.S.*), *41*, 297 (1926).
13. J. Goldberger and G. A. Wheeler, *Public Health Repts.* (*U.S.*), *42*, 2383 (1927).
14. J. Goldberger, G. A. Wheeler, R. D. Lillie, and L. M. Rogers, *Public Health Repts.* (*U.S.*), *43*, 657 (1928).
15. P. J. Fouts, S. Lepkovsky, O. M. Helmer, and T. H. Jukes, *Proc. Soc. Exptl. Biol. Med.*, *35*, 245 (1936).
16. W. H. Sebrell, Jr., R. H. Onstott, and D. J. Hunt, *Public Health Repts.* (*U.S.*), *52*, 427 (1937).
17. C. A. Elvehjem, R. J. Madden, F. M. Strong, and D. W. Woolley, *J. Am. Chem. Soc.*, *59*, 1767 (1937); *J. Biol. Chem.*, *123*, 137 (1938).
18. P. J. Fouts, O. M. Helmer, S. Lepkovsky, and T. H. Jukes, *Proc. Soc. Exptl. Biol. Med.*, *37*, 405 (1937).
19. D. T. Smith, J. M. Ruffin, and S. G. Smith, *J. Am. Med. Assoc.*, *109*, 2054 (1937).
20. T. D. Spies, C. Cooper, and M. A. Blankenhorn, *J. Am. Med. Assoc.*, *110*, 622 (1938).

amounts of corn not only increase the nicotinic acid requirement, but also contain little or no tryptophan. Since such diets also contain little riboflavine and pyridoxol, both of which are required for the biosynthesis of nicotinic acid from tryptophan, they are free of both intrinsic and potentially biosynthetic nicotinic acid.

2. Isolation

A. Nicotinamide

Nicotinamide was isolated from liver as follows.[17,21–23] An ethanol-ether-water (4:5:1) extract of liver paste was concentrated and then extracted with acetone. The acetone extract was concentrated, and the residue was extracted with amyl alcohol. Successive concentration and extraction with ethanol, acetone, and finally water, gave an aqueous concentrate that was passed over a column of Norit. The active substance was eluted with a mixture of methanol and pyridine (4:1), and the eluates were combined and concentrated. The active substance was further purified by extraction with acetone. Concentration of the acetone extract gave a residue that was further purified by distillation *in vacuo*. The distillate was purified by precipitation from an alcohol solution with mercuric chloride, and the precipitate was separated and then decomposed with hydrogen sulfide in dilute hydrochloric acid solution. Filtration of the reaction mixture gave a solution from which pure nicotinamide crystallized.

Nicotinamide was also obtained by the degradation of diphosphopyridine nucleotide (DPN, coenzyme I) and triphosphopyridine nucleotide (TPN, coenzyme II). Obtaining the "natural amide" from these coenzymes is simple, but isolation of the pure coenzyme forms may be difficult. Nicotinamide is liberated from the coenzyme by hydrolysis with dilute sulfuric acid.[4] The adenine is precipitated as the silver complex, and excess silver ion is removed from solution with hydrogen sulfide; the amide is extracted from aqueous solution with amyl alcohol and precipitated with picrolonic acid. The picrolonate is purified by recrystallization from water and is then converted to a crystalline hydrochloride by treatment with hydrochloric acid. The pure amide is obtained in the form of a hydrochloride after recrystallization from ethanol.

B. Nicotinic Acid

The isolation of nicotinic acid from natural sources is relatively easy. After the removal of lipids with suitable solvents, the source material is

21. C. J. Koehn, Jr. and C. A. Elvehjem, *J. Nutr. 11*, 67 (1936).
22. C. A. Elvehjem and C. J. Koehn, Jr., *J. Biol. Chem.*, *108*, 709 (1935).
23. C. J. Koehn, Jr. and C. A. Elvehjem, *J. Biol. Chem.*, *118*, 693 (1937).

hydrolyzed with acid or alkali. Nicotinic acid is extracted from the acidified hydrolyzate and isolated as the free acid, ester, or copper salt. The product is usually purified by recrystallization from water or alcohol, or by sublimation.

3. Structure Determination and Synthesis

Nicotinic acid (**1**) was first obtained by the nitric acid oxidation of nicotine,[1] which was later shown to have structure (**2**).[24] Evidence that

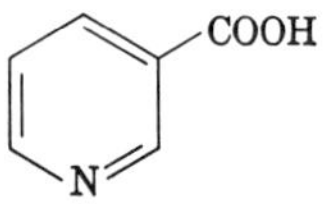

COOH N (1)

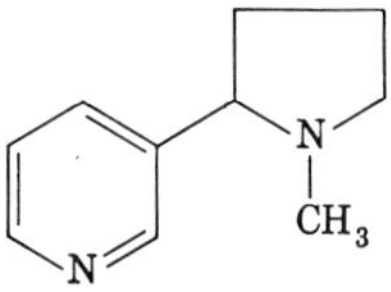

N N CH_3 (2)

the carboxyl group of nicotinic acid was at the 3-position of the pyridine ring was provided by the fact that pyridine-2,3-dicarboxylic acid (quinolinic acid) gave nicotinic acid on thermal monodecarboxylation, and that pyridine-3,4-dicarboxylic acid (cinchomeronic acid) yielded both nicotinic acid and isonicotinic acid under similar conditions.[25]

Nicotinic acid is synthesized commercially by the hydrolysis of 3-cyanopyridine (**4**) or by the oxidation of (a) nicotine from tobacco wastes; (b) refined quinoline or β-picoline from coal tars; or (c) collidine. By far the two most common methods used are the oxidation of quinoline and the hydrolysis of 3-cyanopyridine. The synthesis of 3-cyanopyridine proceeds from pyridine by way of the intermediate sulfonic acid (**3**).

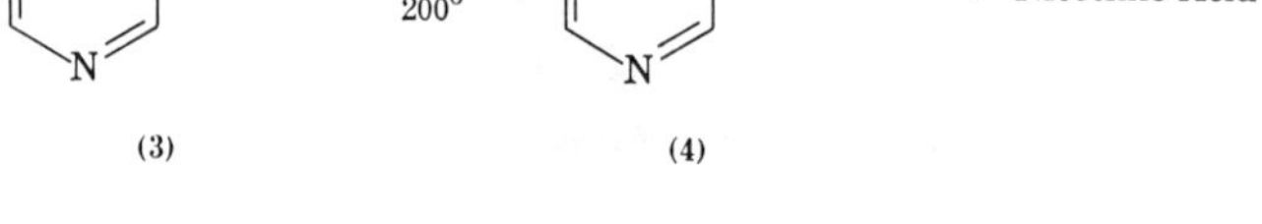

SO_3H N (3) —NaCN, 200°→ CN N (4) ——→ Nicotinic Acid

The most useful commercial syntheses of nicotinamide (**5**) employ partial hydrolysis of 3-cyanopyridine using either dilute sodium hydroxide

24. A. Pinner, *Ber.*, *26*, 292 (1893).
25. V. Von Richter, *The Chemistry of the Carbon Compounds*, Vol. IV, Elsevier, N.Y., 1947, p. 213.

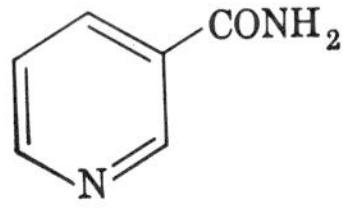

(5)

and hydrogen peroxide or the quaternary ammonium hydroxide resin, Amberlite IRA-400. Yields of the order of 90% are reported for the latter method.[26]

4. Biosynthesis

Almost all living species require some form of nicotinic acid or a precursor. Some organisms utilize tryptophan or an unknown precursor; others require the vitamin itself, and still others need the preformed coenzyme.

The first observation that tryptophan served as a precursor of nicotinic acid in mammalian metabolism was reported in 1945.[27] It was already known that the rat did not require nicotinic acid *per se*, and it was assumed that this species had an effective pathway for the biosynthesis of the substance. However, rats sustained on corn or other protein sources low in tryptophan developed a syndrome which was characterized by poor growth. When such diets were supplemented with tryptophan, normal growth was observed. The precursor relationship between tryptophan and nicotinic acid was established by feeding labeled tryptophan supplements and analyzing the excreted nicotinic acid and other metabolites.[28–32] Animals that were fed 3-C^{14}-*DL*-tryptophan excreted carboxyl-labeled nicotinic acid in their urine;[28–30] with tryptophan labeled with N^{15} in the indole nucleus, ring-labeled nicotinic acid was excreted.[31,32] Partial insight into the metabolic pathway was also gained from these experiments. The urine of animals fed 3-C^{14}-*DL*-tryptophan contained C^{14}-labeled kynurenine (**8**) and 3-hydroxyanthranilic acid (**14**) in addition to the carboxyl-labeled nicotinic acid. If the diets were supplemented with *DL*-tryptophan labeled at the β-position of the side chain, labeled kynurenine (**8**) and

26. A. Galat, *J. Am. Chem. Soc.*, *70*, 3945 (1948).
27. W. A. Krehl, L. J. Teply, P. S. Sarma, and C. A. Elvehjem, *Science*, *101*, 489 (1945).
28. C. Heidelberger, M. E. Gullberg, A. F. Morgan, and S. Lepkovsky, *J. Biol. Chem.*, *175*, 471 (1948); *179*, 143 (1949).
29. C. Heidelberger, E. P. Abraham, and S. Lepkovsky, *J. Biol. Chem.*, *176*, 1461 (1949); *179*, 151 (1949).
30. C. Heidelberger, *J. Biol. Chem.*, *179*, 139 (1949).
31. R. W. Schayer, G. L. Foster, and D. Shemin, *Federation Proc.*, *8*, 248 (1949).
32. R. W. Schayer, *J. Biol. Chem.*, *187*, 777 (1950).

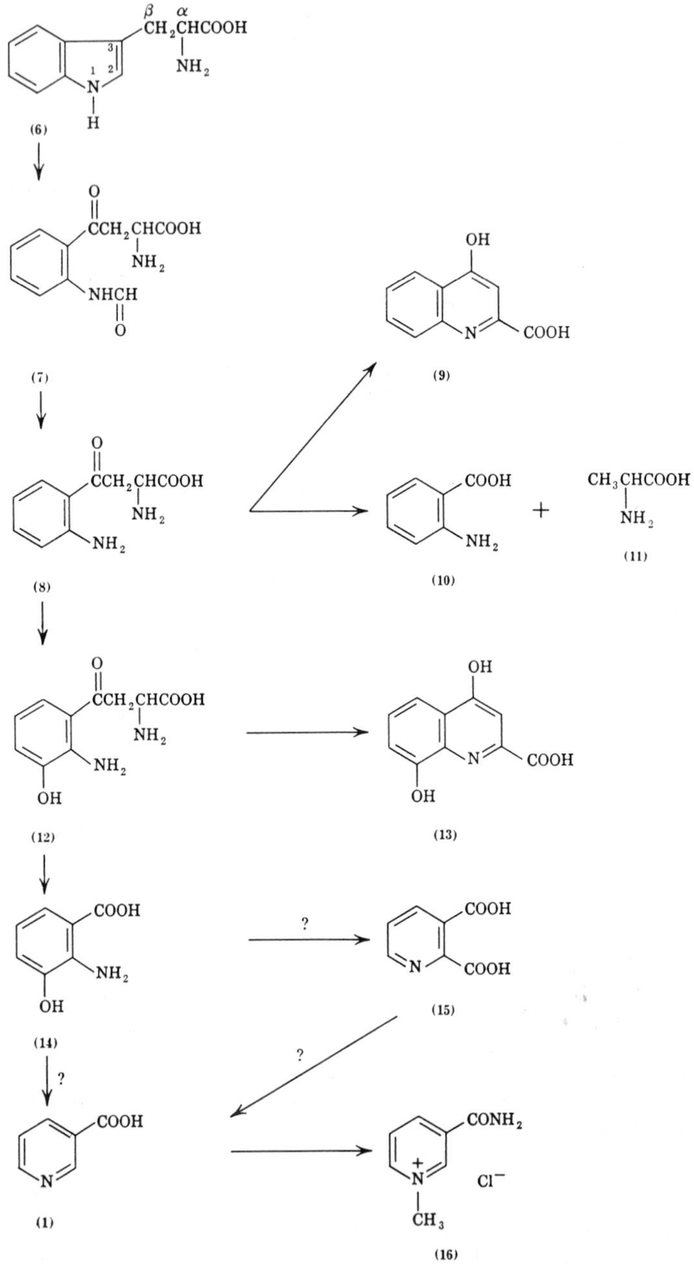

Fig. 1. Proposed pathway and side reactions in biosynthesis of nicotinic acid from tryptophan.[34]

kynurenic acid (**9**) were isolated; the excreted nicotinic acid, however, was not labeled.[28–32] Feeding experiments with carboxyl-labeled *DL*-tryptophan resulted in the isolation of nonlabeled nicotinic acid and N^1-methylnicotinamide (**16**).[33] Thus, it appeared that the nucleus, but not the side chain of tryptophan, was necessary for the biosynthesis of nicotinic acid.

In the ensuing years, more information about the biosynthetic pathway from tryptophan to nicotinic acid was sought in studies with the rat, mutant strains of *Neurospora crassa*, and in isolated enzyme systems.[34,35] Although incomplete, most of the data obtained with variously labeled tryptophan supplements are consistent with the main pathway and side reactions of biosynthesis as depicted in Fig. 1.[34]

The pathway for the biosynthesis of nicotinic acid appears to proceed by the oxidation of tryptophan (**6**) to formylkynurenine (**7**).[34] It has been suggested that this reaction is dependent upon thiamine.[36] Formylkynurenine is hydrolyzed to kynurenine (**8**) which is hydroxylated to 3-hydroxykynurenine (**12**). Kynurenine, however, may also be diverted from the main pathway by side reactions leading to kynurenic acid (**9**) or anthranilic acid (**10**) and alanine (**11**). A pyridoxol-dependent cleavage of the side chain converts 3-hydroxykynurenine to 3-hydroxyanthranilic acid (**14**). Cyclization of 3-hydroxykynurenine to xanthurenic acid (**13**), however, effectively removes a large portion of this precursor from the main biosynthetic pathway. At this point the pathway becomes obscure. The conversion of 3-hydroxyanthranilic acid (**14**) to quinolinic acid (**15**) has been demonstrated, but evidence linking the latter compound with the direct pathway is lacking.

Riboflavine and biotin are reportedly operative at some stage of the biosynthesis of nicotinic acid, but the reactions involved are unknown.

The biosynthesis of nicotinic acid in certain bacteria proceeds by a different and as yet unknown pathway. Early evidence for this conclusion was based on the observations that intermediates in the mammalian biosynthesis of nicotinic acid from tryptophan do not replace nicotinic acid as a growth factor for *Lactobacillus arabinosus*, *Leuconostoc mesenteroides*, *Streptococcus faecalis*, *Bacillus subtilis*, and *Escherichia coli*.[37–39]

33. J. M. Hundley and H. W. Bond, *Arch. Biochem.*, *21*, 313 (1949).
34. L. M. Henderson, *Nutritional Symposium Series*, *13*, The Natl. Vitamin Foundation, Inc., N.Y., 1956, p. 31.
35. C. E. Dalgliesh, *Brit. Med. Bull.*, *12*, 49 (1956).
36. C. E. Dalgliesh, *Biochem. J.*, *61*, 328 (1955).
37. B. E. Volcani and E. E. Snell, *Proc. Soc. Exptl. Biol. Med.*, *67*, 511 (1948).
38. R. Y. Stanier and M. Tsuchida, *J. Bacteriol.*, *58*, 45 (1949).
39. C. Yanofsky, *J. Bacteriol.*, *68*, 577 (1954).

Later it was shown that maximal biosynthesis of nicotinic acid by resting-cell suspensions of *E. coli* was obtained when glycerol, a C_4-dicarboxylic acid, ribose, and adenine were added to the medium.[40] From this observation, it was suggested that the biosynthesis of nicotinic acid in this organism proceeds by condensation between the C_4-dicarboxylic acid and glycerol, or a closely related derivative, to yield a C_7-intermediate. Decarboxylation is visualized as one of the subsequent enzymic reactions which convert the C_7-intermediate to nicotinic acid.

In an independent study, pyridine-3,4-dicarboxylic acid was identified as an intermediate in the biosynthesis of nicotinic acid by a series of *E. coli* mutants.[41] With some mutant strains, pyridine-3,4-dicarboxylic acid promoted the growth of the microorganism in the absence of nicotinic acid; with mutants in which the enzymic conversion of pyridine-3,4-dicarboxylic acid to nicotinic acid was blocked, the dicarboxylic acid accumulated in the medium.

5. Metabolic Role

Nicotinamide is a constituent of the two coenzymes diphosphopyridine nucleotide (DPN, **17**) and triphosphopyridine nucleotide (TPN, **18**). The cofactors have also been designated (a) cozymase and phospho-cozymase; (b) codehydrogenase I and codehydrogenase II; and (c) coenzyme I and

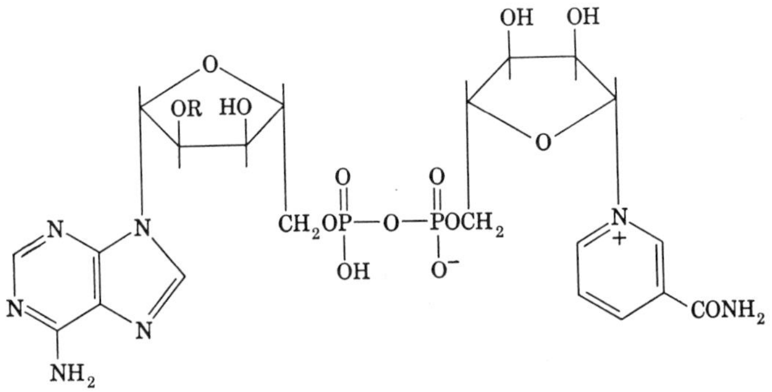

(17), R = H
(18), R = $P(=O)(OH)_2$

40. M. V. Ortega and G. M. Brown, *J. Biol. Chem.*, *235*, 2939 (1960).
41. F. Lingens, *Angew. Chem.*, *72*, 920 (1960).

coenzyme II. Recently it was proposed that the names nicotinamide-adenine dinucleotide (NAD) and nicotinamide-adenine dinucleotide phosphate (NADP) be used to designate DPN and TPN, respectively.[42]

The DPN- and TPN-containing enzymes play an important role in biological oxidation-reduction systems by virtue of their capacity to serve as hydrogen-transfer agents. As previously noted (Chapter IV), hydrogen is effectively transferred from the oxidizable substrate to oxygen through a series of graded enzymic hydrogen transfers. Nicotinamide-containing enzyme systems constitute one such group of hydrogen transfer agents. The nicotinamide moiety of the coenzyme operates in these systems by reversibly alternating between an oxidized quarternary pyridinium ion and a reduced tertiary amine. The transfer of hydrogen is reversible and stereospecific.

A. Diphosphopyridine Nucleotide (DPN, Coenzyme I)

1. STRUCTURE DETERMINATION AND SYNTHESIS. DPN was isolated from brewer's or baker's yeast by fractional precipitation followed by chromatography. Its structure was elucidated by degradation (Fig. 2). Acid hydrolysis cleaved the substance into one molecule of adenine (**19**), two molecules of *D*-ribose-5-phosphoric acid (**20**), and one molecule of nicotinamide.[4,5,43,44] Mild alkaline hydrolysis yielded an adenosine-diphosphate-ribose compound, presumably (**21**), and nicotinamide;[45] vigorous alkaline hydrolysis[46] gave adenosine diphosphate (**22**). Enzymic hydrolysis yielded adenosine (**23**) and nicotinamide riboside (**24**).[47] Consequently, the structure (**17**) proposed for coenzyme I consisted of one molecule of adenosine and one molecule of nicotinamide riboside linked through their 5′-positions by a pyrophosphate group.

DPN has been synthesized from nicotinamide, *D*-ribose, and adenosine 5′-phosphate.[48,49] 1-*O*-Acetyl-2,3,5-tri-*O*-benzoyl-*β*-*D*-ribofuranoside (**25**) was converted to 2,3,5-tri-*O*-benzoyl-*D*-ribofuranosyl chloride (**26**). Condensation of this product with nicotinamide, followed by debenzoylation

42. M. Dixon, *Nature*, *188*, 464 (1960); *Science*, *132*, 1548 (1960).
43. F. Schlenk, *J. Biol. Chem.*, *146*, 619 (1942).
44. H. von Euler, P. Karrer, and B. Becker, *Helv. Chim. Acta*, *19*, 1060 (1936).
45. F. Schlenk, H. von Euler, H. Heiwinkel, W. Gleim, and H. Nyström, *Z. Physiol. Chem.*, *247*, 23 (1937).
46. R. Vestin, F. Schlenk, and H. von Euler, *Ber.*, *70*, 1369 (1937); *Naturwissenschaften*, *25*, 318 (1937).
47. F. Schlenk, *Arch. Biochem.*, *3*, 93 (1943); *Naturwissenschaften*, *28*, 46 (1940).
48. N. A. Hughes, G. W. Kenner, and A. Todd, *J. Chem. Soc.*, 3733 (1957).
49. L. J. Haynes, N. A. Hughes, G. W. Kenner, and A. Todd, *J. Chem. Soc.*, 3727 (1957).

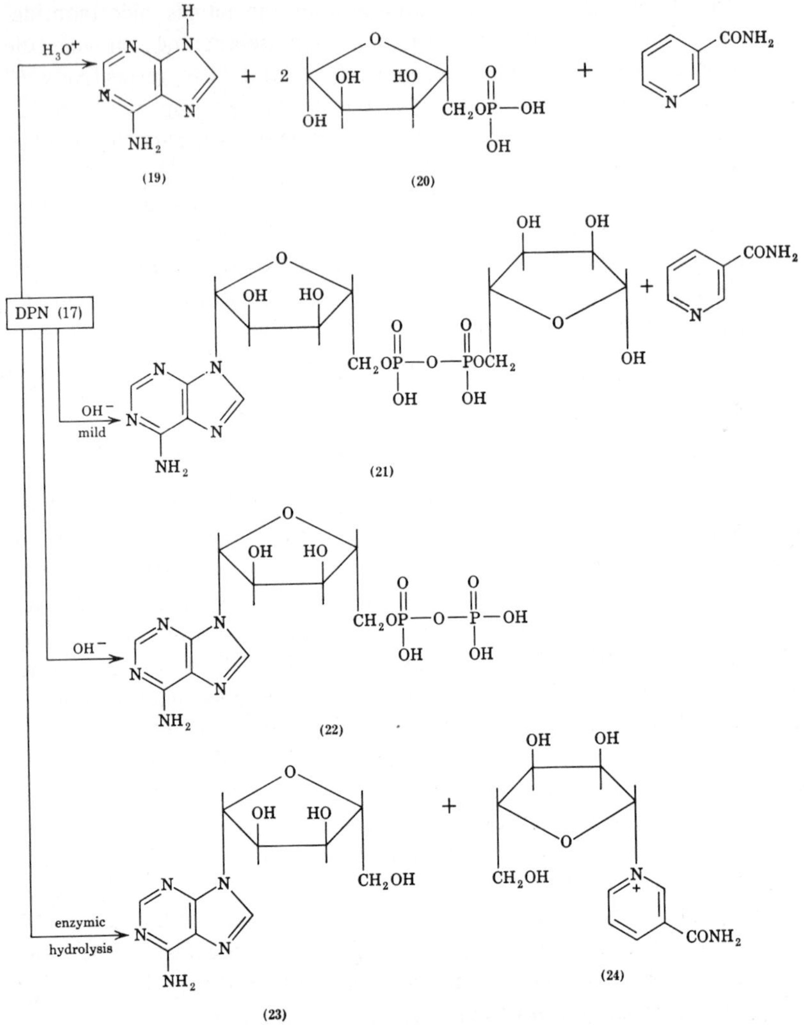

(19) (20) (21) (22) (23) (24)

Fig. 2. Hydrolytic degradation of DPN.[43–47]

with alcoholic ammonia yielded the nicotinamide nucleoside (**27**). This compound was phosphorylated to nicotinamide nucleotide (**28**), which was then condensed with adenosine 5′-phosphate (**29**) to yield diphosphopyridine nucleotide (**17**).

Synthetic nicotinamide nucleotide (**28**) was obtained as a mixture of α- and β-anomers in a 1:4 ratio. On the basis of physical properties, the natural form was assumed to be the β-anomer. Since the intermediate (**28**)

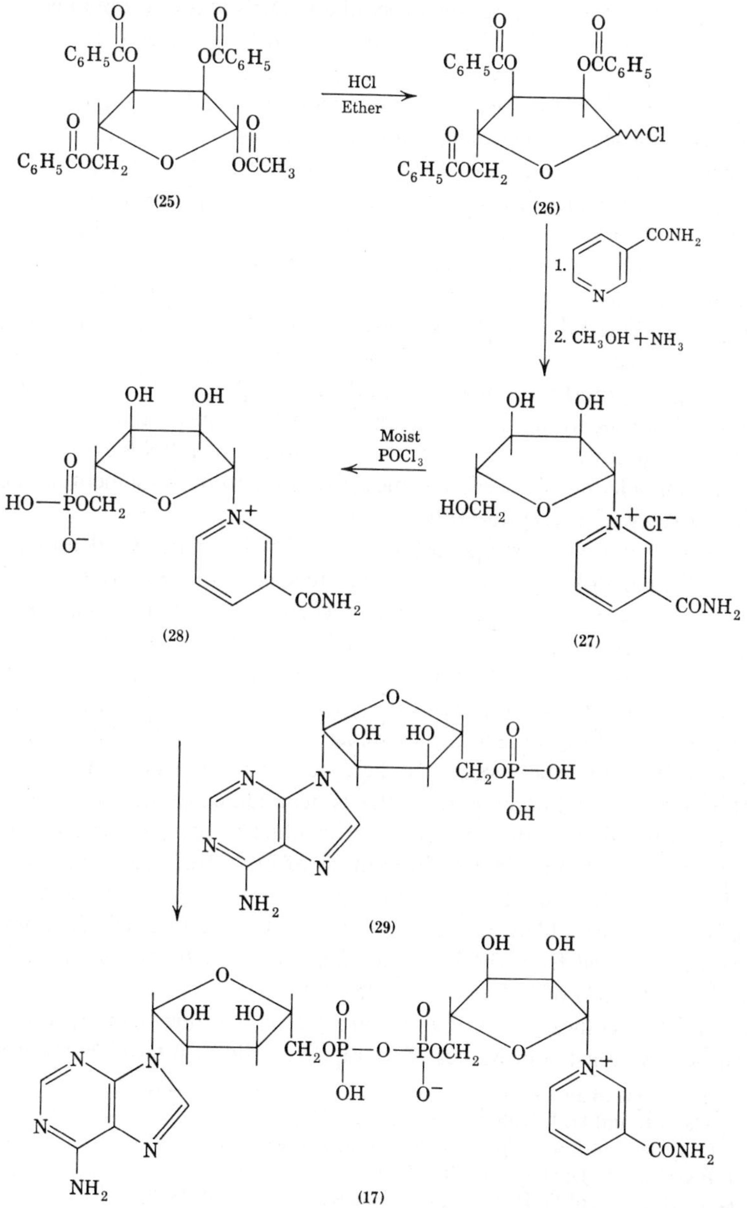

O O
C_6H_5CO OCC_6H_5
O O
$C_6H_5COCH_2$ O $OCCH_3$

(25)

HCl
Ether

O O
C_6H_5CO OCC_6H_5
O Cl
$C_6H_5COCH_2$ O

(26)

1. $CONH_2$ N

2. $CH_3OH + NH_3$

OH OH
$HOCH_2$ O
N^+ Cl^-
$CONH_2$

(27)

Moist
$POCl_3$

OH OH
O
HO—$POCH_2$ O
O^-
N^+
$CONH_2$

(28)

O
OH HO O
N N CH_2OP—OH
N N OH
NH_2

(29)

OH OH
O
OH HO O O
N N CH_2OP—O—$POCH_2$ O
OH O^- N^+
N N
NH_2 $CONH_2$

(17)

was a mixture of α- and β-anomers, synthetic DPN was also obtained as a mixture of anomers; the pure β-anomer of DPN was isolated from the synthetic mixture as follows. The β-anomer in the mixture was converted to the dihydro form by selective enzymic reduction, and the α-anomer was then decomposed by treatment with alkali. Enzymic reoxidation of the purified dihydro β-anomer of DPN yielded pure DPN as the β-anomer. This product was identical with the natural coenzyme; thus, structure was proved, and the coenzyme was established as having a β-furanoside configuration in the nicotinamide nucleotide moiety.

2. BIOSYNTHESIS OF DIPHOSPHOPYRIDINE NUCLEOTIDE. At first it was generally accepted that the biosynthesis of DPN from nicotinic acid or its amide proceeded from nicotinamide mononucleotide. Later it was suggested that alternative metabolic pathways might exist for the synthesis of DPN from nicotinic acid or its amide. Now it appears that a pathway common to many species exists for the biosynthesis of DPN from nicotinic acid mononucleotide; indeed, in some systems the route from nicotinamide is also by way of desamido-DPN.

This new concept is supported by the following data. Oral administration of small doses of nicotinic acid produced a significant increase in the pyridine nucleotide content of human erythrocytes, but an equivalent amount of nicotinamide was, at best, only one-third as effective.[50,51] An enzyme capable of converting nicotinamide to nicotinamide mononucleotide was isolated from human erythrocytes, but its Michaelis constant was sufficiently high to suggest the existence of an alternative biosynthetic pathway.[52,53] In other systems it became apparent that in DPN biosynthesis from nicotinamide, the latter is deamidated at an early stage of the biosynthesis, and the condensation product is then amidated in the final step. For example, in the biosynthesis of DPN from nicotinamide by *L. arabinosus*, the substrate is deamidated so rapidly that nicotinic acid is considered the most likely precursor.[54] In another instance, C^{14}-desamido-DPN was isolated from the livers of mice sacrificed thirty minutes after the administration of C^{14}-nicotinamide.[55–57]

In the biosynthesis of DPN *in vitro* from nicotinic acid by human erythrocytes, yeast autolyzates, and rat liver slices, intermediates were

50. C. L. Hoagland and S. M. Ward, *J. Biol. Chem.*, *146*, 115 (1942).
51. P. Handler and H. I. Kohn, *J. Biol. Chem.*, *150*, 447 (1943).
52. I. G. Leder and P. Handler, *J. Biol. Chem.*, *189*, 889 (1951).
53. J. Preiss and P. Handler, *J. Biol. Chem.*, *225*, 759 (1957).
54. D. E. Hughes and D. H. Williamson, *Biochem. J.*, *51*, 330 (1952).
55. T. A. Langan, Jr. and L. Shuster, *Federation Proc.*, *17*, 260 (1958).
56. T. A. Langan, Jr., N. O. Kaplan, and L. Shuster, *J. Biol. Chem.*, *234*, 2161 (1959).
57. C. J. Threlfall, *Nature*, *184*, 60 (1959).

isolated and identified, and a new biosynthetic pathway was established.[58,59] Later, desamido-DPN was isolated and identified during *in vivo* and *in vitro* biosynthesis of DPN from nicotinamide by rat liver slices.[56,57] The stage at which deamidation takes place is not known, and it cannot be assumed that the pathway from nicotinamide to desamido-DPN goes through the same stages as that from nicotinic acid to desamido-DPN.

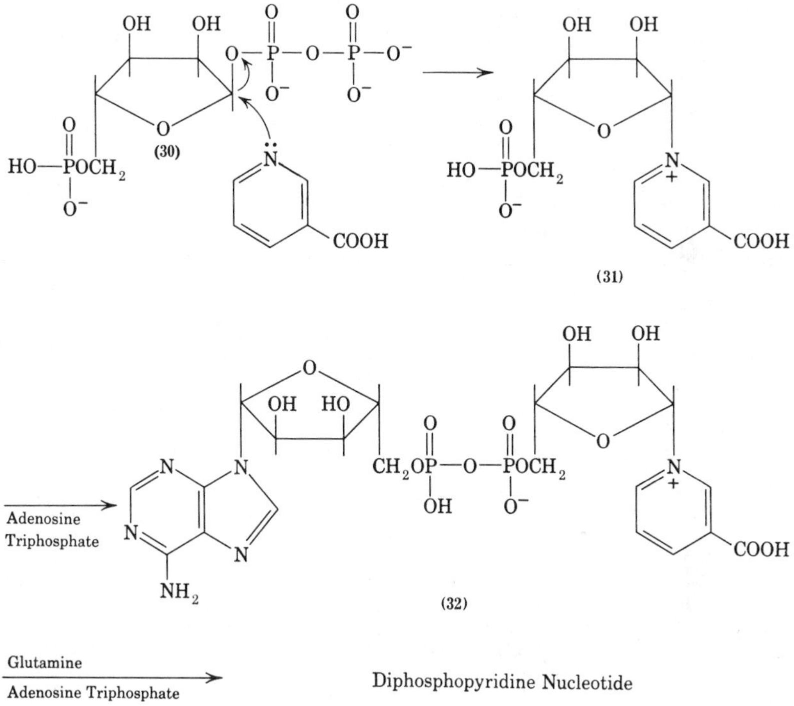

(30) → (31)

$\xrightarrow{\text{Adenosine Triphosphate}}$ (32)

$\xrightarrow[\text{Adenosine Triphosphate}]{\text{Glutamine}}$ Diphosphopyridine Nucleotide

(17)

The biosynthesis of DPN from nicotinic acid in extracts of human erythrocytes, yeast autolyzates, and rat liver preparations is currently visualized as proceeding through three consecutive reactions.[58,59] The reaction of nicotinic acid with 5-phosphoribosyl pyrophosphate (**30**) yields nicotinic acid mononucleotide (**31**); the enzyme that catalyzes this reaction is designated nicotinic acid mononucleotide pyrophosphorylase.[60] Since the pyrophosphate moiety of 5-phosphoribosyl pyrophosphate is in

58. J. Preiss and P. Handler, *J. Am. Chem. Soc.*, *79*, 4246 (1957).
59. J. Preiss and P. Handler, *J. Biol. Chem.*, *233*, 488 (1958); *233*, 493 (1958).
60. J. Imsande and P. Handler, *J. Biol. Chem.*, *236*, 525 (1961).

the α-configuration and the ribose-nicotinamide linkage is in the β-configuration in DPN, it has been suggested that nicotinic acid and 5-phosphoribosyl pyrophosphate are adsorbed simultaneously on the enzyme surface where the reaction proceeds by a single displacement.[60] The second reaction requires a condensation between nicotinic acid mononucleotide and adenosine triphosphate and is catalyzed by DPN-phosphorylase. In the final reaction, nicotinic acid-adenine dinucleotide (desamido-DPN) (**32**) is amidated to DPN. The enzyme that catalyzes this reaction is designated DPN synthetase, and glutamine is the amide-nitrogen donor.

In other studies of the biosynthesis of DPN, it was concluded that the pathway from nicotinic acid is the predominant mechanism with the yeast *Saccharomyces cerevisiae*, and the only pathway with the bacterium *L. mesenteroides*.[61] Growing or resting cells of *S. cerevisiae* deamidate nicotinamide rapidly and consequently can synthesize DPN from either nicotinic acid or nicotinamide. *L. mesenteroides* 9135 lacks this deamidase activity and can synthesize DPN from nicotinic acid but not nicotinamide.

B. *Triphosphopyridine Nucleotide* (*TPN*, *Coenzyme II*)

1. STRUCTURE DETERMINATION. TPN was isolated from hemolyzed horse erythrocytes,[4,62] and its structure was elucidated by degradation.[63–65] Cleavage of TPN (**18**) by a nucleotide phosphatase yielded nicotinamide

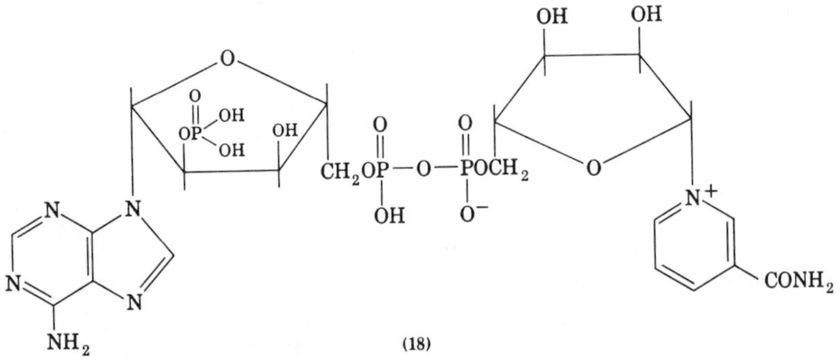

(**18**)

61. T. K. Sundarum, K. V. Rajagopalan, C. V. Pichappa, and P. S. Sarma, *Biochem. J.* *77*, 145 (1960).
62. O. Warburg, W. Christian, and W. Griese, *Biochem. Z.*, *282*, 157 (1935).
63. A. Kornberg, *J. Biol. Chem.*, *174*, 1051 (1948).
64. A. Kornberg and W. E. Pricer, *J. Biol. Chem.*, *186*, 557 (1950).
65. A. Kornberg and W. E. Pricer, *J. Biol. Chem.*, *182*, 763 (1950).

nucleotide (**28**) and a compound established later as adenosine 2′,5′-diphosphate. Selective hydrolysis of the 5′-phosphate group of the diphosphoadenosine fragment yielded adenosine 2′-phosphate; this structural assignment was based on a comparison of the monophosphate with adenylic acids "a" and "b" (adenosine 2′- and 3′-phosphate, respectively).

Preliminary synthetic studies have confirmed the structure (**18**) for TPN,[48] but the pure β-anomer has not been isolated from the synthetic mixture.

C. *Mechanism of Coenzyme Action*

It was formerly considered that the stoichiometry of biological oxidation-reduction reactions required the transfer of protons to and from the

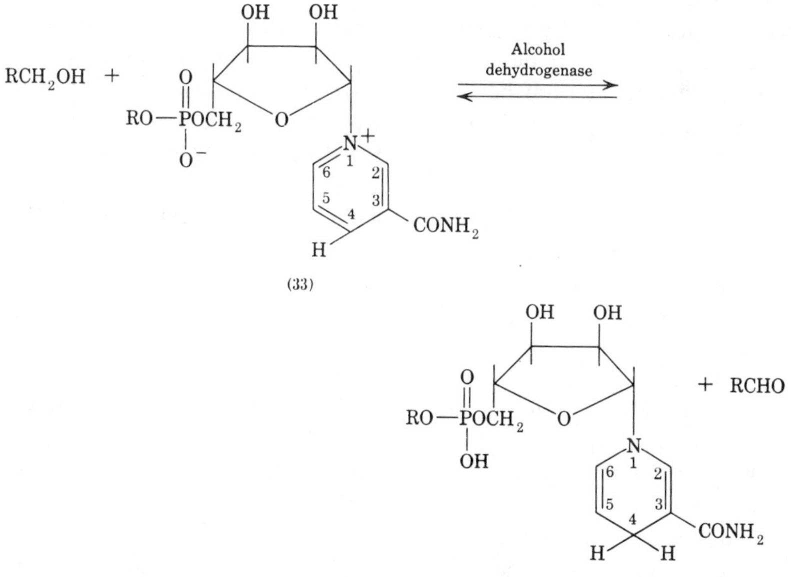

RCH_2OH + (33) $\underset{}{\overset{\text{Alcohol dehydrogenase}}{\rightleftharpoons}}$ (34) + RCHO

(33)

(34)

medium. With the advent of deuterium tracer techniques, actual hydrogen transfer between substrate and coenzyme was demonstrated. The pyridine nucleotide-containing enzymes constitute one such group of hydrogen transferases in which substrate specificity is endowed by the apoenzyme, and the coenzyme moiety participates directly in hydrogen transfer reversibly and stereospecifically by alternating between the quaternary pyridinium ion form (**33**) and the tertiary amine form (**34**). The direct transfer of hydrogen from the α-carbon of ethanol to DPN without participation of the medium was demonstrated using deuterium tracer techniques in the DPN-mediated alcohol dehydrogenase system.[66–69] With 1,1-diproteo-ethanol in deuterium oxide solution, reduced proteo-DPN was obtained; reduced deutero-DPN was obtained using 1,1-dideutero-ethanol in water. The first indications of stereospecificity at the active site were also noted in these experiments.[66,67] When the end point of the reaction was approached slowly so that the DPN molecules had an opportunity of reacting more than once, the deuterium content of reduced DPN never exceeded one atom of deuterium per molecule. In an equilibrium system under these conditions, a nonstereospecific transfer would be expected to yield reduced DPN that contained more than one equivalent of deuterium. Stereospecificity at the active site was proven when only deuterium was transferred between the coenzyme and the substrate during the enzymic reoxidation of enzymically reduced deutero-DPN with acetaldehyde; in contrast, enzymic reoxidation of chemically (i.e., non-stereospecific) reduced deutero-DPN resulted in the exchange of both hydrogen and deuterium between the coenzyme and the substrate.[68,69] Similar results were also obtained with pyruvate in the presence of lactic dehydrogenase. When enzymically reduced deutero-DPN was used, one atom of deuterium was transferred to each molecule of pyruvate to yield lactate; with chemically reduced deutero-DPN, roughly equivalent amounts of hydrogen and deuterium were exchanged between the coenzyme and pyruvate.[69]

Until 1954 it was assumed that the reduction of diphosphopyridine nucleotide resulted in the addition of a hydrogen atom to either the 2- or 6-carbon atom of the pyridine ring. The actual site of enzymic hydrogen transfer in DPN- and TPN-containing enzymes was recently established at the 4-position. To demonstrate this point, DPN was reduced chemically in the presence of deuterium oxide to yield a mixture of the two stereoisomers of reduced deutero-DPN; enzymic reoxidation of this compound yielded a deuterium-containing DPN.[70] Labeled nicotinamide was then isolated from the coenzyme after cleavage with DPN*ase* and was converted to N^1-methylnicotinamide iodide. Alkaline ferricyanide oxidation of this compound yielded the isomeric pyridones (**35**) and (**36**), each of

66. F. H. Westheimer, H. F. Fisher, E. E. Conn, and B. Vennesland, *J. Am. Chem. Soc.*, *73*, 2403 (1951).
67. H. F. Fisher, E. E. Conn, B. Vennesland, and F. H. Westheimer, *J. Biol. Chem.*, *202*, 687 (1953).
68. F. A. Loewus, F. H. Westheimer, and B. Vennesland, *J. Am. Chem. Soc.*, *75*, 5018 (1953).
69. F. A. Loewus, P. Ofner, H. F. Fisher, F. H. Westheimer, and B. Vennesland, *J. Biol. Chem.*, *202*, 699 (1953).
70. M. E. Pullman, A. San Pietro, and S. P. Colowick, *J. Biol. Chem.*, *206*, 129 (1954).

which contained essentially equal amounts of deuterium. If deuterium transfer occurred at either the 2- or 6-position of the pyridine ring, the pyridones would not contain equivalent amounts of deuterium. Therefore, hydrogen transfer is restricted to the 4- or 5-positions of the pyridine ring. Since the rules of aromatic substitution eliminate activation of the 5-position, hydrogen transfer must occur at the 4-position of the pyridine ring.

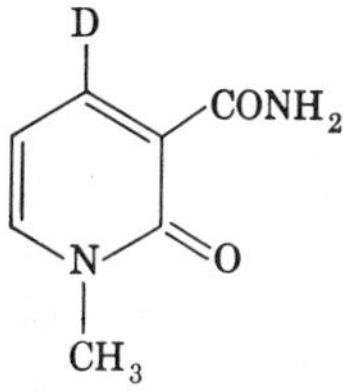

(35) 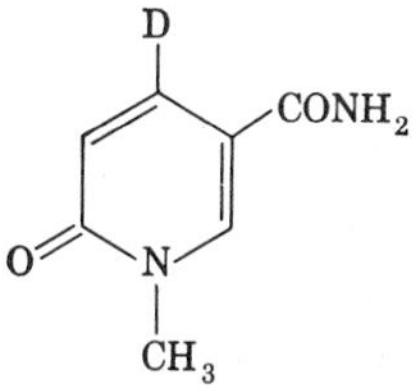 (36)

Hydrogen transfer at the 4-position of the pyridine ring was confirmed by the synthesis and reactions of diphosphopyridine nucleotide containing either 2-, 4-, or 6-deutero-nicotinamide.[71] The 2-, 4- or 6-deutero-nicotinamide moiety was incorporated into DPN by an enzymic exchange reaction. The labeled DPN molecules were then chemically reduced in water and reoxidized enzymically with pyruvate in the presence of lactic dehydrogenase. Only the coenzyme containing the 4-deutero-nicotinamide moiety transferred deuterium to pyruvate. With either the 2- or 6-deutero-nicotinamide-containing coenzyme, no detectable amounts of deuterium were transferred during enzymic reoxidation of the reduced coenzyme.

Evidence for activation at the 4-position of the nicotinamide moiety during hydrogen transfer by DPN was also obtained from studies with model compounds. For example, the reduction of N^1-methylnicotinamide chloride with sodium hydrosulfite in deuterium oxide yielded a deuterated dihydro derivative which was oxidized to the corresponding 2-pyridone derivatives (cf. (**35**) and (**36**)) without the loss of deuterium.[72] In another study, it was shown that 1-benzyl-4-deutero-dihydronicotinamide transferred deuterium to malachite green, but the corresponding 2- and 6-deutero isomers did not.[73] Evidence for a 1,4-dihydro structure in the nicotinamide moiety of the reduced coenzyme was also derived from nuclear magnetic resonance and infrared spectra. N^1-Methylnicotinamide chloride was reduced chemically in deuterium oxide; a detailed comparison

71. F. A. Loewus, B. Vennesland, and D. L. Harris, *J. Am. Chem. Soc.*, *77*, 3391 (1955).
72. G. W. Rafter and S. P. Colowick, *J. Biol. Chem.*, *209*, 773 (1954).
73. D. Mauzerall and F. H. Westheimer, *J. Am. Chem. Soc.*, *77*, 2261 (1955).

of the nuclear magnetic resonance spectrum of this deuterated derivative with those of authentic specimens of 2- and 6-deutero-N^1-methyldihydro-nicotinamide revealed significant differences that were interpreted as conclusive evidence for a 1,4-dihydro structure in the model reduction product.[74] Finally, the 2-, 4-, and 6-deutero isomers of nicotinamide were synthesized, and significant differences were observed in the infrared spectra.[75] The infrared spectrum of deutero-nicotinamide derived from reduced deutero-DPN was identical with that of the authentic specimen of 4-deutero-nicotinamide.

D. DPN- and TPN-Containing Enzymes

DPN- and TPN-containing coenzymes are important links in the series of reactions usually associated with carbohydrate, lipid, and protein metabolism. Important DPN-containing dehydrogenases include the alcohol dehydrogenase system, which converts ethanol to acetaldehyde; the lactic dehydrogenase system, which converts lactic acid to pyruvic acid; and systems that convert 1,3-diphosphoglyceric acid to 3-phosphoglyceraldehyde, *L*-α-glycerophosphate to dihydroxyacetone phosphate, and *L*-glutamic acid to iminoglutaric acid.[76] TPN-containing dehydrogenases include those that convert glucose to gluconic acid, pyruvic acid to malic acid, α-ketoglutaric acid to isocitric acid, and 6-phosphogluconic acid to glucose 6-phosphate.[76]

6. Nutritional and Therapeutic Role

Among the mammalian species, only the dog and the human develop a syndrome characteristic of a deficiency of nicotinic acid. In other species, this deficiency state is not easily differentiated from other nutritional deficiencies.

A. In the Dog

A deficiency of nicotinic acid in the dog results in the syndrome described as canine blacktongue.[77] The animal in this state has no appetite for food or water; oral manifestations such as lesions on the inner surfaces

74. R. Hutton and F. Westheimer, *Tetrahedron*, *3*, 73 (1958).
75. M. S. Brown and H. S. Mosher, *J. Biol. Chem.*, *235*, 2145 (1960).
76. F. Schlenk, *The Enzymes*, Vol. II, Part I, Academic N.Y., 1951, p. 278.
77. J. Goldberger and G. A. Wheeler, *Public Health Repts.* (*U.S.*), *43*, 172 (1928).

of the gums, lips, and cheeks develop, and the tongue assumes a bluish-black color.[78] The nerves in the area of these lesions degenerate, and extensive histological changes take place in the spinal cord and other regions of the central nervous system.[79,80]

B. In the Human

A deficiency of nicotinic acid in the human is designated pellagra. The first deliberate dietary-induced pellagra in man under conditions that eliminated the possibility of concomitant deficiencies of other essential factors was described in 1952,[81] and the resulting deficiency syndrome was essentially the same as that described in 1915.[82,83] The early clinical signs of deficiency include weakness, lassitude, indigestion, and anorexia, usually followed in the course of several months by dermatitis, diarrhea, and finally dementia.[84] Body lesions are usually found in areas most subject to mechanical irritation or body secretion. The mental symptoms usually include irritability, headaches, sleeplessness, and loss of memory. Emotional instability is usually an early sign of pellagra, and advanced cases may develop acute delirium.

Nicotinamide is preferred over nicotinic acid as a therapeutic agent because of better tolerance. It is used in 50-mg. oral doses ten times daily for the treatment of the various stages of the human pellagra syndrome and for overcoming toxicity symptoms incurred during sulfonamide therapy.

The specific requirement for nicotinic acid in man has been difficult to assess for many reasons, but a daily dietary intake of less than 7 mg. of nicotinic acid is usually associated with pellagra.[85] The presently accepted values have been calculated on the basis of body weight and caloric intake, and finally by increasing the value by a 50% safety factor. The recommended daily dietary allowance has been set at 18–21 mg. equivalents for men, 17 mg. equivalents for women, and 6–17 mg. equivalents for children.

78. J. Denton, *Am. J. Pathol.*, *4*, 341 (1928).
79. H. Jensenius and F. Norgaard, *Acta. Pathol. Microbiol. Scand.*, *19*, 433 (1942).
80. R. D. Lillie, *Natl. Insts. Health Bull.*, *162*, 13 (1933).
81. G. A. Goldsmith, H. P. Sarett, U. D. Register, and J. D. Gibbens, *J. Clin. Invest.*, *31*, 533 (1952).
82. J. Goldberger, *Public Health Repts.* (*U.S.*), *31*, 3159 (1916).
83. J. Goldberger, C. H. Waring, and D. G. Willets, *Public Health Repts.* (*U.S.*), *30*, 3117 (1915).
84. N. Joliffe, K. M. Bowman, L. A. Rosenblum, and H. D. Fein, *J. Am. Med. Assoc.*, *114*, 307 (1940).
85. *Recommended Dietary Allowances, Natl. Acad. Sci.-Natl. Res. Council Publ.* 589, Washington, D. C., 1958, p. 13.

The intrinsic and potential nicotinic acid in the diet is usually expressed as equivalents of nicotinic acid; for purposes of calculation, it is assumed that 60 mg. of tryptophan may be converted to 1 mg. of nicotinic acid.[85] For pregnancy and lactation, allowances are increased using 4.4 equivalents for each 1000 calories added to the diet, and further increasing this amount by 50%.

Nicotinic acid is widely distributed in nature. Among the richer sources of the vitamin are wheat germ, brewer's yeast, and meats such as liver, heart, and kidney. The pellagra-preventive efficiency of a given diet, however, is influenced by many other aspects of the diet.

CHAPTER VI

Pantothenic Acid and Coenzyme A

1. Introduction

Pantothenic acid was isolated while the multiple nature of the thermostable fraction of the vitamin B complex was slowly being unfolded. Pantothenic acid and pyridoxol were purified together from liver and yeast and were separated by adsorption chromatography. Since pyridoxol was adsorbed on fuller's earth and pantothenic acid was not, pantothenic acid was sometimes referred to as the filtrate factor and pyridoxol as the eluate factor. During the 1930's several independent research programs were concentrating on either a growth factor for microorganisms or a chick antidermatitis factor. These studies culminated in the isolation, characterization, and synthesis of the vitamin pantothenic acid.

Research on the essential nutrients for yeasts, and particularly *Saccharomyces cerevisiae*,[1,2] was largely responsible for the isolation and partial characterization of pantothenic acid from liver.[3,4] Before the actual isolation of the factor was complete, the fundamental role of the factor was recognized, and sufficient evidence of its chemical nature was obtained to effect partial characterization.[2,5] Since the factor could be obtained from a variety of plant and animal tissues, it was designated pantothenic acid meaning "from everywhere."[2] The compound is also referred to as vitamin B_3.[6]

During this same period, others were independently pursuing the nature of an essential factor for lactic acid bacteria.[7] Later this activity was

1. R. J. Williams, *Advan. Enzymol.*, *3*, 253 (1943).
2. R. J. Williams, C. M. Lyman, G. H. Goodyear, J. H. Truesdail, and D. Holaday, *J. Am. Chem. Soc.*, *55*, 2912 (1933).
3. H. K. Mitchell, H. H. Weinstock, E. E. Snell, S. R. Stanbery, and R. J. Williams, *J. Am. Chem. Soc.*, *62*, 1776 (1940).
4. R. J. Williams, J. H. Truesdail, H. H. Weinstock, E. Rohrman, C. M. Lyman, and C. H. McBurney, *J. Am. Chem. Soc.*, *60*, 2719 (1938).
5. R. J. Williams, H. H. Weinstock, E. Rohrman, J. H. Truesdail, H. K. Mitchell, and C. E. Meyer, *J. Am. Chem. Soc.*, *61*, 454 (1939).
6. R. J. Williams, *Chem. Eng. News*, *37*, 86 (1959).
7. E. E. Snell, F. M. Strong, and W. H. Peterson, *Biochem. J.*, *31*, 1789 (1937).

shown to be identical with pantothenic acid.[8] Another approach to the same vitamin began with studies of a chick dermatitis that was produced by a deficiency of the "thermostable vitamin B complex."[9] The response of this condition to the administration of pantothenic acid concentrates[10] and the effectiveness of calcium pantothenate in stimulating growth and preventing dermatitis in chicks[11] were reported at nearly the same time. The apparent identity of pantothenic acid and the chick antidermatitis factor was evident by a similarity in dissociation constants and a direct relationship between yeast-growth activity and chick activity of pantothenic acid preparations.[11]

2. Isolation

The best sample of pantothenic acid that had been isolated was estimated to be about 90% pure and was a colorless amorphous material about 1100 times as active as the "standard rice bran preparations."[4] The isolation of pantothenic acid from sheep liver was accomplished by starting with an aqueous liver extract[4] or preferably the 90% alcohol-soluble fraction of this extract.[3] Organic bases were removed with fuller's earth, and the vitamin was adsorbed on Norit at pH 3.6. After elution with ammonia, amorphous brucine salts were formed and separated. The mixture of brucine salts was partially purified by a large number of partitions between chloroform and water, and the purified brucine salt was converted to the calcium salt. The amorphous calcium salt was further purified by fractional precipitation from various solvent systems.

3. Structure Determination

The structure of pantothenic acid (**1**) was established as D_g-3-(2′,4′-dihydroxy-3′,3′-dimethylbutyramido)propionic acid by degradation, synthesis, and application of the rules of isorotation.

Even before pantothenic acid was isolated, it had been demonstrated that the substance was a nitrogen-containing polyhydroxy acid with a molecular weight of about 150.[2,5] The nitrogen atom was found to be weakly basic, and no evidence was obtained for the presence of olefinic,

8. E. E. Snell, F. M. Strong, and W. H. Peterson, *J. Am. Chem. Soc.*, *60*, 2825 (1938).
9. L. C. Norris and R. C. Ringrose, *Science*, *71*, 643 (1930).
10. D. W. Woolley, H. A. Waisman, and C. A. Elvehjem, *J. Am. Chem. Soc.*, *61*, 977 (1939); *J. Biol. Chem.*, *129*, 673 (1939).
11. T. H. Jukes, *J. Am. Chem. Soc.*, *61*, 975 (1939); *J. Biol. Chem.*, *129*, 225 (1939).

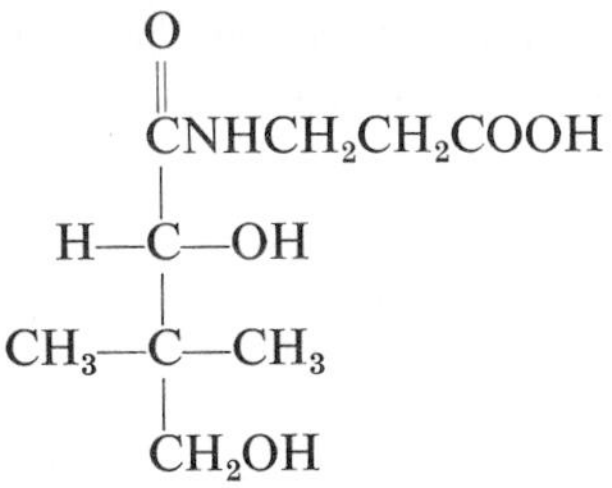

$$\begin{array}{c} O \\ \| \\ CNHCH_2CH_2COOH \\ | \\ H—C—OH \\ | \\ CH_3—C—CH_3 \\ | \\ CH_2OH \end{array}$$

(1)

aldehydic, ketonic, amino, or aromatic functionality. β-Alanine (**2**) was recognized as a constituent of pantothenic acid early in the study, and evidence was presented showing it to be an alkaline cleavage product.[12]

Alkaline hydrolysis of pantothenic acid also gave an acidic compound that was designated pantoic acid (**3**).[3,13] This compound contained two

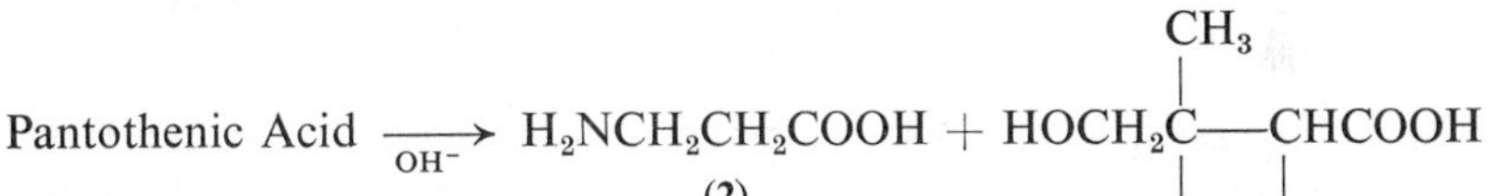

$$\text{Pantothenic Acid} \xrightarrow[OH^-]{} \underset{(2)}{H_2NCH_2CH_2COOH} + \underset{(3)}{HOCH_2\overset{CH_3}{\underset{CH_3}{C}}—\underset{OH}{CH}COOH}$$

hydroxyl groups and formed a lactone readily in acid solution or upon heating. The hydroxyl groups were established in a 2,4-relationship as follows.[3] A 2-hydroxyl group was indicated since pantoic acid gave formic acid on hydrolysis with sulfuric acid and carbon monoxide on dehydration with sulfuric acid. The absence of a 3-hydroxyl group was assumed on the basis of dehydration and oxidation studies and since the acid lactonized readily, the second hydroxyl group was assigned to the 4-position.

Acid hydrolysis of pantothenic acid gave pantolactone (**4**). The presence of a *gem*-dimethyl group in this molecule was established by degradation.[14] A Kuhn-Roth *C*-methyl determination that indicated the presence of a *gem*-dimethyl group was confirmed by the formation of acetone from

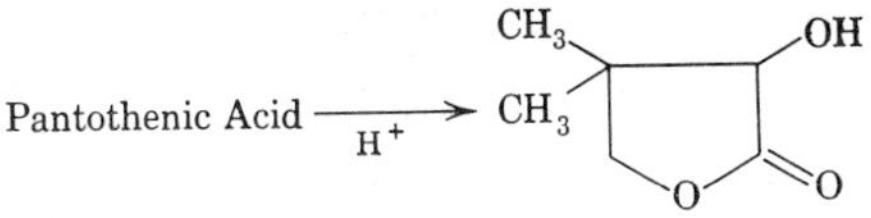

Pantothenic Acid $\xrightarrow[H^+]{}$ [lactone ring: CH_3, CH_3, OH, O, =O]

12. H. Weinstock, Jr., H. K. Mitchell, E. F. Pratt, and R. J. Williams, *J. Am. Chem. Soc.*, *61*, 1421 (1939).
13. R. J. Williams and R. T. Major, *Science*, *91*, 246 (1940).
14. E. T. Stiller, J. C. Keresztesy, and J. Finkelstein, *J. Am. Chem. Soc.*, *62*, 1779 (1940).

pantolactone after oxidation with barium permanganate. Treatment of pantolactone with methyl magnesium iodide followed by oxidation with lead tetraacetate gave 2,2-dimethyl-3-hydroxypropionaldehyde (**5**), which on oxidation with silver oxide yielded the known 2,2-dimethyl-3-hydroxypropionic acid (**6**). These data established the structure of pantolactone as 3,3-dimethyl-2-hydroxybutyro-4-lactone (**4**).

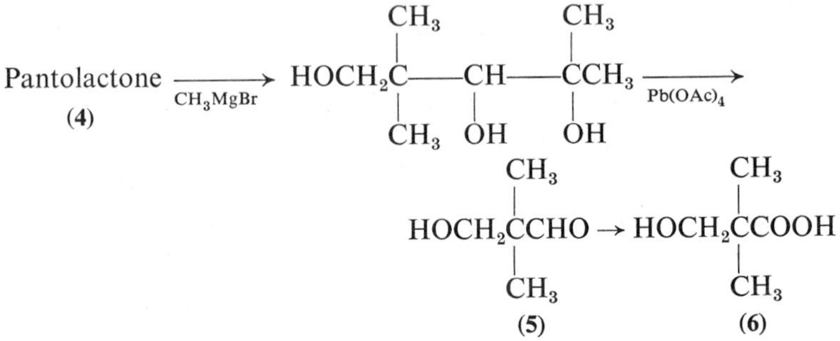

$$\underset{(\mathbf{4})}{\text{Pantolactone}} \xrightarrow[CH_3MgBr]{} HOCH_2\overset{CH_3}{\underset{CH_3}{C}}-\underset{OH}{CH}-\overset{CH_3}{\underset{OH}{C}}CH_3 \xrightarrow[Pb(OAc)_4]{}$$

$$\underset{(\mathbf{5})}{HOCH_2\overset{CH_3}{\underset{CH_3}{C}}CHO} \rightarrow \underset{(\mathbf{6})}{HOCH_2\overset{CH_3}{\underset{CH_3}{C}}COOH}$$

Since it was apparent that an amide linkage served to connect the β-alanine and pantoic acid moieties, several investigators reacted pantolactone, both natural and synthetic, with β-alanine and obtained microbiologically active materials.[15–18]

The biologically active dextrorotatory pantothenic acid and the derived levorotatory pantolactone were related to the D_g series by application of Hudson's hydrazide rule of isorotation.[19] On the basis of the observed optical rotation of (−)-pantolactone and its phenylhydrazide, (−)-pantolactone and (+)-pantothenic acid have been assigned the configurations (**7**) and (**1**), respectively.

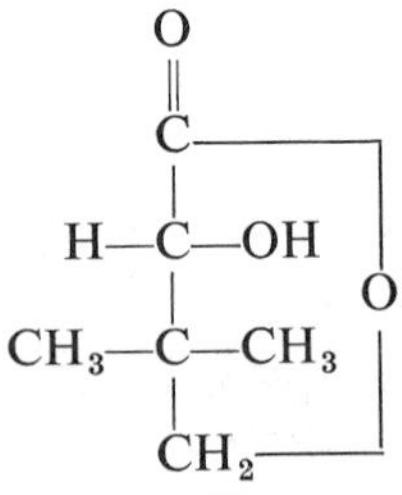

$$\begin{array}{c} O \\ \| \\ C\text{——} \\ | \\ H-C-OH \quad O \\ | \\ CH_3-C-CH_3 \\ | \\ CH_2\text{——} \end{array}$$

(**7**)

15. S. H. Babcock, Jr., and T. H. Jukes, *J. Am. Chem. Soc.*, *62*, 1628 (1940).
16. H. H. Weinstock, A. Arnold, E. L. May, and D. Price, *Science*, *91*, 411 (1940).
17. R. J. Williams, *Science*, *89*, 486 (1939).
18. R. J. Williams, H. K. Mitchell, H. H. Weinstock, and E. E. Snell, *J. Am. Chem. Soc.*, *62*, 1784 (1940).
19. A. Grüssner, M. Gatzi-Fichter, T. Reichstein, and H. Pfaltz, *Helv. Chim. Acta*, *23*, 1276 (1940).

4. Synthesis

For the total synthesis of pantothenic acid, the intermediate pantolactone (**4**) was synthesized and resolved.[20] 2-Methylpropionaldehyde (**8**) was hydroxymethylated with formaldehyde and 2,2-dimethyl-3-hydroxypropionaldehyde (**5**) was obtained. Treatment of this compound with

$$(CH_3)_2CHCHO \ (\mathbf{8}) \xrightarrow{HCHO} HOCH_2C(CH_3)_2CHO \ (\mathbf{5}) \xrightarrow[KCN]{NaHSO_3} HOCH_2C(CH_3)_2CH(OH)CN \ (\mathbf{9}) \xrightarrow{HCl}$$

$$\text{pantolactone } (\mathbf{4}) \xrightarrow{\beta\text{-Alanine}} \text{Pantothenic Acid } (\mathbf{1})$$

potassium cyanide yielded the cyanohydrin (**9**), which was hydrolyzed with acid to give racemic pantolactone (**4**). This intermediate was converted to the sodium salt of pantoic acid, which was resolved into its optical enantiomers with quinine hydrochloride. *D*- and *L*-pantothenic acid were then synthesized from the corresponding isomer of pantolactone and β-alanine.

Most methods for the commercial synthesis of pantothenic acid use the condensation of *D*-(−)-pantolactone with a salt of β-alanine. The *D*-(−)-lactone is obtained from racemic pantolactone by resolution with the methohydroxides of quinine, quinidine, or cinchonidine[21] and with brucine after the esterification of pantolactone with diacetyltartaric anhydride.[22] Pantothenic acid is frequently used commercially as a calcium salt.

5. Coenzyme Forms of Pantothenic Acid

Coenzyme A and the microbial growth factors pantetheine (*Lactobacillus bulgaricus* factor) and pantetheine 4′-phosphate (*Acetobacter suboxydans* factor) are derivatives of pantothenic acid.

20. E. T. Stiller, S. A. Harris, J. Finkelstein, J. C. Keresztesy, and K. Folkers, *J. Am. Chem. Soc.*, *62*, 1785 (1940).
21. R. T. Major and J. Finkelstein, *J. Am. Chem. Soc.*, *63*, 1368 (1941).
22. R. Beutel and M. Tishler, *J. Am. Chem. Soc.*, *68*, 1463 (1946).

A. Coenzyme A

Coenzyme A was discovered as an essential cofactor for the acetylation of sulfonamide in the liver and the acetylation of choline in the brain.[23] Since that time, it has been identified with "active acetate" and has been found to be essential for a variety of biochemical transacetylations.

1. STRUCTURE OF COENZYME A. The structure of coenzyme A (**10**) was established notably by a series of selective enzymic degradations. When

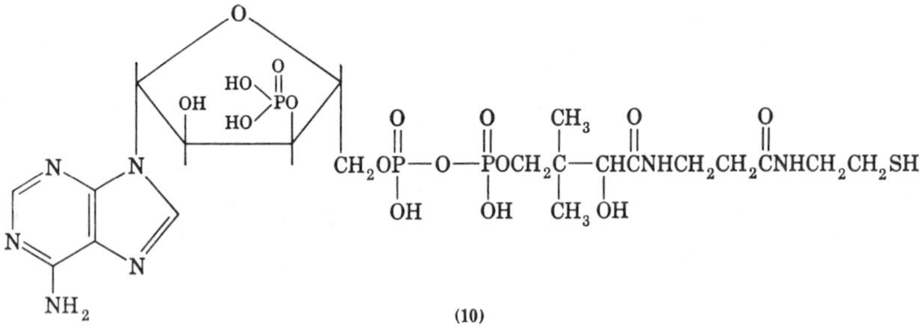

(10)

the first highly purified preparations of coenzyme A became available, the molecule was degraded to pantothenic acid, adenosine, phosphate, and an unidentified sulfur-containing compound.[24] One equivalent of adenosine and three equivalents of phosphate were found for each mole of pantothenic acid.

The three equivalents of phosphate were established as existing in a monophosphate and pyrophosphate ester grouping. Enzymolysis of coenzyme A with prostate phosphomonoesterase released only one of the three potential moles of phosphate.[25] The monophosphate ester was located in the ribose portion of the adenosine moiety of the coenzyme,[26] and was established later at the 3′-position of ribose by observing the rate of enzymic deactivation of coenzyme A by a barley "b"-nucleotidase.[27] The latter is specific for 3′-phosphoribosides. The two remaining moles of phosphate were accounted for as a pyrophosphate bridge that links the adenosine moiety through its 5′-position to the 4′-position of pantothenic acid; the pyrophosphate nature of the linkage was shown by enzymic

23. F. Lipmann and N. O. Kaplan, *J. Biol. Chem.*, *162*, 743 (1946).
24. W. H. De Vries, W. M. Grovier, J. S. Evans, J. D. Gregory, G. D. Novelli, M. Soodak, and F. Lipmann., *J. Am. Chem. Soc.*, *72*, 4838 (1950).
25. J. D. Gregory, G. D. Novelli, and F. Lipmann, *J. Am. Chem. Soc.*, *74*, 854 (1952).
26. J. Baddiley and E. M. Thain, *J. Chem. Soc.*, 246, 2253 (1951).
27. Te Pao Wang, L. Shuster, and N. O. Kaplan, *J. Am. Chem. Soc.*, *74*, 3204 (1952).

deactivation of coenzyme A with pyrophosphatases and dinucleotidases.[28] Location of the pyrophosphate linkage at the 4′-position of pantothenic acid resulted from the identification of pantothenic acid 4′-phosphate **(11)** in an alkaline hydrolyzate of coenzyme A.[26] The structure of this 4′-phosphate was established by comparative chromatography with a group of known synthetic pantothenic acid monophosphates and was confirmed by the synthesis of pantetheine 4′-phosphate (*Acetobacter suboxydans* factor) **(12)**.[29]

$$(HO)_2\overset{O}{\overset{\|}{P}}OCH_2\underset{CH_3}{\overset{CH_3}{C}}-\underset{OH}{CH}\overset{O}{\overset{\|}{C}}NHCH_2CH_2COOH$$

(11)

$$(HO)_2\overset{O}{\overset{\|}{P}}OCH_2\underset{CH_3}{\overset{CH_3}{C}}-\underset{OH}{CH}\overset{O}{\overset{\|}{C}}NHCH_2CH_2\overset{O}{\overset{\|}{C}}NHCH_2CH_2SH$$

(12)

The sulfur-containing moiety of coenzyme A was elucidated by the identification of 2-aminoethanethiol as a degradation product from *N*-pantothenylaminoethanethiol **(13)**.[30] The latter compound is derived from

$$HOCH_2\underset{CH_3}{\overset{CH_3}{C}}-\underset{OH}{CH}\overset{O}{\overset{\|}{C}}NHCH_2CH_2\overset{O}{\overset{\|}{C}}NHCH_2CH_2SH$$

(13)

coenzyme A and is usually referred to as pantetheine (*Lactobacillus bulgaricus* factor). The characterization and synthesis of pantetheine established an amide link between the amino group of the aminoethanethiol moiety and the carboxyl group of the pantothenic acid moiety in coenzyme A.

2. SYNTHESIS OF COENZYME A. The structure of coenzyme A **(10)** established on the basis of degradation data was confirmed by synthesis.[31] Key

28. G. D. Novelli, N. O. Kaplan, and F. Lipmann, *Federation Proc.*, *9*, 209 (1950).
29. J. Baddiley, E. M. Thain, G. D. Novelli, and F. Lipmann, *Nature*, *171*, 76 (1953).
30. E. E. Snell, G. M. Brown, V. J. Peters, J. A. Craig, E. L. Wittle, J. A. Moore, V. M. McGlohon, and O. D. Bird, *J. Am. Chem. Soc.*, *72*, 5349 (1950).
31. J. G. Moffatt and H. G. Khorana, *J. Am. Chem. Soc.*, *81*, 1265 (1959); *83*, 663 (1961).

reactions in the synthesis (Fig. 1) are the carbodiimide-mediated condensation of adenosine 2′(3′),5′-diphosphate with morpholine yielding adenosine 2′,3′-phosphate-5′-phosphoromorpholidate (**14**) and condensation of this activated nucleotide 5′-phosphoromorpholidate with pantetheine 4′-phosphate (**12**). Mild acid hydrolysis of the cyclic phosphate group of the intermediate (**15**) and cleavage of disulfide bonds with 2-mercaptoethanol gave a mixture of coenzyme A and its 2′-phosphate isomer (iso-coenzyme A) which were separated by chromatography. The coenzyme A

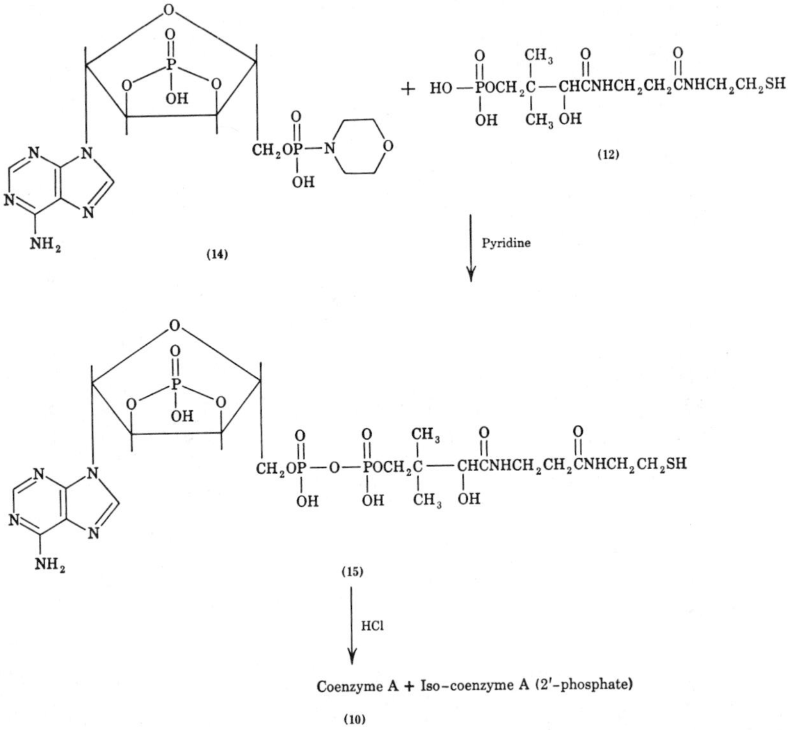

(14) (12)

Pyridine

(15)

HCl

Coenzyme A + Iso-coenzyme A (2′-phosphate)

(10)

Fig. 1. Synthesis of coenzyme A.[31]

that was prepared from *D*-(+)-pantetheine 4′-phosphate was identical with natural coenzyme A chromatographically, electrophoretically, and by biochemical assay. Iso-coenzyme A had no coenzyme A activity in the biochemical assay.

3. METABOLIC ROLE OF COENZYME A. Coenzyme A participates in two-carbon unit metabolism by facilitating acyl transfer. In this process currently regarded as occurring in three stages,[32] the coenzyme serves as

32. T. C. Chou and F. Lipmann, *J. Biol. Chem.*, *196*, 89 (1952).

a shunt between acyl donors such as pyruvate, acetoacetate, or acetyl phosphate and acyl acceptors such as oxaloacetate, hydroxylamine, and acetoacetate. *S*-Acetyl coenzyme A, one form of active acetate, has been isolated from natural materials such as yeast,[33,34] and until recently was the only form of the coenzyme depicted in acyl transfer. Recently malonyl coenzyme A was found to be the form of active acetate participating in fatty acid biosynthesis in cytoplasm. In this mechanism, the acyl coenzyme A molecule is further activated by reaction with carbon dioxide to form the malonyl derivative.[35–38]

The acyl group of acetyl or malonyl coenzyme A may be regarded as being activated at either its alkyl carbon atom or at the carbonyl carbon atom since condensations involving "active acetate" are known to result in either simple carbon-carbon condensations (tail condensations) or in carbon-carbonyl condensations (head condensations). With the exception of fatty acid biosynthesis, acyl coenzyme A in biochemical processes is depicted as participating as an acetyl rather than a malonyl derivative. Further research may determine whether the malonyl rather than acetyl form of acyl coenzyme A participates in some of these other processes.

In the Krebs cycle, the acetyl group of acetyl coenzyme A (**17**) is "tail condensed"[39] through its methyl group with oxaloacetic acid (**16**) yielding citric acid (**18**).

$$
\begin{array}{c}
\mathrm{COOH} \\
| \\
\mathrm{O{=}C} \\
| \\
\mathrm{CH_2} \\
| \\
\mathrm{COOH} \\
\textbf{(16)}
\end{array}
\quad + \quad
\begin{array}{c}
\mathrm{O} \\
\| \\
\mathrm{HCH_2CS{-}CoA} \\
\textbf{(17)}
\end{array}
\quad \longrightarrow \quad
\begin{array}{c}
\mathrm{COOH} \\
| \\
\mathrm{HO{-}C{-}CH_2COOH} \\
| \\
\mathrm{CH_2} \\
| \\
\mathrm{COOH} \\
\textbf{(18)}
\end{array}
$$

Acetoacetate biosynthesis and fatty acid biosynthesis in mitochondria may be regarded as being initiated by a "head and tail condensation" of acetyl coenzyme A.[40–42] After such condensation, the carbonyl group is

33. F. Lynen and E. Reichert, *Angew. Chem.*, *63*, 47 (1951).
34. F. Lynen, E. Reichert, and L. Rueff, *Ann.*, *574*, 1 (1951).
35. S. J. Wakil, *J. Am. Chem. Soc.*, *80*, 6465 (1958).
36. R. O. Brady, *Proc. Natl. Acad. Sci.* (*U.S.*), *44*, 993 (1958).
37. S. J. Wakil, *Am. J. Clin. Nutr.*, *8*, 630 (1960).
38. S. J. Wakil and D. M. Gibson, *Biochim. et Biophys. Acta*, *41*, 122 (1960).
39. S. Ochoa, J. R. Stern, and M. C. Schneider, *J. Biol. Chem.*, *193*, 691 (1951).
40. F. Lipmann, *Science*, *120*, 855 (1954).
41. E. R. Stadtman, M. Doudoroff, and F. Lipmann, *J. Biol. Chem.*, *191*, 377 (1951).
42. F. Lynen, *Federation Proc.*, *12*, 683 (1953).

converted stepwise to a methylene group, and the resulting molecule condenses with another equivalent of active acetate. Each participation by acetyl coenzyme A results in building up the chain by two carbon atoms through acyl transfer.

According to later evidence, fatty acid biosynthesis in cytoplasm requires the conversion of acetyl coenzyme A to malonyl coenzyme A prior to condensation.[35–38] This conversion is dependent upon a biotin-containing enzyme fraction, ATP, and carbon dioxide. The sequence may be depicted as follows.[35,37] Acetyl coenzyme A is carboxylated to malonyl coenzyme A (**19**) which then condenses with either acetyl coenzyme A or another molecule of malonyl coenzyme A. The resulting intermediate (**20**) loses carbon dioxide, forming acetoacetyl coenzyme A (**21**). DPNH reduction of acetoacetyl coenzyme A yields the intermediate β-hydroxybutyryl coenzyme A (**22**), which after dehydration and reduction gives butyryl coenzyme A (**23**). The cycle is then repeated; condensation

$$CH_3\overset{O}{\overset{\|}{C}}S{-}CoA \xrightarrow{CO_2} \underset{\underset{(\mathbf{19})}{COOH}}{CH_2}\overset{O}{\overset{\|}{C}}S{-}CoA \xrightarrow{CH_3\overset{O}{\overset{\|}{C}}S-CoA}$$

$$\left[CH_3\overset{O}{\overset{\|}{C}}\underset{COOH}{\underset{|}{C}H}\overset{O}{\overset{\|}{C}}S{-}CoA\right]_{(\mathbf{20})} \xrightarrow[-CO_2]{}$$

$$\underset{(\mathbf{21})}{CH_3\overset{O}{\overset{\|}{C}}CH_2\overset{O}{\overset{\|}{C}}S{-}CoA} \xrightarrow{DPNH} \underset{(\mathbf{22})}{CH_3\overset{OH}{\overset{|}{C}}HCH_2\overset{O}{\overset{\|}{C}}S{-}CoA} \longrightarrow$$

$$CH_3CH{=}CH\overset{O}{\overset{\|}{C}}S{-}CoA \longrightarrow \underset{(\mathbf{23})}{CH_3CH_2CH_2\overset{O}{\overset{\|}{C}}S{-}CoA} \xrightarrow{\underset{COOH}{\underset{|}{CH_2}}\overset{O}{\overset{\|}{C}}S-CoA}$$

$$\underset{(\mathbf{24})}{CH_3CH_2CH_2\overset{O}{\overset{\|}{C}}\underset{COOH}{\underset{|}{C}H}\overset{O}{\overset{\|}{C}}S{-}CoA} \xrightarrow{-CO_2} \underset{(\mathbf{25})}{CH_3CH_2CH_2\overset{O}{\overset{\|}{C}}CH_2\overset{O}{\overset{\|}{C}}S{-}CoA}$$

of butyryl coenzyme A with malonyl coenzyme A results in the intermediate (**24**), which after the loss of carbon dioxide yields butyroacetyl coenzyme A (**25**). The latter is converted to caproyl coenzyme A, and the process continues. Since the free carboxyl group of malonyl coenzyme A is eliminated immediately following each acyl transfer step, none of the carbon atoms in the final product come from carbon dioxide. Consequently, the condition that all carbon atoms of the acid come from acetyl coenzyme A is satisfied.

This reaction mechanism is valid for the biosynthesis of butyryl, hexanoyl, and octanoyl coenzyme A, but there are objections to its application without modification to the biosynthesis of palmityl coenzyme A from acetyl and malonyl coenzyme A. In the cytoplasm, acetyl and malonyl coenzyme A are converted to palmitate, but other fatty acid derivatives of coenzyme A are not incorporated. To account for this observation, it has been suggested that the biosynthesis of palmitate from malonyl coenzyme A may proceed by

(a) Synthesis of polycarboxylic acid intermediates and ultimate polydecarboxylation at the C_{16}-stage;

(b) Synthesis of polyketo acid intermediates and ultimate reduction at the C_{16}-stage; or

(c) Formation of intermediate tightly-bound acylthio-enzyme complexes and ultimate dissociation at the C_{16}-stage.

The enzymic synthesis of fatty acids from aldehydes by aldol condensation also proceeds from malonyl rather than acetyl coenzyme A.[36] The reaction is depicted with the aldehyde condensing at the activated methylene carbon atom of malonyl coenzyme A. After the loss of the free carboxyl carbon atom as carbon dioxide, the resulting β-hydroxyacyl coenzyme A is dehydrated and the product is reduced in a TPNH mediated reaction to yield the fatty acid.

Methylmalonyl coenzyme A (**27**) is an intermediate in propionic acid metabolism at the isomerization step which is mediated by the cobamide coenzymes. The reaction sequence proceeds through the stages propionyl coenzyme A (**26**), methylmalonyl coenzyme A (**27**), and succinyl coenzyme A (**28**).[43–45] The conversion of propionyl coenzyme A to methylmalonyl coenzyme A is mediated by biotin and is discussed in Chapter VIII. The mechanism of the isomerization of methylmalonyl coenzyme A to succinyl coenzyme A as mediated by dimethylbenzimidazolyl cobamide coenzyme is described in Chapter X.

43. M. Flavin and S. Ochoa, *J. Biol. Chem.*, *229*, 965 (1957).
44. W. S. Beck, M. Flavin, and S. Ochoa, *J. Biol. Chem.*, *229*, 997 (1958).
45. W. S. Beck and S. Ochoa, *J. Biol. Chem.*, *232*, 931 (1958).

$$\underset{(26)}{CH_3\text{—}CH_2\text{—}\overset{\overset{}{}}{C}(=O)S\text{—}CoA} \underset{-CO_2}{\overset{CO_2}{\rightleftharpoons}} \underset{(27)}{CH_3\text{—}CH(COOH)\text{—}C(=O)S\text{—}CoA} \underset{+H\cdot}{\overset{-H\cdot}{\rightleftharpoons}}$$

$$\left[\cdot CH_2\text{—}CH(COOH)\text{—}C(=O)S\text{—}CoA \rightleftharpoons CH_2\text{—}\dot{C}H(COOH)\text{—}C(=O)S\text{—}CoA \right] \rightleftharpoons \underset{(28)}{COOH\text{—}CH_2\text{—}CH_2\text{—}C(=O)S\text{—}CoA}$$

$$\underset{(28)}{COOH\text{—}CH_2\text{—}CH_2\text{—}C(=O)\text{—}S\text{—}CoA} + \underset{(29)}{H\bar{C}(COO^-)\text{—}N\text{=}C\text{—}[\text{pyridine ring: HO, }CH_3\text{, N, }CH_2O\text{—}P(=O)(OH)\text{—}OH]} \longrightarrow \underset{(30)}{COOH\text{—}CH_2\text{—}CH_2\text{—}C(=O)\text{—}CH(NH_2)\text{—}COOH}$$

$$(28) + (29) \xrightarrow{-CO_2} (31); \quad (30) \xrightarrow{-CO_2} (31)$$

$$\underset{(31)}{COOH\text{—}CH_2\text{—}CH_2\text{—}C(=O)\text{—}CH_2\text{—}NH_2} \longrightarrow \underset{(32)}{\text{pyrrole (N—H) with } CH_2COOH,\ CH_2CH_2COOH,\ CH_2NH_2}$$

Succinyl coenzyme A (**28**) also participates in erythrocyte metabolism. It was suggested that the pyrrole (**32**), which is a precursor for heme synthesis, is formed by the reaction of glycine with two equivalents of "activated succinate,"[46] and it was demonstrated that succinate is activated by conversion to succinyl coenzyme A prior to condensation.[47–49] The reaction appears to proceed in two stages. Succinate is activated by coenzyme A and ATP, yielding succinyl coenzyme A (**28**), which may then be considered to condense with a stabilized carbanion of the pyridoxal derivative of glycine (**29**).[49,50] It is not known whether α-amino-β-keto-adipic acid (**30**) is an intermediate in this sequence leading to the pyrrole precursor, δ-aminolevulinic acid (**31**).

The role of coenzyme A in fatty acid degradation is evident in amino acid metabolism when isovaleric acid, an intermediate in leucine metabolism, is degraded to acetoacetic acid.[51] The reaction scheme is depicted as follows.[51,52] Isovaleryl coenzyme A (**33**) is converted to 3-methylcrotonyl coenzyme A (**34**) which is carboxylated in the presence of ATP and bicarbonate to yield 3-methylglutaconyl coenzyme A (**35**). Enzymic hydration of the latter yields 3-hydroxy-3-methylglutaryl coenzyme A (**36**) which is then enzymically cleaved in the presence of cysteine or glutathione yielding acetoacetic acid and acetyl coenzyme A.

$$\underset{\mathbf{(33)}}{CH_3CH(CH_3)CH_2C(=O)S\text{—}CoA} \rightarrow \underset{\mathbf{(34)}}{CH_3C(CH_3){=}CHC(=O)S\text{—}CoA} \rightarrow$$

$$\underset{\mathbf{(35)}}{HOOCCH_2C(CH_3){=}CHC(=O)S\text{—}CoA} \rightarrow \underset{\mathbf{(36)}}{HOOCCH_2C(CH_3)(OH)CH_2C(=O)S\text{—}CoA} \xrightarrow[\text{glutathione}]{\text{Cysteine or}}$$

$$CH_3C(=O)CH_2COOH + CH_3C(=O)S\text{—}CoA$$

46. D. Shemin and R. Rittenberg, *J. Biol. Chem.*, *192*, 315 (1951).
47. D. Shemin and C. S. Russel, *J. Am. Chem. Soc.*, *75*, 4873 (1953).
48. G. Kikuchi, A. Kumar, P. Talmage, and D. Shemin, *J. Biol. Chem.*, *233*, 1214 (1958).
49. D. Shemin and G. Kikuchi, *Ann. N.Y. Acad. Sci.*, *75*, 122 (1958).
50. K. D. Gibson, W. G. Laver, and A. Neuberger, *Biochem. J.*, *70*, 71 (1958).
51. B. K. Bachhawat, W. G. Robinson, and M. J. Coon, *J. Am. Chem. Soc.*, *76*, 3098 (1954); *J. Biol. Chem.*, *216*, 727 (1955); *219*, 539 (1956).
52. E. E. Dekker, M. J. Schlesinger, and M. J. Coon, *J. Biol. Chem.*, *233*, 434 (1958); A. del Campillo-Campbell, E. E. Dekker, and M. J. Coon, *Biochim. et Biophys. Acta*, *31*, 290 (1959).

Observations on enzymic syntheses of 3-methylcrotonic acid, 3-hydroxy-3-methylglutaric acid, and cholesterol from acetoacetic acid led to the concept that coenzyme A plays a role in sterol and terpene biogenesis.[53–55] Enzymic biosynthesis of 3-hydroxy-3-methylglutaryl coenzyme A (**36**) from acetyl coenzyme A and acetoacetyl coenzyme A[56] or from 3-methylcrotonyl coenzyme A (**34**) by carboxylation followed by hydroxylation[57] substantiated the participation of coenzyme A at this step of sterol biosynthesis. It was shown next that the acetate-replacing growth factor mevalonic acid (3,5-dihydroxy-3-methylpentanoic acid) (**37**) plays a key role in sterol biosynthesis.[58] Incorporation of radioactivity from *DL*-2-C^{14}-mevalonic acid into cholesterol was 10-fold that observed with 4-C^{14}-3-methylcrotonic acid and 240 times that found with 3′-C^{14}-3-hydroxy-3-methylglutaric acid. The results also suggested that the pathway from mevalonic acid to cholesterol is direct rather than by cleavage to smaller molecules. In addition, it was reported that the enzymic synthesis

CH_3 OH

C

$HOCH_2CH_2$ CH_2COOH

(37)

of squalene from mevalonic acid is direct and not by preliminary cleavage.[59,60] The enzymic reduction of 3-hydroxy-3-methylglutaryl coenzyme A (**36**) to mevalonic acid (**37**) in baker's yeast was also demonstrated.[61] These data were interpreted as evidence for the participation of coenzyme A in isoprenoid biosynthesis during the conversion of acetate to mevalonate by way of 3-hydroxy-3-methylglutaryl coenzyme A.

Evidence is available that leads to the suggestion of a role for coenzyme A in phosphorylations that are coupled with electron transport.[62,63] Coenzyme A maintains rather than stimulates the rate of phosphorylation

53. K. Bloch, L. C. Clark, and I. Harary, *J. Biol. Chem.*, *211*, 687 (1954).
54. J. L. Rabinowitz and S. Gurin, *J. Am. Chem. Soc.*, *76*, 5168 (1954).
55. H. Rudney, *J. Am. Chem. Soc.*, *76*, 2595 (1954); *77*, 1698 (1955).
56. H. Rudney and J. J. Ferguson, Jr., *J. Am. Chem. Soc.*, *79*, 5580 (1957).
57. H. Hilz, J. Knappe, E. Ringelmann, and F. Lynen, *Biochem. Z.*, *329*, 476 (1958).
58. P. A. Tavormina, M. H. Gibbs, and J. W. Huff, *J. Am. Chem. Soc.*, *78*, 4498 (1956).
59. B. H. Admur, H. Rilling, and K. Bloch, *J. Am. Chem. Soc.*, *79*, 2646 (1957).
60. F. Dituri, S. Gurin, and J. L. Rabinowitz, *J. Am. Chem. Soc.*, *79*, 2650 (1957).
61. J. J. Ferguson, Jr., I. F. Durr, and H. Rudney, *Federation Proc.*, *17*, 219 (1958).
62. W. C. McMurray and H. A. Lardy, *J. Am. Chem. Soc.*, *79*, 6563 (1957).
63. W. C. McMurray and H. A. Lardy, *J. Biol. Chem.*, *233*, 754 (1958).

accompanying the oxidation of substrates such as *D*-β-hydroxybutyric acid, DPNH, or succinic acid by submitochondrial particles of rat liver. Although such activity might arise from a protective nonspecific effect of the sulfhydryl group of the coenzyme, other mercapto compounds do not act in a similar fashion. This activity is not due to an adenosine triphosphate-sparing effect of the coenzyme since nucleotides such as the mono-, di-, and triphosphates of cytidine, inosine, guanosine, and uridine were ineffective in maintaining catalytic oxidative phosphorylation. Although speculative, it was suggested that a bound-form of coenzyme A is necessary for this reaction.

Acyl coenzyme A also plays a role in the synthesis of fatty acid ester bonds in phospholipid synthesis. An enzyme prepared from rat liver facilitates the synthesis of phosphate-containing lipids from *L*-α-glycerophosphate and long chain fatty acids.[64] This system, which requires ATP and coenzyme A, has been depicted with stearyl coenzyme A acylating *L*-α-glycerophosphate.

4. BIOSYNTHESIS OF COENZYME A. Until recently, the biosynthetic pathway (Fig. 2) from pantothenic acid to coenzyme A was assumed to proceed exclusively through the sequence, pantothenylcysteine (**39**), pantetheine (**13**), pantetheine 4′-phosphate (**12**), and dephospho-coenzyme A. However, an alternate and perhaps even more significant pathway exists for both mammalian and microbial systems. In many systems this newly discovered sequence is the only operative pathway.

In the sequence that was recently discovered[65] in rat liver, rat kidney, *Proteus morganii*, and *L. arabinosus*, pantothenic acid (**1**) is phosphorylated to pantothenic acid 4′-phosphate (**11**) by the enzyme pantothenic acid kinase. Pantothenic acid 4′-phosphate is then condensed with cysteine (**38**) in the presence of an enzyme designated "coupling enzyme" to yield 4′-phosphopantothenylcysteine (**40**), which in turn is decarboxylated to pantetheine 4′-phosphate (**12**) by the enzyme phosphopantothenylcysteine decarboxylase. Pantetheine 4′-phosphate is then converted to coenzyme A with adenosine triphosphate.

If 2-mercaptoethylamine is substituted for cysteine in these enzyme systems, the sequence proceeds directly from pantothenic acid 4′-phosphate (**11**) to pantetheine 4′-phosphate (**12**). This observation was unexpected since 2-mercaptoethylamine is not nearly as effective as cysteine for the biosynthesis of coenzyme A in either rat liver or in resting cell suspensions of *L. arabinosus* or *P. morganii*. It has been suggested, however, that insufficient substrate was used in the latter experiment.[65]

64. A. Kornberg and W. E. Pricer, Jr., *J. Am. Chem. Soc.*, *74*, 1617 (1952).
65. G. M. Brown, *J. Biol. Chem.*, *234*, 370 (1959).

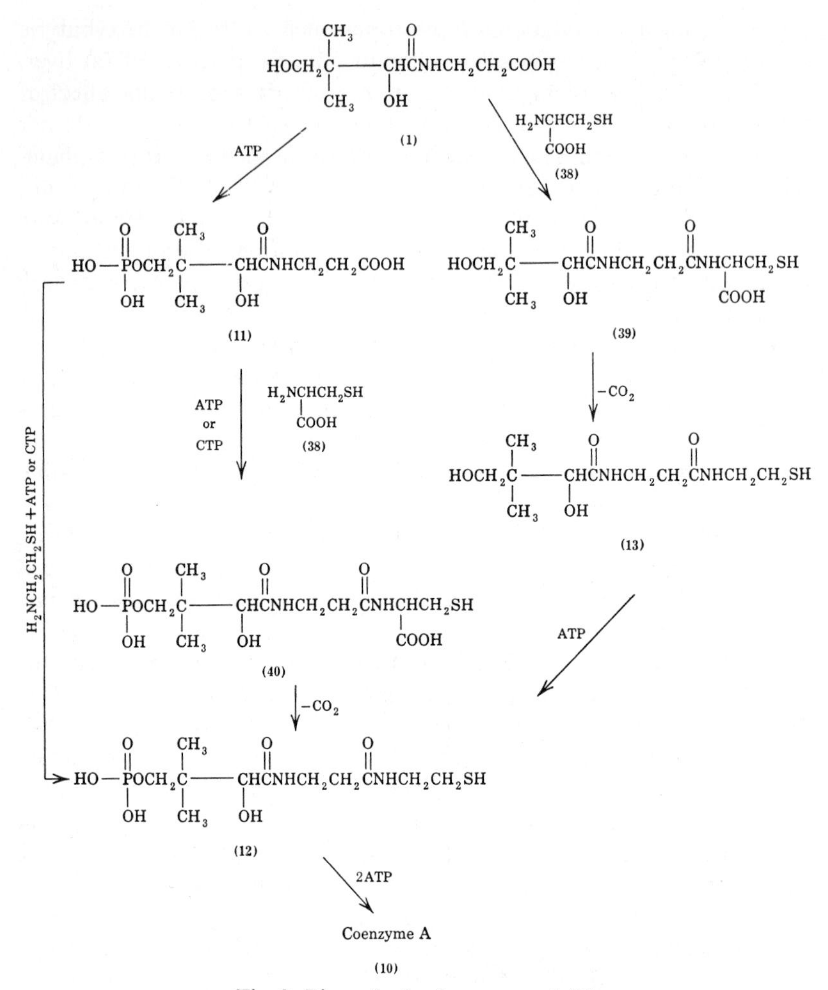

Fig. 2. Biosynthesis of coenzyme A.[65]

In view of the discovery of a biosynthetic pathway for coenzyme A that does not require pantetheine **(13)** and because of the apparent major importance of this new sequence, the metabolic importance of pantothenylcysteine and pantetheine has been reconsidered.[65] The importance of pantothenylcysteine in metabolism is questioned on the basis of its ineffectiveness in replacing pantothenic acid in chick and rat nutrition under conditions in which pantetheine is effective.[66] The reported failures to

66. R. Q. Thompson and O. D. Bird, *Science*, *120*, 763 (1954).

phosphorylate pantothenylcysteine to 4′-phosphopantothenylcysteine or to hydrolyze it to pantothenic acid, and the low yields obtained on decarboxylation to pantetheine also suggest a minor metabolic role for pantothenylcysteine.

Although pantetheine is abundantly distributed throughout nature, it does not appear to be on the main biosynthetic pathway to coenzyme A. The abundance of pantetheine is attributed to side reactions resulting in the degradation of either pantetheine 4′-phosphate or coenzyme A.[65]

B. Pantetheine (Lactobacillus bulgaricus Factor) and Pantetheine 4′-Phosphate (Acetobacter suboxydans Factor)

Two fragments of coenzyme A have been identified as microbial growth factors. The *Lactobacillus bulgaricus* factor was characterized as pantetheine (**13**)[67] and was synthesized by the ammonolysis of methyl pantothenate (**41**) with 2-mercaptoethylamine.[30]

$$HOCH_2C(CH_3)_2\text{—}CH(OH)C(=O)NHCH_2CH_2COOCH_3 + H_2NCH_2CH_2SH \longrightarrow \text{Pantetheine (LBF)}$$

(**41**) → Pantetheine (LBF) (**13**)

The *Acetobacter suboxydans* factor has been identified as pantetheine 4′-phosphate (**12**)[68] and was synthesized (Fig. 3) from the 2′-benzyl derivative (**42**) of pantothenic acid.[29]

6. Nutritional and Therapeutic Role

A. In Animals

The pathological symptoms of pantothenic acid deficiency are clearly defined in most animals but not in man.[69,70] The deficiency syndrome, however, varies with the species.

Pantothenic acid deficiency in chicks is characterized by growth failure, dermatitis, spinal cord degeneration, and poor feathering.

In rats, pantothenic acid deficiency leads to pathological changes in

67. W. L. Williams, E. Hoff-Jorgensen, and E. E. Snell, *J. Biol. Chem.*, *177*, 933 (1949).
68. T. E. King, I. G. Fells, and V. H. Cheldelin, *J. Am. Chem. Soc.*, *71*, 131 (1949).
69. B. C. Johnson, *Ann. Rev. Biochem.*, *24*, 419 (1955).
70. G. M. Briggs and F. S. Daft, in W. H. Sebrell, Jr. and R. S. Harris, eds., *The Vitamins: Chemistry, Physiology, and Pathology*, Vol. II, Academic, N.Y., 1954, p. 649.

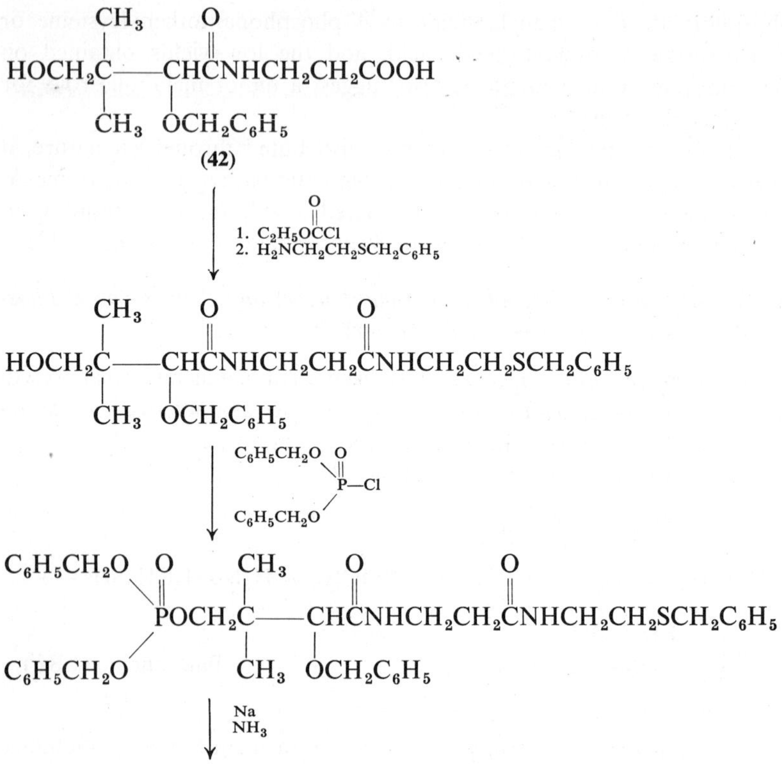

$$\begin{array}{l} \quad\ \ CH_3 \quad\ \ O \\ \quad\ \ \ | \qquad\quad \| \\ HOCH_2C\text{—}CHCNHCH_2CH_2COOH \\ \quad\ \ \ | \qquad\ | \\ \quad\ \ CH_3 \ \ OCH_2C_6H_5 \end{array}$$

(42)

$\downarrow$ 1. $C_2H_5OC(=O)Cl$ 2. $H_2NCH_2CH_2SCH_2C_6H_5$

$$\begin{array}{l} \quad\ \ CH_3 \quad\ \ O \qquad\qquad\qquad\quad O \\ \quad\ \ \ | \qquad\quad \| \qquad\qquad\qquad\quad \| \\ HOCH_2C\text{—}CHCNHCH_2CH_2CNHCH_2CH_2SCH_2C_6H_5 \\ \quad\ \ \ | \qquad\ | \\ \quad\ \ CH_3 \ \ OCH_2C_6H_5 \end{array}$$

$\downarrow$ $(C_6H_5CH_2O)_2P(=O)Cl$

$$\begin{array}{l} C_6H_5CH_2O \ \ O \qquad CH_3 \qquad O \qquad\qquad\qquad O \\ \qquad\quad \diagdown \| \qquad\quad | \qquad\quad \| \qquad\qquad\qquad \| \\ \qquad\qquad POCH_2C\text{—}CHCNHCH_2CH_2CNHCH_2CH_2SCH_2C_6H_5 \\ \qquad\quad \diagup \qquad\quad\ \ | \qquad\ | \\ C_6H_5CH_2O \qquad\quad CH_3 \ \ OCH_2C_6H_5 \end{array}$$

$\downarrow$ Na, NH_3

Pantetheine 4′-phosphate (*Acetobacter suboxydans* factor)

(12)

Fig. 3. Synthesis of the *Acetobacter suboxydans* factor.[29]

several organs. Adrenal necrosis and hemorrhage is perhaps the most common manifestation of avitaminosis in this species. Gastrointestinal disturbances and duodenal ulcers are a pronounced feature of a deficiency state in the adult rat;[71,72] absence of the vitamin apparently creates increased vulnerability of tissue to cortical hormones which leads to ulceration. Severe cases of pantothenic acid deficiency in the growing rat also lead to degeneration of testicular interstitial tissue.[73] A marked impairment of antibody formation to influenza virus PR-8 was also observed in the pantothenic acid- and pyridoxine-deficient rat.[74] Other

71. T. F. Zucker, *Am. J. Clin. Nutr.*, *6*, 65 (1958).
72. B. N. Berg, *Brit. J. Exptl. Pathol.*, *40*, 371 (1959).
73. J. J. Barboriak, G. W. Cowgill, and A. D. Whedon, *J. Nutr.*, *66*, 457 (1958).
74. A. E. Axelrod and S. Hopper, *J. Nutr.*, *72*, 325 (1960).

more classical signs of deficiency in the rat include blood dyscrasias and achromotrichia.

In the dog, a pantothenic acid deficiency is characterized by hypoglycemia, rapid labored respiration, rapid irregular heart rate, convulsion, and sudden coma.[75] Pathologic manifestations of the deficiency include fatty liver, kidney degeneration, and mottled thymus.

B. In the Human

Pantothenic acid plays an important role in human nutrition, but a pantothenic acid deficiency in the human is apparently rare and is not recognized to occur under normal circumstances. Early studies on a pantothenic acid depletion induced in humans by the combined use of a pantothenic acid-free diet and the antagonist ω-methylpantothenic acid are of special interest.[76–79] The depletion syndrome was characterized by a burning sensation, muscle weakness, abdominal disorder, vasomotor instability, infection, and depression. Metabolically, erratic changes in acetylation, 17-ketosteroid excretion, and the excretion of water-soluble vitamins were noted. In addition, a change in glucose tolerance, increased insulin sensitivity, and diminished eosinopenic response to ACTH were observed. Although administration of pantothenic acid did not alleviate the depletion syndrome completely, adjunctive cortisone therapy resulted in complete remission of these symptoms.

The adrenal symptoms appeared to accent a potential role of coenzyme A in adrenosteroid synthesis. A more recent study of pantothenic acid depletion in humans, however, has revealed certain inconsistencies in the early data.[80,81] The general symptoms of malaise,fatigue, mental changes, and low cholesterol levels in plasma developed as described earlier; lowered cholesterol levels, however, were attributed to large quantities of corn oil in the diet. Adrenal dysfunction as observed earlier in 17-ketosteroid excretion and diminished eosinopenic response to ACTH was not as evident in the later study. Despite the disparity between certain of the data, a depletion syndrome has been conclusively demonstrated in man by pantothenic acid restriction, and it is reasonable to conclude that pantothenic acid is essential for health.

75. A. E. Schaefer, J. M. McKibbin, and C. A. Elvehjem, *J. Biol. Chem.*, *143*, 321 (1942).
76. W. B. Bean and R. E. Hodges, *Proc. Soc. Exptl. Biol. Med.*, *86*, 693 (1954).
77. W. B. Bean, R. E. Hodges, and K. Daum, *J. Clin. Invest.*, *34*, 1073 (1955).
78. W. B. Bean, R. Lubin, and K. Daum, *J. Lab. Clin. Med.*, *46*, 793 (1955).
79. R. Lubin, K. A. Daum, and W. B. Bean, *Am. J. Clin. Nutr.*, *4*, 420 (1956).
80. R. E. Hodges, M. A. Ohlson, and W. B. Bean, *J. Clin. Invest.*, *37*, 1642 (1958).
81. *Nutr. Revs.*, *17*, 200 (1959).

Pantothenic acid in combination with other vitamins has been used in the treatment of certain states of shock such as might occur in the postoperative patient.[82,83] It is especially useful for major abdominal postoperative patients in alleviating postoperative paralytic ileus.[84]

Sodium or calcium pantothenate has also been used in the treatment of certain types of vertigo,[85,86] but the effectiveness of the treatment has not been confirmed. Sodium pantothenate is claimed to be both a preventative and curative for post-streptomycin vertigo and has been used in combination with antibiotics such as streptomycin, neomycin, viomycin, and dihydrostreptomycin to eliminate the ear-involvement features of these antibiotics. Since these antibiotics do not damage the hearing nerve, the action of pantothenic acid in this combination has been described as "detoxifying."[87]

Pantothenic acid is widely distributed in cells and tissue. Among the best sources of the vitamin are liver, kidney, yeast, egg yolk, and fresh vegetables. The vitamin is relatively stable in foodstuffs during long periods of storage, and the usual methods of preparation destroy little if any of it.

Minimum dietary requirements of the vitamin are unknown. However, it has been estimated that a 2500-calorie diet selected from both plant and animal food will provide about 10 mg. of pantothenic acid per day.[88]

82. J. H. Crandon, *J. Am. Med. Assoc.*, *158*, 264 (1955).
83. E. P. Ralli, *J. Am. Dietet. Assoc.*, *28*, 1082 (1952).
84. C. Orecchia, *Minerva Med.*, *46*, 1610 (1955); abstr. *J. Am. Med. Assoc.*, *160*, 1367 (1956).
85. J. Aubry and S. Sigwald, *Presse Med.*, *64*, 709 (1956).
86. J. Célice, M. Aubry, F. Pias, and G. Duchesnay, *Presse Med.*, *64*, 2124 (1956).
87. *Science News Letter*, *68*, 328 (1955).
88. R. J. Williams, *J. Am. Med. Assoc.*, *119*, 1 (1942).

CHAPTER VII

Pteroylmonoglutamic Acid and the Folic Acid Coenzymes

1. Introduction

Pteroylmonoglutamic acid and its related derivatives and conjugate forms are also referred to as the folic acid group. The vitamin, isolated from spinach, yeast, and liver extracts, is an essential nutrient for man, lower animals, insects, and microorganisms. Apparently the earliest publication of an activity of this vitamin group appeared in 1931 under the designation Wills factor;[1] the activity was extracted from autolyzed yeast and was effective in the treatment of tropical macrocytic anemia. By 1938 reports on vitamin M and factor U were published. One study showed that monkeys being maintained on diets similar to those associated with human tropical macrocytic anemia developed a blood condition that responded to the administration of yeast or liver extracts; the activity in these extracts was designated vitamin M.[2] In the same period, it was reported that chicks being sustained on highly purified diets responded to an unknown growth factor in yeast, alfalfa, and wheat bran; this activity was designated factor U.[3] About a year later an activity designated vitamin B_c, which prevented a macrocytic anemia in chicks, was discovered in liver extracts.[4] In 1940 an essential nutrient for lactic acid bacteria was isolated from liver and yeast. This substance, first designated Norit eluate factor, later became known as the *Lactobacillus casei* factor.[5] Further purification of the factor from liver showed that it was also an essential nutrient for the chick which indicated a possible identity of the bacterial and chick factors.[6] By 1943 it was possible to differentiate between the Norit eluate

1. L. Wills, M. A. Contab, and B. S. Lond, *Brit. Med. J.*, *1*, 1059 (1931).
2. P. L. Day, W. C. Langston, and W. J. Darby, *Proc. Soc. Exptl. Biol. Med.*, *38*, 860 (1938).
3. E. L. R. Stokstad and P. D. V. Manning, *J. Biol. Chem.*, *125*, 687 (1938).
4. A. G. Hogan and E. M. Parrott, *J. Biol. Chem.*, *128*, xlvi (1939).
5. E. E. Snell and W. H. Peterson, *J. Bacteriol.*, *36*, 273 (1940).
6. B. L. Hutchings, N. Bohonos, D. M. Hegsted, C. A. Elvehjem, and W. H. Peterson, *J. Biol. Chem.*, *141*, 521 (1941).

factor from yeast and that from liver; although the factor from liver stimulated the growth of both *Lactobacillus helveticus* and *Streptococcus faecalis* R, the extract from yeast fully stimulated the growth of *L. helveticus*, but showed only one-half the activity of the factor from liver toward *S. faecalis* R.[7] In time it became popular to designate the *casei* factors as either the liver *L. casei* factor or the fermentation *L. casei* factor. The fermentation product was also designated the yeast *L. casei* factor. In the meantime an activity in a spinach extract designated folic acid, was observed to stimulate the growth of *S. faecalis* R and was also active for *L. casei*. This extract appeared to have the same microbiological properties as the original Norit eluate factor.[8] In 1943 a fermentation product was isolated which stimulated the growth of *Streptococcus lactis* R but was inactive for *L. casei*.[9] This product, originally referred to as the SLR factor, became known as rhizopterin when the structure was elucidated.

Although there were indications from time to time that one or more of these activities were identical and related to a common organic molecule, the keystone was set only after the isolation and characterization of pteroylmonoglutamic acid. Only at this stage were all of these nutritional deficiencies categorized as manifestations of a pteroylglutamic acid deficiency. For example, the activities that had been designated factor U, vitamin M, vitamin B_c, and the *L. casei* factor from liver were found to be pteroylmonoglutamic acid. The activity of the *L. casei* factor from yeast occurred owing to pteroyldiglutamylglutamic acid, and that of the yeast vitamin B_c conjugate occurred owing to pteroylhexaglutamylglutamic acid. The SLR factor, or rhizopterin, was identified as N^{10}-formylpteroic acid, a substance that lacked the glutamic acid moiety. In view of the development of this phase of nutritional chemistry, it has been referred to as the most complicated chapter in the story of the vitamin B complex.

2. Isolation

Pteroylmonoglutamic acid was obtained from a number of sources by degradation of the conjugate form by enzymolysis and isolation by extraction, adsorption chromatography, ion exchange, and precipitation. Final stages of purification usually required recrystallization from water. The following brief description of the isolation of pteroylmonoglutamic acid from liver will typify the general procedure.[10]

7. E. L. R. Stokstad, *J. Biol. Chem.*, *149*, 573 (1943).
8. H. K. Mitchell, E. E. Snell, and R. J. Williams, *J. Am. Chem. Soc.*, *63*, 2284 (1941).
9. J. C. Keresztesy, E. L. Rickes, and J. L. Stokes, *Science*, *97*, 465 (1943).
10. B. L. Hutchings, E. L. R. Stokstad, N. Bohonos, N. H. Sloan, and Y. SubbaRow, *J. Am. Chem. Soc.*, *70*, 3 (1948).

An aqueous solution of a liver extract was acidified to pH 3.0, and the factor was adsorbed on Norit A. After the removal of inert materials with 60% ethanol, the factor was eluted with 0.5*N* ammonium hydroxide in 60% ethanol. Inert material was precipitated at pH 3.5, and then the factor in the filtrate was adsorbed at pH 1.3 on Superfiltrol. Elution with 1.0*N* ammonium hydroxide in 60% ethanol gave a solution representing a 17-fold increase in activity. After the eluate was concentrated and its pH was adjusted to 7.0, a mixture of barium salts was precipitated by the addition of ethanol and barium chloride. The salt of the factor precipitated too, but little increase in activity was achieved by this step. The factor was also precipitated as a phosphotungstate or as a lead or silver salt, but slight increase in activity was achieved by these precipitations. At the next step of purification, the barium salts were converted to methyl esters by treatment with 0.2*N* methanolic hydrogen chloride. After the esterification mixture was cautiously neutralized and concentrated, the material was dissolved in water; the aqueous solution was then acidified to pH 6–7 and extracted with *n*-butanol. The methyl esters were adsorbed on Superfiltrol and the majority of highly colored impurities were eluted with 92.5% acetone. Following this treatment, the methyl ester of the factor was eluted with 75% acetone. The ester was purified by several crystallizations from hot methanol and was then converted to the free acid by treatment with 0.01*N* sodium hydroxide. Pure pteroylmonoglutamic acid was obtained by recrystallization, once from 0.1*N* sodium chloride solution and twice from water.

3. Structure Determination

The elucidation of structure began with the degradation of the *L. casei* factor from yeast and led to the formulation of pteroylmonoglutamic acid

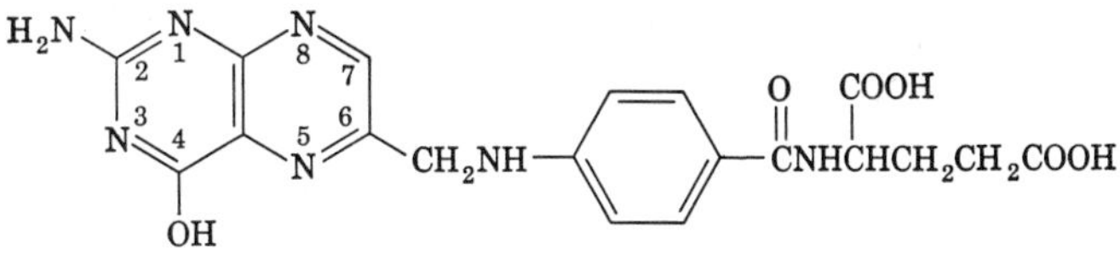

(1)

(**1**) as *N*-[4-{[(2-amino-4-hydroxy-6-pteridinyl)methyl]amino}benzoyl]glutamic acid.

A. Pteroylmonoglutamic and Pteroyltriglutamic Acids

The structure of the pteridine moiety was established from the following data. Aerobic hydrolysis of the *L. casei* factor from fermentation gave a dibasic acid, $C_7H_5N_5O_3$ (**2**).[11] Electrometric titration of this acid showed the presence of two acidic groups, one carboxylic and one enolic in nature. When oxidation of this dibasic acid with chlorine water followed by hydrolysis gave guanidine, the presence of a 2-aminopyrimidine moiety was evident. These data in combination with the elemental composition

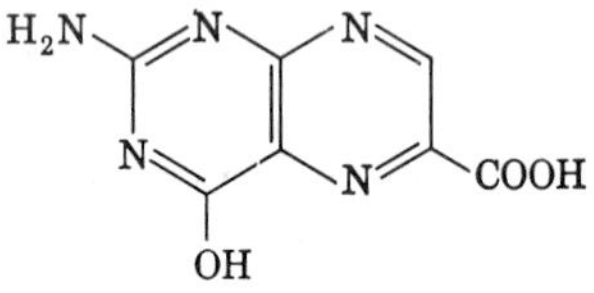

(2) 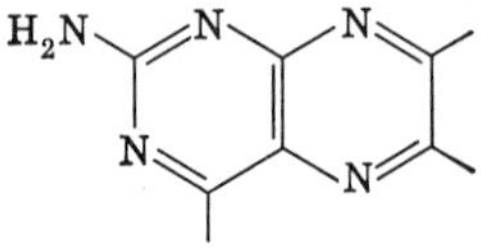 (3)

indicated either a 2-aminopurine or a 2-aminopteridine structure for the dibasic acid. The purine formulation was eliminated in favor of the pteridine moiety (**3**) because the dibasic acid exhibited fluorescence and absorption above 300 mμ in the ultraviolet region of the spectrum.

The positions of the carboxylic and enolic functions on the pteridine nucleus were established by studying the reaction of sulfurous acid on the

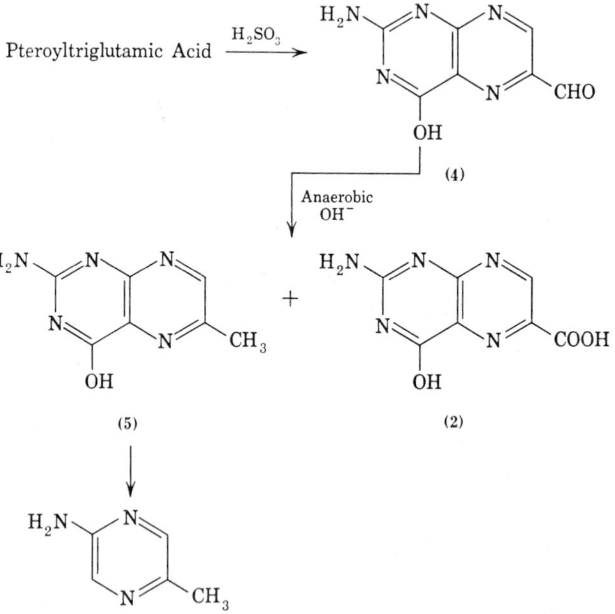

Pteroyltriglutamic Acid $\xrightarrow{H_2SO_3}$ (4)

Anaerobic OH^-

(5) + (2)

(6)

11. E. L. R. Stokstad, B. L. Hutchings, J. H. Mowat, J. H. Boothe, C. W. Waller, R. B. Angier, J. Semb, and Y. SubbaRow, *J. Am. Chem. Soc.*, *70*, 5 (1948).

L. casei factor from fermentation.[12] One product of this reaction was the highly unstable fluorescent aldehyde (**4**). When a dilute alkaline solution of this reactive aldehyde was allowed to stand in the absence of air, the aldehyde underwent a Cannizzaro-like oxidation-reduction reaction, yielding equimolar quantities of the acid (**2**) and the methyl compound (**5**). The latter was degraded to 2-methyl-5-aminopyrazine (**6**). On the basis of the position of the methyl group in the pyrazine, the formyl group of the aldehyde (**4**) was established at the 6-position; it was assumed that the carboxyl group in the acid (**2**) occupied the same position.

Decarboxylation of the pteridine-6-carboxylic acid (**2**) apparently gave 2-amino-4-hydroxypteridine which indicated the 4-position of the acid (**2**) as the most probable location of the enolic hydroxyl group.

The formulation of the dibasic acid (**2**) as 2-amino-4-hydroxypteridine-6-carboxylic acid was confirmed by synthesis.[13] 4-Hydroxy-2,5,6-triaminopyrimidine (**7**) on condensation with a dialkyl mesoxalate yielded the isoxanthopterincarboxylic acid (**8**). Chlorination of the latter gave the intermediate (**9**) which was reduced with hydrogen iodide to yield the dibasic acid (**2**). Since either the 4- or 7-hydroxyl group of the intermediate (**8**) could have been eliminated in this series of reactions, decarboxylation of the synthetic dibasic acid (**2**) to 2-amino-4-hydroxypteridine (**10**) was necessary in order to establish its structure. The authentic specimen of the pteridine (**10**) was prepared from the condensation of 4-hydroxy-2,5,6-triaminopyrimidine and glyoxal.

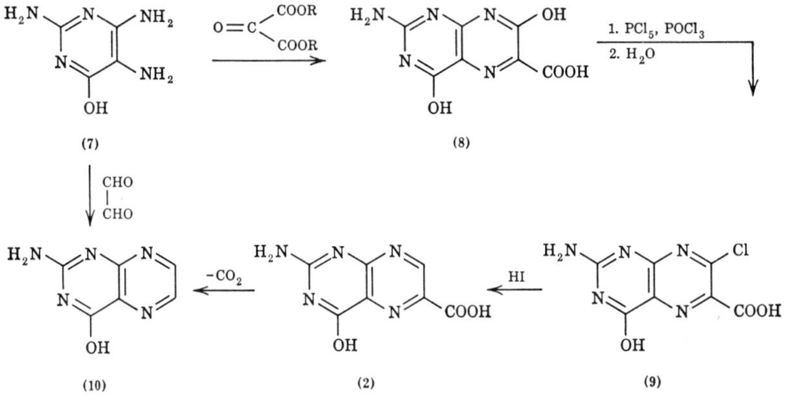

12. B. L. Hutchings, E. L. R. Stokstad, J. H. Mowat, J. H. Boothe, C. W. Waller, R. B. Angier, J. Semb, and Y. SubbaRow, *J. Am. Chem. Soc.*, *70*, 10 (1948).
13. J. H. Mowat, J. H. Boothe, B. L. Hutchings, E. L. R. Stokstad, C. W. Waller, R. B. Angier, J. Semb, D. B. Cosulich, and Y. SubbaRow, *J. Am. Chem. Soc.*, *70*, 14 (1948).

The presence of the pteridine moiety 2-amino-4-hydroxy-6-pteridinylmethylene (**11**) in the vitamin was established from the structure of the dibasic acid (**2**) and the following observations. Aerobic alkaline hydrolysis of the factor yielded a pteridine derivative and a primary aromatic amine which indicated a linking group between the pteridine and the nitrogen atom of the aromatic amine moiety. This linking group must be a single-carbon unit since the derived pteridines had one-carbon substituents and carbon dioxide was not a product of the degradation reaction. The dibasic acid was formed by aerobic hydrolysis but not by anaerobic hydrolysis;

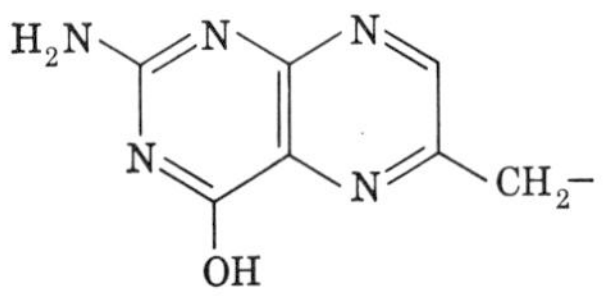

(11)

consequently it appeared that oxidation of the atom linking the pteridine ring to the rest of the molecule was necessary before hydrolytic cleavage could take place. Therefore the single-carbon unit was visualized as a methylene group rather than a carbonyl group of an amide or the carbon of an azomethine group. This deduction was confirmed with the synthesis and study of the two model compounds, *N*-benzylidene-*p*-aminobenzoic acid and *N*-benzyl-*p*-aminobenzoic acid.[13] The former was cleaved rapidly in the presence of weak acids. The latter was stable when subjected to acidic or anaerobic alkaline hydrolysis, but was cleaved rapidly by aerobic alkaline hydrolysis. Since the behavior of pteroyltriglutamic acid paralleled that of *N*-benzyl-*p*-aminobenzoic acid, the concept of a pteridinylmethylene moiety in the vitamin was strengthened.

The relationship between the *L. casei* factor (**1**) from liver and the *L. casei* factor (**12**) from yeast and the nature of the *p*-aminobenzoylglutamic acid moiety in each was established by the aerobic and anaerobic hydrolysis of the *L. casei* factor (**12**) from yeast.[11] Anaerobic alkaline hydrolysis of the latter gave the racemic *L. casei* factor (**1**) from liver and two equivalents of glutamic acid (**13**). Aerobic hydrolysis of the factor (**12**) from fermentation gave the aromatic amine (**14**), which on hydrolysis with 2*N* sulfuric acid yielded one equivalent of *p*-aminobenzoic acid and one of glutamic acid. Consequently, the factor from yeast differed from the one from liver by the presence of two additional units of glutamic acid in the *p*-aminobenzoyl moiety. With these data, the *p*-aminobenzoyl moiety of the *L. casei* factor from liver was formulated as *p*-aminobenzoylglutamic acid, and that of the *L. casei* factor from yeast was formulated as *p*-aminobenzoylglutamylglutamylglutamic acid. Hydrolysis of the factor from fermentation at pH 4 gave (−)-pyrrolidonecarboxylic acid, which upon alkaline hydrolysis yielded *L*-(+)-glutamic acid.[12]

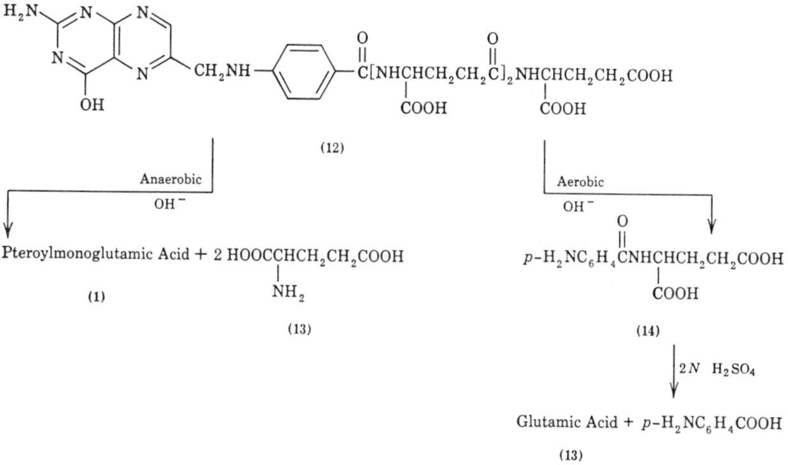

(2-amino-4-hydroxypteridin-6-yl)CH_2NH–C_6H_4–$\overset{O}{\overset{\|}{C}}[NH\underset{COOH}{CH}CH_2CH_2\overset{O}{\overset{\|}{C}}]_2NH\underset{COOH}{CH}CH_2CH_2COOH$

(12)

Anaerobic, OH^- → Pteroylmonoglutamic Acid + 2 $HOOC\underset{NH_2}{CH}CH_2CH_2COOH$

(1) (13)

Aerobic, OH^- → p-$H_2NC_6H_4\overset{O}{\overset{\|}{C}}NH\underset{COOH}{CH}CH_2CH_2COOH$

(14)

$\downarrow$ 2*N* H_2SO_4

Glutamic Acid + p-$H_2NC_6H_4COOH$

(13)

Since it had already been established that the pteridine ring system was joined from its 6-position through a saturated single-carbon unit to the amino group of the *p*-aminobenzoylglutamic acid moiety, and since the hydrolytic stability of the two model compounds *N*-benzylidene-*p*-aminobenzoic acid and *N*-benzyl-*p*-aminobenzoic acid supported this deduction,[12] the structure of the *L. casei* factor from liver was depicted as (**1**). On the same basis, the structure of the *L. casei* factor from yeast was depicted as (**12**). The exact mode of linkage in the tripeptide sequence of the *p*-aminobenzoylglutamic acid moiety in (**12**) was resolved by synthesis which demonstrated that the residues are linked as in γ-glutamyl-γ-glutamylglutamic acid.[14]

B. Vitamin B$_c$ *Conjugate*

The structure of vitamin B$_c$ conjugate was shown to be pteroylhexaglutamylglutamic acid, but the mode of linkage of the glutamic acid units has not been established directly.

14. J. H. Boothe, J. H. Mowat, B. L. Hutchings, R. B. Angier, C. W. Waller, E. L. R. Stokstad, J. Semb, A. L. Gazzola, and Y. SubbaRow, *J. Am. Chem. Soc.*, *70*, 1999 (1948).

C. *Rhizopterin*

The structure of rhizopterin (SLR Factor) was established as N^{10}-formylpteroic acid (**15**). Alkaline hydrolysis of this substance gave pteroic acid (**16**);[15] acid hydrolysis gave formic acid. The location of the formyl

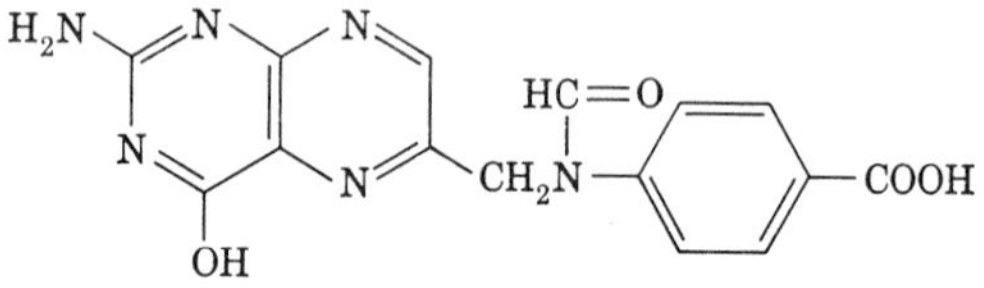

(15)

group was established as follows. Benzoylation of rhizopterin followed by oxidation yielded benzoylguanidine, proving that the 2-amino group of rhizopterin was benzoylated prior to oxidation and is therefore unsubstituted. Since rhizopterin contains only one acylatable group whereas its

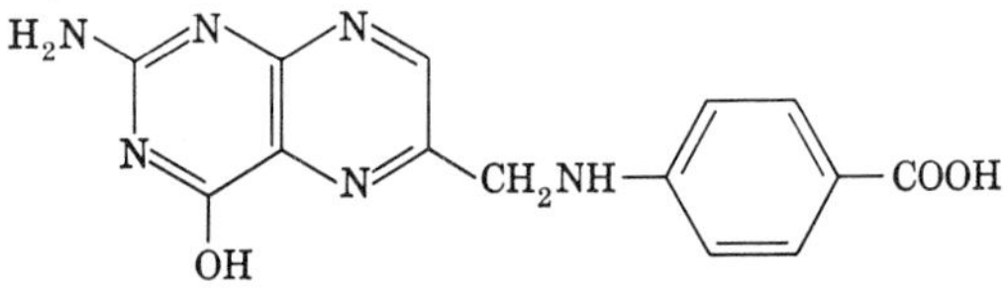

(16)

alkaline hydrolysis product pteroic acid (**16**) contains two, it followed that the 10-amino group of rhizopterin must be formylated.[15]

4. Synthesis

Pteroylmonoglutamic acid has been synthesized by two basic approaches. The first method requires the simultaneous condensation between a triaminopyrimidine, a three-carbon intermediate, and *p*-aminobenzoylglutamic acid. This approach was used for confirmation of the structure of pteroylmonoglutamic acid by synthesis.[16] Equimolar quantities of

15. D. E. Wolf, R. C. Anderson, E. A. Kaczka, S. A. Harris, G. E. Arth, P. L. Southwick, R. Mozingo, and K. Folkers, *J. Am. Chem. Soc.*, *69*, 2753 (1947).
16. C. W. Waller, B. L. Hutchings, J. H. Mowat, E. L. R. Stokstad, J. H. Boothe, R. B. Angier, J. Semb, Y. SubbaRow, D. B. Cosulich, M. J. Fahrenbach, M. E. Hultquist, E. Kuh, E. H. Northey, D. R. Seeger, J. P. Sickels, and J. M. Smith, Jr., *J. Am. Chem. Soc.*, *70*, 19 (1948).

4-hydroxy-2,5,6-triaminopyrimidine (**7**), 2,3-dibromopropionaldehyde (**17**), and *p*-aminobenzoyl-*L*-glutamic acid (**14**) were allowed to react in aqueous solution in the presence of an acetate buffer. The reaction mixture contained about 50% of the desired compound, and the pure compound was isolated after removal of impurities by alkaline precipitation, butanol extraction, and recrystallization.

H_2N, N, NH_2, N, NH_2, OH (**7**) + $BrCH_2$–CH(Br)–CHO (**17**) + $p\text{-}H_2NC_6H_4C(=O)NHCH(COOH)CH_2CH_2COOH$ (**14**)

→ Pteroylmonoglutamic Acid (**1**)

Since pteridines are usually high-melting compounds with limited solubility, the purification of intermediates and the final product has been a major difficulty in a number of synthetic approaches. Many efforts to circumvent this difficulty led to a second basic approach to synthesis in which a 2-amino-4-hydroxy-6-pteridinyl intermediate is synthesized and then condensed with *p*-aminobenzoyl-*L*-glutamic acid. An especially productive example of this approach gave crystalline intermediates of such high purity that the final condensation reaction gave a product requiring a minimum of purification.[17] In this synthesis (Fig. 1) the intermediate 2-acetamido-6-formyl-4-hydroxypteridine (**22**) was synthesized from 1,3,3-triethoxy-1-propene (**18**). Bromination of the latter compound followed by treatment with sodium bicarbonate yielded the intermediate α-bromo-β,β-diethoxypropionaldehyde (**20**), which on treatment with 4-hydroxy-2,5,6-triaminopyrimidine (**7**) yielded 2-amino-6-diethoxymethyl-4-hydroxypteridine (**21**). This intermediate was purified by crystallization of the sodium salt. Treatment of the intermediate (**21**) with acetic anhydride at 100° gave an excellent yield of the crystalline 2-acetamido derivative which was easily purified by recrystallization; selective cleavage of the acetal group was achieved by treatment with 88% formic acid, and as the reaction proceeded, the formic acid salt of 2-acetamido-6-formyl-4-hydroxypteridine (**22**) crystallized from solution.

17. M. Sletzinger, D. Reinhold, J. Grier, M. Beachem, and M. Tishler, *J. Am. Chem. Soc.*, *77*, 6365 (1955).

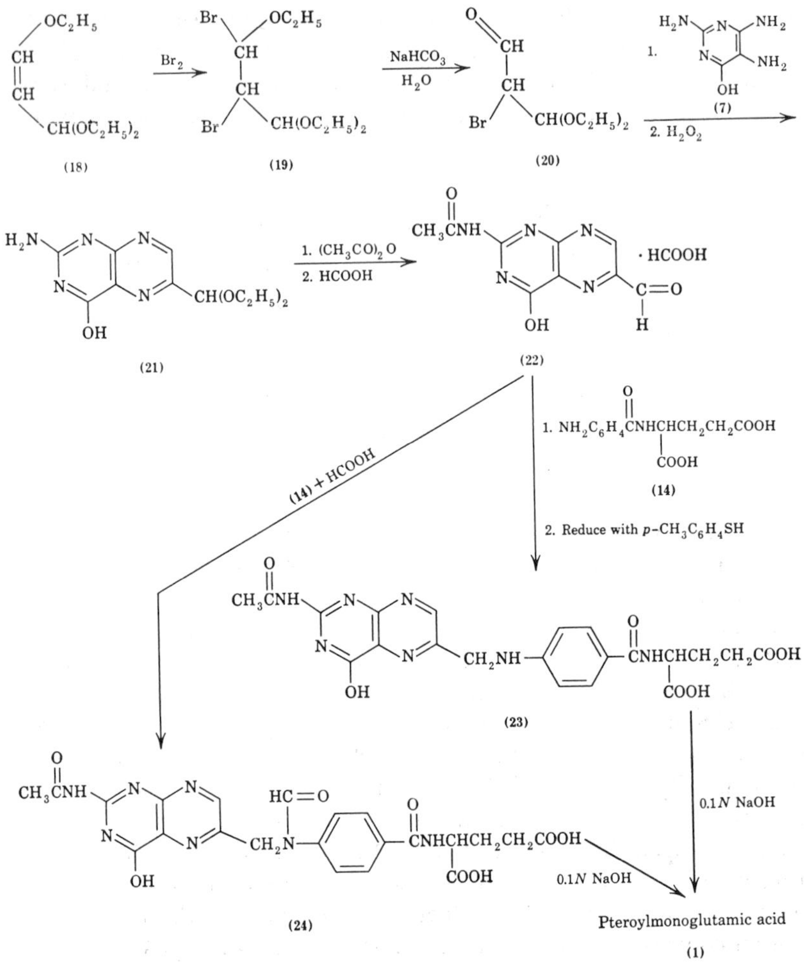

OC_2H_5 CH=CH $CH(OC_2H_5)_2$ (18)
$\xrightarrow{Br_2}$
Br OC_2H_5 CH CH Br $CH(OC_2H_5)_2$ (19)
$\xrightarrow[H_2O]{NaHCO_3}$
O=CH CH Br $CH(OC_2H_5)_2$ (20)
1. H_2N N NH_2 N NH_2 OH (7)
2. H_2O_2

H_2N N N N N $CH(OC_2H_5)_2$ OH (21)
1. $(CH_3CO)_2O$
2. HCOOH
O $CH_3\overset{\|}{C}NH$ N N N N · HCOOH C=O H OH (22)

1. $NH_2C_6H_4\overset{O}{\overset{\|}{C}}NHCHCH_2CH_2COOH$ COOH (14)
2. Reduce with p-$CH_3C_6H_4SH$
(14) + HCOOH

O $CH_3\overset{\|}{C}NH$ N N N N CH_2NH O $\overset{\|}{C}NHCHCH_2CH_2COOH$ COOH OH (23)

0.1N NaOH

O $CH_3\overset{\|}{C}NH$ N N N N HC=O CH_2N O $\overset{\|}{C}NHCHCH_2CH_2COOH$ COOH OH (24)

0.1N NaOH

Pteroylmonoglutamic acid (1)

Fig. 1. A two-stage synthesis of pteroylmonoglutamic acid.[17]

Reductive condensations involving pteridines usually lead to many by-products since the pteridine ring is apparently very susceptible to reduction. In this second method, however, it was found that the aryl thiols were excellent selective reducing agents for the reductive condensation of the 6-formylpteridine (**22**) with *p*-aminobenzoyl-*L*-glutamic acid (**14**). The resulting acetylpteroylmonoglutamic acid (**23**) was a crystalline product that was easily purified by recrystallization from water and readily converted to pure pteroylmonoglutamic acid by hydrolysis in hot $0.1N$ sodium hydroxide.

5. Metabolic Role

Coenzymes containing pteroylmonoglutamic acid participate in animal, plant, and microbial metabolism by controlling the transfer of single-carbon units at the oxidation level of formic acid or formaldehyde.[18–22] Five distinct pteroylmonoglutamic acid-C_1 complexes have been encountered in living systems. In three of these forms the single-carbon unit is at the oxidation state of formic acid; in the other two the C_1 unit is at the oxidation state of formaldehyde. In all of them pteroylmonoglutamic acid is in the reduced state as tetrahydropteroylmonoglutamic acid.

Among the important metabolic reactions mediated by coenzymes containing pteroylmonoglutamic acid are:

(a) the conversion of glycine to serine;
(b) the methylation of ethanolamine to choline;
(c) the methylation of homocysteine to methionine;
(d) the methylation of nicotinamide to N^1-methylnicotinamide;
(e) the methylation of a pyrimidine intermediate to thymine;
(f) the introduction of C-2 and C-8 in purine biosynthesis; and
(g) the introduction of the amidine-carbon atom in histidine.

During the investigation of the role of pteroylmonoglutamic acid in one-carbon metabolism, it had been suggested that 5,6,7,8-tetrahydropteroylmonoglutamic acid, N^5-formyl-5,6,7,8-tetrahydropteroylmonoglutamic acid (citrovorum factor, folinic acid-SF), N^{10}-formyl-5,6,7,8-tetrahydropteroylmonoglutamic acid, N^5-hydroxymethyl-5,6,7,8-tetrahydropteroylmonoglutamic acid, and corresponding N^5,N^{10}-derivatives were cofactors for given enzymic processes. A brief review follows on these and other developments leading to the present-day concept of the participation of pteroylmonoglutamic acid in metabolism.

A. The Citrovorum Factor

At first it was believed that the citrovorum factor (**25**) was the predominant form of pteroylmonoglutamic acid which participated in enzymic reactions. This factor was recognized in nutritional studies with the organism *Leuconostoc citrovorum*.[23] A close structural relationship

18. F. M. Huennekens, H. R. Whitely, and M. J. Osborn, *J. Cellular Comp. Physiol.*, *54*, Suppl. 1, 109 (1959).
19. F. M. Huennekens, M. J. Osborn, and H. R. Whiteley, *Science*, *128*, 120 (1958).
20. O. A. Bessey, H. J. Lowe, and L. L. Salomon, *Ann. Rev. Biochem.*, *22*, 545 (1953).
21. G. R. Greenberg, *Federation Proc.*, *12*, 651 (1953).
22. W. Shive, *Federation Proc.*, *12*, 639 (1953).
23. H. E. Sauberlich and C. A. Baumann, *J. Biol. Chem.* *176*, 165 (1948).

between the citrovorum factor and pteroylmonoglutamic acid was established independently by three groups of investigators studying pteroylglutamic acid antagonism.[24–26] One study showed that citrovorum factor concentrates overcame the effect of the pteroylglutamic acid

(25)

antagonist, 4-aminopteroylmonoglutamic acid.[24] Another showed that fractions of a liver extract were from 10 to 100 times as active as pteroylmonoglutamic acid in overcoming the toxic effects of methylfolic acid on the growth of *L. casei*; this active principle had properties corresponding to those of the citrovorum factor and was apparently accompanied by at least two other active forms as evidenced by paper chromatography.[25] A third investigation demonstrated a competitive reversal of the antagonism of 4-aminopteroylmonoglutamic acid for pteroylmonoglutamic acid by citrovorum factor concentrates.[26] In partition and chromatographic studies of the citrovorum factor, a close structural relationship to pteroylmonoglutamic acid was also evident.[26]

Belief that the citrovorum factor was an *N*-formylperhydro derivative of pteroylmonoglutamic acid followed from the facts that N^{10}-formylpteroylmonoglutamic acid was more effective than pteroylmonoglutamic acid in reversing the growth inhibition of *S. faecalis* R by methylfolic acid[27] and that *N*-formylperhydropteroylmonoglutamic acid approached the growth-promoting activity of the citrovorum factor for *S. faecalis* R[28,29] and chicks.[30] For the chick growth studies, biologically-active

24. H. E. Sauberlich, *Arch. Biochem.*, *24*, 224 (1949).
25. T. J. Bond, T. J. Bardos, M. Sibley, and W. Shive, *J. Am. Chem. Soc.*, *71*, 3852 (1949).
26. H. F. Broquist, E. L. R. Stokstad, and T. H. Jukes, *J. Biol. Chem.*, *185*, 399 (1950).
27. M. Gordon, J. M. Ravel, R. E. Eakin, and W. Shive, *J. Am. Chem. Soc.*, *70*, 878 (1948).
28. E. H. Flynn, T. J. Bond, T. J. Bardos, and W. Shive, *J. Am. Chem. Soc.*, *73*, 1979 (1951).
29. W. Shive, T. J. Bardos, T. J. Bond, and L. L. Rogers, *J. Am. Chem. Soc.*, *72*, 2817 (1950).
30. J. A. Brockman, Jr., B. Roth, H. P. Broquist, M. E. Hultquist, J. M. Smith, Jr., M. J. Fahrenbach, D. B. Cosulich, R. P. Parker, E. L. R. Stokstad, and T. H. Jukes, *J. Am. Chem. Soc.*, *72*, 4325 (1959).

N^5-formyl-5,6,7,8-tetrahydropteroylmonoglutamic acid (**25**) was synthesized and isolated in pure crystalline form.[30] The synthetic citrovorum factor has been given two designations, leucovorin[31] and folinic acid-SF.[28]

Structural studies on the factor (**25**) proceeded as follows. Guanidine, oxalic acid, and chloranil were found among the oxidation products of the citrovorum factor.[32] The identity of these products with those from N^{10}-formylpteroic acid (**15**) established a certain structural similarity between the two compounds. Folinic acid-SF, however, was more resistant to sulfurous acid cleavage than pteroylmonoglutamic acid. This evidence was cited to support the presence of a saturated pyrazine ring in the molecule. Comparison of the ultraviolet absorption spectrum of folinic acid-SF with the spectra of certain model pyrimidines suggested an intact pyrimidine moiety within the factor. Since electrometric titration showed that the hydroxyl group of folinic acid-SF (pKa 10.4) was attached to a "completely aromatic" pyrimidine ring, the possibility that the pyrimidine ring might be reduced was eliminated. Consequently, it was concluded that the citrovorum factor contained the 5,6,7,8-tetrahydropteroyl moiety. This conclusion was confirmed from a study of the polarographic behavior of leucovorin (**25**) and related compounds.[33]

The final question to be answered in the elucidation of structure was the location of the formyl group in the factor. In the synthesis of the factor by the catalytic reduction of N^{10}-formylpteroylmonoglutamic acid, it soon became apparent that the formyl group had to migrate from the 10-position before appreciable citrovorum activity was obtained. This migration occurred on standing and was facilitated by treatment with alkali.[32,34] It was concluded that the formyl group was at the 5-position of the 5,6,7,8-tetrahydropteroyl moiety on the basis of

(a) reference to analogous acyl migrations in certain tetrahydroquinolines and tetrahydroisoquinolines;

(b) increased absorption at 282 mμ in the ultraviolet absorption spectrum;

(c) the stability of folinic acid-SF in alkali as compared to the relatively

31. B. Roth, M. E. Hultquist, M. J. Fahrenbach, D. B. Cosulich, H. P. Broquist, J. A. Brockman, Jr., J. M. Smith, Jr., R. P. Parker, E. L. R. Stokstad, and T. H. Jukes, *J. Am. Chem. Soc.*, *74*, 3247 (1952).
32. A. Pohland, E. H. Flynn, R. G. Jones, and W. Shive, *J. Am. Chem. Soc.*, *73*, 3247 (1951).
33. W. Allen, R. L. Pasternak, and W. Seaman, *J. Am. Chem. Soc.*, *74*, 3264 (1952).
34. D. B. Cosulich, B. Roth, J. M. Smith, Jr., M. E. Hultquist, and R. P. Parker, *J. Am. Chem. Soc.*, *74*, 3252 (1952).

easy hydrolysis of N^{10}-formylpteroylmonoglutamic acid with alkali; and (d) absence of a titratable basic group in the pH range 2–10.5.[32]

The possibility of a formyl migration from the 10- to the 7-position of the tetrahydropteridine ring was eliminated by demonstrating the absence of 2-amino-4-hydroxypteridine-6,7-dicarboxylic acid in the alkaline permanganate oxidation products of leucovorin.[34] Migration of the formyl group from the 10-position to the 5-position of the tetrahydropteroyl moiety was demonstrated as most feasible using the model compound 2-amino-6,7-diphenyl-8-ethyl-5-formyl-4-hydroxy-5,6,7,8-tetrahydropteridine (**26**). The polarographic behavior, stability toward alkali, and

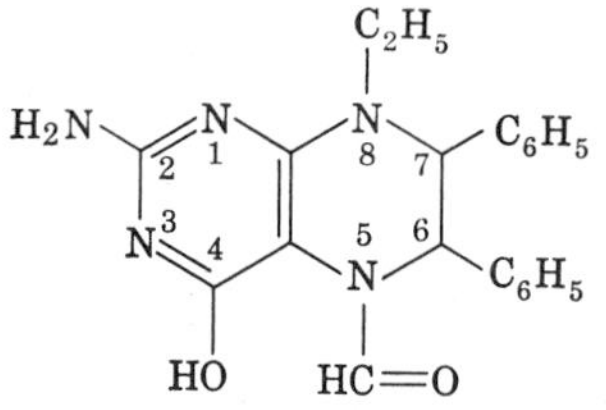

C_2H_5 | H_2N | N | N | C_6H_5 | C_6H_5 | N | N | HO | HC=O

(26)

nitrosation reactions exhibited by this compound and leucovorin were essentially identical. In addition, the nitrosation of both leucovorin and pteroylmonoglutamic acid and the failure of N^{10}-formylpteroylmonoglutamic acid to nitrosate under similar conditions were assumed to eliminate the possibility of the formyl group bridging the 5- and 10-positions in leucovorin.

On the basis of these data, the synthetic citrovorum factor (folinic acid-SF and leucovorin) was assigned the structure N^5-formyl-5,6,7,8-tetrahydropteroylmonoglutamic acid. At this stage, however, the identity of the natural and synthetic factor had not been established by direct comparison of appropriate samples.

The first pure sample of the natural citrovorum factor was isolated from horse liver as a crystalline barium salt.[35] The natural compound was identical with the synthetic compound in most properties, but it was twice as active as the synthetic sample for the growth of *L. citrovorum*. After the synthetic compound (leucovorin or folinic acid-SF) was resolved,[36] the (—)*L*-diastereoisomer was found to be identical with the natural citrovorum factor.

35. J. C. Keresztesy and M. Silverman, *J. Am. Chem. Soc.*, *73*, 5510 (1951).
36. D. B. Cosulich, J. M. Smith, Jr., and H. P. Broquist, *J. Am. Chem. Soc.*, *74*, 4215 (1952).

In the course of structural investigations, several interesting acid-catalyzed rearrangements of leucovorin were observed.[34] These rearrangements to cyclic anhydro forms are of major importance to the present understanding of pteroylmonoglutamic acid participation in one-carbon

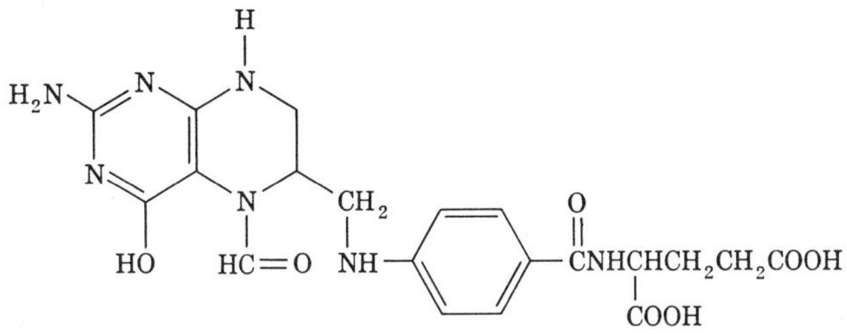

(25)

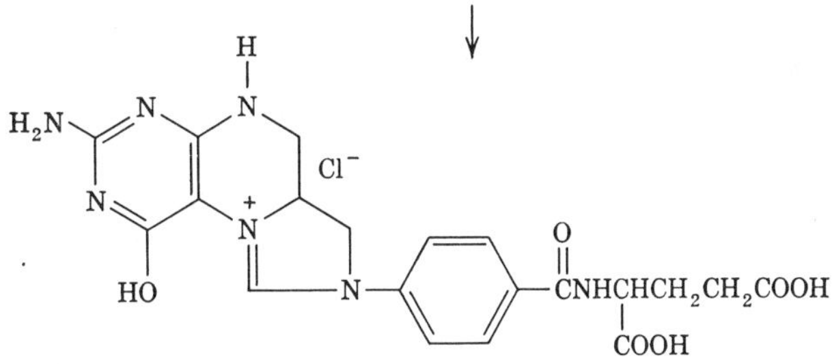

(27)

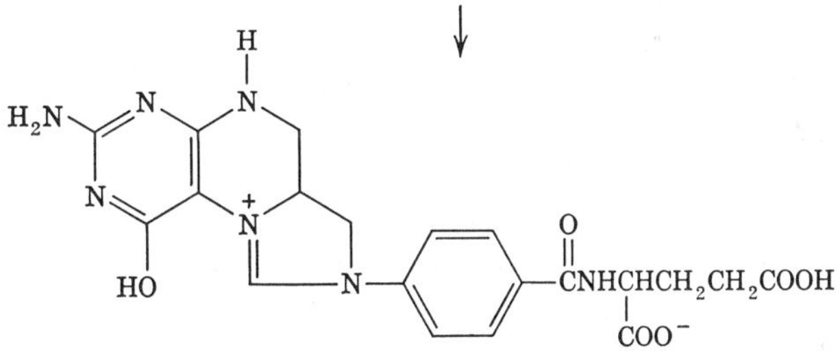

(28)

metabolism. At a pH of 1.3 or less, leucovorin (**25**) was converted by hydrochloric acid to the cyclic intermediate, isoleucovorin chloride (**27**). When this intermediate was dissolved in boiling water and the solution was cooled, anhydroleucovorin A (**28**) was obtained; further treatment of this cyclic isomer with boiling water yielded anhydroleucovorin B, an isomer of unknown structure.

Later it was found that the specific requirement of *L. citrovorum* for N^5-formyl-5,6,7,8-tetrahydropteroylmonoglutamic acid was only apparent and could be traced to the unique stability of N^5-formyl derivatives of pteroylmonoglutamic acid.[37] Under the conditions of assay, only the N^5-formyl derivative withstands autoclaving; by aseptic addition or in pad-plate assays, other derivatives such as 7,8-dihydropteroylmonoglutamic acid, 5,6,7,8-tetrahydropteroylmonoglutamic acid, and anhydroleucovorin show citrovorum factor activity.

B. 5,6,7,8-*Tetrahydropteroylmonoglutamic Acid*

The requirement for N^5-formyl-5,6,7,8-tetrahydropteroylmonoglutamic acid in the enzymic formylation of glutamate might be considered an exception since mounting evidence made it apparent that N^5-formyltetrahydropteroylmonoglutamic acid was relatively unimportant as a coenzyme form of pteroylmonoglutamic acid. Consequently, increasing interest was focused on tetrahydropteroylmonoglutamic acid *per se* and especially on its N^{10}- and N^5,N^{10}-derivatives.

In 1954 it was reported that the addition of tetrahydropteroylmonoglutamic acid restored the ability of inactivated pigeon liver extracts to utilize formaldehyde but not formate in serine biosynthesis.[38] It was also reported that inactivated rat liver preparations were reactivated for serine biosynthesis by the addition of ATP plus leucovorin or by tetrahydropteroylmonoglutamic acid alone.[39] Later observations on these and other systems made it apparent that "active formate" and "active formaldehyde" consisted of "formyl" and "hydroxymethyl" groups, respectively, bound to tetrahydropteroylmonoglutamic acid.

Pteroylmonoglutamic acid is susceptible to reduction in the pyrazine moiety. In the presence of a platinum catalyst, pteroylmonoglutamic acid is reduced to a dihydro derivative in alkaline solution and to a tetrahydro derivative in acetic acid solution. In strongly acidic media, these derivatives undergo hydrogenolysis between the pteridinylmethylene group and the nitrogen atom of the *p*-aminobenzoyl moiety.[12] In alkaline solution, the dihydro and tetrahydro derivatives react readily with oxygen, regenerating pteroylmonoglutamic acid.[40]

The enzymic reduction of pteroylmonoglutamic acid to 5,6,7,8-tetrahydropteroylmonoglutamic acid in avian and mammalian systems

37. C. A. Nichol, *Nutritional Symposium Series, 13*, The National Vitamin Foundation, Inc., N.Y., 1956, p. 77.
38. R. S. Kisliuk and W. J. Sakami, *J. Am. Chem. Soc.*, *76*, 1456 (1954); *J. Biol. Chem.*, *214*, 47 (1955).
39. N. Alexander and D. M. Greenberg, *J. Biol. Chem.*, *214*, 821 (1955).
40. B. L. O'Dell, J. M. Vandenbelt, E. S. Bloom, and J. J. Pfiffner, *J. Am. Chem. Soc.*, *69*, 250 (1947).

requires DPNH or TPNH, or both. It is regarded as occurring stepwise by direct reduction, and 7,8-dihydropteroylmonoglutamic acid is considered to be the product of the first step in the reduction sequence.[41,42] Direct evidence for the enzymic synthesis of dihydropteroylmonoglutamic acid was first obtained from studies with an enzyme system derived from *Clostridium sticklandii*.[43] The purified enzyme, which converts serine to glycine and formate in the presence of a pteroylglutamic acid, was unique since it reduced the pteridinyl moiety to a dihydropteridinyl function but no further. Consequently, the dihydropteroyl derivative accumulates in the system. After pteroylmonoglutamic acid was incubated in the enzyme system, a reduced pteroylmonoglutamic acid derivative was isolated and identified as dihydropteroylmonoglutamic acid. The spectral characteristics and chromatographic behavior of the enzymic product were identical to those of synthetic dihydropteroylmonoglutamic acid.

A 7,8-dihydro formulation was deduced for dihydropteroylmonoglutamic acid as follows. Synthetic tetrahydropteroylmonoglutamic acid and synthetic citrovorum factor are only about 50% active in the various enzyme systems. Synthetic dihydropteroylmonoglutamic acid is fully active. Since differences in enzymic activity are most likely to occur owing to asymmetry and the 6-position is the only point at which an asymmetric center could be introduced, it may be concluded that hydrogen did not enter this position at the dihydro stage.[41] Furthermore, 5-formyltetrahydropteroylmonoglutamic acid is fully stable toward air oxidation but tetrahydropteroylmonoglutamic acid is relatively labile. Consequently, the reoxidation of 5,6,7,8-tetrahydropteroylmonoglutamic acid to dihydropteroylmonoglutamic acid and finally to pteroylmonoglutamic acid must proceed first by the removal of hydrogen from the 5- and 6-positions of the pteridine ring yielding the 7,8-dihydro derivative.[40]

C. *N^{10}-Formyl-*5,6,7,8-*tetrahydropteroylmonoglutamic Acid*

N^{10}-Formyl-5,6,7,8-tetrahydropteroylmonoglutamic acid has never been isolated from natural sources because of its susceptibility to oxidation. It has, however, been encountered as an unstable intermediate during the synthesis of the citrovorum factor from pteroylmonoglutamic acid. The formation of N^{10}-formyltetrahydropteroylmonoglutamic acid was observed in several enzyme systems derived from pigeon liver preparations, and the

41. M. J. Osborn and F. M. Huennekens, *J. Biol. Chem.*, *233*, 969 (1958).
42. J. M. Peters and D. M. Greenberg, *J. Am. Chem. Soc.*, *80*, 6679 (1958); *Nature*, *181*, 1669 (1958).
43. B. E. Wright, M. L. Anderson, and E. C. Herman, *J. Biol. Chem.*, *230*, 271 (1958).

compound was designated "active formate."[44,45] A year later it was also encountered during a study of formiminoglycine degradation by extracts of *Clostridium cylindrosporum.*[46] The enzymic conversion of tetrahydropteroylmonoglutamic acid to N^{10}-formyltetrahydropteroylmonoglutamic acid is ATP-dependent. The first step in formate activation is an ATP-dependent phosphorylation of tetrahydropteroylmonoglutamic acid;[47] subsequent reaction of the N^{10}-phosphoryl derivative of tetrahydropteroylmonoglutamic acid with formate yields N^{10}-formyl-5,6,7,8-tetrahydropteroylmonoglutamic acid.

The N^5- and N^{10}-formyl-5,6,7,8-tetrahydropteroylmonoglutamic acids are chemically and enzymically interconvertible, and the reaction proceeds through a cyclic N^5,N^{10}-methenyl intermediate.

D. N^5-*Formimino*-5,6,7,8-*tetrahydropteroylmonoglutamic Acid*

In a detailed study of the enzymic synthesis of N^{10}-formyl-5,6,7,8-tetrahydropteroylmonoglutamic acid in systems converting formiminoglycine (**29**) to glycine (**31**), two forms of tetrahydropteroylmonoglutamic acid were encountered which are intermediate in the path from tetrahydropteroylmonoglutamic acid to N^{10}-formyltetrahydropteroylmonoglutamic acid.[46] The reaction sequence proceeds from tetrahydropteroylmonoglutamic acid (**30**) by the transfer of the formimino group from formiminoglycine (**29**), yielding glycine (**31**) and N^5-formimino-5,6,7,8-tetrahydropteroylmonoglutamic acid (**32**), which in turn eliminates ammonia yielding the cyclic form, anhydroleucovorin A (**28**).[48,49] Enzymic cleavage of the imidazoline ring of the latter yields N^{10}-formyl-5,6,7,8-tetrahydropteroylmonoglutamic acid (**33**). The same sequence of tetrahydropteroylmonoglutamic acid derivatives has also been observed in the enzymic conversion of formimino-*L*-glutamic acid to *L*-glutamic acid.[49,50]

E. N^5,N^{10}-*Methenyl*-5,6,7,8-*tetrahydropteroylmonoglutamic Acid*

This form (**28**) of tetrahydropteroylmonoglutamic acid was first encountered during studies with the synthetic citrovorum factor. It was

44. G. R. Greenberg, *Federation Proc.*, *13*, 745 (1954).
45. G. R. Greenberg, L. Jaenicke, and M. Silverman, *Biochim. et Biophys. Acta*, *17*, 589 (1955).
46. J. C. Rabinowitz and W. E. Pricer, Jr., *J. Am. Chem. Soc.*, *78*, 4176 (1956).
47. H. R. Whiteley, M. J. Osborn, and F. M. Huennekens, *J. Am. Chem. Soc.*, *80*, 757 (1958).
48. J. C. Rabinowitz and W. E. Pricer, Jr., *J. Am. Chem. Soc.*, *78*, 5702 (1956).
49. J. C. Rabinowitz and W. E. Pricer, Jr., *J. Am. Chem. Soc.*, *78*, 5705 (1956).
50. H. Tabor and L. Wyngarden, *J. Biol. Chem.*, *234*, 1830 (1959).

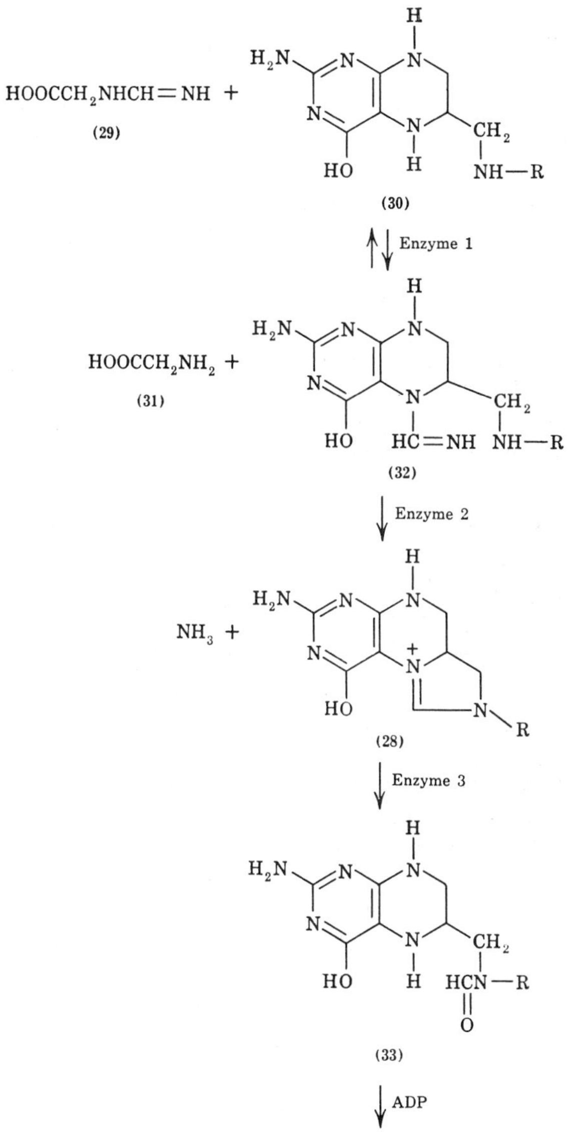

$HOOCCH_2NHCH{=}NH$ +

(29)

(30)

↑↓ Enzyme 1

$HOOCCH_2NH_2$ +

(31)

(32)

↓ Enzyme 2

NH_3 +

(28)

↓ Enzyme 3

(33)

↓ ADP

ATP + HCOOH + 5, 6, 7, 8-Tetrahydropteroylmonoglutamic Acid

(30)

$R = C_6H_4C(=O)NHCH(COOH)CH_2CH_2COOH$

observed that treatment of leucovorin with strong acid yielded a cyclic intermediate, which on treatment with boiling water gave the N^5,N^{10}-methenyl-bridged intermediate, anhydroleucovorin A.[34] Its relationship to "active formate" was unknown at the time. Later it was observed as an intermediate in the pathway for the enzymic synthesis of N^{10}-formyl-5,6,7,8-tetrahydropteroylmonoglutamic acid from tetrahydropteroylmonoglutamic acid in systems converting formiminoglycine and formimino-*L*-glutamic acid to glycine and *L*-glutamic acid, respectively.[48,50] The N^5,N^{10}-methenyl derivative is the intermediate form in chemical and enzymic interconversions of N^5-formyl- and N^{10}-formyl-5,6,7,8-tetrahydropteroylmonoglutamic acid.

F. "Active Formaldehyde"

A participating form of the vitamin in enzymic reactions requiring "active formaldehyde" is believed to be the corresponding N^5,N^{10}-methylene-bridged derivative (**34**) of 5,6,7,8-tetrahydropteroylmonoglutamic

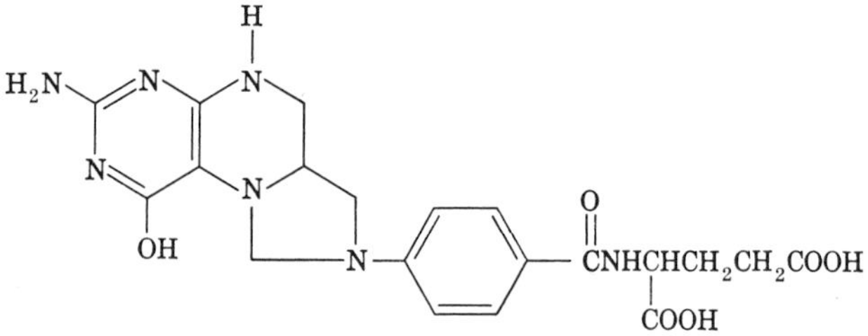

(34)

acid. The term N^5-hydroxymethyl-5,6,7,8-tetrahydropteroylmonoglutamic acid is still used, but the isolated form is an N^5,N^{10}-methylene rather than an N^5-hydroxymethyl derivative.

"Active formaldehyde" is readily synthesized from tetrahydropteroylmonoglutamic acid on treatment with an excess of formaldehyde;[51] pH 4.2 is optimum for the condensation reaction.[52] Although there is a multiplicity of reaction sites, e.g., N^3, N^5, N^8, and N^{10}, good yields of "active formaldehyde" are obtained. A purified formaldehyde-activating enzyme from pigeon liver has also been used to convert tetrahydropteroylmonoglutamic acid to "active formaldehyde."[53] The substance, which is

51. R. L. Kisliuk, *Federation Proc.*, *15*, 289 (1956); *J. Biol. Chem.*, *227*, 805 (1957).
52. M. J. Osborn, P. T. Talbert, and F. M. Huennekens, *J. Am. Chem. Soc.*, *82*, 4921 (1960).
53. M. J. Osborn, E. N. Vercamer, P. T. Talbert, and F. M. Huennekens, *J. Am. Chem. Soc.*, *79*, 6565 (1957).

reasonably stable in the presence of air, was purified by chromatography on Solka-floc columns or on Whatman No. 1 paper. Product authenticity was established by enzymic assay and by conversion to N^5,N^{10}-methenyl-5,6,7,8-tetrahydropteroylmonoglutamic acid in the presence of hydroxymethyltetrahydrofolic acid dehydrogenase.

The structure of "active formaldehyde" has been formulated as the N^5,N^{10}-methylene derivative (**34**) of 5,6,7,8-tetrahydropteroylmonoglutamic acid on the basis of the following observations:[18,51–55]

(a) The optimum pH curve for the synthesis from formaldehyde and tetrahydropteroylmonoglutamic acid suggests participation of two prototropic groups having pKa values closely corresponding to those of the N^{10}- and N^5-atoms of tetrahydropteroylmonoglutamic acid.

(b) The equilibrium constant for this reaction ($\sim 10^4$ at pH 7) is greater than anticipated for the formation of a single linkage between formaldehyde and one of the nitrogen atoms.

(c) The compound exhibits an unusual stability to air oxidation in spite of the presence of a readily available active formaldehyde group.

(d) In systems freed from cyclohydrolase, only N^5,N^{10}-methenyl-5,6,7,8-tetrahydropteroylmonoglutamic acid can be enzymically reduced to "active formaldehyde;" conversely, only N^5,N^{10}-methenyl-5,6,7,8-tetrahydropteroylmonoglutamic acid is produced from the enzymic oxidation of "active formaldehyde." None of the related N^5- or N^{10}-compounds respond similarly.

(e) Only N^5,N^{10}-methenyl-5,6,7,8-tetrahydropteroylmonoglutamic acid can be chemically reduced to "active formaldehyde."

Although "active formaldehyde" is commonly depicted as the N^5,N^{10}-methylene-bridged derivative, the transient occurrence of a single-bonded adduct such as N^5-hydroxymethyl-5,6,7,8-tetrahydropteroylmonoglutamic acid or N^{10}-hydroxymethyl-5,6,7,8-tetrahydropteroylmonoglutamic acid during enzymic C_1-transfer is possible; actual transfer of the single carbon unit from "active formaldehyde" to the acceptor probably requires opening of the bridged structure just prior to transfer.

The mechanism for chemical synthesis of N^5,N^{10}-methylene-5,6,7,8-tetrahydropteroylmonoglutamic acid is depicted as proceeding by the intermediate formation of N^{10}-hydroxymethyl-5,6,7,8-tetrahydropteroylmonoglutamic acid.[18] Maximum synthesis of "active formaldehyde" is achieved at pH 4.2 when the N^5-atom is charged and the N^{10}-atom is uncharged. Consequently, hydroxymethylation of the N^{10}-atom is favored. The final stage of synthesis is accomplished by a concerted displacement

54. M. J. Osborn and F. M. Huennekens, *Biochim. et Biophys. Acta*, *26*, 646 (1957).
55. R. L. Blakely, *Nature*, *182*, 719 (1958).

of electrons resulting in expulsion of a hydroxyl ion from the hydroxymethyl group and a hydrogen ion from the N^5-atom. Condensation between the N^5-atom and the methylene carbonium ion on the N^{10}-atom follows. Further support for this mechanism may be derived from pH stability studies of "active formaldehyde." In the presence of formaldehyde-trapping agents such as hydroxylamine, formaldehyde is generated rapidly in strongly acidic solution whereas in alkaline solution there is little or no tendency toward formaldehyde generation. This pH dependence for reversal of synthesis is fully compatible with the mechanism.

6. Biosynthesis

The biosynthesis of pteroylmonoglutamic acid apparently proceeds through an ATP and coenzyme A-mediated condensation of *p*-aminobenzoic acid with glutamic acid yielding *p*-aminobenzoylglutamic acid; condensation of this moiety with an as yet unknown pteridine yields pteroylmonoglutamic acid.[56]

After it was known that pteroylmonoglutamic acid contains a *p*-aminobenzoyl moiety and that certain similarities exist in the metabolic functions of pteroylmonoglutamic acid and *p*-aminobenzoic acid, it was suggested that pteroylmonoglutamic acid would eliminate the *p*-aminobenzoic acid requirement of most organisms. It appears, however, that *p*-aminobenzoic acid does not function solely as a precursor for pteroylmonoglutamic acid in all organisms. Pteroylmonoglutamic acid can replace the requirement of some organisms for *p*-aminobenzoic acid if the latter compound is concerned solely with the biosynthesis of purines and pyrimidines. With organisms in which *p*-aminobenzoic acid also participates in the biosynthesis of methionine, pteroylmonoglutamic acid cannot replace the requirement for *p*-aminobenzoic acid.[57]

7. Nutritional and Therapeutic Role

A. In Animals

Pteroylglutamic acid avitaminosis in man and animals is evident almost exclusively from blood pathology. The avitaminosis syndrome is characterized by the various anemias usually described in terms of red and white

56. F. M. Huennekens and M. J. Osborn, *Advan. Enzymol.*, *21*, 393 (1959).
57. J. O. Lampen, M. J. Jones, and R. R. Roepke, *J. Biol. Chem.*, *180*, 423 (1949).

blood cell counts and the degree of maturation of these cells. Since bone marrow is almost the exclusive source of blood in the adult, a deficiency of pteroylglutamic acids is sometimes evident in structural changes in the bone marrow itself. Normal circulating blood contains erythrocytes and leucocytes. Since these particles cannot reproduce and are destroyed, maintenance of normal "healthy" blood becomes dependent upon at least two factors: (a) the manufacture of erythrocytes and leucocytes, and (b) the normal maturation of these particles through various stages of development. Pteroylmonoglutamic acid participates in both of these processes.

The various animal species show strikingly different requirements for pteroylmonoglutamic acid which have been attributed to varying degrees of intestinal synthesis of the factor.[58] A pteroylglutamic acid deficiency has been created in animals by the use of one of the three following methods.

Animals such as the chick, monkey, and guinea pig develop deficiency symptoms on a diet deficient in pteroylglutamic acids. In the chick, the avitaminosis syndrome is characterized by slow growth, decreased feathering, and the presence of abnormally large erythrocytes in the blood. The latter condition is usually described as macrocytic anemia. A deficiency in the monkey is accompanied by a low leucocyte count (leucopenia), a reduction in polynuclear leucocytes (agranulocytosis), the presence of abnormally large erythrocytes, and an increased susceptibility to intestinal infection.

In the rat and pig, a pteroylglutamic acid deficiency develops only when intestinal "antiseptics" are used with a diet devoid of pteroylglutamic acids. The deficiency syndrome is characterized by decreased growth, low leucocyte count, and a reduction in polynuclear leucocytes. An altered or hypocellular bone marrow is also a manifestation of pteroylglutamic acid deficiency in such animals.

Animals such as the dog are very resistant to pteroylglutamic acid deficiency, and it is necessary to use a pteroylglutamic acid antagonist to create the deficiency.

B. In The Human

Pteroylglutamic acid deficiency in man is characterized by a deficiency of normal polynuclear erythrocytes and is usually accompanied by the

58. E. L. R. Stokstad, in W. H. Sebrell, Jr., and R. S. Harris, eds., *The Vitamins: Chemistry, Physiology, and Pathology*, Vol. III, Academic, N.Y., 1954, p. 171.

presence of abnormally large erythrocytes (megaloblastic erythropoiesis).[59,60] The nutritional macrocytic anemia is characterized by

(a) altered blood manufacture resulting in a decrease in blood platelets (thrombocytopenia);

(b) reduction in polynuclear leucocytes;

(c) glossitis; and

(d) gastrointestinal disturbances.

The megaloblastic erythropoiesis is characterized by changes in bone marrow structure.

In addition to its use in the therapy of nutritional megaloblastic anemia, pteroylglutamic acid therapy has been used in treating the anemia of pregnancy, the megaloblastic anemia of infancy, and vitamin B_{12}-refractory megaloblastic anemia. It has also been used to relieve the anemia, glossitis, and gastrointestinal disturbances of tropical sprue.

The exact biochemical relationship between pteroylglutamic acid and vitamin B_{12} is not clear although both are necessary for erythropoiesis. All forms of anemia characterized by failure to develop polynuclear erythrocytes respond to pteroylglutamic acid provided there is adequate vitamin B_{12}. On the other hand, anemias characterized by added neurological degeneration, e.g., Addisonian pernicious anemia, respond to vitamin B_{12} therapy. In this instance pteroylglutamic acid, which relieves the anemia and glossitis symptoms, does not relieve, but accentuates in some instances, the neurological degeneration.

The minimum daily requirement of pteroylglutamic acid by man has not been established.[61] Although the pteroylglutamic acid content of many foods is known, the usual daily dietary intake of the vitamin by man is largely unknown. The vitamin, however, is classified as an essential human nutrient since

(a) the macrocytic anemias of animals that respond to pteroylglutamic acid also occur in man;

(b) the compound is an essential metabolite for the synthesis of nucleic acid and for the mediation of enzymic processes requiring one-carbon transfer; and

(c) administration of pteroylglutamic acid antagonists to man during the treatment of various disease states produces deficiency syndromes bearing a marked resemblance to those induced in various animals.

59. F. H. Bethell, in W. H. Sebrell, Jr., and R. S. Harris, eds., *The Vitamins: Chemistry, Physiology, and Pathology*, Vol. III, Academic, N.Y., 1954, p. 202.
60. L. J. Witts, *Brit. Med. Bull.*, *12*, 14 (1956).
61. *Recommended Dietary Allowances*, Natl. Acad. Sci., Natl. Res. Council Publication 589, Washington, D.C., 1958, p. 23.

The minimum nutritional need of pteroylglutamic acid by man has been estimated at 0.5 mg. per day on the basis of extrapolation from animal studies.

The vitamin is found in liver, kidney, yeast, mushrooms, and is produced by microorganisms such as *Bacillus subtilis*, *Bacillus vulgatus*, and *Serratia marcescens*. Among the best vegetable sources of the factor are asparagus, broccoli, spinach, and lima beans; the richest sources of the factor in fruits are lemons, bananas, strawberries, and cantaloupes.[62]

62. E. W. Toepfer, E. G. Zook, M. L. Orr, and L. R. Richardson, *U.S. Dept. Agr., Agr. Handbook*, *29*, (1952).

CHAPTER VIII

Biotin, Biocytin, and *N*-Carboxybiotin

1. Introduction

It could be said that records dealing with the importance of biotin activity for microbial growth date back to the Pasteur-Liebig controversy concerning essential ingredients for microbial growth. In 1860 Pasteur declared that yeast could be grown in solutions containing only water, sugar, yeast ash, and ammonium tartrate; however, he also noted the value of "albuminoid materials" for the stimulation of growth of yeast and other microbes.[1] Liebig questioned the possibility of cultivating yeast without such "albuminoid materials." From 1872 to 1901 the position of Pasteur held and the concept of "essential factors" for the growth of microorganisms was dormant. In the latter year, however, evidence was presented proving that "a healthy crop" of yeast could not be grown in salt-and-sugar solutions unless a little wort, yeast water, peptone, or beef extract was added.[2] The activity was designated "bios," and the first attempt at isolation and chemical identification was made. In the thirty years which followed, bios was found to be a mixture of essential factors, and the requirements of the various yeasts for such activity were found to vary widely. By 1924 bios was fractionated and three substances, all essential for microbial growth, were isolated.[3] The first, designated bios I, was later identified as *meso*-inositol. The second, bios IIA, was replaced by pantothenic acid in some strains and by β-alanine supplemented with *L*-leucine in other organisms. The third, bios IIB, was identified with biotin.

During the 1930's, independent investigations of the yeast growth factor (bios IIB), a growth- and respiration-promoting factor for *Rhizobium trifolii* (coenzyme R), and a factor essential in rat nutrition (vitamin H) were in progress; each of the studies dealt with the same factor, biotin.

1. L. Pasteur, *Ann. Chim. Phys.*, 3rd ser., *58*, 323 (1860).
2. E. Wildiers, *Cellule Rec. Cytol. Histol.*, *18*, 313 (1901).
3. W. Lash Miller, *Science*, *58*, 197 (1924).

The activity of bios IIB was provisionally designated as biotin[4] and studies with yeast concentrates were begun. Since the process for isolation of the active principle was long and tedious, investigators eventually turned to alternate sources; dried egg yolk proved to be the best source of activity. It was an exceedingly fine choice since the preliminary crude aqueous extracts were of the same degree of purity as the earlier best preparations from yeast. Biotin, isolated from this source in the form of a crystalline methyl ester, was later shown to be identical with the activity of bios IIB.

During this same period, a group of factors designated "protective factor X,"[5] vitamin H,[6] and "the factor protective against egg-white injury"[7] were fractionated from liver; these activities, essential for nutrition in the rat, were subsequently shown to be the same factor and to possess properties remarkably similar to those of biotin from egg yolk.[8,9] During the period immediately following the isolation and structure determination of biotin, it was suggested that the compound isolated from liver and that isolated from egg yolk, although very similar in chemical and biological properties, were not identical.[10] On the basis of what seemed to be significant differences in melting points and optical rotations of the compounds derived from the two sources, the factor from egg yolk was designated α-biotin and that from liver, β-biotin. Recent evidence, however, showed no significant variation in the biological activity of α- and β-biotin in five microbial systems;[11] consequently, the concept of distinguishing biotin on the basis of its source is no longer valid.

Research on growth and respiration factors for several strains of legume nodule bacteria also led to the fractionation of biotin activity. The respiration factor designated coenzyme R was obtained by extracting commercial sucrose with absolute ethanol and was studied mostly with the red clover root nodule organism, *R. trifolii.*[12] In these early studies, coenzyme R was inactive under the test conditions for a yeast-growth factor;

4. F. Kögl and B. Tönnis, *Z. Physiol. Chem.*, *242*, 43 (1936).
5. M. A. Boas-Fixen, *Biochem. J.*, *21*, 712 (1927).
6. P. György, *Z. ärztl. Fortbild.*, *28*, 377, 417 (1931); *J. Biol. Chem.*, *119*, xliii (1937); *131*, 733 (1939).
7. J. G. Lease and H. T. Parsons, *Z. Physiol. Chem.*, *269*, 61 (1941).
8. P. György, D. B. Melville, D. Burk, and V. du Vigneaud, *Science*, *91*, 243 (1940).
9. V. du Vigneaud, D. B. Melville, P. György, and C. S. Rose, *Science*, *92*, 62 (1940).
10. F. Kögl, and E. J. ten Ham, *Naturwissenschaften*, *31*, 208 (1943); *Z. Physiol. Chem.*, *279*, 140 (1943).
11. K. K. Krueger and W. H. Peterson, *J. Biol. Chem.*, *173*, 497 (1948).
12. F. E. Allison, S. H. Hoover, and D. Burk, *Science*, *78*, 217 (1933).

therefore, the identical nature of coenzyme R and biotin was not suspected. When the requirement of the yeast system for β-alanine became known and sufficient quantities of the amino acid were added to the test medium, coenzyme R was active for the stimulation of yeast growth, and it was concluded that coenzyme R and biotin were identical.[13]

2. Isolation

During the various studies, biotin was isolated from fresh and dried egg yolk, autolyzed yeast, and papain or pepsin digests of liver. The following description for the isolation of biotin from egg yolk is typical of the general procedure for the isolation of this vitamin from a variety of sources.[4] Fractionation was guided by the activity of the substance for the growth of yeast.

Biotin was extracted from the yolks of 1000 fresh eggs by acetone treatment and was precipitated from the filtrate with four volumes of alcohol. An aqueous solution of the active precipitate was freed from certain impurities by treatment with lead acetate, and the active principle was precipitated with phosphotungstic acid. Further purification was achieved by decomposition of the phosphotungstate with barium hydroxide and charcoal adsorption of biotin from the filtrate. After preliminary washing of the adsorbate with 50% ethanol, the biotin was eluted with 60% acetone containing 2.5% ammonia. Precipitation with phosphotungstic acid followed by decomposition with barium hydroxide yielded an active alcohol-soluble fraction. The alcohol solution was purified by treatment with mercuric chloride prior to the esterification of the active fraction with methanol. Solutions of the methyl ester were further purified by precipitation of impurities; first, bromopicrolonic acid and then rufianic acid were used as precipitants. Biotin was finally purified as a crystalline reineckate.

When dried egg yolk was used as the starting material, the procedure was essentially the same up to the methyl ester purification with bromopicrolonic acid. At this stage, the methyl ester was further purified by high vacuum distillation and then by crystallization from a mixture of chloroform and petroleum ether. By this method, 1.1 mg. of crystalline biotin was isolated from 250 kg. of dried egg yolk; since the starting material contained approximately 80 mg. by assay, isolation was achieved in a yield of 1.4%.

13. P. M. West and P. W. Wilson, *Science*, *89*, 607 (1939).

3. Structure Determination

Biotin is (+)-*cis*-hexahydro-2-keto-1*H*-thieno(3,4)-imidazole-4-valeric acid (**1**). The highlights of the structural elucidation are as follows.[14–22]

O
||
C
H—N N—H
H H
$(CH_2)_4COOH$
S

(1)

Biotin, $C_{10}H_{16}N_2O_3S$, is an optically active compound and behaves as a monocarboxylic acid. Ninhydrin tests and Van Slyke nitrous acid tests established the absence of amino- and basic ring-nitrogen atoms. Absence of OCH_3, NCH_3, and SCH_3 groups was ascertained after treatment with hydrogen iodide.

Hydrolysis of biotin with barium hydroxide yielded the diaminocarboxylic acid (**2**) which gave adipic acid (**3**) on oxidation. To establish the

Biotin (1) ⟶ H_2N NH_2 $(CH_2)_4COOH$ S (2) ⟶ $HOOC(CH_2)_4COOH$ (3)

14. V. du Vigneaud, K. Hofmann, D. B. Melville, and J. R. Rachele, *J. Biol. Chem.*, *140*, 763 (1941).
15. G. B. Brown and V. du Vigneaud, *J. Biol. Chem.*, *141*, 85 (1941).
16. K. Hofmann, D. B. Melville, and V. du Vigneaud, *J. Biol. Chem.*, *141*, 207 (1941).
17. K. Hofmann, D. B. Melville, and V. du Vigneaud, *J. Am. Chem. Soc.*, *63*, 3237 (1941); *J. Biol. Chem.*, *144*, 513 (1942).
18. D. B. Melville, K. Hofmann, and V. du Vigneaud, *J. Biol. Chem.*, *145*, 101 (1942).
19. G. W. Kilmer, M. D. Armstrong, G. B. Brown, and V. du Vigneaud, *J. Biol. Chem.*, *145*, 495 (1942).
20. K. Hofmann, G. W. Kilmer, D. B. Melville, V. du Vigneaud, and H. H. Darby, *J. Biol. Chem.*, *145*, 503 (1942).
21. V. du Vigneaud, D. B. Melville, K. Folkers, D. E. Wolf, R. Mozingo, J. C. Keresztesy, and S. A. Harris, *J. Biol. Chem.*, *146*, 475 (1942).
22. D. B. Melville, A. W. Mayer, K. Hofmann, and V. du Vigneaud, *J. Biol. Chem.*, *146*, 487 (1942).

fact that one of the carboxyl groups of adipic acid was originally present in biotin, the methyl ester of biotin (**4**) was subjected to a Curtius degradation; hydrolysis of the derived urethane (**5**) with barium hydroxide yielded the triamine (**6**) which failed to give adipic acid on oxidation. These data were interpreted as evidence for a δ-valeric acid side chain in biotin.

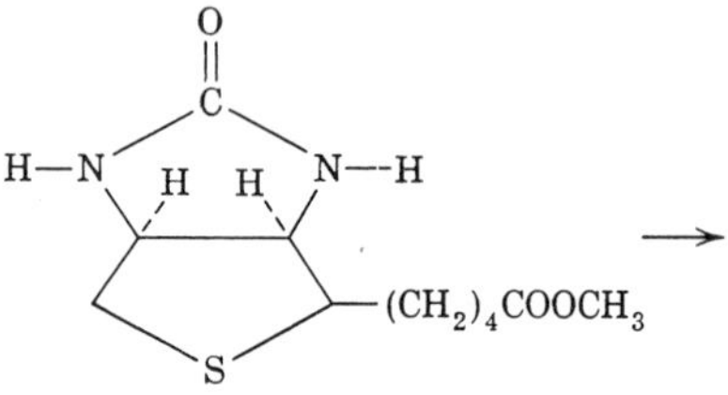

(4) 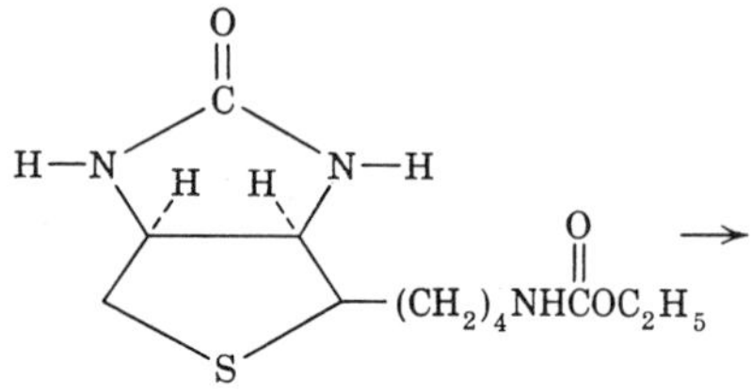 (5)

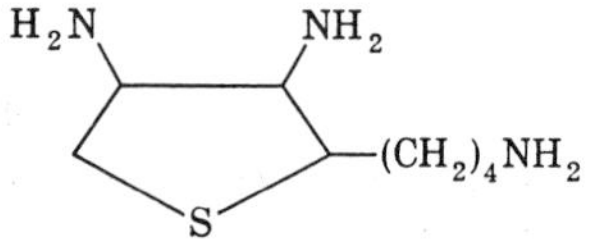

(6)

The imidazolidone ring was established by the following reactions. When biotin was hydrolyzed with barium hydroxide, formation of the diaminocarboxylic acid (**2**) was accompanied by the loss of one carbon and one oxygen atom. The presence of two primary amino groups in the hydrolysis product was confirmed by Van Slyke titration. Treatment of the diaminocarboxylic acid (**2**) with phosgene regenerated biotin. Although these data confirmed the existence of a cyclic urea function in biotin, they did not distinguish between a five- or six-membered ring. The 1,2-relationship of the amino groups in the diaminocarboxylic acid and the five-membered imidazolidone ring in biotin were established from the reaction of the diaminocarboxylic acid (**2**) with phenathraquinone. The product of

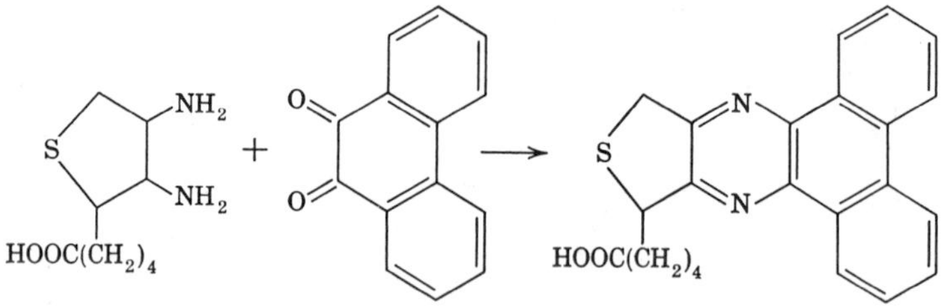

(2) (7)

this reaction was the dibenzoquinoxaline derivative (**7**); its structure followed from color reactions and the ultraviolet absorption spectrum.

At this stage the size and nature of the sulfur-containing moiety remained to be established. The sulfur atom was assumed to be in a cyclic thioether linkage on the basis of the absence of SCH_3, a negative nitroprusside test, and the ease of oxidation of biotin to biotin sulfone. Although all but four of the carbon atoms were apparently assigned, the possibility of a six-membered sulfur-containing ring was still considered on the premise that biotin might have a side chain of four rather than five carbon atoms. In either case it would be possible to obtain adipic acid by the oxidation of a derived diaminocarboxylic acid. If biotin contained a γ-butyric acid side chain, the intermediate diaminocarboxylic acid would be the tetrahydrothiapyran derivative (**8**). Oxidation of the latter could yield either the α-keto-dicarboxylic acid (**9**) or the tricarboxylic acid (**10**),

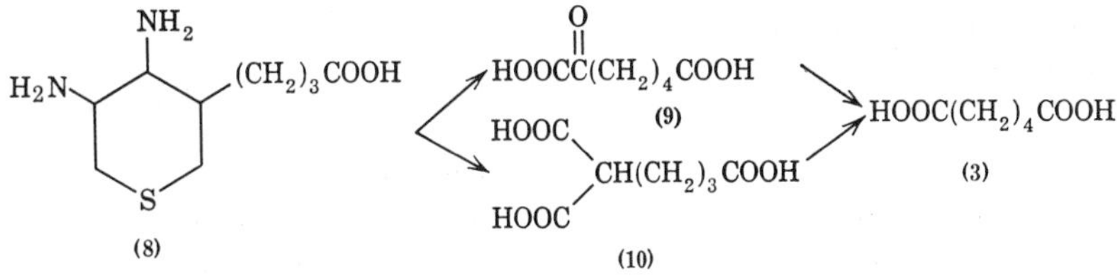

NH_2, H_2N, $(CH_2)_3COOH$, S (8) → $HOOCC(=O)(CH_2)_4COOH$ (9) or $(HOOC)_2CH(CH_2)_3COOH$ (10) → $HOOC(CH_2)_4COOH$ (3)

both of which on decarboxylation would give adipic acid. A five-membered sulfur-containing ring in biotin was firmly established by Raney nickel desulfurization. This method for the desulfurization of organic thioethers had just been established[23] as a general reaction proceeding usually in yields of 65–90% and its usefulness for structural studies on sulfur-containing natural products was realized. The application of this reaction

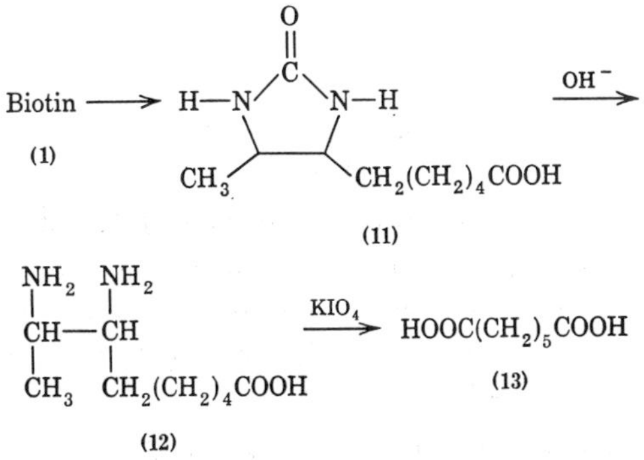

Biotin (1) → H—N–C(=O)–N—H, CH_3, $CH_2(CH_2)_4COOH$ (11) $\xrightarrow{OH^-}$

NH_2 NH_2, CH—CH, CH_3 $CH_2(CH_2)_4COOH$ (12) $\xrightarrow{KIO_4}$ $HOOC(CH_2)_5COOH$ (13)

23. R. Mozingo, D. E. Wolf, S. A. Harris, and K. Folkers, *J. Am. Chem. Soc.*, *65*, 1013 (1943).

to biotin gave desthiobiotin (**11**). Hydrolysis of the latter gave the desthiodiamino acid (**12**) which yielded pimelic acid (**13**) on periodate oxidation. Consequently, the presence of the five-membered sulfur-containing ring was established and the existence of the δ-valeric acid side chain was confirmed.

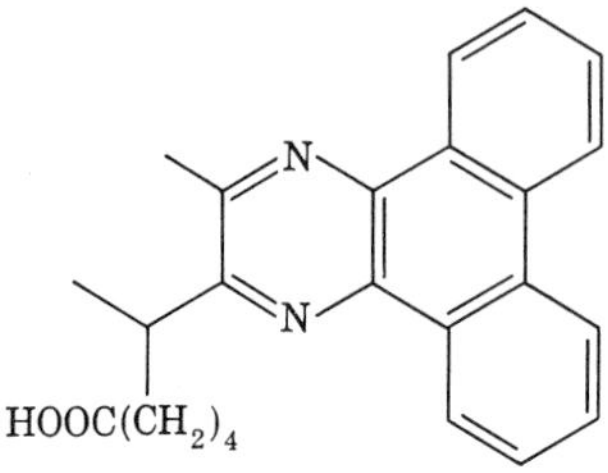

(14) 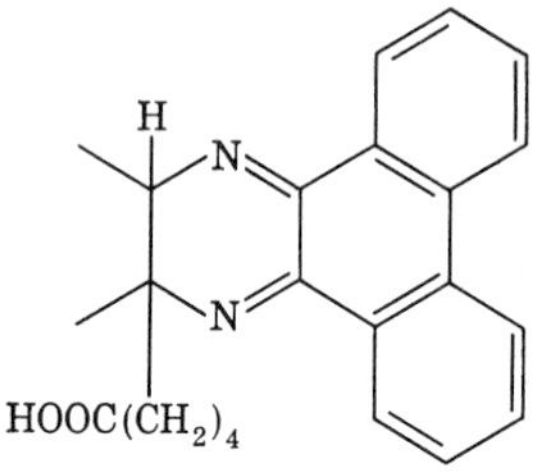 (15)

Location of the side chain at the α-position of the thiophane moiety was deduced from the reactions of the diaminocarboxylic acid (**2**) and the desthiodiamino acid (**12**) with phenanthraquinone. Both compounds gave dibenzoquinoxaline derivatives (**14**) rather than dihydrodibenzoquinoxaline derivatives (**15**). If the acid chain were attached at the β-position of the thiophane ring, the dihydrodibenzoquinoxaline derivative would have been formed. The presence of the thiophane ring with the side chain in the α-position was also demonstrated by the conversion of the diaminocarboxylic acid (**2**) to the known δ-(2-thienyl)valeric acid (**16**) by exhaustive methylation.

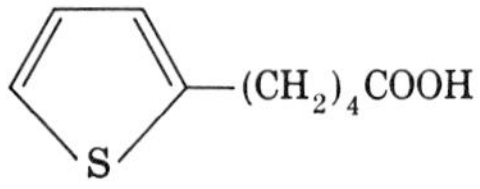

(16)

4. Synthesis

Biotin contains three asymmetric centers and since the molecule is capable of existing in either a *cis*- or *trans*-orientation at the bridgehead of the two fused rings, there are four racemic pairs or eight stereoisomers corresponding to this structure. All four racemates have been synthesized[24,25] and related to a *cis*- or *trans*-configuration at the line of

24. A. Grüssner, J. P. Bourquin, and O. Schnider, *Helv. Chim. Acta*, *28*, 517 (1945).
25. R. Baker, W. L. McEwen, and W. N. Kinley, *J. Org. Chem.*, *12*, 323 (1947).

fusion.[26] The two *cis*-forms are represented by (±)-biotin and (±)-epibiotin; the *trans*-forms are (±)-allobiotin and (±)-epiallobiotin. Of all eight isomers, however, only (+)-biotin is biologically active.

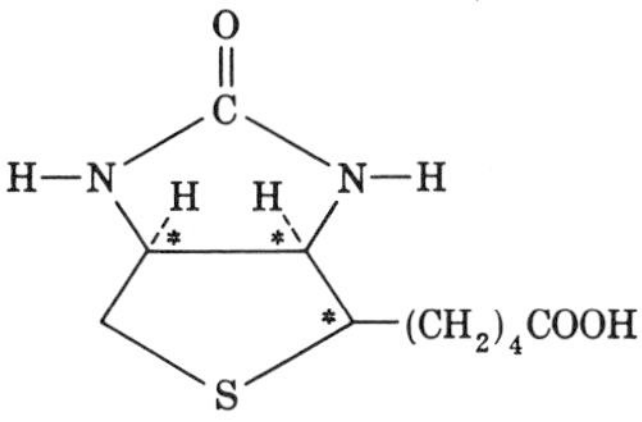

cis 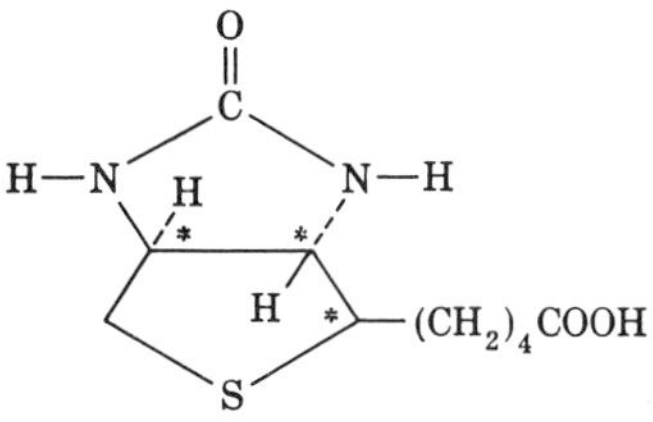 *trans*

The first synthesis (Fig. 1) of (+)-biotin yielded (±)-allobiotin, (±)-epiallobiotin, and (±)-biotin. Resolution of the latter gave (+)-biotin.[27–29] In this synthesis the key thiophane derivative (**19**) was constructed by starting with the condensation of chloroacetic acid and the sodio derivative of cysteine. The intermediate amino acid (**17**) was benzoylated and then esterified, yielding the corresponding benzamido ester (**18**). Alkali-induced cyclization of the latter followed by acid catalyzed decarboxylation yielded 4-benzamido-3-ketothiophane (**19**).

At this stage the δ-valeric acid side chain was introduced starting with the condensation of (**19**) with γ-carbomethoxybutyraldehyde. Treatment of the intermediate α,β-unsaturated ketone (**20**) with hydroxylamine gave the corresponding unsaturated oxime (**21**), which on reduction with zinc and acetic acid followed by acetylation yielded 3-acetamido-4-benzamido-2-(4-carbomethoxybutyl)-4,5-dihydrothiophene (**22**). Hydrogenation of the latter in the presence of palladium yielded the corresponding thiophane derivative (**23**). Two racemates were isolated from the reaction mixture at this stage. The next step of the synthesis was accomplished by hydrolysis of the thiophane derivative (**23**) with barium hydroxide; the diamino hydrolysis product (**24**) on treatment with phosgene in the presence of sodium bicarbonate yielded biotin.

The (±)-biotin was resolved through its mandelic acid ester to an isomer

26. S. A. Harris, R. Mozingo, D. E. Wolf, A. N. Wilson, and K. Folkers, *J. Am. Chem. Soc.*, *67*, 2102 (1945).
27. S. A. Harris, D. E. Wolf, R. Mozingo, and K. Folkers, *Science*, *97*, 447 (1943).
28. S. A. Harris, D. E. Wolf, R. Mozingo, R. C. Anderson, G. E. Arth, N. R. Easton, D. Heyl, A. N. Wilson, and K. Folkers, *J. Am. Chem. Soc.*, *66*, 1756 (1944).
29. S. A. Harris, N. R. Easton, D. Heyl, A. N. Wilson, and K. Folkers, *J. Am. Chem. Soc.*, *66*, 1757 (1944).

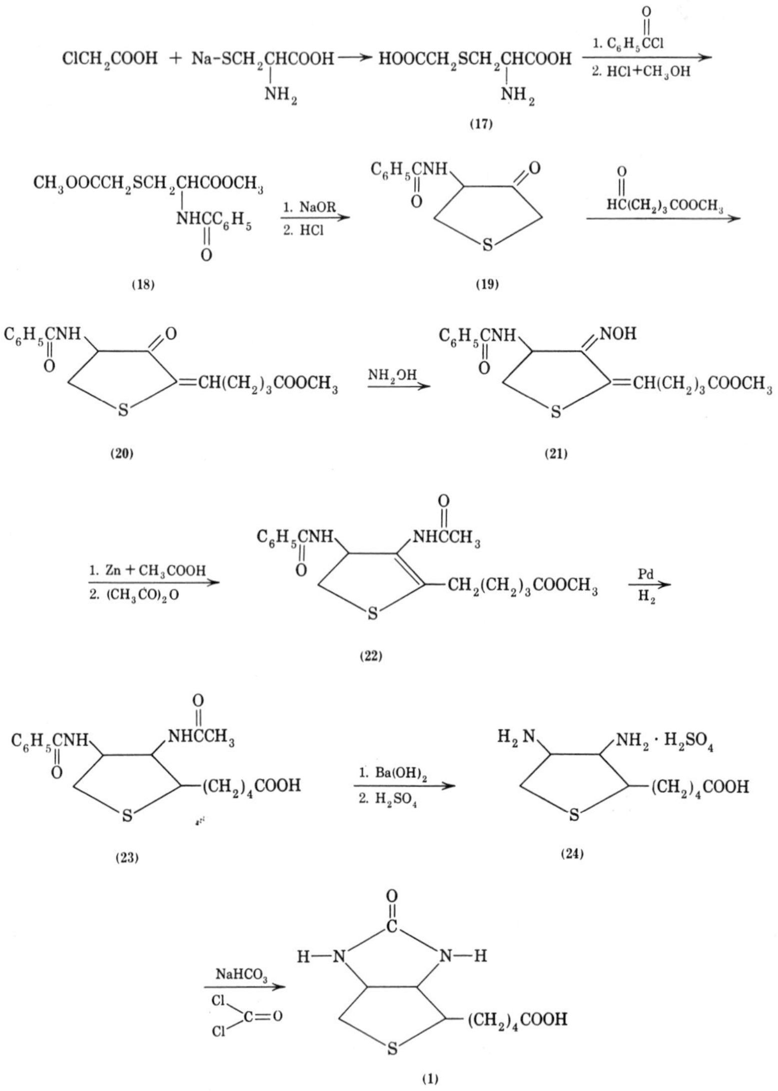

$ClCH_2COOH + Na\text{-}SCH_2CHCOOH(NH_2) \longrightarrow HOOCCH_2SCH_2CHCOOH(NH_2)$ (17) $\xrightarrow[\text{2. } HCl+CH_3OH]{\text{1. } C_6H_5\overset{O}{\overset{\|}{C}}Cl}$

$CH_3OOCCH_2SCH_2CHCOOCH_3$ with $NH\overset{O}{\overset{\|}{C}}C_6H_5$ (18) $\xrightarrow[\text{2. HCl}]{\text{1. NaOR}}$ $C_6H_5\overset{O}{\overset{\|}{C}}NH$, =O, S (19) $\xrightarrow{H\overset{O}{\overset{\|}{C}}(CH_2)_3COOCH_3}$

$C_6H_5\overset{O}{\overset{\|}{C}}NH$, =O, S, $=CH(CH_2)_3COOCH_3$ (20) $\xrightarrow{NH_2OH}$ $C_6H_5\overset{O}{\overset{\|}{C}}NH$, =NOH, S, $=CH(CH_2)_3COOCH_3$ (21)

$\xrightarrow[\text{2. } (CH_3CO)_2O]{\text{1. } Zn + CH_3COOH}$ $C_6H_5\overset{O}{\overset{\|}{C}}NH$, $NH\overset{O}{\overset{\|}{C}}CH_3$, S, $-CH_2(CH_2)_3COOCH_3$ (22) $\xrightarrow[H_2]{Pd}$

$C_6H_5\overset{O}{\overset{\|}{C}}NH$, $NH\overset{O}{\overset{\|}{C}}CH_3$, S, $-(CH_2)_4COOH$ (23) $\xrightarrow[\text{2. } H_2SO_4]{\text{1. } Ba(OH)_2}$ H_2N, $NH_2 \cdot H_2SO_4$, S, $-(CH_2)_4COOH$ (24)

$\xrightarrow[Cl_2C{=}O]{NaHCO_3}$ O=C, H—N, N—H, S, $-(CH_2)_4COOH$ (1)

Fig. 1. The first synthesis of biotin[27–29].

CHCOOH
||
HOOCCH
→
BrCHCOOH
|
BrCHCOOH
meso
→
$C_6H_5CH_2$—NHCHCOOH
|
$C_6H_5CH_2$—NHCHCOOH
(25)
Cl
C=O
Cl
→

O
||
C
$C_6H_5CH_2$—N N—$CH_2C_6H_5$
COOH COOH
cis
(26)
$(CH_3CO)_2O$
→

O
||
C
$C_6H_5CH_2$—N N—$CH_2C_6H_5$
O=C C=O
O
(27)
1. Zn + CH_3COOH
2. $(CH_3CO)_2O$
→

O
||
C
$C_6H_5CH_2$—N N—$CH_2C_6H_5$
O
||
CH_3COCH C=O
O
1. H_2S + HCl
2. KHS
3. Zn + CH_3COOH
→

O
||
C
$C_6H_5CH_2$—N N—$CH_2C_6H_5$
CH_2 C=O
S
(28)
$BrMg(CH_2)_4OCH_3$
→

O
||
C
$C_6H_5CH_2$—N N—$CH_2C_6H_5$
OH
S $(CH_2)_4OCH_3$
(29)
CH_3COOH
Heat
→
O
||
C
$C_6H_5CH_2$—N N—$CH_2C_6H_5$
=$CH(CH_2)_3OCH_3$
S

H_2
Pd
→
O
||
C
$C_6H_5CH_2$—N N—$CH_2C_6H_5$
—$(CH_2)_4OCH_3$
S
2 Na
NH_3
→
O
||
C
H—N N—$CH_2C_6H_5$
—$(CH_2)_4OCH_3$
S
(30)

1. HBr
2. KCN
3. Hydrolysis
→
O
||
C
H—N N—$CH_2C_6H_5$
—$(CH_2)_4COOH$
S
(31)
Na
NH_3
→
O
||
C
H—N N—H
—$(CH_2)_4COOH$
S
(1)

Fig. 2. A stereoselective synthesis of biotin.[31]

that was identical with natural biotin. (±)-Biotin was also resolved with quinidine methohydroxide, and very effectively with *L*(+)-arginine.[30]

Another synthesis of (±)-biotin is noteworthy.[31] By this method the imidazolidone ring is formed before the thiophane ring in such a manner that the amino groups are *cis*-oriented; thus, the formation of allo- and epiallobiotin is obviated. This synthesis (Fig. 2) is as follows.

meso-Dibromosuccinic acid was converted to *meso*-bis-benzylamino-succinic acid (**25**), which on treatment with phosgene yielded 1,3-dibenzyl-2-imidazolidone-*cis*-4,5-dicarboxylic acid (**26**). At this stage formation of the thiophane ring was started by converting the *cis*-acid (**26**) to the corresponding anhydride (**27**); reduction of the latter with zinc in acetic acid and acetic anhydride yielded a cyclic aldehydo acid derivative that was converted to the thiolactone (**28**). Introduction of the side chain began at this stage with condensation between the thiolactone (**28**) and the Grignard derivative of 4-methoxybutyl bromide. Dehydration of the carbinol derivative (**29**) followed first by reduction of the double bond and then by cleavage of one of the benzyl groups yielded (**30**) or its corresponding 1′-benzyl isomer. Cleavage of the methoxyl group in (**30**) with hydrobromic acid, conversion of the derived bromo derivative to a nitrile, and then hydrolysis yielded monobenzylbiotin (**31**). Cleavage of the remaining benzyl group yielded (±)-biotin.

5. Biologically Active Analogs and Derivatives

The biological activity of many analogs and homologs of biotin has been studied. Desthiobiotin (**11**), one of the key degradation products from structural investigation, has been synthesized both totally[32] and from degradation products of biotin.[33] The growth-stimulating activity of this compound for certain microorganisms is attributed to their apparent ability to convert this compound to biotin.

Oxybiotin (**32**), also synthesized totally,[34] exists only in the *cis*-configuration at the ring junction. Of the two racemates, (±)-*epi*-oxybiotin is inactive; (±)-oxybiotin has about 25% of the growth-stimulating

30. D. E. Wolf, R. Mozingo, S. A. Harris, R. C. Anderson, and K. Folkers, *J. Am. Chem. Soc.*, *67*, 2100 (1945).
31. M. W. Goldberg and L. J. Sternbach, U.S. Pat. 2,489,232 (Nov. 22, 1949).
32. R. Duschinsky and L. A. Dolan, *J. Am. Chem. Soc.*, *67*, 2079 (1945).
33. D. B. Melville, *J. Am. Chem. Soc.*, *66*, 1422 (1944).
34. K. Hofmann, *J. Am. Chem. Soc.*, *67*, 694, 1459 (1945).

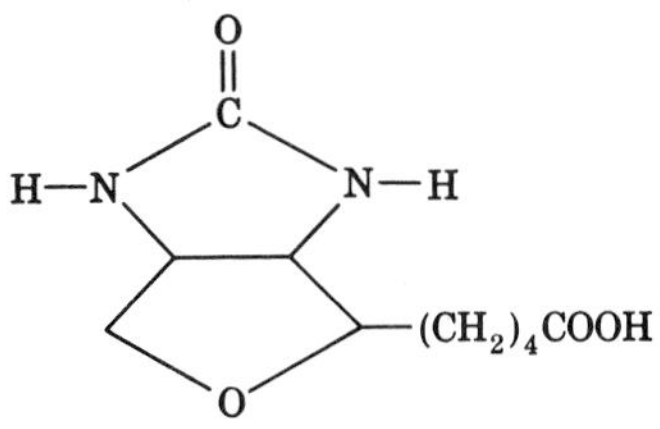

O
C
H—N N—H
$(CH_2)_4COOH$
O

(32)

activity of (+)-biotin, and its effectiveness in curing egg-white injury in rats is 10% that of biotin. The activity of oxybiotin is not due to its conversion to biotin.[35]

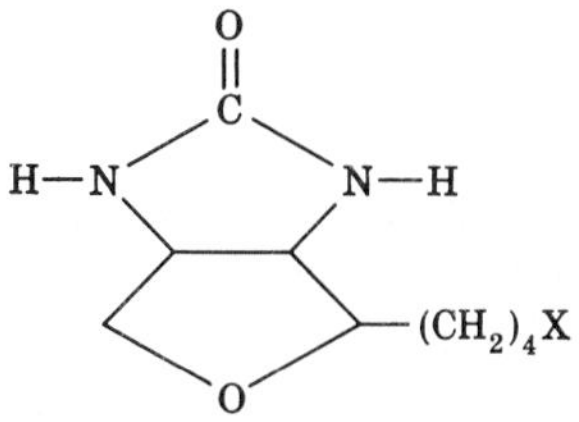

O
C
H—N N—H
$(CH_2)_4X$
O

X= SO_3H, SH, $SCH_2C_6H_5$

(33)

(±)-Oxybiotin sulfonic acid and the corresponding thiol and benzylthioether (**33**) are effective biotin antagonists for certain microorganisms.[36]

Biotin (−)-sulfoxide (**34**) has been synthesized.[37] Later this compound (AN factor) was isolated from culture filtrates of *Aspergillis niger*,[38] and

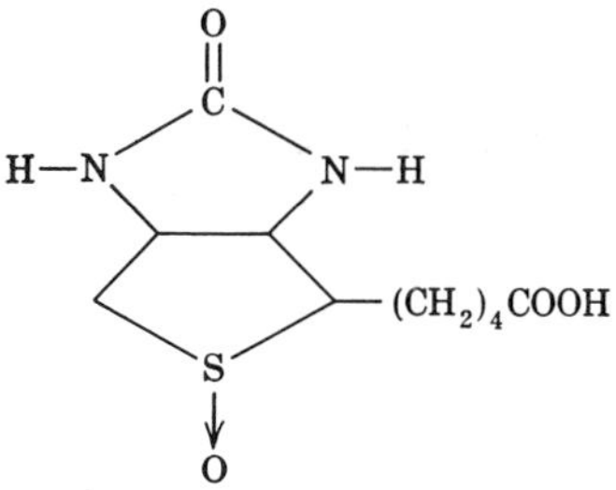

O
C
H—N N—H
$(CH_2)_4COOH$
S
↓
O

(34)

35. K. Hofmann and T. Winnick, *J. Biol. Chem.*, *160*, 449 (1945).
36. A. F. Axelrod and K. Hofmann, *J. Biol. Chem.*, *180*, 525 (1949).
37. D. B. Melville, *J. Biol. Chem.*, *208*, 495 (1954).
38. L. D. Wright and E. L. Cresson, *J. Am. Chem. Soc.*, *76*, 4156 (1954).

is now believed to have metabolic significance.[39] Biotin (−)-sulfoxide also combines with avidin, the causative factor in egg-white injury.

Biotin sulfone[16] (**35**) acts as a growth promoter for yeast, but inhibits the growth of certain *Lactobacilli* and *Staphylococci*.[40,41]

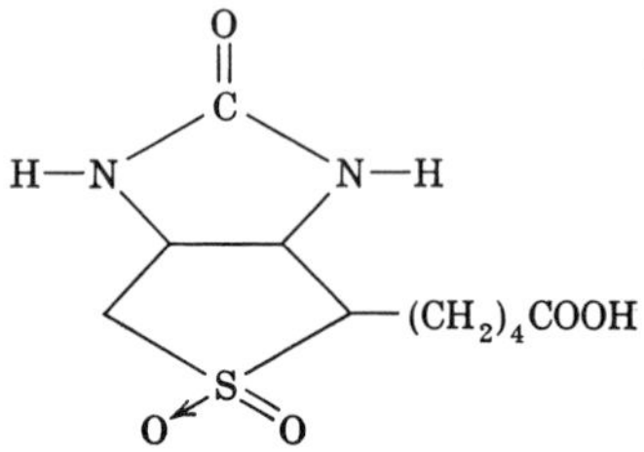

(35)

Biotin occurs in tissue and natural materials in a bound form. Biocytin (**36**), found in extracts of actively metabolizing yeasts, was isolated and characterized as (+)-ε-*N*-biotinyl-*L*-lysine[42] and was synthesized from biotin acid chloride and the copper chelate of *L*-lysine.[43]

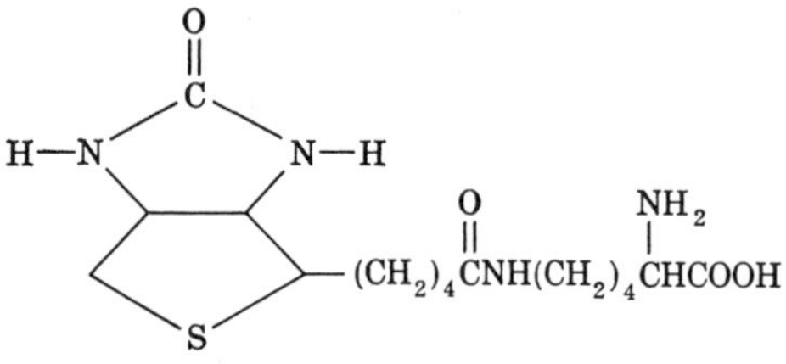

(36)

Avidin, the protein responsible for egg-white injury, combines with biotin; since the complex is a nonabsorbable form, a deficiency develops. The exact mode of bonding of biotin to avidin is unknown, but it is believed to be associated with the imidazolidone ring.

39. L. D. Wright, E. L. Cresson, J. Valiant, D. E. Wolf, and K. Folkers, *J. Am. Chem. Soc.*, *76*, 4160, 4163 (1954).
40. K. Dittmer and V. du Vigneaud, *Science*, *100*, 129 (1944).
41. K. Dittmer, V. du Vigneaud, P. György, and C. S. Rose, *Arch. Biochem.*, *4*, 229 (1944).
42. L. D. Wright, E. L. Cresson, H. R. Skeggs, R. L. Peck, D. E. Wolf, T. R. Wood, J. Valiant, and K. Folkers, *Science*, *114*, 635 (1951).
43. D. E. Wolf, J. Valiant, and K. Folkers, *J. Am. Chem. Soc.*, *73*, 4142 (1951).

6. Metabolic Role

In the course of studies to establish a role for biotin in metabolism, it has been suggested that biotin may participate directly or indirectly in a variety of biological reactions that include the deamination of aspartic acid, threonine, and serine; the carboxylation of pyruvate, adenine, and guanine; the decarboxylation of oxalacetate and succinate; the oxidation of pyruvate and lactate; and the biosynthesis of citrulline and oleic acid.[44–54] Of these, the role of biotin in carboxylation-decarboxylation is the one most clearly elucidated.

The first association of biotin with an enzymic role was in the microbial biosynthesis of aspartic acid. In 1942 the growth stimulatory effect of biotin for *Torula cremoris* was associated with the biosynthesis of aspartic acid;[46] this amino acid promoted growth of the organism in the absence of biotin, but at much higher levels. On the basis of this and subsequent studies, it appeared that biotin participates in the microbial biosynthesis of aspartic acid by influencing either the carboxylation of pyruvate to oxalacetate or the amination of oxalacetate to yield aspartate.

Confirmatory evidence for the participation of biotin in microbial carboxylation-decarboxylation consisted of the following observations:

(a) With *Lactobacillus arabinosis* in media deficient in aspartic acid,[49] bicarbonate was found to stimulate growth in the presence of biotin, but not in biotin-deficient media; thus, deficient organisms failed to condense pyruvate with carbon dioxide to form oxalacetate from which aspartate can be formed by transamination.

(b) Partially deactivated cells of *Escherichia coli* lost their ability to liberate carbon dioxide from aspartate;[50] activity was restored, however, after the addition of biotin.

(c) Biotin participation in the biosynthesis of oxalacetic and α-keto-glutaric acids was demonstrated in *E. coli* and *L. arabinosis*, respectively, by inhibition analysis.[51] After the antibacterial index of a given competitive antagonist for biotin biosynthesis was determined, the effect of

44. H. C. Lichstein, *Vitamins & Hormones*, *9*, 27 (1951).
45. R. J. Winzler, D. Burk, and V. du Vigneaud, *Arch. Biochem.*, *5*, 25 (1944).
46. S. A. Koser, M. H. Wright, and A. Dorfman, *Proc. Soc. Exptl. Biol. Med.*, *51*, 204 (1942).
47. J. L. Stokes, A. Larsen, and M. Gunness, *J. Biol. Chem.*, *167*, 613 (1947); *J. Bacteriol.*, *54*, 219 (1947).
48. H. C. Lichstein and W. W. Umbreit, *J. Biol. Chem.*, *170*, 423 (1947).
49. H. A. Lardy, R. L. Potter, and C. A. Elvehjem, *J. Biol. Chem.*, *169*, 451 (1947).
50. H. C. Lichstein and W. W. Umbreit, *J. Biol. Chem.*, *170*, 329 (1947).
51. W. Shive and L. L. Rogers, *J. Biol. Chem.*, *169*, 453 (1947).

various added intermediates on this index was determined. With *E. coli* only α-ketoglutaric acid or glutamic acid exerted a sparing effect as evidenced by a change in antibacterial index; thus, the first system affected by decreased biotin biosynthesis was the α-ketoglutaric acid system. Similarly, only oxalacetic acid or aspartic acid provoked a change in the antibacterial index for *L. arabinosis*; consequently, the first system affected by decreased biosynthesis of biotin in this organism was the biosynthesis of oxalacetic acid.

(d) A liver enzyme from biotin-deficient turkeys showed a decreased capacity for the oxidative decarboxylation of malate and oxalacetate, although the activities of several other enzymes were within normal range.[52]

(e) A study of C^{14}-bicarbonate utilization by *L. arabinosis* established that cells grown in biotin-deficient media failed almost completely in fixing carbon dioxide, whereas cells grown in the presence of adequate biotin converted C^{14} from the bicarbonate of the medium into cellular aspartic acid.[53]

(f) Using C^{13}-bicarbonate and the biotin inactivator avidin in a cell-free system, carbon dioxide fixation yielding oxalacetate was prevented; the addition of adequate biotin resulted in restoration of normal activity.[54]

Shortly after it was established that carboxylation reactions by micro-organisms are biotin dependent, studies were initiated to determine the effect of a biotin deficiency in the animal on the incorporation of carbon dioxide into various tissue components. One manifestation of a biotin deficiency in the rat is decreased incorporation of C^{14}-labeled bicarbonate into tissue arginine.[55] Since carbon dioxide is incorporated into arginine (**39**) as a result of the conversion of ornithine (**37**) to citrulline (**38**) in the Krebs-Henseleit urea cycle,[56] it was suggested that the decrease in arginine biosynthesis was related to a decreased rate in the biosynthesis of citrulline.[57] These studies showed that liver particles from biotin-deficient rats convert ornithine to citrulline at about one-fifth the rate observed with similar preparations from normal rats; biotin injection, however, restored citrulline synthesis to normal within twenty-four hours. After it was

52. S. Ochoa, A. Mehler, M. L. Blanchard, T. H. Jukes, C. E. Hoffmann, and M. Regan, *J. Biol. Chem.*, *170*, 413 (1947).
53. H. A. Lardy, R. L. Potter, and R. H. Burris, *J. Biol. Chem.*, *179*, 721 (1949).
54. G. E. Wessman and C. H. Werkman, *Arch. Biochem. Biophys.*, *26*, 214 (1950).
55. P. R. MacLeod and H. A. Lardy, *J. Biol. Chem.*, *179*, 733 (1949).
56. S. Grisolia and P. P. Cohen, *J. Biol. Chem.*, *176*, 929 (1948).
57. P. R. MacLeod, S. Grisolia, P. P. Cohen, and H. A. Lardy, *J. Biol. Chem.*, *180*, 1003 (1949).

shown that carbamyl *L*-glutamate is an essential metabolite for the enzymic conversion of ornithine to citrulline,[58] studies were undertaken

$$\underset{(37)}{H_2NCH_2(CH_2)_2\underset{\displaystyle NH_2}{\underset{|}{C}}HCOOH} \xrightarrow{HOOCCH_2CH_2\underset{\underset{\underset{\displaystyle O}{\|}}{NHCNH_2}}{\underset{|}{C}}HCOOH}$$

$$\underset{(38)}{H_2N\overset{\overset{\displaystyle O}{\|}}{C}NHCH_2(CH_2)_2\underset{\displaystyle NH_2}{\underset{|}{C}}HCOOH} \rightarrow \underset{(39)}{H_2N\overset{\overset{\displaystyle NH}{\|}}{C}NHCH_2(CH_2)_2\underset{\displaystyle NH_2}{\underset{|}{C}}HCOOH}$$

to determine whether biotin participates directly in the enzymic trans-carbamylation reaction or indirectly by influencing the biosynthesis of carbamyl *L*-glutamate.[59] The rate of citrulline synthesis from ornithine in the presence of *L*-glutamate is decreased in the biotin-deficient rat, but in the presence of carbamyl *L*-glutamate the rate of biosynthesis was the same in the normal and biotin-deficient animals. Therefore it appeared that biotin might be required for the conversion of *L*-glutamate to carbamyl *L*-glutamate. More recent data also indicate that the effect of biotin on citrulline biosynthesis is indirect.[60,61] In one study no significant differences were observed in either the ornithine- or aspartate carbamyl transferase activity of liver mitochondria from normal and biotin-deficient rats.[60] In another study a biotin deficiency in *Streptococcus lactis* 8039 was associated with decreased ornithine transcarbamylase activity, but the highly purified active enzyme preparations did not contain significant amounts of biotin.[61] The role of biotin in this system is assumed to be indirect and is probably associated with the production of an active four-carbon unit.

The conversion of propionate to succinate by the fixation of carbon dioxide was demonstrated with soluble enzymes from mammalian liver.[62,63] Preparations from biotin-deficient rats were far less effective

58. S. Grisolia and P. P. Cohen, *J. Biol. Chem.*, *191*, 189 (1951).
59. G. Feldott and H. A. Lardy, *J. Biol. Chem.*, *192*, 447 (1951).
60. S. P. Mistry and M. A. Grillo, *Biochim. et Biophys. Acta*, *41*, 166 (1960).
61. J. Ravel and W. Shive, *Federation Proc.*, *19*, 413 (1960).
62. H. A. Lardy and R. Peanasky, *Physiol. Rev.*, *33*, 560 (1953).
63. H. A. Lardy and J. Adler, *J. Biol. Chem.*, *219*, 933 (1956).

than those from normal rats in catalyzing this reaction, but the metabolic defect was alleviated upon the injection of biotin. This reaction appears to be the major metabolic pathway for propionate oxidation in animal tissue.[63] Further study[64] has shown that the oxidation proceeds through the stages:

(a) conversion of propionate to propionyl coenzyme A;

(b) an ATP-dependent carboxylation of propionyl coenzyme A to methylmalonyl (isosuccinyl) coenzyme A by an enzyme containing biotin;

(c) quantitative isomerization of methylmalonyl coenzyme A to succinyl coenzyme A. Details of this conversion are included in a discussion of its coenzyme B_{12} dependence (Chapter X); and

(d) oxidation of succinyl coenzyme A by way of the citric acid cycle. More recent studies on the incorporation of C^{14}-propionate into succinate by cell-free extracts of *Propionibacterium shermanii* confirm the participation of biotin in the carboxylation of propionate to methylmalonate.[65]

In fatty acid biosynthesis one of two purified avian liver enzymes catalyzing the synthesis of palmitate from acetyl coenzyme A is rich in protein-bound biotin and is severely inhibited by avidin.[66–68] The biotin-containing enzyme participates in fatty acid biosynthesis by catalyzing the carboxylation of acetyl coenzmye A to malonyl coenzyme A in the presence of ATP. Details of these conversions are included in a discussion of coenzyme A (Chapter VI).

Isovaleric acid is an intermediate in the enzymic conversion of leucine to acetoacetate. The α-, β-, and γ-carbon atoms of acetoacetate are derived from the isopropyl moiety of isovalerate and the carboxyl group is derived by the fixation of carbon dioxide.[69] Biotin participation in leucine metabolism was evident since: (a) the ability of liver homogenates to incorporate labeled carbon dioxide during isovalerate metabolism was directly related to the biotin level of the animal,[70] and (b) mitochondria from biotin-deficient rats failed to convert isovalerate, β-methylcrotonate, or β-methylvinylacetate to acetoacetate.[71] In the metabolism of leucine, isovaleryl coenzyme A is converted to β-methylcrotonyl coenzyme A

64. M. Flavin and S. Ochoa, *J. Biol. Chem.*, *229*, 965 (1957).
65. E. R. Stadtman, P. Overath, H. Eggerer, and F. Lynen, *Biochem. Biophys. Res. Commun.*, *2*, 1 (1960).
66. S. J. Wakil, *J. Am. Chem. Soc.*, *80*, 6465 (1958).
67. S. J. Wakil, E. B. Titchener, and D. M. Gibson, *Biochim. et Biophys. Acta*, *29*, 225 (1958).
68. S. J. Wakil and D. M. Gibson, *Biochim. et Biophys. Acta*, *41*, 122 (1960).
69. M. J. Coon, *J. Biol. Chem.*, *187*, 71 (1950).
70. G. W. E. Plaut, *Proc. Soc. Exptl. Biol. Med.*, *78*, 769 (1951).
71. J. E. Fischer, *Proc. Soc. Exptl. Biol. Med.*, *88*, 227 (1955).

which in turn is carboxylated to β-methylglutaconyl coenzyme A. The latter is then hydrated to β-hydroxy-β-methylglutaryl coenzyme A which is cleaved to acetoacetate and acetyl coenzyme A. Later studies showed that this carboxylase activity was completely lacking in biotin-deficient systems, and it was concluded that biotin participated in the carboxylation of β-methylcrotonyl coenzyme A by "activated carbon dioxide."[72]

1′-*N*-Carboxybiotin and δ-(3-amino-4-carboxyamino-2-tetrahydrothienyl)valeric acid are both being considered as forms of "activated carbon dioxide" in biotin-dependent enzymic carboxylation-decarboxylation reactions. First it was established that a β-methylcrotonyl coenzyme A carboxylase was a biotin-containing enzyme in which biotin is the prosthetic group. This conclusion, based on the fact that the biotin content of the enzyme increased as a function of purity, was further demonstrated when the purified enzyme could be inhibited by avidin and protected against avidin by the addition of free biotin.[73] Once biotin was actually related to enzyme activity, it was concluded that "activated carbon dioxide" was a carboxylated biotin enzyme. The requirement for (+)-biotin was specific, and since the compound could also function as substrate in the β-methylcrotonyl coenzyme A carboxylase system, "C^{14}-activated carbon dioxide" was enzymically prepared from (+)-biotin and studied *in situ*. On the basis of certain theoretical considerations and in view of such properties as lability in dilute acid solution (pH 2) and stability in neutral or slightly alkaline (pH 8) media, "active carbon dioxide" was formulated as either 3′- or 1′-carboxybiotin (**40** or **41**).[73,74] The structure of this enzymic biotin-carbon dioxide compound was established as 1′-*N*-carboxybiotin (**41**) by converting the enzymic product to its

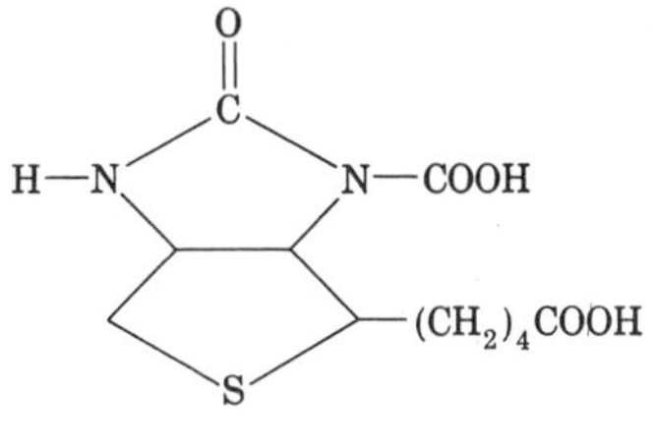

(40)

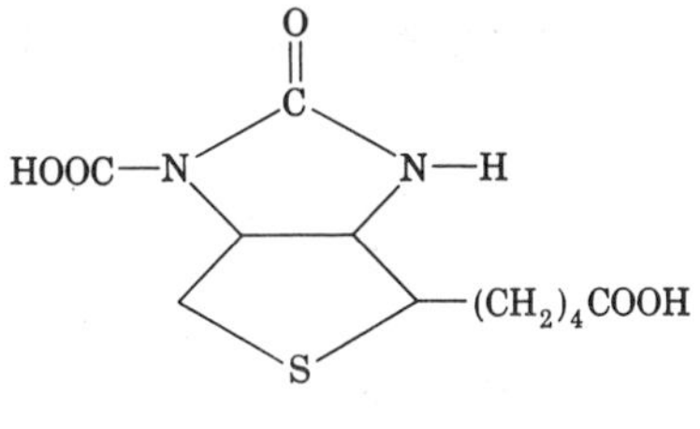

(41)

72. J. F. Woessner, Jr., B. K. Bachhawat, and M. J. Coon, *J. Biol. Chem.*, *233*, 520 (1958). A. del Campillo-Campbell, E. E. Dekker, and M. J. Coon, *Biochim. et Biophys. Acta*, *31*, 290 (1959).
73. F. Lynen, J. Knappe, E. Lorche, G. Jutting, and E. Ringelmann, *Angew. Chem.*, *71*, 481 (1959).
74. F. Lynen, *J. Cellular Comp. Physiol.*, *54*, *Suppl. 1*, 43 (1959).

corresponding methyl ester and comparing this with synthetic 1′- and 3′-*N*-carbomethoxybiotin derivatives prepared from (+)-biotin.[74a]

Coenzyme formation from biotin has been formulated starting with the phosphorylation of biotin by ATP to yield inorganic phosphate and the biotin enol ester of adenosine diphosphate (**42**).[75] Reaction of the latter with carbon dixoide yields 1′-carboxybiotin and adenosine diphosphate.

P—O—P—O—Adenosine; HOH; HOOC—N; N—H; $(CH_2)_4COOH$; + ADP

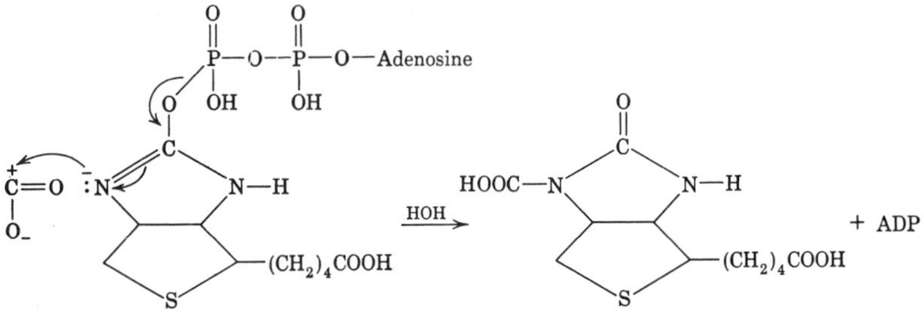

(42) **(41)**

Studies on the nature of "activated carbon dioxide" in the acetyl coenzyme A carboxylase system suggest that δ-(3-amino-4-carboxyamino-2-tetrahydrothienyl)valeric acid is the reactive moiety of the carboxylating enzyme from this system.[75a,75b] Hydrolysis of the carboxylating enzyme prepared by incubation with labeled bicarbonate yielded labeled biotin. The radioactivity of the biotin thus isolated accounted for over 80% of that added to the enzyme system, and the C^{14} was located exclusively in the ureido carbonyl group. When the "native carboxylating enzyme" was first reacted with acetyl coenzyme A and then hydrolyzed, the major biotin-like product was tentatively identified as δ-(3,4-diamino-2-tetrahydrothienyl)valeric acid (**2**).

These studies of "activated carbon dioxide" in the acetyl coenzyme A carboxylase system suggest that the ureido ring of bound biotin is open and that the amino group at the 4-position of the bound diaminothiophane moiety is the site for activation of carbon dioxide.[75a,75b] According to this concept, carboxylation in the acetyl coenzyme A carboxylase system may proceed by reaction of the bound 4-carboxyaminothiophane derivative (**43**) with acetyl coenzyme A to yield the bound diaminothiophane derivative (**44**) and malonyl coenzyme A.

74a. J. Knappe, E. Ringelmann, and F. Lynen, *Biochem. Z.*, *335*, 168 (1961).
75. M. Calvin and N. G. Pon, *J. Cellular Comp. Physiol.*, *54*, *Suppl. 1*, 64 (1959).
75a. S. J. Wakil and M. Waite, *Biochem. Biophys. Res. Commun.*, *9*, 18 (1962).
75b. M. Waite and S. J. Wakil, *J. Biol. Chem.*, *238*, 81 (1963).

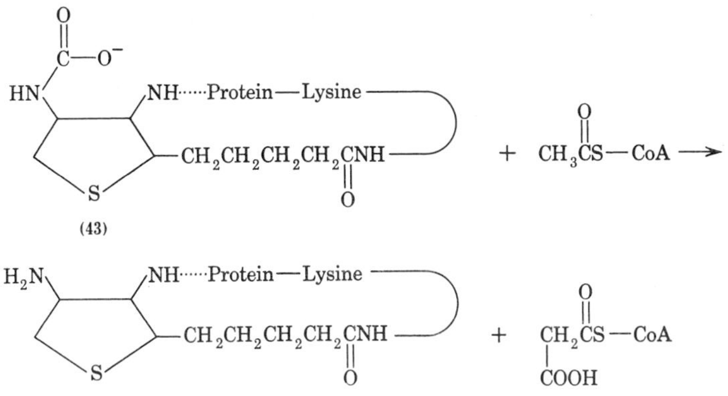

$$\text{HN(C(=O)O}^-\text{)}\cdots\text{NH}\cdots\text{Protein—Lysine—}\text{CH}_2\text{CH}_2\text{CH}_2\text{CH}_2\text{C(=O)NH} \quad (43) \quad + \quad \text{CH}_3\text{C(=O)S—CoA} \longrightarrow$$

$$\text{H}_2\text{N}\cdots\text{NH}\cdots\text{Protein—Lysine—}\text{CH}_2\text{CH}_2\text{CH}_2\text{CH}_2\text{C(=O)NH} \quad (44) \quad + \quad \text{HOOC—CH}_2\text{C(=O)S—CoA}$$

The biotin dependence of such carboxylation-decarboxylation systems and the role of biotin in fatty acid and carbohydrate metabolism are now understood in terms of the substrate acid being an acyl coenzyme A derivative and the carboxylating agent being an *N*-carboxylated derivative of either biotin or "descarbonyl biotin." The reaction is visualized as proceeding by carboxylation at the α-carbanion or at a vinylogous α-carbanion of the substrate with concomitant cleavage of ATP to ADP and inorganic phosphate.

7. Nutritional and Therapeutic Role

A. In Animals

Rats consuming abnormally large quantities of uncooked egg white develop the biotin deficiency syndrome, "egg-white injury,"[6] characterized by an eczema-like dermatitis, an alopecia about the eyes, and paralysis of the hind legs. The deficiency state, characterized by dermatitis and perosis, has been produced in the turkey and in the chick, and experimental avitaminosis has been induced in the dog, calf, pig, monkey, and fish.[76]

B. In the Human

A "natural" biotin avitaminosis appears to have been demonstrated for infants, but not conclusively for the adult human. Clinical manifestations of induced biotin deficiency are generally mild and unspecific. The induced

76. P. György in W. H. Sebrell, Jr. and R. S. Harris, eds., *The Vitamins: Chemistry, Physiology and Pathology*, Vol. 1, Academic, N.Y., 1954, p. 600.

syndrome in man is characterized by a fine nonpruritic dermatitis that disappears in seven to ten days.[77] After the fifth week symptoms such as lassitude, muscular pains, and hyperanesthesia become prominent; at the tenth week patients show signs of anorexia, nausea, anemia, and hypercholesterolemia. Biotin therapy at an average daily dose of 150 μg. caused all symptoms to disappear within five days.

Clinical and experimental studies linking infant seborrheic dermatitis and Leiner's disease to a biotin deficiency have been reviewed recently.[78] These conditions are believed to be different degrees of the same disease with Leiner's disease probably being an intensified form of seborrheic dermatitis. The seborrheic dermatitis occurs most commonly in infants under four years of age and often begins with "cradle cap." This form of the disease is essentially characterized by scaling on an inflammed base usually on the scalp, cheeks, neck, and sometimes around the umbilicus and groin. In Leiner's disease the dermatitis spreads over the entire skin area.

A review of European literature beginning in 1950 shows a marked increase in Leiner's disease and seborrheic dermatitis in Europe after World War II.[78] In Czechoslovakia, favorable response was reported in sixteen cases of Leiner's disease and one case of seborrheic dermatitis after treatment with biotin or meat hydrolyzates;[79] in the same country, twenty-six cases of Leiner's disease were cured with biotin.[80] In Germany, cures were reported in seborrheic dermatitis after the daily oral or parenteral administration of 5 mg. of biotin for three weeks.[81] In France, improvement was noted in six cases of localized seborrhea and four cases of extensive seborrhea after biotin therapy.[82] Seborrheic skin was usually replaced by normal skin about fifteen days after biotin treatment. Dramatic cures were also observed in seborrheic dermatitis when biotin was injected with the other factors of the vitamin B-complex, and a synergism was postulated between biotin and the vitamin B-complex.[83] In Italy, excellent results were reported for the treatment of seven cases of Leiner's disease

77. V. P. Sydenstricker, S. A. Singal, A. P. Briggs, N. M. DeVaughn, and H. Isbell, *Science*, *95*, 176 (1942).
78. A. Nisenson, *J. Pediat.*, *51*, 537 (1957).
79. A. F. Palacky and R. Strycek, *Pediatricke Listy*, *5*, 270 (1950); through *J. Pediat.*, *51*, 537 (1957).
80. J. Svejcar and J. Homolka, *Ann. Paediat.*, *174*, 175 (1950); through *J. Pediat.*, *51*, 537 (1957).
81. S. Kokil, *Ann. Paediat.*, 183, 28 (1954); through *J. Pediat.*, *51*, 537 (1957).
82. C. Martin, *Arch. franc. pediat.*, *8*, 337 (1951); through *J. Pediat.*, *51*, 537 (1957).
83. H. Lemke, *Monatschr. Kinderheilk*, *98*, 350 (1950); through *J. Pediat.*, *51*, 537 (1957).

and five cases of seborrheic dermatitis with biotin; parenteral administration was more effective than oral administration.[84]

In the United States, marked improvement was reported in nine cases of seborrheic dermatitis and two cases of Leiner's disease after biotin therapy.[78] The daily administration of 5 mg. of biotin intramuscularly for one to two weeks was recommended for Leiner's disease; oral administration of 2–4 mg. of biotin for two to three weeks was recommended for mild cases. Parenteral administration of biotin was the method of choice and concomitant daily injections of the vitamin B-complex was also recommended.

Biotin is apparently without effect in the seborrheic dermatitis of the older child and the adult, suggesting that the disease is one of different etiology in these age groups.[78]

The minimum daily biotin requirement has not been established, but diets containing from 150 to 300 μg. of biotin daily are considered adequate.[85] Among the richest sources of biotin are egg yolk, liver, kidney, and yeast. In animal and yeast products the factor is found in a bound, water-insoluble form; in vegetables and plants it is found in a water-soluble form.

84. S. Petrocini and P. Debernardi, *Lattante*, 360 (1954); through *J. Pediat.*, *51*, 537 (1957).
85. *Recommended Dietary Allowances*, Natl. Acad. Sci.-Natl. Res. Council Publ. 589, Washington. D.C., 1958, p. 25.

CHAPTER IX

Pyridoxine and Codecarboxylase

1. Introduction

Early studies on the nature of the "vitamin B_2-complex" were based primarily upon cures for certain dermatoses in the rat; unfortunately, these conditions developed irregularly and were characterized by at least two different types of skin lesions. Before this situation was realized investigators were misled by the lack of a critical assay that could differentiate between the various activities of the "B_2-complex." In 1934 vitamin B_6 activity was defined[1] precisely as "that part of the vitamin B-complex responsible for the cure of a specific dermatitis developed by rats on a vitamin-free diet supplemented with vitamin B_1 and lactoflavin."[2] This condition, previously designated "rat pellagra" during investigations for the factor preventing human pellagra, consisted of a symmetrical florid dermatitis spreading over the limbs and trunk; it was further characterized by swollen red digits and ears. In contrast, the dermatological condition related to riboflavine deficiency appeared on the head and chest and was characterized by inflammation about the eyelids and nostrils.

With this definition of an "acrodynia-like" dermatitis to measure vitamin B_6 activity, only a few years spanned the gap between the recognition of activity and the isolation, characterization, and synthesis of pyridoxol. By 1936 significant purification studies on vitamin B_6 activity were described, and an account was given of the behavior of this activity after the materials were treated with various chemical reagents.[2] With this information, progress on the purification and isolation of pyridoxol was rapid, and within the first five months of 1938 five research groups reported the isolation of crystalline salts.[3–7] Although the salts originally isolated by

1. P. György, *Nature*, *133*, 498 (1934).
2. T. W. Birch and P. György, *Biochem. J.*, *30*, 304 (1936).
3. J. C. Keresztesy and J. R. Stevens, *Proc. Soc. Exptl. Biol. Med.*, *38*, 64 (1938).
4. S. Lepkovsky, *Science*, *87*, 169 (1938).
5. R. Kuhn and G. Wendt, *Ber.*, *71*, 780 (1938).
6. P. György, *J. Am. Chem. Soc.*, *60*, 983 (1938).
7. A. Ichiba and K. Michi, *Sci. Papers Inst. Phys. Chem. Res.* (*Tokyo*), *34*, 623 (1938); *Chem. Abstracts*, *32*, 7534[8] (1938).

these workers were of 4,5-di-(hydroxymethyl)-3-hydroxy-2-methylpyridine (**1**), later investigation of vitamin B_6 activity revealed the additional active companion compounds, pyridoxal (**2**), pyridoxamine (**3**), pyridoxal phosphate (**4**), and pyridoxamine phosphate (**5**). Recognition of the multiple forms of the vitamin made it more appropriate to use the designations vitamin B_6 and pyridoxine for the group and to designate each characterized member of the group with a generic name. Today the term

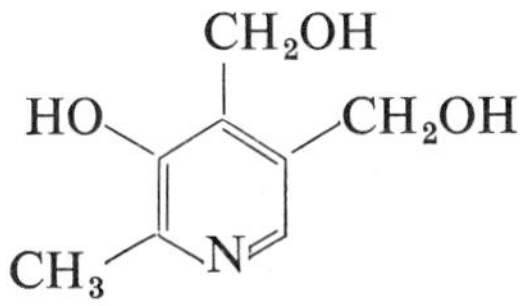

(1) 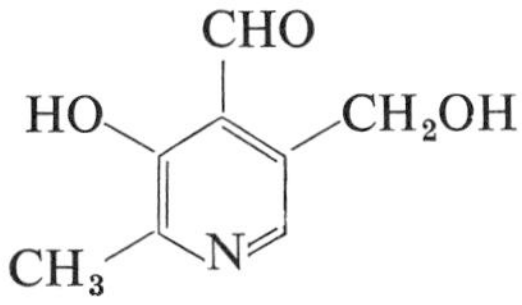 **(2)**

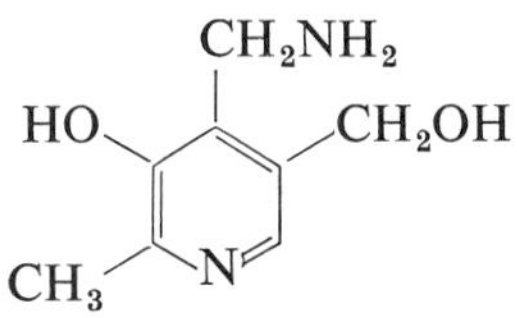

(3) 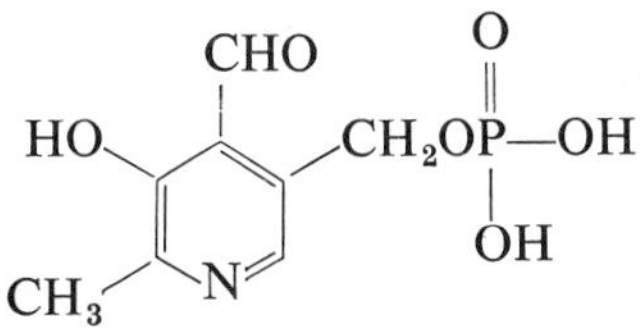 **(4)**

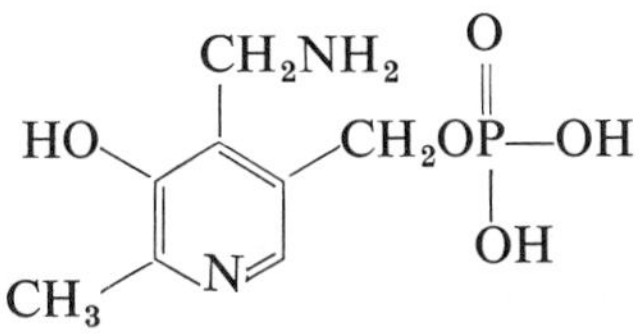

(5)

pyridoxine is generally used to designate this group of naturally occurring pyridine derivatives.

2. Isolation

Pyridoxol, originally designated pyridoxine, was isolated from rice bran[3,4,7,8] and from yeast.[5,6] The factor was removed from extracts by adsorption on either fuller's earth or charcoal and was eluted with a base, usually barium hydroxide. Impurities were generally precipitated as heavy metal salts, and the factor was purified as a crystalline phosphotungstate. Final stages of purification were accomplished by fractional crystallization, and the vitamin was isolated either as a hydrochloride or the free base.

8. S. Lepkovsky, *J. Biol. Chem.*, *124*, 125 (1938).

A typical procedure for the isolation of pyridoxol from rice bran follows.[8] The factor in a rice bran extract was adsorbed on fuller's earth and then eluted with aqueous barium hydroxide. The alkaline solution was concentrated under reduced pressure, barium ion was precipitated as the sulfate, and the extract was concentrated to a syrup. The factor was dissolved in ethanol, and the alcoholic solution was treated first with solid barium hydroxide and then with mercuric chloride to remove accompanying impurities. The alcoholic filtrate was concentrated, diluted with water, and the solution was filtered. Alcohol was removed by distillation, barium ion was precipitated as the sulfate, and mercuric ion as the sulfide. Excess hydrochloric acid generated in solution was neutralized with lead hydroxide, and excess lead ion was removed as the sulfide. The factor was precipitated from solution as the phosphotungstate. The phosphotungstate was purified by recrystallization from water and was decomposed with barium hydroxide; after barium phosphotungstate was removed by filtration and excess barium ion was removed as the sulfate, the filtrate was concentrated under reduced pressure yielding a thin syrup. The factor was finally crystallized from ethanol-acetone solution.

By another procedure, the vitamin-protein complex of Münchner Löwenbraü yeast was purified by low temperature dialysis prior to thermal treatment which liberated the vitamin.[5] The vitamin was converted to a chloroform-soluble acetyl derivative which was extracted. After purification by recrystallization, the derivative was hydrolyzed with hydrochloric acid and yielded a crystalline hydrochloride.

In another method a yeast side fraction obtained during the purification of thiamine was concentrated by fuller's earth adsorption and elution with barium hydroxide.[6] Accompanying impurities were precipitated with aqueous platinic chloride, and the factor was precipitated as the phosphotungstate. The vitamin was then isolated as the free base.

3. Structure Determination

The structure of pyridoxol was established as 4,5-di-(hydroxymethyl)-3-hydroxy-2-methylpyridine (**1**) by degradation. Proof of structure was provided by two independent groups. The first group proposed this structure on the basis of the following data.[9] The substance $C_8H_{11}NO_3$ is an optically inactive base that is stable to acid and alkali. It contains a *C*-methyl group, an aromatic hydroxyl group, and three active hydrogen atoms; there was no evidence for an alkoxyl or alkylamino group, and the

9. E. T. Stiller, J. C. Keresztesy, and J. R. Stevens, *J. Am. Chem. Soc.*, *61*, 1237 (1939).

compound did not react with nitrous acid. From these data, it was assumed that the nitrogen atom is tertiary and bound in a cyclic system. Treatment of the substance with ferric chloride gave a red color similar to that produced by the action of ferric chloride on 3-hydroxypyridine. The pK_b of pyridoxol was of the same order as that of 3-hydroxypyridine, and variations in the ultraviolet absorption spectrum of pyridoxol with changing pH were analogous to those observed with three 3-hydroxypyridine derivatives. Consequently, it was assumed that pyridoxol was a substituted 3-hydroxypyridine.

The nature and location of the other functional groups were established by oxidation. Treatment of pyridoxol with diazomethane yielded the methyl ether (**6**) which consumed about four equivalents of potassium permanganate, yielding the lactone (**7**) and the dibasic acid (**8**). The pK_a

Pyridoxol (1) $\xrightarrow{CH_2N_2}$

CH_2OH, CH_3O, CH_2OH, CH_3, N $\xrightarrow{KMnO_4}$

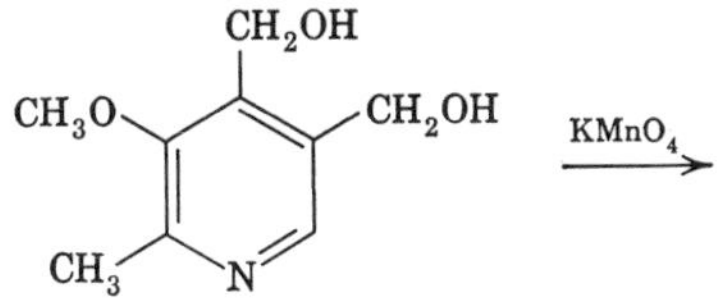

(6)

CH_2—O, C=O, CH_3O, CH_3, N + COOH, CH_3O, COOH, CH_3, N

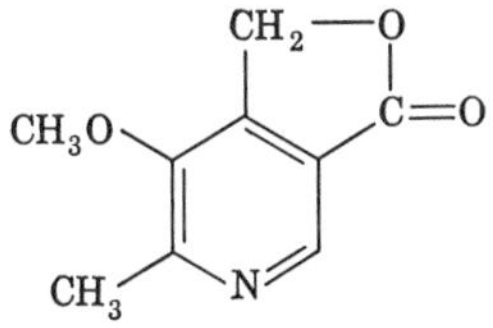

(7) 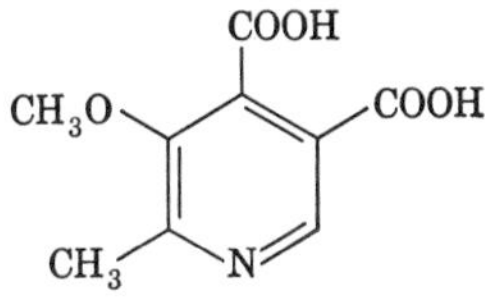 (8)

and ultraviolet absorption spectrum of the dibasic acid were similar to those of 2,6-dimethylcinchomeronic acid (**9**). A vicinal relationship of carboxyl groups was also evident by the reaction of the dibasic acid (**8**)

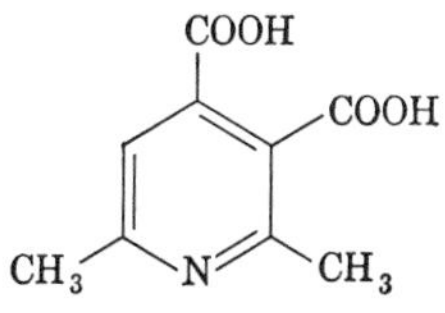

COOH, COOH, CH_3, N, CH_3

(9)

with resorcinol yielding a yellow fluorescent phthalein. Neither carboxyl group of the dibasic acid was in the 2-, or 6-position since the dibasic acid

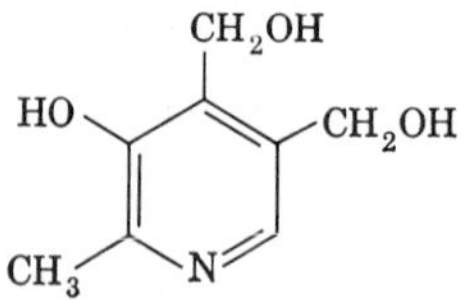

(1) 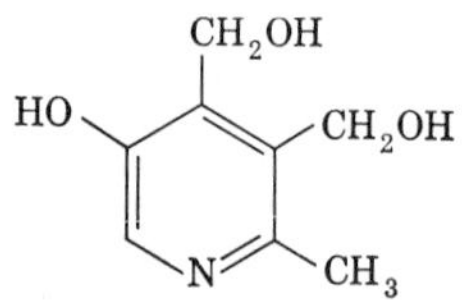 (10)

failed to give a color on treatment with ferrous sulfate. Based on these data, the carboxyl groups were assigned to the 4- and 5-positions of the 3-hydroxypyridine nucleus of the dicarboxylic acid.

Since the dibasic acid was derived from pyridoxol by the addition of two oxygen atoms and the loss of four hydrogen atoms, it was assumed that the 4- and 5-positions of pyridoxol were occupied by hydroxymethyl groups. At this stage of the study the structure of pyridoxol was restricted to the two possibilities 4,5-di-(hydroxymethyl)-3-hydroxy-2-methylpyridine

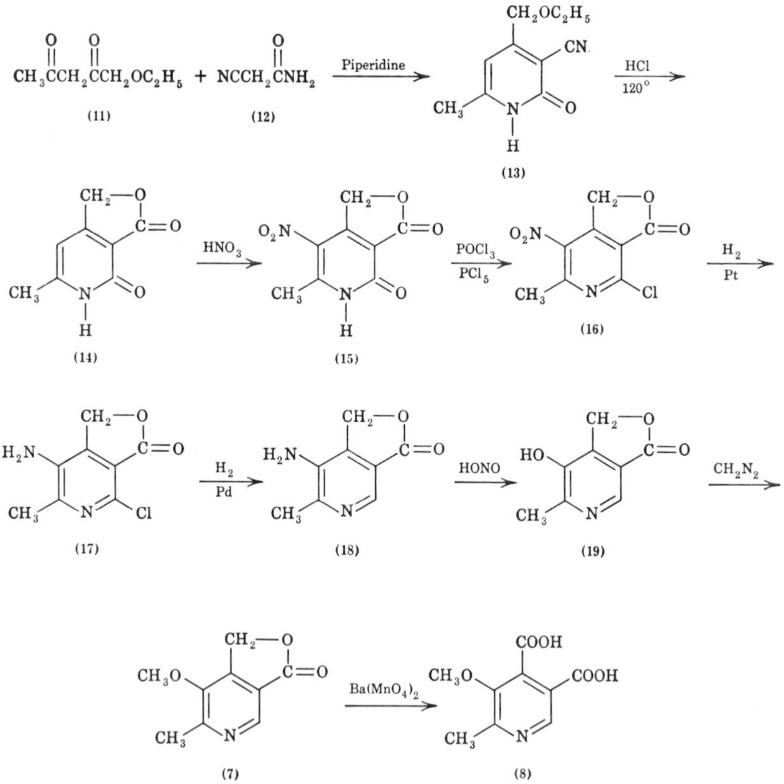

Fig. 1. Synthesis of pyridoxol degradation products.[10]

(**1**) and 4,5-di-(hydroxymethyl)-3-hydroxy-6-methylpyridine (**10**). A 2-methyl group was indicated by the Gibb's indophenol test. Treatment of pyridoxol with 2,6-dichloroquinonechloroimide in alkaline solution gave a blue color; since *para*-substituted phenols do not normally give a blue color with this reagent, the 6-position of pyridoxol was assumed to be unsubstituted and structure (**1**) was assigned to the vitamin.

Synthesis (Fig. 1) of the lactone (**7**) and the dibasic acid (**8**), starting with α-acetyl-α′-ethoxyacetone (**11**) and cyanoacetamide (**12**), confirmed these structural conclusions.[10] Condensation of these two reagents catalyzed by piperidine yielded 3-cyano-4-ethoxymethyl-6-methyl-2-pyridone (**13**) which was treated with hot hydrochloric acid to give the lactone (**14**) of 3-carboxy-4-hydroxymethyl-6-methyl-2-pyridone. The latter compound was converted to the 5-nitro derivative (**15**) which was treated with phosphorus oxychloride and phosphorus pentachloride to yield the lactone (**16**) of 6-chloro-4-hydroxymethyl-2-methyl-3-nitropyridine-5-carboxylic acid. Catalytic reduction yielded the 3-amino derivative (**17**), which was converted by hydrogenolysis to the lactone (**18**) of 3-amino-4-hydroxymethyl-2-methylpyridine-5-carboxylic acid. Diazotization of this intermediate, followed by hydrolysis and then methylation with diazomethane yielded the same lactone (**7**) as encountered during degradation studies. Oxidation of this lactone by barium permanganate yielded 3-methoxy-2-methylpyridine-4,5-dicarboxylic acid (**8**), which was identical with the dicarboxylic acid obtained during degradation studies.

The structure of pyridoxol was independently established by the following oxidative and synthetic studies.[11–14] Mild permanganate oxidation of the monomethyl ether of pyridoxol (**6**) yielded the lactone (**7**), constituting evidence for a vicinal relationship of the original hydroxymethyl groups in pyridoxol. The *C*-methyl group of pyridoxol was located at the 2-position of the pyridine nucleus by alkaline potassium permanganate oxidation of the methyl ether (**6**) to the tricarboxylic acid (**20**); since the latter gave a red color on treatment with ferrous sulfate, at least one carboxyl group of the tricarboxylic acid was in the 2- or 6-position of the pyridine nucleus. Monodecarboxylation and dehydration of the tricarboxylic acid yielded the anhydride (**21**), which failed to give a red color with ferrous sulfate; consequently, neither of the vicinal carboxyl

10. S. A. Harris, E. T. Stiller, and K. Folkers, *J. Am. Chem. Soc.*, *61*, 1242 (1939).
11. R. Kuhn and G. Wendt, *Ber.*, *72*, 305 (1939).
12. R. Kuhn, H. Andersag, K. Westphal, and G. Wendt, *Ber.*, *72*, 309 (1939).
13. R. Kuhn, G. Wendt, and K. Westphal, *Ber.*, *72*, 310 (1939).
14. R. Kuhn, K. Westphal, G. Wendt, and O. Westphal, *Naturwissenschaften*, *27*, 469 (1939).

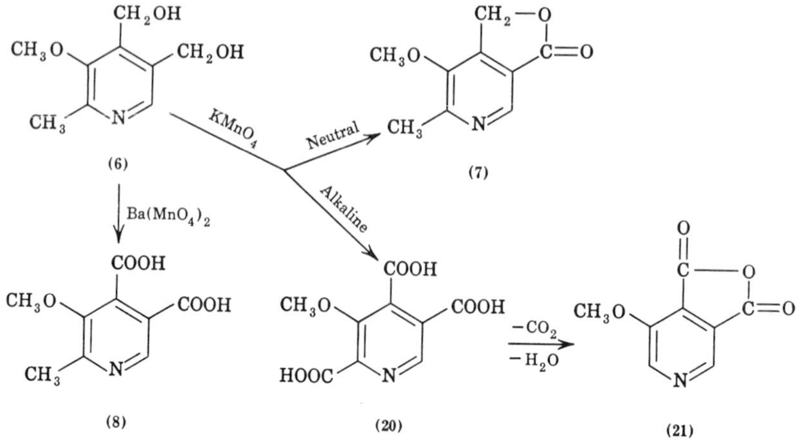

(6) (7) (8) (20) (21)

groups was in the 2- or 6-position. Since the tricarboxylic acid was obtained only by vigorous oxidation, it was assumed that the carboxyl group responsible for the positive ferrous sulfate test of the tricarboxylic acid was derived from a 2-methyl group in the pyridine nucleus.

The aromatic hydroxyl group of pyridoxol was established in the 3-position of the pyridine nucleus by a positive reaction with the Folin-Denis reagent. It had already been shown that 3-hydroxypyridine derivatives give a deep blue color with this reagent and that 2- and 4-hydroxypyridine derivatives do not give such colored products. In the final assignment of structure, the 4- and 5-positions of the pyridine ring were designated for the vicinal hydroxymethyl groups.

These structural conclusions were confirmed by a synthesis of 3-methoxy-2-methylpyridine-4,5-dicarboxylic acid (**8**) from 4-methoxy-3-methylisoquinoline (**22**).[14] Nitration of the latter yielded a mononitro compound, most probably the 5-nitro derivative (**23**), which was reduced to the corresponding amine (**24**). Oxidation of this intermediate with

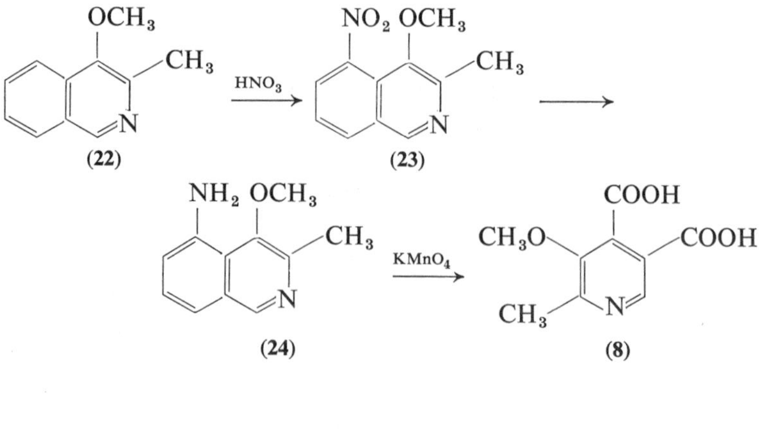

(**22**) (**23**) (**24**) (**8**)

potassium permanganate yielded the dibasic acid (**8**) identical with the product obtained from the oxidation of pyridoxol methyl ether (**6**) by barium permanganate.

4. Synthesis

Pyridoxol was synthesized by starting with the piperidine-catalyzed condensation (Fig. 2) of α-acetyl-α'-ethoxyacetone (**11**) and cyanoacetamide (**12**).[15–17] The condensation product, 3-cyano-4-ethoxymethyl-6-

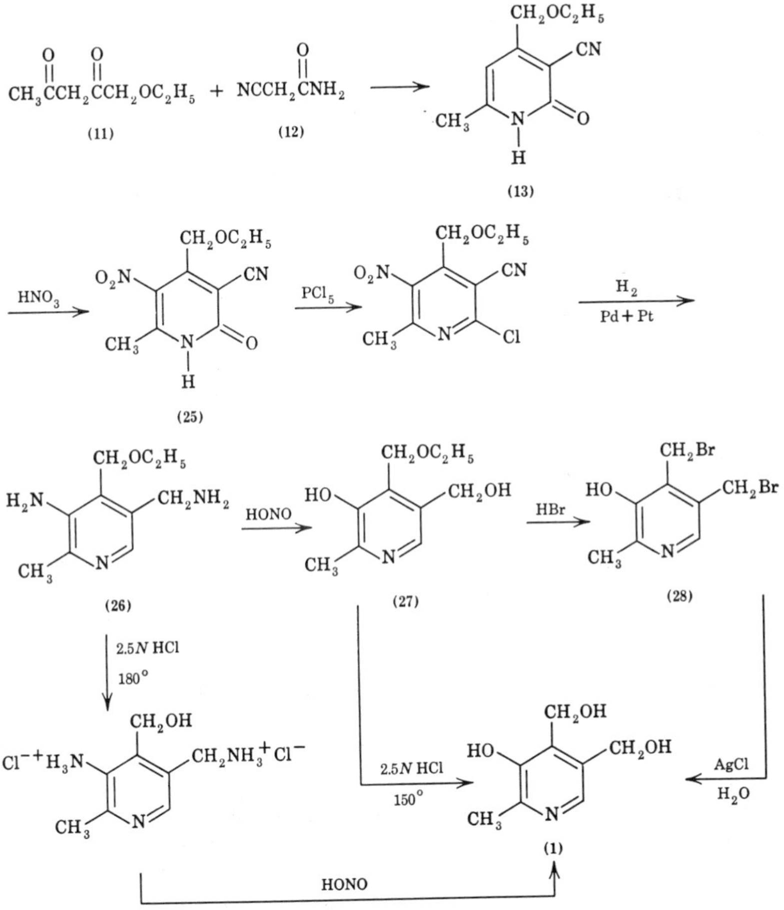

Fig. 2. Synthesis of pyridoxol.[15–17]

15. S. A. Harris and K. Folkers, *Science*, *89*, 347 (1939).
16. S. A. Harris and K. Folkers, *J. Am. Chem. Soc.*, *61*, 1245 (1939).
17. S. A. Harris and K. Folkers, *J. Am. Chem. Soc.*, *61*, 3307 (1939).

methyl-2-pyridone (**13**), was converted to the 5-nitro-2-pyridone derivative (**25**) which was chlorinated and then reduced to 3-amino-5-aminomethyl-4-ethoxymethyl-2-methylpyridine (**26**). On diazotization, this diamino intermediate was converted to 4-ethoxymethyl-3-hydroxy-5-hydroxymethyl-2-methylpyridine (**27**) which was converted to pyridoxol through the intermediate dibromide (**28**). Variations and improvements in this method,[17] starting with the key compound 3-amino-5-aminomethyl-4-ethoxymethyl-2-methylpyridine (**26**) eliminated the use of constant boiling hydrobromic acid for ether cleavage and subsequent hydrolysis of the intermediate dibromide (**28**); cleavage of the ethers (**26**) or (**27**) with dilute hydrochloric acid at 150° under pressure yielded the corresponding 4-hydroxymethyl compounds directly.

Another approach (Fig. 3) to synthesis started with 3-methoxy-2-methylpyridine-4,5-dicarboxylic acid (**8**).[14] The carboxyl groups were converted to nitrile groups which were reduced to aminomethyl groups; these were diazotized and hydrolyzed to hydroxymethyl groups. The synthesis was completed by cleavage of the *O*-methyl group with hydrobromic acid and hydrolysis of the resulting dibromide in the presence of silver acetate to give pyridoxol.

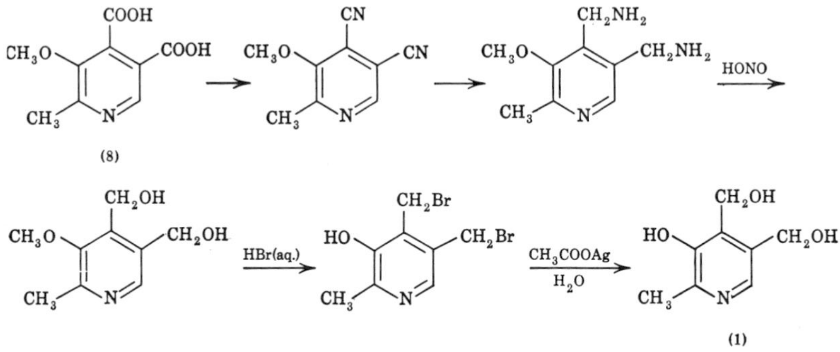

Fig. 3. Synthesis of pyridoxol from a degradation product.[14]

Until the 1950's most syntheses of pyridoxol required that at least one of the two hydroxymethyl groups be derived from a nitrile group by reduction and subsequent diazotization. The nitrile groups were either derived from carboxyl groups or were introduced during the initial condensation step. The advent of the powerful and specific complex metal hydrides, however, provided an excellent opportunity for simplified syntheses of pyridoxol.[18,19] For example, a study of the lithium aluminum

18. R. G. Jones and E. C. Kornfeld, *J. Am. Chem. Soc.*, *73*, 107 (1951).
19. H. M. Wuest, J. A. Bigot, T. J. DeBoer, B. v.d. Wal, and J. P. Wibaut, *Rec. Trav. Chim.*, *78*, 226 (1959).

hydride reduction of vicinal diesters of heterocyclic compounds provided a facile method for converting diester precursors directly to pyridoxol.[18] Reduction of dimethyl 3-hydroxy-2-methylpyridine-4,5-dicarboxylate (**29**) and dimethyl 3-acetoxy-2-methylpyridine-4,5-dicarboxylate (**30**) by lithium

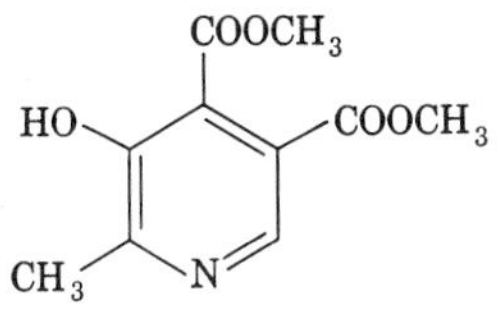

(29) 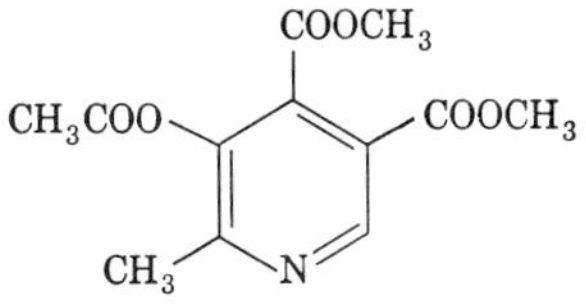 (30)

aluminum hydride gave pyridoxol in yields of about 80%. Likewise, 3-amino-4,5-di-(hydroxymethyl)-2-methylpyridine (**32**) was synthesized in 90% yield by reduction of dimethyl 3-amino-2-methylpyridine-4,5-dicarboxylate (**31**) with lithium aluminum hydride.

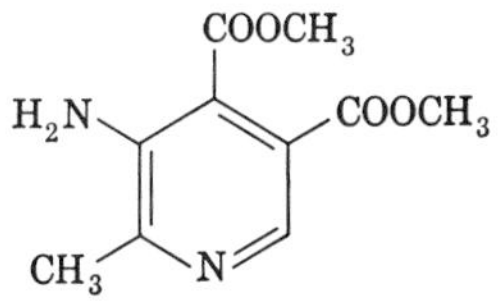

(31) 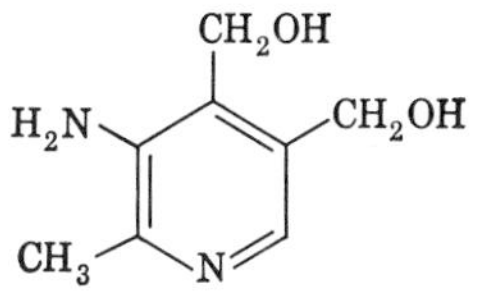 (32)

Several effective syntheses of pyridoxol proceed by the addition of a suitably substituted dienophile to 5-ethoxy-4-methyloxazole (**32b**).[19a] The requisite oxazole derivative was synthesized from ethyl *N*-formyl-*DL*-alaninate (**32a**).

The addition of diethyl maleate to 5-ethoxy-4-methyloxazole yielded the adduct (**32c**) which on treatment with hydrogen chloride in ethanol yielded diethyl 3-hydroxy-2-methylpyridine-4,5-dicarboxylate (**32d**). Reduction of the diester with lithium aluminum hydride yielded pyridoxol.

The reaction of fumaronitrile with 5-ethoxy-4-methyloxazole gave the adduct (**32e**), which yielded 4,5-dicyano-3-hydroxy-2-methylpyridine after treatment with concentrated hydrochloric acid. The dicyano intermediate was converted to 4,5-di-(aminomethyl)-3-hydroxy-2-methylpyridine (**32f**) by reduction, and the di-(aminomethyl) intermediate was diazotized in water to yield pyridoxol.

The condensation of 2,5-dihydrofuran with 5-ethoxy-4-methyloxazole at elevated temperature and pressure and in the presence of trichloroacetic

19a. E. E. Harris, R. A. Firestone, K. Pfister, 3rd, R. R. Boettcher, F. J. Cross, R. B. Currie, M. Monaco, E. R. Peterson, and W. Reuter, *J. Org. Chem.*, *27*, 2705, (1962).

$CH_3CHCOOC_2H_5$ — NH — HC=O (**32a**) $\xrightarrow{1.\ P_2O_5;\ 2.\ KOH}$ C_2H_5O, CH_3, O, N (**32b**)

$CHCOOC_2H_5$ ‖ $CHCOOC_2H_5$ → $COOC_2H_5$, C_2H_5O, $COOC_2H_5$, O, CH_3, N (**32c**) $\xrightarrow{H^+}$ $COOC_2H_5$, HO, $COOC_2H_5$, CH_3, N (**32d**) $\xrightarrow{LiAlH_4}$ (**1**)

CHCN ‖ CHCN → CN, C_2H_5O, CN, O, CH_3, N (**32e**) $\xrightarrow{1.\ H^+;\ 2.\ H_2/Pd}$ CH_2NH_2, HO, CH_2NH_2, CH_3, N (**32f**) $\xrightarrow{HONO}$ CH_2OH, HO, CH_2OH, CH_3, N (**1**)

(2,5-dihydrofuran, O) → CH_2—O, CH_2, C_2H_5O, CH_3, N (**32g**) $\xrightarrow{HBr\ (aq.)}$ CH_2Br, HO, CH_2Br, CH_3, N (**28**) $\xrightarrow{OH^-}$ (**1**)

acid yielded the cyclic ether derivative (**32g**) of pyridoxol, which on treatment with hydrobromic acid yielded 4,5-di-(bromomethyl)-3-hydroxy-2-methylpyridine (**28**). Hydrolysis of the latter intermediate yielded pyridoxol.

5. Pyridoxamine and Pyridoxal

The existence of one or more pyridoxol-like substances in natural materials with even greater growth-promoting activity than pyridoxol was proposed during a study of the growth-promoting activity of pyridoxol for lactic acid bacteria.[20] This activity was designated "pseudopyridoxine." About two years later it was shown that simple amination and mild oxidation reactions greatly enhanced the activity of pyridoxol as a growth factor for these organisms.[21–23] Syntheses in the same year established the biologically active amine and aldehyde forms as 4-aminomethyl-3-hydroxy-5-hydroxymethyl-2-methylpyridine (**3**) and 4-formyl-3-hydroxy-5-hydroxymethyl-2-methylpyridine (**2**), respectively.[24,25]

A. Pyridoxamine

Pyridoxamine (**3**) was synthesized by the amination of either pyridoxol diacetate (**33**) or 3-hydroxy-5-hydroxymethyl-4-methoxymethyl-2-methylpyridine (**34**) with ammonia in methanol solution at 140°; the synthetic

(33) $\xrightarrow{NH_3}$ (3) $\xleftarrow{NH_3}$ (34)

amine was biologically active.[24,25] Further confirmation of the identity of the active amine was established by the synthesis (Fig. 4) of the inactive isomer 5-aminomethyl-3-hydroxy-4-hydroxymethyl-2-methylpyridine (**38**).

(34) $\xrightarrow{SOCl_2}$ (35) $\xrightarrow{NH_3}$ (36) $\xrightarrow[170^\circ]{HCl\ (aq.)}$ (37) $\xrightarrow{NaHCO_3}$ (38)

Fig. 4. Synthesis of an inactive isomer of pyridoxamine.[24,25]

20. E. E. Snell, B. M. Guirard, and R. J. Williams, *J. Biol. Chem.*, *143*, 519 (1942).
21. E. E. Snell, *J. Biol. Chem.*, *154*, 313 (1944).
22. E. E. Snell, *J. Am. Chem. Soc.*, *66*, 2082 (1944).
23. L. E. Carpenter and F. M. Strong, *Arch. Biochem.*, *3*, 375 (1944).
24. S. A. Harris, D. Heyl, and K. Folkers, *J. Am. Chem. Soc.*, *66*, 2088 (1944).
25. S. A. Harris, D. Heyl, and K. Folkers, *J. Biol. Chem.*, *154*, 315 (1944).

3-Hydroxy-5-hydroxymethyl-4-methoxymethyl-2-methylpyridine (**34**) was converted to the 5-chloromethyl derivative (**35**). Amination followed by cleavage of the methoxyl group gave the dihydrochloride (**37**), which was treated with sodium bicarbonate solution to yield 5-aminomethyl-3-hydroxy-4-hydroxymethyl-2-methylpyridine (**38**). This isomeric amine not only differed from pyridoxamine in chemical properties, but also had no significant activity in promoting growth of lactic acid bacteria.

B. Pyridoxal

Pyridoxal (**2**) was synthesized by the oxidation of pyridoxol with potassium permanganate and was isolated as the oxime (**39**).[24,25] Treatment of the oxime with sodium nitrite and hydrochloric acid gave pyridoxal; it may exist either as the aldehyde (**2**) or as the cyclic acetal (**40**).

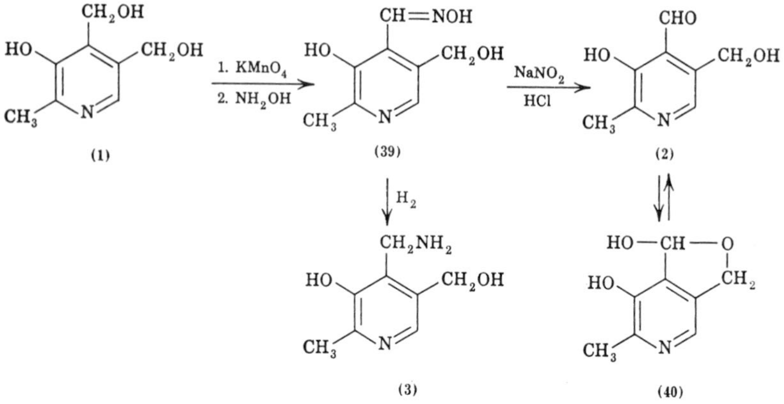

Fig. 5. Synthesis and proof of structure of pyridoxal.[24,25]

The formyl group of pyridoxal was established (Fig. 5) in the 4-position by the catalytic hydrogenation of pyridoxal oxime (**39**) to pyridoxamine (**3**).

6. Metabolic Role

The coenzyme form of vitamin B_6 activity is now established as pyridoxal phosphate. This compound, designated codecarboxylase, is responsible for all nonoxidative enzymic amino acid transformations and catalyzes such reactions as decarboxylation, transamination, racemization, β-elimination, and γ-elimination in amino acid metabolism.

A. Codecarboxylase—Discovery, Structure, and Synthesis

In 1944 an enzyme exhibiting retarded ability to decarboxylate tyrosine was isolated from *Streptococcus faecalis* R which was grown in a "pseudo-pyridoxine"-deficient medium.[26] The enzymic activity of this preparation was increased only slightly by the addition of pyridoxal, but a marked increased rate of tyrosine decarboxylation was observed after the addition of pyridoxal and adenosine triphosphate. The same activation was also observed when phosphorylated pyridoxal alone was added to the enzyme preparation. In the following year, tyrosine decarboxylase was isolated from *S. faecalis* R, and its coenzyme portion was characterized as a pyridoxal derivative.[27] The coenzyme codecarboxylase, which was previously isolated[28] from yeast, was also shown to be a derivative of pyridoxal.[27] It was replaced in a variety of enzyme systems by coenzymes synthesized or biosynthesized from pyridoxal; on hydrolysis it yielded a compound that behaved as pyridoxal in the tyrosine decarboxylase system from *S. faecalis* R. Codecarboxylase was also shown to function as a coenzyme for the decarboxylation of arginine.[29] Consequently, the concept of a coenzyme function for this pyridoxal derivative was extended to include α-amino acid decarboxylases in general.[29,30]

On the basis of biological and chemical syntheses of codecarboxylase, it was assumed that the coenzyme was a phosphorylated pyridoxal and it was designated pyridoxal phosphate.[29] The coenzyme was synthesized in low yield by the action of phosphorus oxychloride on pyridoxal in the presence of water[31] and was isolated from the reaction mixture as the calcium salt.[32] On the basis of analytical data, pyridoxal phosphate could have either of the three structures (**4**), (**41**), or (**42**). Its structure was established as 4-formyl-3-hydroxy-2-methyl-5-pyridinylmethylphosphoric acid (**4**) as follows.[32]

The structure (**41**) depicting a phosphorylated aromatic hydroxyl group was eliminated on the basis of (a) positive ferric chloride color tests for a free aromatic hydroxyl group with both the calcium salt and the oxime of pyridoxal phosphate and (b) synthesis of the oxime (**45**) of 3-pyridoxal-phosphoric acid.[33] Synthesis of the latter was accomplished by converting

26. I. C. Gunsalus, W. D. Bellamy, and W. W. Umbreit, *J. Biol. Chem.*, *155*, 685 (1944).
27. W. W. Umbreit, W. D. Bellamy, and I. C. Gunsalus, *Arch. Biochem.*, *7*, 185 (1945).
28. E. F. Gale and H. M. R. Epps, *Biochem. J.*, *38*, 250 (1944).
29. W. W. Umbreit and I. C. Gunsalus, *J. Biol. Chem.*, *159*, 333 (1945).
30. J. Baddiley and E. F. Gale, *Nature*, *155*, 727 (1945).
31. I. C. Gunsalus, W. W. Umbreit, W. D. Bellamy, and C. E. Foust, *J. Biol. Chem.*, *161*, 745 (1945).
32. D. Heyl, E. Luz, S. A. Harris, and K. Folkers, *J. Am. Chem. Soc.*, *73*, 3430 (1951).
33. D. Heyl and S. A. Harris, *J. Am. Chem. Soc.*, *73*, 3434 (1951).

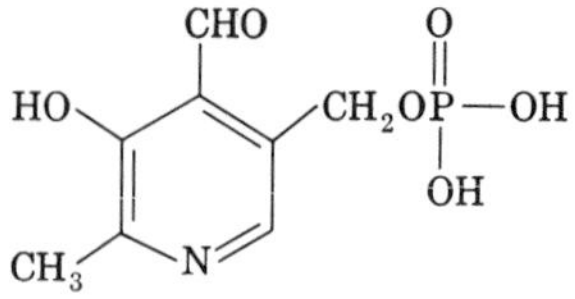

(4)

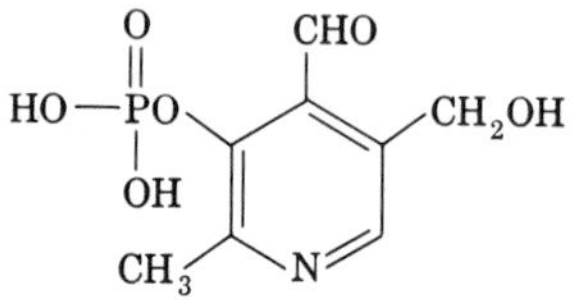

(41)

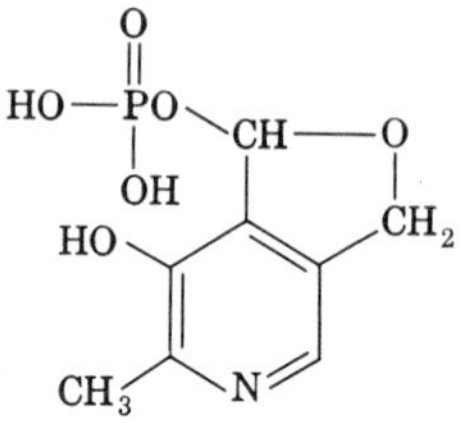

(42)

pyridoxal monoethylacetal (**43**) to the corresponding monoethylacetal (**44**) of 3-pyridoxalphosphoric acid; the final step was accomplished by acid hydrolysis of the acetal group in the presence of hydroxylamine hydrochloride.

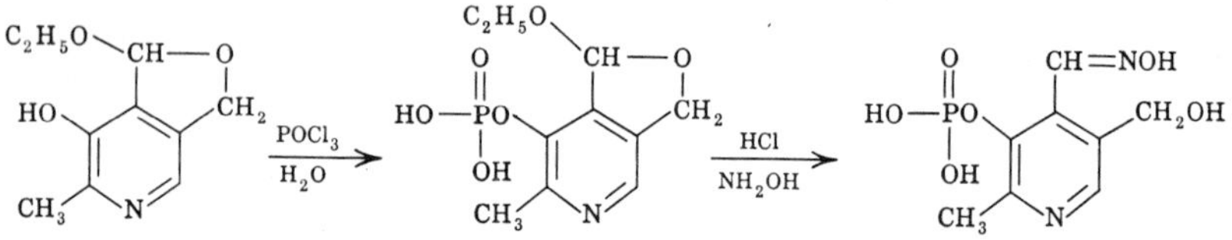

$POCl_3$, H_2O; HCl, NH_2OH

(43) (44) (45)

The structure (**42**) containing a phosphorylated hemiacetal carbon atom at the 4-position was eliminated from further consideration since the same oxime (**46**) of pyridoxal phosphate was synthesized either (a) by the phosphorylation of pyridoxal oxime (**39**) or (b) by the oxidation of pyridoxol phosphate (**47**) followed by conversion to the oxime

Although only structure (**4**) remained to account for pyridoxal phosphate, there were two properties of the substance that required further study. Pyridoxal phosphate does not give a positive Gibb's indophenol test; this indicated the absence of a "free" aromatic hydroxyl group in the usual sense. The second anomaly became apparent when the maxima of the ultraviolet absorption spectrum of pyridoxal phosphate in alkaline solution were observed to shift to longer wavelengths than those of pyridoxal. Both properties were explained, however, on the basis of the existence of a keto-form (**48**) of pyridoxal phosphate at certain pH's.

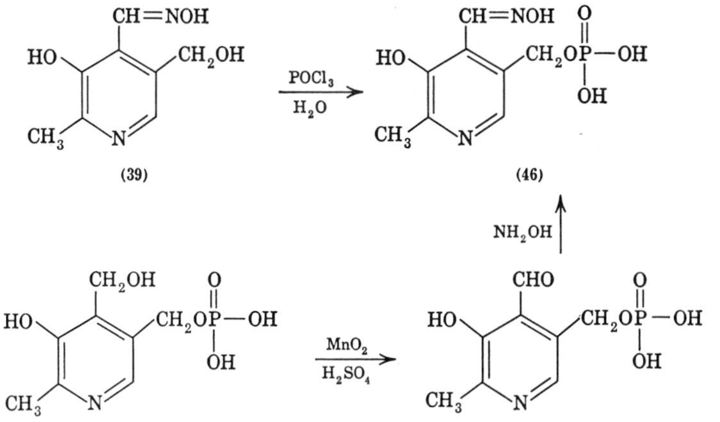

CH=NOH HO CH₂OH CH₃ N (39) $\xrightarrow[H_2O]{POCl_3}$ CH=NOH O HO $CH_2OP(O)(OH)-OH$ CH₃ N (46)

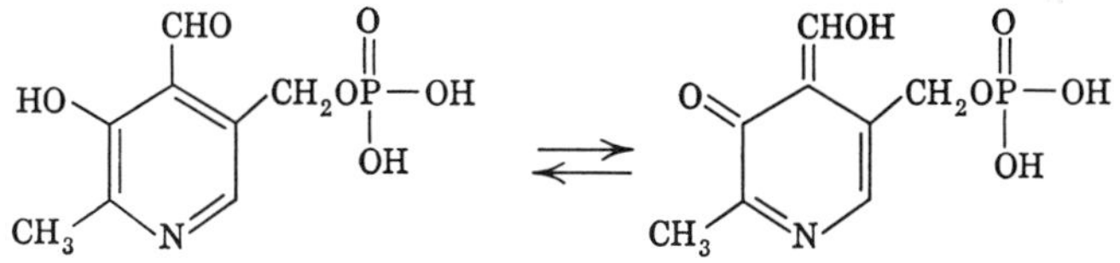

NH_2OH ↑

CH_2OH O HO $CH_2OP(O)(OH)-OH$ CH_3 N (47) $\xrightarrow[H_2SO_4]{MnO_2}$ CHO O HO $CH_2OP(O)(OH)-OH$ CH_3 N (4)

CHO O HO $CH_2OP(O)(OH)-OH$ CH_3 N (4) $\rightleftharpoons$ CHOH O O= $CH_2OP(O)(OH)-OH$ CH_3 N (48)

Pyridoxal phosphate was synthesized from pyridoxamine.[34] The latter after phosphorylation with anhydrous phosphoric acid gave the intermediate (**50**), which was adsorbed on a column of activated charcoal;

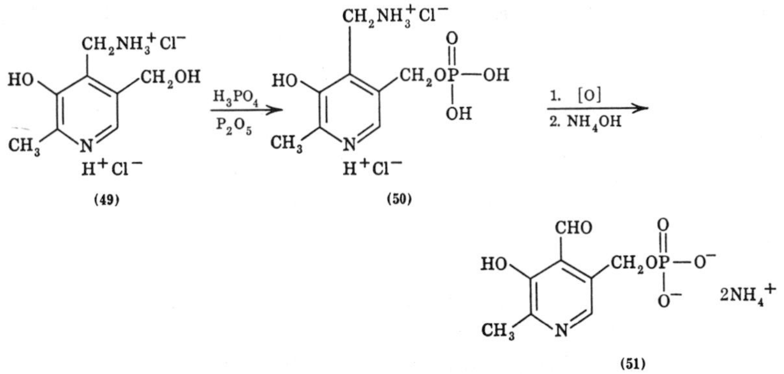

$CH_2NH_3^+Cl^-$ HO CH_2OH CH_3 N H^+Cl^- (49) $\xrightarrow[P_2O_5]{H_3PO_4}$ $CH_2NH_3^+Cl^-$ O HO $CH_2OP(O)(OH)-OH$ CH_3 N H^+Cl^- (50) $\xrightarrow[2.\ NH_4OH]{1.\ [O]}$

CHO O HO $CH_2OP(O)(O^-)-O^-$ $2NH_4^+$ CH_3 N (51)

oxygen adsorbed on the charcoal converted the amino group to a formyl group so that on elution with ammonium hydroxide, the ammonium salt (**51**) of pyridoxal phosphate was obtained. In a similar synthesis, manganese

34. A. N. Wilson and S. A. Harris, *J. Am. Chem. Soc.*, *73*, 4693 (1951).

dioxide was used to oxidize the aminomethyl group to a formyl group, and the crude product was purified by ion exchange chromatography.[35]

The synthesis of pyridoxal phosphate was also accomplished by first converting pyridoxal to the *N,N*-dimethylglycylhydrazone (**53**) which was

HO—CH—O, CH_2, HO, CH_3, N (40)

$(CH_3)_2NCH_2CONHNH_2$ (52) →

CH=N—$NHCOCH_2N(CH_3)_2$, CH_2OH, HO, CH_3, N (53)

$(HPO_3)_3$ →

CH=N—$NHCOCH_2\overset{H}{N}^{+}(CH_3)_2$, HO, CH_3, N, H^+, $CH_2OP(=O)(HO)$—O—$P(=O)(O^-)$—O—$P(=O)(O^-)$—OH (54)

1. HCl+HONO; 2. $Ca(OH)_2$ →

CHO, HO, CH_3, N, $CH_2OP(=O)(O^-)$—O^- Ca^{++} (55)

then phosphorylated with metaphosphoric acid.[36] The resulting triphosphoric acid ester (**54**) was hydrolyzed with hydrochloric acid in the presence of nitrous acid giving pyridoxal phosphate. The product was isolated as the calcium salt (**55**).

B. Codecarboxylase—Coenzyme Reactions

1. TRANSAMINATION REACTIONS. In addition to its role in the enzymic decarboxylation of α-amino acids, pyridoxal phosphate catalyzes other important amino acid transformations. The first clue to its role in enzymic transamination of *L*-α-amino acids came with the observation that tissue of rats raised on pyridoxine-deficient diets had lower transaminase activity than that of rats supplied with adequate amounts of the vitamin.[37] In addition, transaminase activity of tissue from the deficient rat was stimulated by the combined addition of pyridoxal and adenosine triphosphate. The observed nonenzymic interconversion of pyridoxal and pyridoxamine by heating either pyridoxal and glutamic acid or pyridoxamine and α-ketoglutaric acid was also cited as evidence for the role of a pyridoxal derivative in enzymic transamination.[38]

35. E. A. Peterson and H. A. Sober, *J. Am. Chem. Soc.*, *76*, 169 (1954).
36. M. Viscontini, C. Ebnöther, and P. Karrer, *Helv. Chim. Acta*, *34*, 1834 (1951).
37. F. Schlenk and E. E. Snell, *J. Biol. Chem.*, *157*, 425 (1945).
38. E. E. Snell, *J. Am. Chem. Soc.*, *67*, 194 (1945).

Pyridoxal phosphate activates the apoenzyme of the transaminase isolated from *S. faecalis* R; the enzyme catalyzes the glutamic acid (**56**)-aspartic acid (**57**) transamination system.[39] A pure glutamic acid-alanine

$$\left.\begin{array}{r} \mathrm{HOOCCH_2CH_2CH(NH_2)COOH} \\ \mathbf{(56)} \\ \mathrm{HOOCCH_2C(=O)COOH} \end{array}\right\} \rightleftarrows \left\{\begin{array}{l} \mathrm{HOOCCH_2CH_2C(=O)COOH} \\ \\ \mathrm{HOOCCH_2CH(NH_2)COOH} \\ \mathbf{(57)} \end{array}\right.$$

(**59**) transaminase was also isolated and although it was shown to be different from the glutamate-aspartate enzyme,[40] pyridoxal phosphate was present.[39–42] Pyridoxal phosphate was also found to be the coenzyme in

$$\left.\begin{array}{r} \mathrm{HOOCCH_2CH_2CH(NH_2)COOH} \\ \mathbf{(56)} \\ \mathrm{CH_3C(=O)COOH} \end{array}\right\} \rightleftarrows \left\{\begin{array}{l} \mathrm{HOOCCH_2CH_2C(=O)COOH} \\ \mathbf{(58)} \\ \mathrm{CH_3CH(NH_2)COOH} \\ \mathbf{(59)} \end{array}\right.$$

enzymic transaminations between α-ketoglutaric acid (**58**) and the *L*-α-amino acids, aspartic acid, alanine, valine, leucine, norleucine, tryptophan, tyrosine, phenylalanine, and methionine,[43] as well as in transamination systems with α-keto acids such as pyruvic acid, α-ketobutyric acid, and α-ketoisocaproic acid.[44] It is also the coenzyme responsible for the enzymic racemization of *D*- or *L*-alanine[45] and *D*- or *L*-glutamic acid.[46]

2. ELIMINATION REACTIONS. Enzymes containing pyridoxal phosphate catalyze α,β-elimination reactions (Fig. 6) such as the dehydration and

39. H. C. Lichstein, I. C. Gunsalus, and W. W. Umbreit, *J. Biol. Chem.*, *161*, 311 (1945).
40. D. E. Green, L. F. Leloir, and V. Nocito, *J. Biol. Chem.*, *161*, 559 (1945).
41. M. G. Kritzmann and O. Samarina, *Nature*, *158*, 104 (1946).
42. D. E. O'Kane and I. C. Gunsalus, *J. Biol. Chem.*, *170*, 425 (1947).
43. L. I. Feldman and I. C. Gunsalus, *J. Biol. Chem.*, *187*, 821 (1950).
44. E. V. Rowsell, *Nature*, *168*, 104 (1951).
45. W. A. Wood and I. C. Gunsalus, *J. Biol. Chem.*, *190*, 403 (1951).
46. S. A. Narrod and W. A. Wood, *Arch. Biochem. Biophys.*, *35*, 462 (1952).

$$HOCH_2CH(NH_2)COOH \longrightarrow H_2O + \left[\begin{array}{c} CH_2{=}C(NH_2)COOH \\ \upharpoonleft\downharpoonright \\ CH_3C({=}NH)COOH \end{array}\right] \xrightarrow{H_2O} CH_3C({=}O)COOH + NH_3$$

(60)

$$CH_3CH(OH)CH(NH_2)COOH \longrightarrow H_2O + \left[\begin{array}{c} CH_3CH{=}C(NH_2)COOH \\ \upharpoonleft\downharpoonright \\ CH_3CH_2C({=}NH)COOH \end{array}\right] \xrightarrow{H_2O} CH_3CH_2C({=}O)COOH + NH_3$$

(61)

$$HSCH_2CH(NH_2)COOH \longrightarrow H_2S + \left[CH_2{=}C(NH_2)COOH\right] \xrightarrow{H_2O} CH_3C({=}O)COOH + NH_3$$

(62)

$$\text{Indol-3-yl-}CH_2CH(NH_2)COOH \longrightarrow \text{Indole} + \left[CH_2{=}C(NH_2)COOH\right] \xrightarrow{H_2O} CH_3C({=}O)COOH + NH_3$$

(63) (64)

Fig. 6. α,β-Elimination reactions catalyzed by pyridoxal phosphate.[47,48]

subsequent deamination of serine (**60**) and threonine (**61**),[47] the desulfhydration and subsequent deamination of cysteine (**62**),[48] and the cleavage of tryptophan (**63**) to indole (**64**), pyruvic acid, and ammonia.

Pyridoxal phosphate also functions in α,γ-elimination reactions such as the enzymic dehydration and subsequent deamination of homoserine

$$HOCH_2CH_2CH(NH_2)COOH \rightarrow H_2O + \left[CH_3CH_2C({=}NH)COOH\right] \searrow$$

(65)

$$CH_3CH_2C({=}O)COOH + NH_3$$

$$HSCH_2CH_2CH(NH_2)COOH \rightarrow H_2S + \left[CH_3CH_2C({=}NH)COOH\right] \nearrow$$

(66)

47. D. E. Metzler and E. E. Snell, *J. Biol. Chem.*, *198*, 363 (1952).
48. R. E. Kallio, *J. Biol. Chem.*, *192*, 371 (1951).

(65),[49] and the enzymic desulfhydration and subsequent deamination of homocysteine **(66)**.[48]

The enzymic cleavage of cystathione **(67)** to cysteine **(61)** and α-keto-butyric acid or to homocysteine **(66)** and pyruvic acid are also α,γ- and

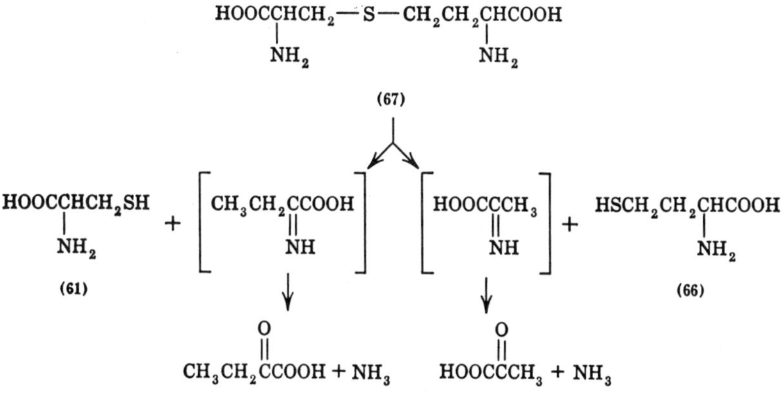

$HOOCCH(NH_2)CH_2{-}S{-}CH_2CH_2CH(NH_2)COOH$

(67)

$HOOCCH(NH_2)CH_2SH$ **(61)** + $[CH_3CH_2C({=}NH)COOH]$ → $CH_3CH_2C({=}O)COOH + NH_3$

$[HOOCC({=}NH)CH_3]$ + $HSCH_2CH_2CH(NH_2)COOH$ **(66)**; $[HOOCC({=}NH)CH_3]$ → $HOOCC({=}O)CH_3 + NH_3$

α,β-elimination reactions, respectively, catalyzed by pyridoxal phosphate.[50–51]

C. Codecarboxylase—Mechanism of Action

Current interpretation of the mechanism of pyridoxal phosphate catalysis in amino acid biochemistry began with observations on trace

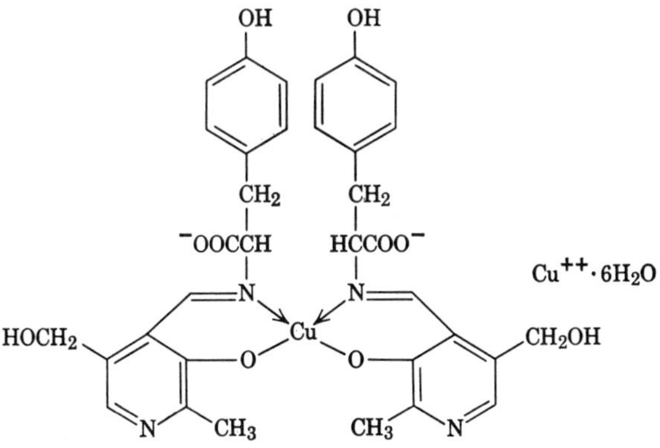

OH OH

CH_2 CH_2

$^{-}OOCCH$ $HCCOO^{-}$

N N Cu O O

$HOCH_2$ CH_2OH

N CH_3 CH_3 N

$Cu^{++} \cdot 6H_2O$

(68)

49. F. Binkley and C. K. Olson, *J. Biol. Chem.*, *185*, 881 (1950).
50. F. Binkley and G. M. Christensen, *J. Am. Chem. Soc.*, *73*, 3535 (1951).
51. F. Binkley, *Federation Proc.*, *12*, 178 (1953).

metal ion (Cu^{2+}, Fe^{3+}, Al^{3+}) catalysis of nonenzymic pyridoxal-catalyzed transamination of α-amino acids.[52]

The synthesis of water-soluble green copper chelates of pyridoxal with the α-amino acids glycine, alanine, serine, lysine, isoleucine, valine, threonine, and methionine was recorded,[53] and the copper chelate compound (**68**) of tyrosine and pyridoxal was isolated and characterized by analysis. On the basis of these observations, nonenzymic transamination

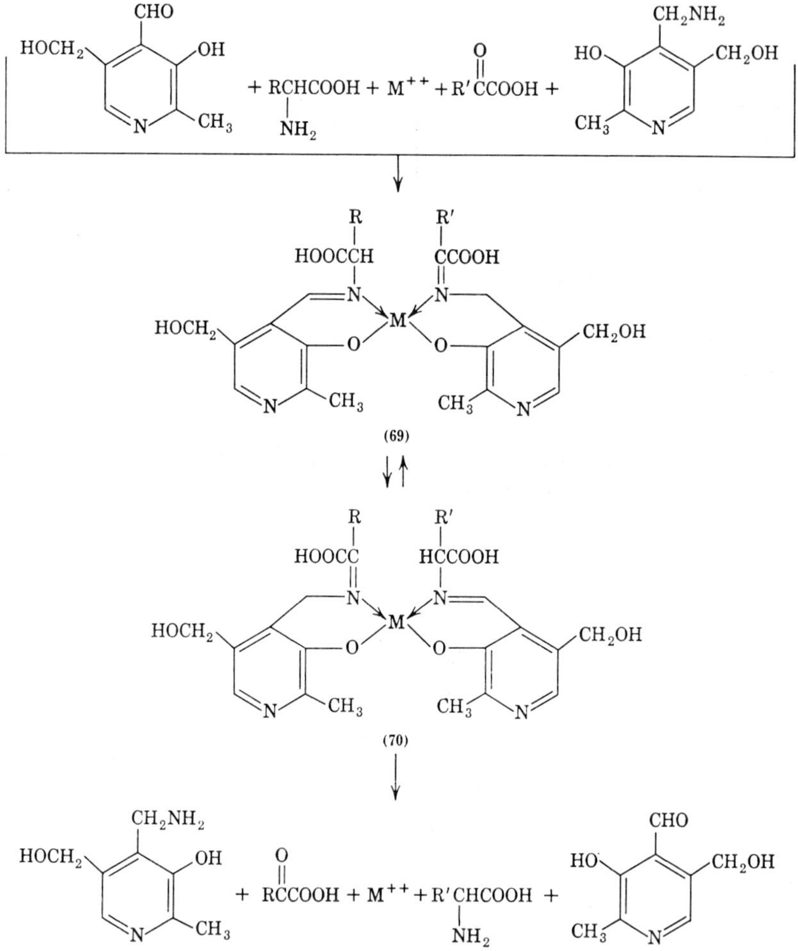

Fig. 7. Visualization of nonenzymic transamination of α-amino acids by pyridoxal.[53]

52. D. E. Metzler and E. E. Snell, *J. Am. Chem. Soc.*, *74*, 979 (1952).
53. J. Baddiley, *Nature*, *170*, 711 (1952).

of α-amino acids by pyridoxal was visualized (Fig. 7) as proceeding through the formation of the copper chelate complex (**69**) containing one moiety each of pyridoxal, pyridoxamine, α-amino acid, and α-keto acid and one metal ion. In this mechanism, the transamination step involves isomerization of the complex (**69**) to (**70**) which on hydrolysis would furnish the deaminated amino acid and aminated keto acid. Since the transaminases had not been isolated in sufficient purity for an accurate determination of the metal ion requirement, the mechanism was considered for biological transamination but with reservation.

Other typical enzymic amino acid transformations have also been reproduced in nonenzymic systems by using combinations of pyridoxal and a metal ion (Cu^{2+}, Fe^{3+}, or Al^{3+}). Among them are transamination,[52,54] serine deamination,[55] decarboxylation,[56] and racemization.[57] Since these nonenzymic reactions parallel the enzymic reactions closely, it has been assumed that both proceed by similar mechanisms.[58,59]

The 4-formyl group, 3-hydroxyl group, and basic ring-nitrogen atom are the only structural features of pyridoxal essential for nonenzymic catalysis. Although the hydroxymethyl group is physiologically important as the point of attachment of the phosphate group, it is not necessary for nonenzymic catalysis.[58]

The general mechanism (Fig. 8) for pyridoxal catalysis of α-amino acid reactions proceeds with the formation of the Schiff base (**71**) from the amino acid and pyridoxal.[58] This conjugated intermediate is then stabilized by the metal ion which promotes planarity in the conjugated system through chelate-ring formation yielding the complex (**72**). A concerted electrophilic action by the basic ring-nitrogen atom of the pyridoxal moiety and the chelated metal ion is transmitted through the conjugated system of the chelate (**72**) potentiating the displacement of an electron pair from the α-carbon atom of the amino acid. One of three electron pairs may be displaced. Displacement of the electron pair binding the hydrogen atom to the α-carbon atom leads to racemization, transamination, β-elimination, or γ-elimination. Decarboxylation is caused by the release of the electron pair between the α-carbon atom and the carboxyl group. Release of the electron pair between the α-carbon atom and the alkyl group results in degradation of the amino acid. The nature of the

54. D. E. Metzler, J. Olivard, and E. E. Snell, *J. Am. Chem. Soc.*, *76*, 644 (1954).
55. D. E. Metzler and E. E. Snell, *J. Biol. Chem.*, *198*, 353 (1952).
56. E. Werle and W. Koch, *Biochem. Z.*, *319*, 305 (1949).
57. J. Olivard, D. E. Metzler, and E. E. Snell, *J. Biol. Chem.*, *199*, 669 (1952).
58. D. E. Metzler, M. Ikawa, and E. E. Snell, *J. Am. Chem. Soc.*, *76*, 648 (1954).
59. E. E. Snell, *Physiol. Revs.*, *33*, 509 (1953).

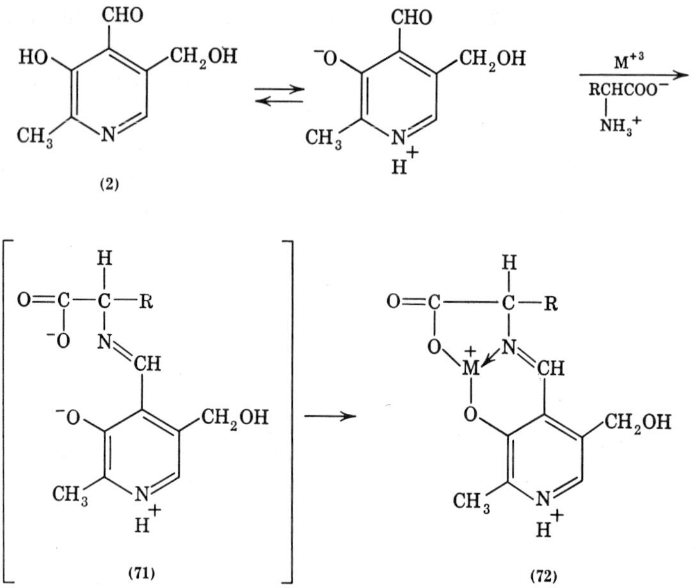

CHO
HO
CH_2OH
CH_3
N
(2)

CHO
^-O
CH_2OH
CH_3
N^+
H

M^{+3}
$RCHCOO^-$
NH_3^+

H
O=C—C—R
^-O
N=CH
^-O
CH_2OH
CH_3
N^+
H
(71)

H
O=C——C—R
O
M
N=CH
O
CH_2OH
CH_3
N^+
H
(72)

Fig. 8. General mechanism for pyridoxal catalysis in amino acid chemistry.[58]

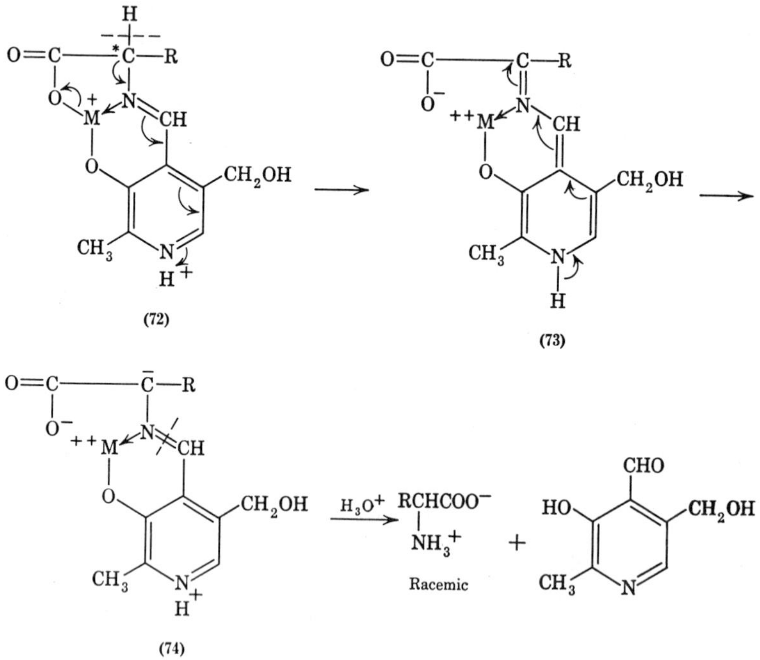

H
O=C——*C—R
O
M
N=CH
O
CH_2OH
CH_3
N
H^+
(72)

O=C——C—R
O^-
++M
N
CH
O
CH_2OH
CH_3
N
H
(73)

O=C——C—R
O^-
++M
N
CH
O
CH_2OH
CH_3
N^+
H
(74)

H_3O^+
$RCHCOO^-$
NH_3^+
Racemic
+

CHO
HO
CH_2OH
CH_3
N

Fig. 9. Pyridoxal in amino acid racemization.[58]

amino acid, the metal ion, and the environment presumably determine the nature of the electron pair displaced and which of the three α-carbon bonds is cleaved.

In the mechanism for racemization (Fig. 9), the α-carbon-hydrogen bond in the chelate intermediate **(72)** is cleaved, and the intermediate **(73)** is apparent. After a migration of electrons and the creation of an electronegative center at the α-carbon atom, a proton adds to the carbanion **(74)**. Subsequent hydrolysis at the carbon-nitrogen double bond of **(74)** yields the racemized amino acid and pyridoxal.(58)

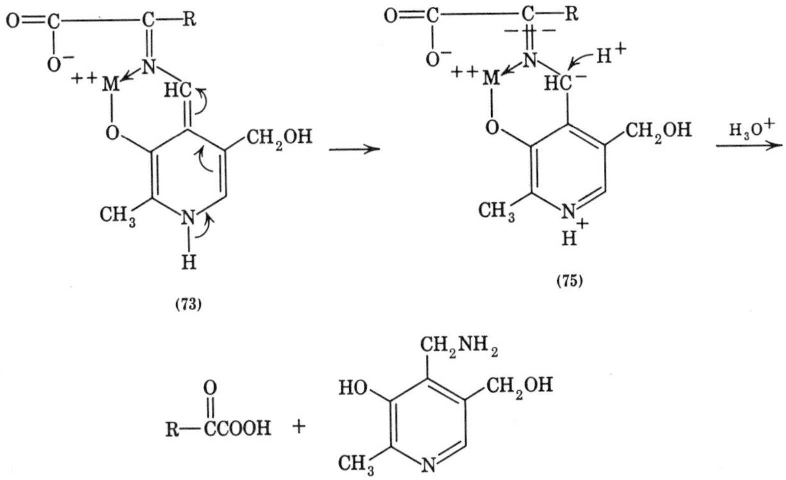

(73)

(75)

$$R{-}\overset{O}{\overset{\|}{C}}COOH \; + $$

Fig. 10. Pyridoxal in transamination.(58)

In the transamination mechanism the chelate **(72)** loses a proton, yielding the same intermediate **(73)** (Fig. 10) as proposed for racemization.(58) The carbanion **(75)** is formed by rearrangement of **(73)**, and cleavage of the carbon-nitrogen double bond yields the α-keto acid and pyridoxamine.

When the β-carbon of the amino acid is substituted with an electron-attracting group, the complex **(76)** (Fig. 11) eliminates the β-substituent as the anion **(78)**. In contrast to the racemization and transamination reactions, the resulting Schiff base **(77)** is stabilized without the formation of a carbanion.(58) Hydrolysis of this intermediate gives a keto acid, ammonia, and pyridoxal. Examples of such β-eliminations are the dehydration of serine and threonine, the desulfhydration of cysteine, and the cleavage of indole from tryptophan.

It was also suggested that an intermediate of type **(77)** could ultimately result in the formation of another amino acid either by reduction of the double bond with a thiol compound, yielding an unsubstituted amino acid, or by the addition of a second compound to the double bond to yield after hydrolysis a new β-substituted amino acid.

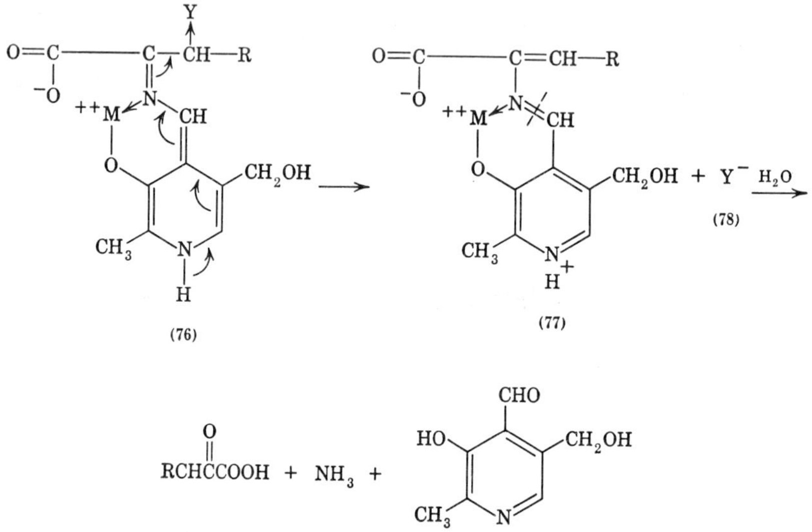

Fig. 11. Pyridoxal in β-elimination.[58]

Two mechanisms (Fig. 12) have been suggested for the nonenzymic γ-elimination reaction.[58] The intermediate (**79**) undergoes a Wagner-Meerwein-type rearrangement to the complex (**80**) which is then hydrolyzed. Alternatively, the intermediate (**81**) undergoes β,γ-elimination to yield the form (**82**) which may be isomerized, presumably by a second catalyst, to the complex (**80**). Among the enzymic γ-elimination reactions catalyzed by pyridoxal phosphate are the conversion of homocysteine and homoserine to α-ketobutyric acid and ammonia.

In the decarboxylation mechanism (Fig. 13), the release of the carboxyl group as carbon dioxide from the intermediate (**72**) yields (**83**). A migration of electrons occurs to form a carbanion at the α-position of the amino acid moiety.[58] After the addition of a proton to the carbanion and hydrolytic cleavage of the carbon-nitrogen double bond of the intermediate (**84**), the amine corresponding to the α-amino acid is obtained.

Pyridoxal-catalyzed reactions such as the nonenzymic cleavage of threonine or allothreonine to glycine and acetaldehyde, and the nonenzymic cleavage of serine to glycine and formaldehyde have been

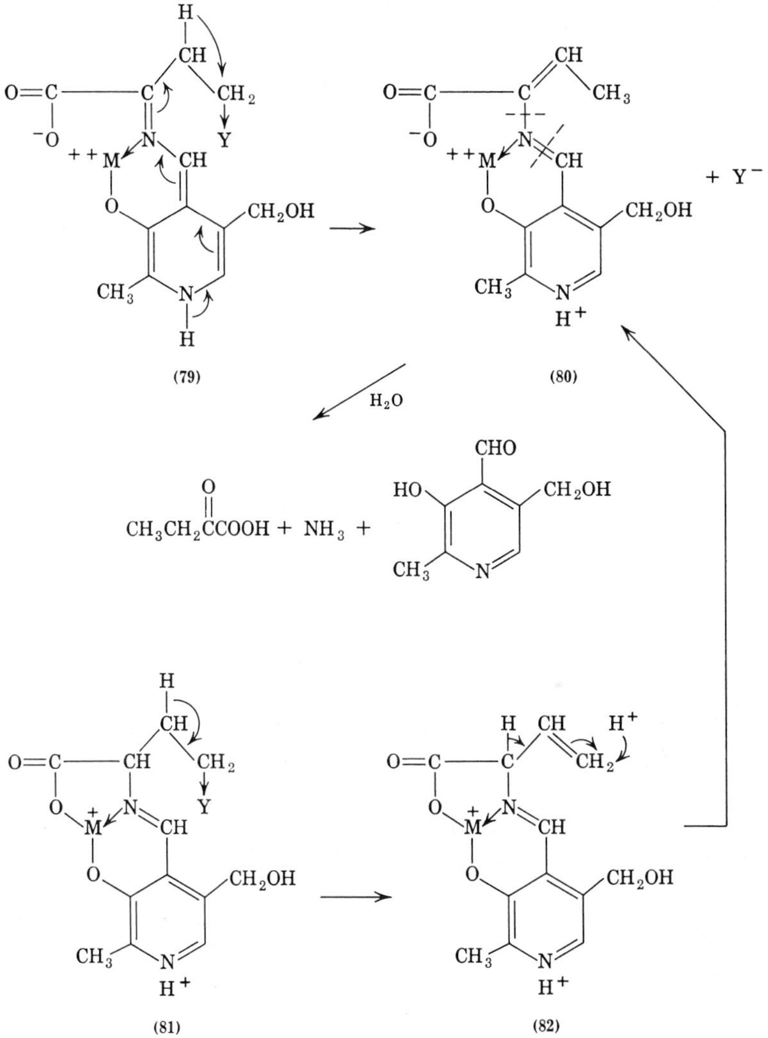

H
CH
O=C——C CH$_2$
$^-$O N Y
++M CH
O CH$_2$OH
CH$_3$ N
H

(79)

→

CH
O=C——C CH$_3$
$^-$O N
++M CH
O CH$_2$OH
CH$_3$ N
H$^+$

(80)

+ Y$^-$

H$_2$O

O
‖
CH$_3$CH$_2$CCOOH + NH$_3$ +

CHO
HO CH$_2$OH
CH$_3$ N

H
CH
O=C——CH CH$_2$
O N Y
M$^+$ CH
O CH$_2$OH
CH$_3$ N
H$^+$

(81)

→

H CH H$^+$
O=C——C CH$_2$
O N
M$^+$ CH
O CH$_2$OH
CH$_3$ N
H$^+$

(82)

Fig. 12. Alternative paths for pyridoxal participation in γ-elimination.[58]

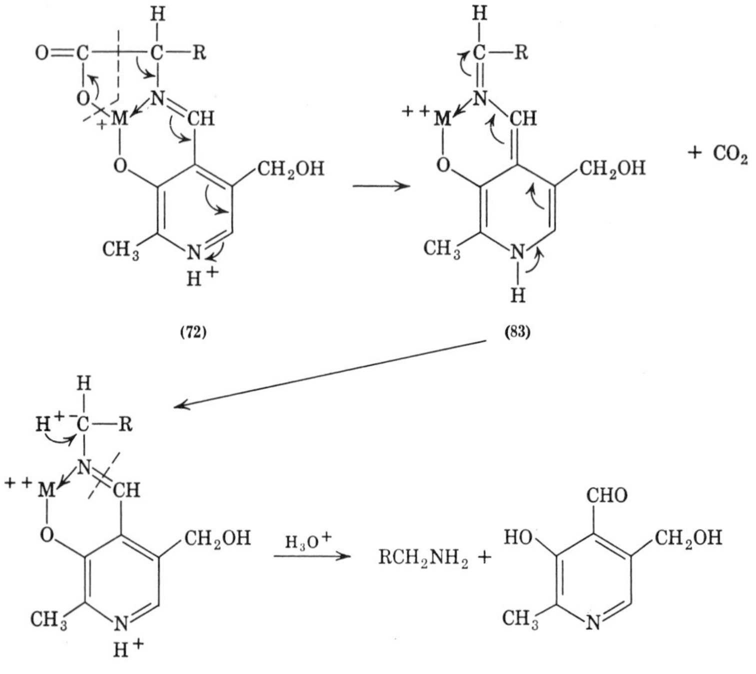

(72)

(83)

(84)

Fig. 13. Pyridoxal in decarboxylation.[58]

depicted (Fig. 14) as proceeding through the release of the α-alkyl substituent from the Schiff base (**85**) to yield the intermediate (**86**). An α-carbanion is created in this intermediate by a migration of electrons to yield the form (**87**). The addition of a proton to the carbanion, followed by hydrolytic cleavage gives a lower amino acid analog and an aldehyde corresponding to the hydroxyalkyl substituent of the original amino acid.[58]

When several metal chelates of pyridoxylidene-amino acids were prepared in crystalline form, two types of chelate compounds were observed.[60] The formation of a given type depended upon the metal ion used. The Cu^{2+} and Fe^{3+} chelates are comprised of pyridoxal, amino acid, and metal ion in a 1:1:1 ratio. The molecule is depicted (**72**) with three coplanar rings, and the metal ion is bound to the 3-hydroxyl group of pyridoxal. Chelates of the metal ions Mn^{2+}, Zn^{2+}, Fe^{2+}, and Ni^{2+} with pyridoxylidene-amino acids are comprised of pyridoxal, amino acid, and metal ion in a 2:2:1 ratio. The 3-hydroxyl group of pyridoxal is not bound

60. H. N. Christensen, *J. Am. Chem. Soc.*, *79*, 4073 (1957).

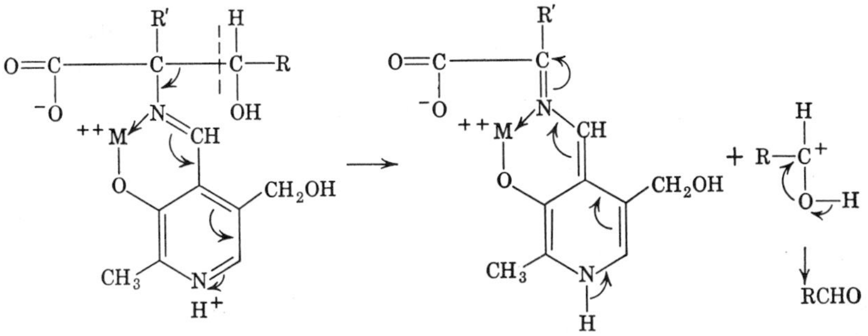

R′ H
O=C—C—C—R
$^-$O OH
$^{++}$M N CH
O CH_2OH
CH_3 N
H^+

(85)

R′
O=C—C
$^-$O
$^{++}$M N CH
O CH_2OH
CH_3 N
H

+ H
R—C^+
O—H
RCHO

(86)

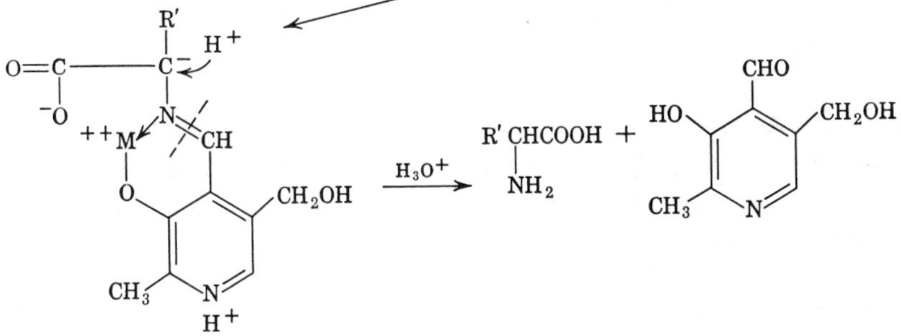

R′
O=C—C^- H^+
$^-$O
$^{++}$M N CH
O CH_2OH
CH_3 N
H^+

(87)

$\xrightarrow{H_3O^+}$ R′ CHCOOH +
NH_2

CHO
HO CH_2OH
CH_3 N

Fig. 14. Pyridoxal in carbon–carbon cleavage.[58]

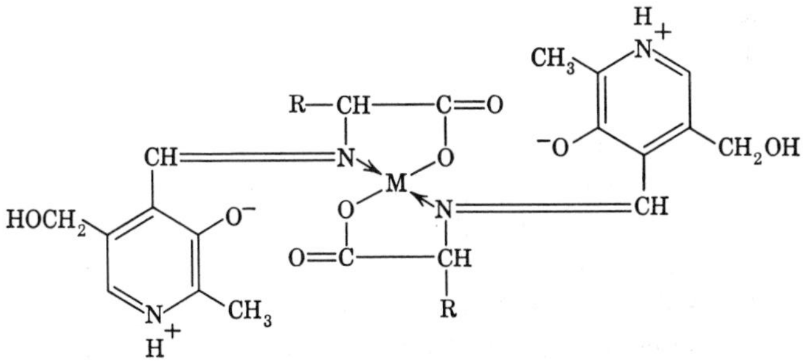

H
CH_3 N^+
R—CH—C=O
$^-$O CH_2OH
CH=N O
M
$HOCH_2$ O^- O N=CH
O=C—CH
N CH_3 R
H^+

(88)

in these complexes (**88**). Consequently, it is suggested that chelation to the 3-hydroxyl group is probably not essential for catalytic activity.

D. Pyridoxamine Phosphate

Pyridoxamine phosphate (**5**) was synthesized by the direct phosphorylation of pyridoxamine in aqueous solution with phosphorus oxychloride.[61]

61. D. Heyl, E. Luz, S. A. Harris, and K. Folkers, *J. Am. Chem. Soc.*, *73*, 3436 (1951).

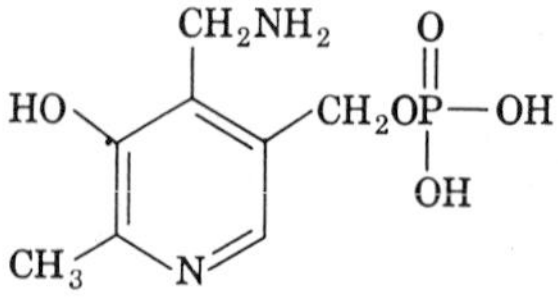

CH_2NH_2 O ‖ HO CH_2OP—OH | OH CH_3 N

(5)

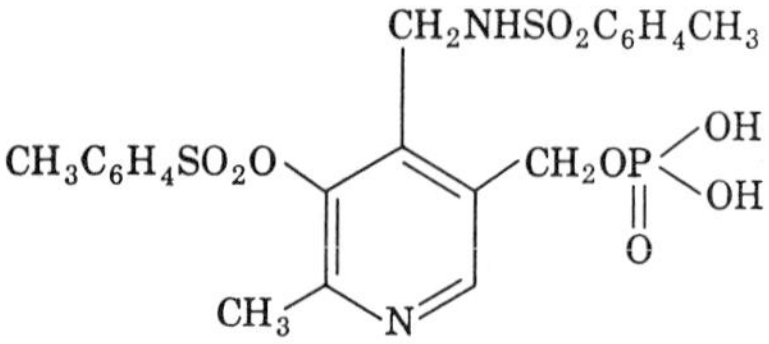

$CH_2NHSO_2C_6H_4CH_3$ $CH_3C_6H_4SO_2O$ CH_2OP OH OH ‖ O CH_3 N

(89)

The product was characterized by enzymic assay and by conversion to the crystalline di-*p*-toluenesulfonyl derivative (**89**). Pyridoxamine phosphate is a growth factor for lactic acid bacteria.[62,63]

7. Nutritional and Therapeutic Role

A. In Animals

Pyridoxine is essential for several animal species. The avitaminosis syndrome varies with the species, but differences appear to be in degree rather than in kind. The general characteristics of deficiency in animals include retarded growth, acrodynia, anemia, epileptiform convulsions, and partial alopecia.

The deficiency state is induced in animals by the use of synthetic diets, pyridoxine antagonists such as 4-deoxypyridoxol (**90**), or both. In the rat,

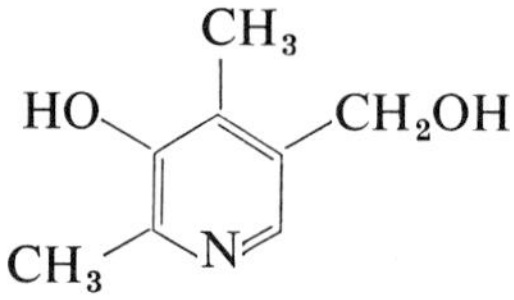

CH_3 HO CH_2OH CH_3 N

(**90**)

the syndrome is characterized by poor growth, usually evident within the first five days.[64] The effects of pyridoxine-deficient diets on reproduction in the rat are slight; the pregnant rat fails to make the normal weight gain during the gestation period, and there is a slight increase in the number of stillborn.[65] With a deoxypyridoxol-induced deficiency, however, the effects on reproduction are severe. There is a decrease in the number of young per litter, a high incidence of fetal resorption, and a greater number of stillborn. A prolonged deficiency results in a termination of the estrus cycle. The survival of suckling young of pyridoxine-deficient mothers is

62. D. Hendlin, M. C. Caswell, V. J. Peters, and T. R. Wood, *J. Biol. Chem.*, *186*, 647 (1950).
63. W. S. McNutt and E. E. Snell, *J. Biol. Chem.*, *182*, 557 (1950).
64. H. Sherman, L. M. Campling, and R. S. Harris, *Federation Proc.*, *9*, 371 (1950).
65. M. M. Nelson and H. M. Evans, *J. Nutr.*, *43*, 281 (1951).

rare regardless of the method used to induce the deficiency state. Epileptiform convulsions are observed in some of the progeny; they were most evident in suckling young when pyridoxol was withdrawn from the mother's diet the day they were born. Epileptiform convulsions are also observed in rats maintained on a pyridoxine-deficient diet for periods of four to five months.[66] The convulsions usually occur after about the twentieth week of deficiency and are prevented or cured by the daily administration of 10–15 μg. of pyridoxol.

The most distinguishing characteristic of pyridoxine deficiency in the rat is the symmetrical dermatitis designated acrodynia. The characteristic skin lesions in the most peripheral parts of the body (e.g., paws, nose, and ears) clearly differentiated pyridoxol from other pellagra-preventive factors and facilitated its isolation.[67]

The effects of pyridoxine deficiency on erythropoiesis in the rat are not as consistent as those observed in the dog and pig, but there are occasional occurrences of moderately severe anemia in rats that are fed pyridoxine-deficient diets. An impairment in the rate of red blood cell regeneration is consistently observed when pyridoxine-deficient rats are subjected to the stress of repeated bleedings.[68] A marked suppression of circulating antibodies is also observed in rats that are fed pyridoxine-deficient diets prior to immunization.[69,70] With influenza virus, an antigen of clinical interest, antibody formation in the rat is impaired by deficiencies of pantothenic acid and pyridoxol.[71]

The influence of pyridoxol on fat metabolism in the rat is evident from the observation that the pyridoxine-deficient rat is unable to synthesize fat from carbohydrate[72] or protein.[73] Pyridoxol also functions in essential fatty acid metabolism of the rat.

There is no evidence of atherosclerosis, arteriolar or arterial disease in the albino rat that is fed a pyridoxine-deficient diet for thirty-four weeks. An elevated systolic blood pressure observed in these animals, however, indicates damage to the cardiovascular system.[74] Studies of the pyridoxine deficiency state in the monkey reveal pathologic alterations bearing a

66. H. Chick, M. M. El Sadr, and A. N. Worden, *Biochem. J.*, *34*, 595 (1940).
67. T. W. Birch, P. W. György, and L. J. Harris, *Biochem. J.*, *29*, 2830 (1935).
68. A. Kornberg, H. Tabor, and W. H. Sebrell, *Am. J. Physiol.*, *143*, 434 (1945).
69. H. C. Stoerk and H. N. Eisen, *Proc. Soc. Exptl. Biol. Med.*, *62*, 88 (1946).
70. P. P. Ludovici, A. E. Axelrod, and B. B. Carter, *Proc. Soc. Exptl. Biol. Med.*, *76*, 665 (1951).
71. A. E. Axelrod and S. Hopper, *J. Nutr.*, *72*, 325 (1960).
72. C. W. Carter and P. J. Phizackerley, *Biochem. J.*, *49*, 227 (1951).
73. E. W. McHenry and G. Gavin, *J. Biol. Chem.*, *138*, 471 (1941).
74. N. Olson, *Am. J. Clin. Nutr.*, *4*, 318 (1956).

strong similarity to atherosclerosis in man. The occurrence of degenerative vascular lesions in pyridoxine-deficient Rhesus monkeys was observed,[75] and the close similarity between these experimental lesions and those of arteriosclerosis in the human was demonstrated.[76] In the experimental primate, vascular lesions develop about five to six months after deprivation of pyridoxol; an unusually high incidence of dental caries also occurs in the second dentition of these pyridoxine-deficient monkeys.[77] Cirrhosis of the liver is another pathologic change frequently observed in these animals.

These initial observations on lesions and caries in both Rhesus monkeys and dogs were confirmed[78] and in addition, arteriosclerosis was detected microscopically in organs such as the heart, kidney, testis, ovary, uterus, liver, adrenal, and lung. In pyridoxol-deprived dogs, arteriosclerosis is observed predominantly in the lower abdominal aorta, in the ascending aorta, or in both. Besides dental abnormalities, relative enlargement of the liver, heart, kidneys, adrenals, thyroid, pituitary, as well as fatty metamorphosis in the liver and kidneys are observed in the pyridoxine-deficient dogs and monkeys. The deficient monkey also loses weight and becomes anemic, listless, and apathetic. A partial alopecia develops, and the remaining fur becomes rough and lusterless. Daily administration of 2 mg. of pyridoxol hydrochloride to one monkey after forty weeks of pyridoxol deprivation produced a dramatic increase in weight and a general improvement.[79]

Pigs fail to grow on a pyridoxine-deficient diet; they have poor appetites, develop rough coats, and become anemic.[80] Epileptiform convulsions and anemia develop in the young pig that is fed a pyridoxine-deficient diet. Other studies revealed that pigs failing to get adequate pyridoxol show symptoms of degeneration in the peripheral sensory nerves and develop an abnormal gait.[81]

In the chick, a pyridoxine deficiency is characterized[82,83] by slow

75. J. F. Rinehart and L. D. Greenberg, *Am. J. Pathol.*, *25*, 481 (1949).
76. J. F. Rinehart and L. D. Greenberg, *A.M.A. Arch. Pathol.*, *51*, 12 (1951).
77. J. F. Rinehart and L. D. Greenberg, *Am. J. Clin. Nutr.*, *4*, 318 (1956).
78. C. W. Mushett and G. A. Emerson, *Federation Proc.*, *15*, 526 (1956); *16*, 367 (1957).
79. C. F. Hutchison, G. E. Boxer, B. Esser, and G. A. Emerson, *Personal Communication.*
80. E. H. Hughes and R. L. Squibb, *J. Animal Sci.*, *1*, 320 (1942).
81. M. M. Wintrobe, M. H. Miller, R. H. Follis, Jr., H. J. Stein, C. W. Mushett, and S. Humphries, *J. Nutr.*, *24*, 345 (1942).
82. T. H. Jukes, *Proc. Soc. Exptl. Biol. Med.*, *42*, 180 (1939).
83. S. Lepkovsky and F. H. Kratzer, *J. Nutr.*, *24*, 515 (1942).

growth, convulsions, and other nervous manifestations. The pyridoxine-deficient chick, however, shows no sign of dermatitis.

B. In The Human

There is conclusive evidence that pyridoxol is essential for human nutrition. In 1948 mild changes in the white blood cells were observed in a male subject who was maintained on a pyridoxine-free diet for fifty-six days.[84] Excretion of the abnormal tryptophan metabolite xanthurenic acid, following test doses of tryptophan is one of the earliest detectable signs of pyridoxine deficiency in the monkey and human.[85] Administration of pyridoxol for one week, following a three-week period of deficiency reduces the excretion of xanthurenic acid substantially. The test is known as the tryptophan load test.

A deoxypyridoxol-induced deficiency in human subjects has been described.[86,87] The syndrome is characterized by skin lesions about the eyes, nose, and mouth, and by a mild but definite lymphocytopenia without accompanying anemia. Administration of a vitamin B complex that contained no pyridoxol was without effect; when daily doses as low as 5 mg. of pyridoxol were administered alone, however, dramatic responses were produced. Similar results were observed in two mentally defective infants being maintained on a pyridoxine-deficient diet for therapeutic reasons.[88]

Pyridoxol plays a role in the prevention of convulsive seizure in infants.[89] A daily dietary intake of less than 0.1 mg. of pyridoxol was associated with the development of clinical manifestations such as hyperirritability and convulsions in a significant number of infants. A daily consumption of 0.3 mg. or more of pyridoxol has not been associated with these symptoms nor with increased xanthurenic acid excretion following a tryptophan load test. Two or three cases are reported, however, where at least 2 mg. of pyridoxol was necessary to suppress convulsions; an abnormality in pyridoxol metabolism was advanced as the probable cause for such observations.

There is also conclusive evidence that pregnancy usually produces a

84. W. W. Hawkins and J. Barsky, *Science*, *108*, 284 (1948).
85. L. D. Greenberg, D. F. Bohr, H. McGrath, and J. F. Rinehart, *Arch. Biochem.*, *21*, 237 (1949).
86. R. W. Vilter, J. F. Mueller, H. S. Glazer, T. Jarrold, J. Abraham, C. Thompson, and V. R. Hawkins, *J. Lab. Clin. Med.*, *42*, 335 (1953).
87. J. F. Mueller and R. W. Vilter, *J. Clin. Invest.*, *29*, 193 (1950).
88. S. E. Snyderman, L. E. Holt, R. Carretero, and K. Jacobs, *Am. J. Clin. Nutr.*, *1*, 200 (1953).
89. *Nutr. Revs.*, *16*, 10 (1958).

conditioned deficiency of pyridoxol in humans.[90] On the basis of the influence of various amounts of pyridoxol on the tryptophan load test in pregnant women, a daily supplement of 10 mg. of pyridoxol hydrochloride has been recommended during pregnancy. Pyridoxol when administered orally,[91] intravenously, or intramuscularly[92] in 50–100 mg. doses three times weekly, is reported to be effective in controlling the nausea and vomiting of pregnancy in some patients.

Pyridoxol is also reported to be effective for the prevention and treatment of nausea and vomiting following X-ray treatment; intravenous injection of 200 mg. of pyridoxol thirty minutes before X-ray treatment produced an excellent or good response in at least two-thirds of the cases treated.[93]

The role of pyridoxol in the prevention of dental caries in humans is a topic of current interest. In a ten-month study, hamsters fed a cariogenic diet suboptimal in pyridoxol developed tooth decay resulting in a 26% loss of tooth structure. Those hamsters that were fed the same diet supplemented with pyridoxol showed an over-all loss of only 4% of tooth structure.[94] By 1957 attention was called to the potential importance of pyridoxol in effecting changes in oral microflora and the beneficial effects this might have on the prevention of dental caries in humans;[95,96] a relationship was cited between the high incidence of dental caries in subjects with high counts of *Lactobacillus acidophilus* and the low incidence of dental caries in subjects with high saliva counts of *Lactobacillus casei*. Since pyridoxol stimulates the growth of *L. casei* but not *L. acidophilus*, it was implied that pyridoxol would stimulate the growth of *L. casei* at the expense of *L. acidophilus* and substantially reduce the incidence of dental caries. Further support for a relationship between pyridoxol and the incidence of dental caries was drawn from the high incidence of caries usually associated with pregnancy or massive cortisone therapy; both stress states are usually characterized by a pyridoxine deficiency.

Only two field studies to test the possible effect of pyridoxol in the suppression of dental caries have been completed.[97,98] A lower incidence

90. M. Wachstein and A. Gudaitis, *J. Lab. Clin. Med.*, *40*, 550 (1952).
91. B. B. Weinstein, Z. Wohl. G. J. Mitchell, and G. F. Sustendal, *Am. J. Obstet. Gynecol.*, *47*, 389 (1944).
92. B. B. Weinstein, G. J. Mitchell, and G. F. Sustendal, *Am. J. Obstet. Gynecol.*, *46*, 283 (1943).
93. J. J. Wells and W. C. Popp, *Proc. Staff Meetings Mayo Clinic*, *22*, 482 (1947).
94. L. P. Strean, E. W. Gilfillian, and G. A. Emerson, *N. Y. State Dental J.*, *22*, 325 (1956).
95. L. P. Strean, *Schweiz. Monatsschr. Zahnheilk.*, *67*, 981 (1957).
96. L. P. Strean, *N.Y. State Dental J.*, *23*, 85 (1957).
97. L. P. Strean, F. T. Bell, E. W. Gilfillian, G. A. Emerson, and E. E. Howe, *N.Y. State Dental J.*, *24*, 133 (1958).
98. A. Cohen and C. Rubin, *Bull. Philadelphia County Dent. Soc.*, *22*, 84 (1958).

of diseased, missing, or filled teeth was observed in children taking pyridoxol in lozenges as compared with a similar group taking placebo lozenges.

A daily dietary intake of 1–2 mg. of pyridoxol should be provided;[(99)] this quantity of the vitamin is available in many ordinary diets. It is widely distributed in foods, and good sources include liver, vegetables, whole grain cereals, and muscle meats.

99. *Recommended Dietary Allowances*, *Natl. Acad. Sci.-Natl. Res. Council Publ.*, 589, Washington, D.C., 1958, p. 22.

CHAPTER X

Cyanocobalamin and the Cobamide Coenzymes

1. Introduction

The history of vitamin B_{12} presents several marked departures from the usual pattern of vitamin discovery and elucidation. The pathologic condition, pernicious anemia, responding to the active substance is generally regarded as a "conditioned" rather than a primary deficiency state. The activity of the substance was discovered in the course of human and not animal studies; efforts to find an animal assay had failed, so evaluation of purification and fractionation procedures was obtained only at the clinical level. The structure of the chemical substance is unique and complex, and X-ray crystallographic data were necessary in conjunction with degradative chemical evidence for the complete structural elucidation.

The first real stride toward the elucidation of pernicious anemia was made in 1926 with the discovery of the effectiveness of whole liver therapy for the therapeutic control of the disease.[1] This highly significant medical discovery stimulated efforts in several laboratories to seek the active principle or principles responsible for the therapeutic effect; twenty years of effort achieved a 1-mg. mass of material equivalent in activity to 400 g. of whole liver. Much was yet to be done, and fractionation studies were painfully slow, particularly because of the very limited number, in any one area, of human subjects with pernicious anemia. Details of this early search for the antipernicious anemia principle have been reviewed.[2] In these and even in subsequent studies, fractionation of liver extracts was guided solely by tests on human subjects with pernicious anemia; later, attention was also given to the conditions for the growth of a microorganism, *Lactobacillus lactis* Dorner, as a guide.

In 1948 a red crystalline compound designated vitamin B_{12} was

1. G. R. Minot and W. P. Murphy, *J. Am. Med. Assoc.*, *87*, 470 (1926); *89*, 759 (1927).
2. Y. SubbaRow, A. B. Hastings, and M. Elkin, in R. S. Harris and K. V. Thimann, eds., *Vitamins and Hormones*, Vol. III, Academic, N.Y., 1948, p. 237.

described.[3] This new crystalline vitamin was found to be clinically active,[4] producing hematological responses in patients with pernicious anemia at a single dose level of 3–6 μg.; it was also found to possess activity for the growth of *L. lactis* Dorner at a concentration of 0.000013 μg./ml. of culture medium.[5] With this knowledge, a patient in relapse was no longer essential for a test of activity of liver fractions. Microbiological evaluation of activity was subsequently extended to other microorganisms, and the red color of the vitamin also provided guidance not only for vitamin B_{12}, but for all related cobalt complexes in chromatographic and related manipulations.

Shortly afterwards another group reported crystalline vitamin B_{12},[6] and in the following year still another group obtained the crystalline vitamin.[7]

Crystalline vitamin B_{12} from a fermentation source utilizing the microorganism *Streptomyces griseus* was first reported in 1948.[8] There were several subsequent reports concerning fermentation materials. For example, vitamin B_{12} was obtained from the broth of *Streptomyces aureofaciens*[9] and the related product, vitamin B_{12b}, was obtained from neomycin fermentations.[10]

2. Fractionation and Crystallization of Vitamin B_{12}

The concentration of vitamin B_{12}-active substances in liver is approximately 1 ppm. Consequently, the processes of fractionation were lengthy and based almost entirely upon such methods as adsorption chromatography, partition chromatography, and extraction.[3,6,7,11,12] Most fractionation studies were initiated using either minced liver or proteolyzed liver extracts.

3. E. L. Rickes, N. G. Brink, F. R. Koniuszy, T. R. Wood, and K. Folkers, *Science*, *107*, 396 (1948).
4. R. West, *Science*, *107*, 398 (1948).
5. M. S. Shorb, *Science*, *107*, 398 (1948).
6. E. L. Smith and L. F. J. Parker, *Biochem. J.*, *43*, viii (1948).
7. B. Ellis, V. Petrow, and G. F. Snook, *J. Pharm. Pharmacol.*, *1*, 60 (1949).
8. E. L. Rickes, N. G. Brink, F. R. Koniuszy, T. R. Wood, and K. Folkers, *Science*, *108*, 634 (1948).
9. J. V. Pierce, A. C. Page, E. L. R. Stokstad, and T. H. Jukes, *J. Am. Chem. Soc.*, *71*, 2952 (1949).
10. W. G. Jackson, G. B. Whitfield, W. H. DeVries, H. A. Nelson, and J. S. Evans, *J. Am. Chem. Soc.*, *73*, 337 (1951).
11. K. H. Fantes, J. E. Page, L. F. J. Parker, and E. L. Smith, *Proc. Roy. Soc.* (*London*), *Ser. B*, *136*, 592 (1949).
12. E. L. Smith, *Proc. Intern. Soc. Hematology*, Paper 1 (1950).

Starting with a minced liver preparation, a representative fractionation proceeded with an aqueous alcohol extraction, followed by the adsorption of the vitamin on either activated carbon or fuller's earth.[11] After preliminary elution, the vitamin could be eluted with 65% ethanol, aqueous phenol, or an aqueous pyridine mixture. The adsorption and elution steps were usually repeated once more. If the liver was first proteolyzed with papain and then extracted with aqueous alcohol, only one charcoal adsorption and elution step was necessary. The vitamin was eluted from charcoal and the mixture was further fractionated by partition chromatography. Supports such as starch, kieselguhr, and damp silica were used, and solvents such as butanol containing 11–25% water, *n*-propanol or isopropanol containing 10–25% water, and butanol-phenol-water mixtures proved especially advantageous for partition. Adsorption chromatography on either silica or alumina was also effective for fractionation; columns of bentonite or aluminum silicate, run under carefully controlled conditions, were eminently satisfactory for purification.[7]

At various stages of these fractionation schemes, it was advantageous to remove the vitamin from aqueous solution. Butanol extraction from aqueous solutions containing relatively high concentrations of ammonium sulfate was especially effective.[7] Phenol or cresol in combination with less effective solvents such as butanol or toluene were also useful.

Pure crystalline vitamin B_{12} was usually obtained from aqueous acetone solutions. A concentrated aqueous solution of the vitamin was treated with about two volumes of acetone, and any trace of flocculent material was removed by centrifugation; the resulting solution was then slowly diluted with acetone until the solvent composition reached nine volumes of acetone for one volume of water. The solution was cooled, and pure crystalline vitamin B_{12} was obtained.

3. Structure Determination

In the course of the structural elucidation of vitamin B_{12}, several novel structural features were encountered which were without precedent, and a new very detailed nomenclature was eventually needed to name systematically the array of structural modifications and fragments of this very complex molecule. This new nomenclature and its rules are included in an appropriate section of this chapter. The name cyanocobalamin was adopted for vitamin B_{12} shortly after certain basic structural features of the vitamin were recognized; in the later nomenclature, the vitamin was named α-(5,6-dimethylbenzimidazolyl)cobamide cyanide. The highlights of this structural elucidation are summarized in the following sections; more details may be found in several reviews.[13–16]

A. General Observations

The ultraviolet absorption spectrum of an aqueous solution of cyanocobalamin exhibits three maxima at 278, 361, and 550 mμ. with extinction coefficients ($E^{1\%}_{1\ cm.}$) of 115, 207, and 63, respectively.[3,11,17,18] The absorption spectrum is essentially unchanged by changing the pH of the aqueous solution. The vitamin is optically active and behaves as a polyacidic base on electrometric titration in glacial acetic acid;[17] titration in aqueous solution revealed neither acidic nor basic groups.

An ebullioscopic determination of molecular weight in methanol gave a value of 1490 $\pm$ 150 for the vitamin,[17] and an early molecular weight of 1360–1575 was calculated from X-ray crystallographic data.[19] Early determinations of the molecular formula resulted in the expressions $C_{61-64}H_{86-92}N_{14}O_{13}PCo$ for the vitamin[17] and $C_{63}H_{84}N_{14}O_{14}PCo \cdot 6HClO_4$ for a perchloric acid salt.[20] The precise determination of the number of atoms of each of the constituent elements in a molecule of such a large molecular weight presented difficulties, but the significance of these early expressions is evident when they are compared with the molecular formula $C_{63}H_{88}N_{14}O_{14}PCo$ and the molecular weight 1355 corresponding to the accepted structure (**1**) for cyanocobalamin.

The vitamin is a cobalt coordination complex containing one replaceable cyano group which is tightly and coordinately bound to the cobalt atom.[21] Magnetic susceptibility measurements,[22–24] which indicated the

13. R. S. Harris, G. F. Marrian, and K. V. Thimann, eds., *Vitamins and Hormones*, Vol. XII, Academic, N.Y., 1954, p. 1.
14. W. H. Sebrell, Jr. and R. S. Harris, eds., *The Vitamins: Chemistry, Physiology, and Pathology*, Vol. I, Academic, N.Y., 1954, p. 395.
15. R. T. Williams, ed., *The Biochemistry of Vitamin B_{12}*, Biochem. Soc. Symposia (Cambridge, Eng.) *No. 13*, 1955.
16. H. C. Heinrich, ed., *Vitamin B_{12} und Intrinsic Factor*, Ferdinand Enke Verlag, Stuttgart, 1957.
17. N. G. Brink, D. E. Wolf, E. Kaczka, E. L. Rickes, F. R. Koniuszy, T. R. Wood, and K. Folkers, *J. Am. Chem. Soc.*, *71*, 1854 (1949).
18. H. G. Wijmenga, J. Lens, and A. Middelbeek, *Chem. Weekblad.*, *45*, 342 (1949).
19. D. C. Hodgkin, M. W. Porter, and R. C. Spiller, *Proc. Roy. Soc.* (*London*), *Ser. B*, *136*, 609 (1949).
20. J. F. Alicino, *J. Am. Chem. Soc.*, *73*, 4051 (1951).
21. N. G. Brink, F. A. Kuehl, and K. Folkers, *Science*, *112*, 354 (1950).
22. H. Diehl, R. W. Vander Haar, and R. R. Sealock, *J. Am. Chem. Soc.*, *72*, 5312 (1950).
23. F. Grun and R. Menasse, *Experientia*, *6*, 263 (1950).
24. J. C. Wallmann, B. B. Cunningham, and M. Calvin, *Science*, *113*, 55 (1951).

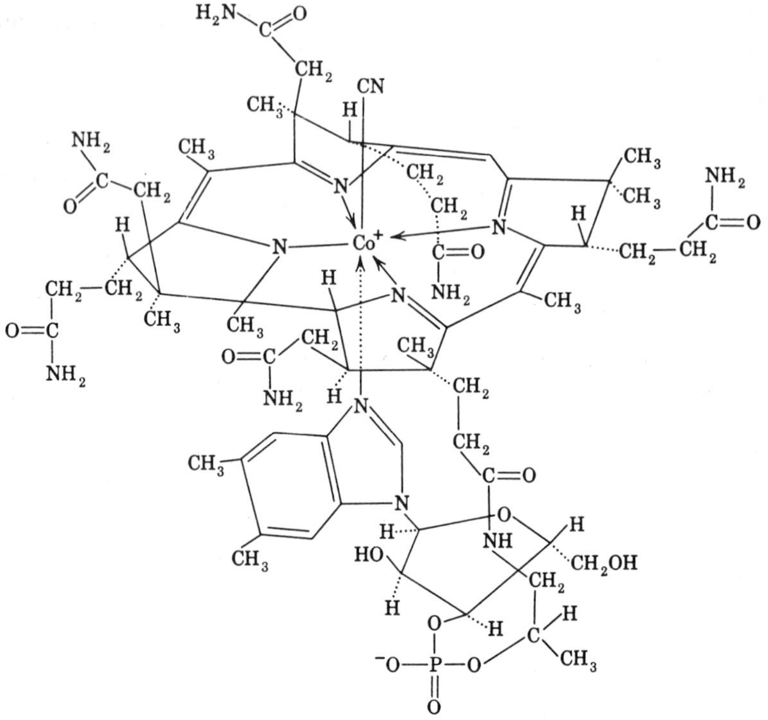

(1)

diamagnetic character of the vitamin, resulted in assignment of the trivalent state to the cobalt atom. A polarographic study of cyanocobalamin and of a titrimetric reduction product also led to the conclusion that the cobalt is trivalent and that the valence states of cobalt in vitamin B_{12} compounds and reduction products are the normal Co^{3+} and Co^{2+} states, respectively.[25]

B. The α-Ribazole Phosphate Moiety

1. 5,6-DIMETHYLBENZIMIDAZOLE. Acid hydrolysis of cyanocobalamin in 6*N* hydrochloric acid at 150° for 20 hrs., followed by chloroform extraction and other purification steps, yielded a new basic compound identified by degradation and synthesis as 5,6-dimethylbenzimidazole (**3**).[26] Degradation of this product with benzoyl chloride in aqueous alkali yielded 4,5-dibenzamido-1,2-dimethylbenzene (**4**), which was identified by comparison with an authentic synthetic sample. The benzimidazole fragment

25. R. N. Boos, J. E. Carr, and J. Conn, *Science*, *117*, 603 (1950).
26. N. G. Brink and K. Folkers, *J. Am. Chem. Soc.*, *71*, 2951 (1949); *72*, 4442 (1950).

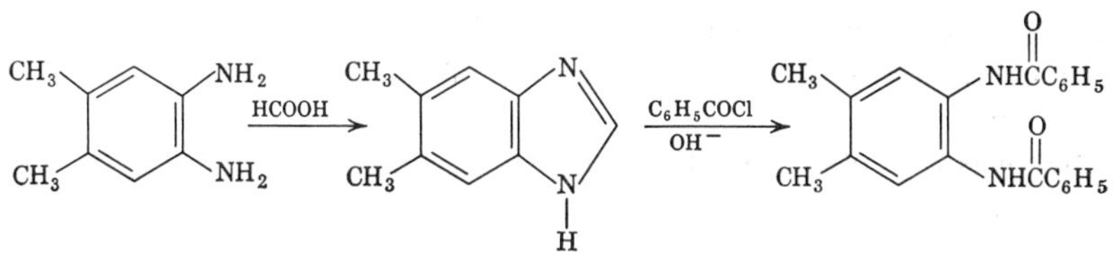

(2) (3) (4)

(**3**) from cyanocobalamin was synthesized by the reaction of formic acid with 4,5-diamino-1,2-dimethylbenzene (**2**). Although the 5,6-dimethyl-benzimidazole moiety in cyanocobalamin is a new heterocycle in the

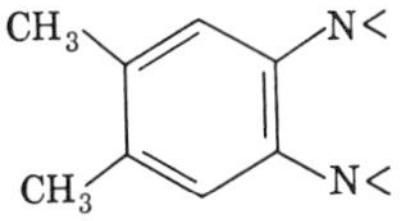

(5)

chemistry of vitamins, the 4,5-diamino-1,2-dimethylbenzene fragment (**5**) is also a moiety of riboflavine.

5,6-Dimethylbenzimidazole (**3**) was also identified as a degradation product of cyanocobalamin by skillful manipulations and spectrophotometric evidence on both the degradation product and a series of synthetic model benzimidazoles.[27] Paper chromatograms of an acid hydrolyzate of cyanocobalamin exhibited three closely related blue fluorescent spots. Comparison of the ultraviolet absorption spectra of eluates from these areas with those of twenty-two different methylated benzimidazoles led to the identification of one component as 5,6-dimethylbenzimidazole.

2. α-RIBAZOLE. Acid hydrolysis of cyanocobalamin in 6*N* hydrochloric acid at 120° for 8 hrs. yielded a glycosyl benzimidazole that was identified by degradation and synthetic studies as 1-α-*D*-ribofuranosyl-5,6-dimethyl-benzimidazole (**6**).[28,29] This compound is usually referred to as α-ribazole or "the nucleoside."

Hydrolysis of cyanocobalamin in 6*N* hydrochloric acid at 120° yielded mixtures of a glycosyl benzimidazole and 5,6-dimethylbenzimidazole. Similar hydrolyses at 100°, however, resulted in only negligible cleavage of the glycosidic link; consequently, the picrate of the glycoside could be isolated more readily and in purer form using this reaction condition. On the basis of elemental analysis, the glycosyl moiety was formulated as a

27. E. R. Holiday and V. Petrow, *J. Pharm. Pharmacol.*, *1*, 734 (1949).
28. N. G. Brink and K. Folkers, *J. Am. Chem. Soc.*, *74*, 2856 (1952).
29. F. W. Holly, C. H. Shunk, E. W. Peel, J. Cahill, J. B. Lavigne, and K. Folkers, *J. Am. Chem. Soc.*, *74*, 4521 (1952).

pentose rather than a hexose. The picrate of the glycoside (**6**) reacted with one equivalent of periodate yielding the picrate of α-(5,6-dimethylbenz-imidazolyl-1)-α′-hydroxymethyldiglycolic aldehyde (**7**). The structure of the latter was formulated on the basis of comparison with the presumably

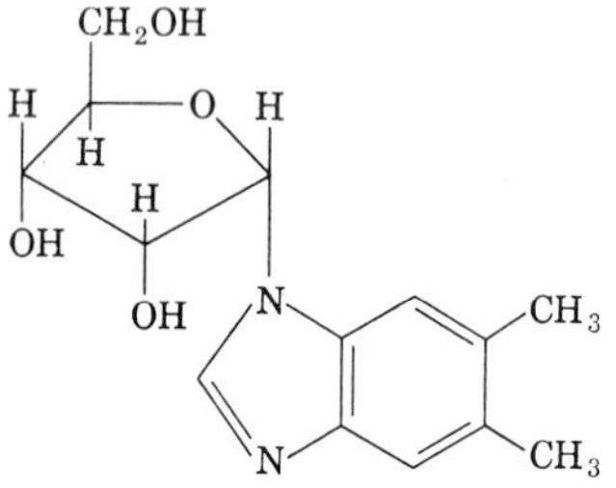

(6)

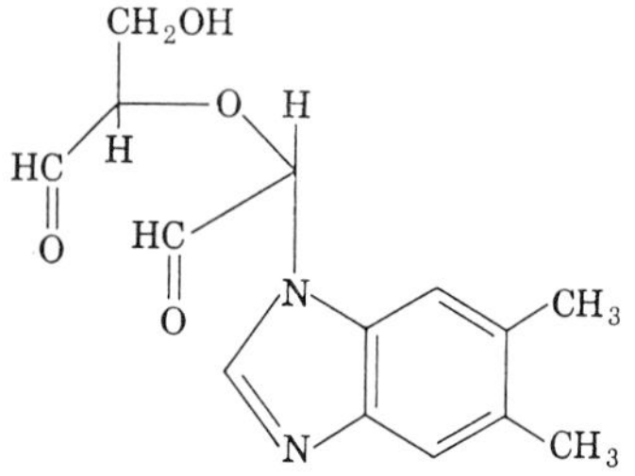

(7)

anomeric dialdehyde prepared by the periodate oxidation of the synthetic model compound, 1-β-*D*-glucopyranosyl-5,6-dimethylbenzimidazole.

Since the glycoside consumed only one equivalent of periodate, a furanose structure was assigned to the pentose moiety. Hydrolytic conditions that were sufficient to cleave the glycosidic link of the degradation product (**6**) also caused extensive decomposition of the pentose so that its identification was not possible. On the basis of the stability of the glycosidic linkage to acid hydrolysis, the degradation product was assumed to be a 1-pentofuranosyl-5,6-dimethylbenzimidazole, and an α-configuration about the glycosidic carbon atom was deduced from a comparison of the oxidation products from the degradation product and the synthetic model compound, 1-β-*D*-glucopyranosyl-5,6-dimethylbenzimidazole.

Final identification of the degradation product as 1-α-*D*-ribofuranosyl-5,6-dimethylbenzimidazole was accomplished by synthesis.[29] The reaction of 4,5-dimethyl-2-nitroaniline with 5-trityl-*D*-ribofuranose in refluxing benzene solution in the presence of acetic acid yielded 4,5-dimethyl-2-nitro-*N*-(5-trityl-*D*-ribofuranosyl)aniline (**8**). Reduction of the nitro group in the latter yielded the amino derivative (**9**) which, on treatment with ethyl- or isopropylformimino ether hydrochloride, yielded the 5′-trityl derivative (**10**) of the benzimidazole. Hydrolysis of the trityl group yielded α-ribazole (**6**) which was isolated as the crystalline picrate. Identity of the picrates from the degradation product and the synthetic specimen was established by comparison of physical properties and a mixed melting point. Furthermore, periodate oxidation of the synthetic α-ribazole picrate gave a crystalline α-(5,6-dimethylbenzimidazolyl-1)-α′-hydroxy-methyldiglycolic aldehyde picrate identical with the corresponding compound from the picrate of the degradation product.[28]

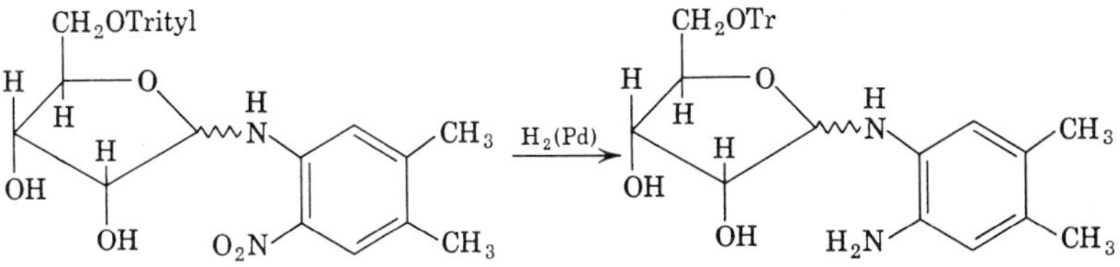

(8) $\xrightarrow{H_2(Pd)}$ (9)

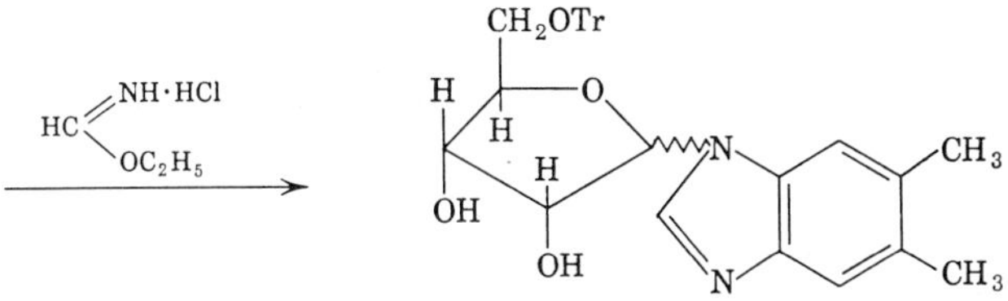

$\xrightarrow{HC(=NH \cdot HCl)OC_2H_5}$ (10)

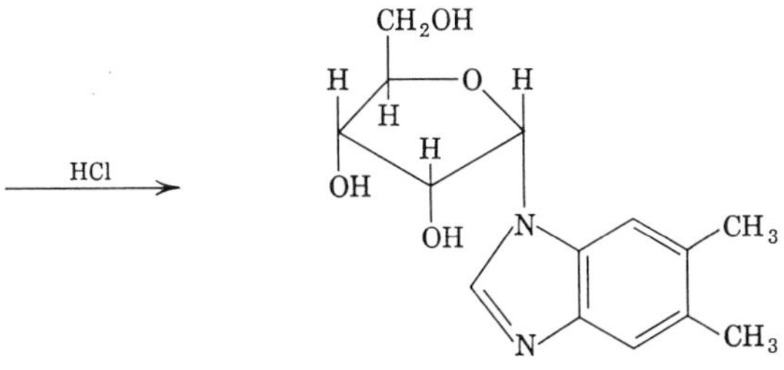

$\xrightarrow{HCl}$ (6)

It is particularly noteworthy that the ribazole moiety of cyanocobalamin has an α-configuration at the glycosidic carbon atom whereas other naturally occurring pyrimidine and purine ribosides have a β-configuration. Apparently the stereochemical requirements of cobalt coordination complexes having structures like that of cyanocobalamin restrict the ribosides of the bases to the α-configuration.[30]

3. α-RIBAZOLE PHOSPHATE. When cyanocobalamin was hydrolyzed in 1*N* hydrochloric acid at 100° for 1–20 hours, an organic phosphate having the composition of a benzimidazolyl nucleotide was isolated.[31] The compound, isolated as an amorphous barium salt, failed to react with

30. D. C. Hodgkin, in R. T. Williams, ed., *The Biochemistry of Vitamin* B_{12}, Biochem. Soc. Symposia (Cambridge, Eng.) *No. 13*, 1955, p. 28.
31. J. G. Buchanan, A. W. Johnson, J. A. Mills, and A. R. Todd, *J. Chem. Soc.*, 2845 (1950).

periodic acid; after hydrolysis with 6*N* HCl at 100° for 48 hours, it yielded an *N*-substituted benzimidazole which reacted with periodic acid. On the basis of knowledge derived from studies with 1-α-*D*-ribofuranosyl-5,6-dimethylbenzimidazole, it was evident that the phosphate group is attached to either C-2 or C-3 of the ribose moiety of the nucleotide.

α-Ribazole phosphate, the crystalline free phosphate of 1-α-*D*-ribofuranosyl-5,6-dimethylbenzimidazole, was obtained both by the degradation of cyanocobalamin and by synthesis.[32] After the acid hydrolysis of cyanocobalamin, α-ribazole phosphate was separated as a lead salt. The free phosphate, obtained after treatment with hydrogen sulfide, was purified by countercurrent distribution and was further characterized as a crystalline dibrucine salt.

The nucleotide was synthesized by either of two procedures. The better method began with the reaction of 5′-trityl-α-ribazole (**10**) with diphenylphosphorochloridate. Hydrolytic cleavage of the phenyl and trityl groups

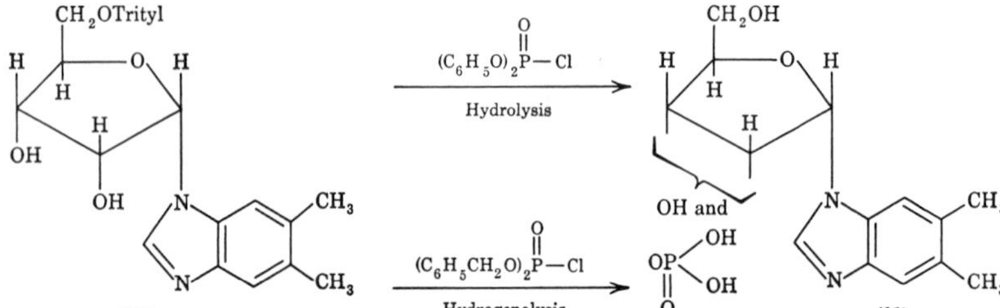

$(C_6H_5O)_2P(=O)-Cl$, Hydrolysis; $(C_6H_5CH_2O)_2P(=O)-Cl$, Hydrogenolysis

(10) → (11)

yielded α-ribazole phosphate (**11**). Alternatively, treatment of the trityl derivative (**10**) with dibenzylphosphorochloridate followed by hydrogenolysis yielded α-ribazole phosphate.

The synthetic methods did not permit the identification of the crystalline α-ribazole phosphate as the 2′-phosphate (**12**) or the 3′-phosphate (**13**).

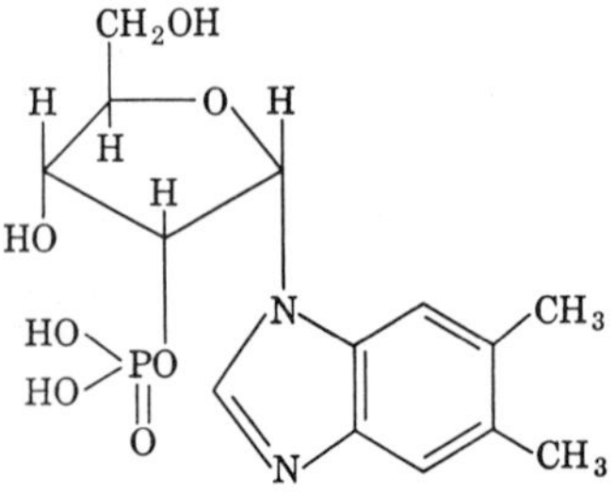

(12) 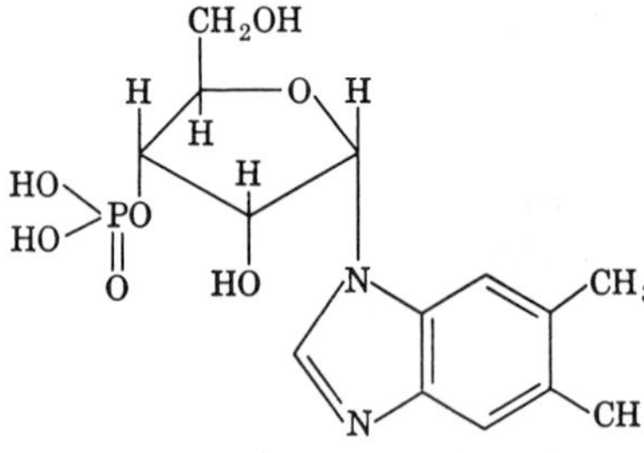 (13)

32. E. A. Kaczka, D. Heyl, W. H. Jones, and K. Folkers, *J. Am. Chem. Soc.*, *74*, 5549 (1952).

Comparison of α-ribazole phosphate with the known adenosine-2′ and 3′-phosphates by paper chromatography showed that the degradation product was very probably the 3′-phosphate (**13**).[33] This conclusion was further substantiated by the partial isomerization of α-ribazole phosphate in 80% acetic acid solution; paper chromatography of the equilibrium mixture revealed a second fluorescent spot corresponding to an isomerized product containing a 2′-phosphate group. Attachment of the phosphate group to the 3′-position of the ribazole moiety in cyanocobalamin was revealed later by X-ray crystallographic studies.[34]

Since early spectroscopic studies revealed that the nitrogen atom in the 3-position of the 5,6-dimethylbenzimidazole moiety and the cobalt atom

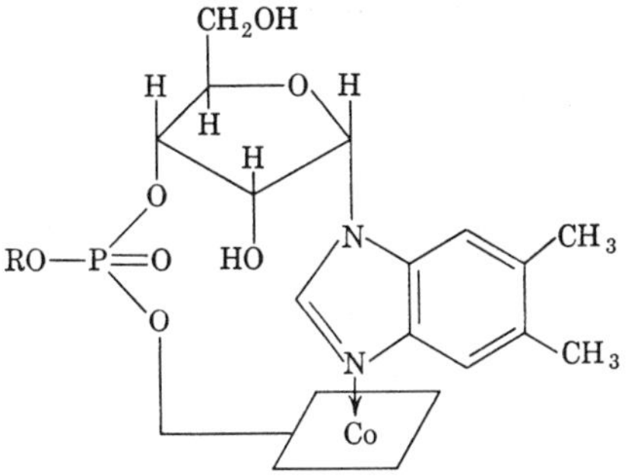

(14)

of the vitamin molecule form a coordinate link,[7] the α-ribazole phosphate moiety of the vitamin was visualized (**14**) as covalently bound through its phosphate group and coordinately bound through the 3-position.

C. The Aminopropanol Moiety

Among the products of hydrolysis of cyanocobalamin with 20% hydrochloric acid in a sealed tube at 100° was a "ninhydrin-reacting" substance that was first recognized in unidimensional paper chromatography.[7,35,36]

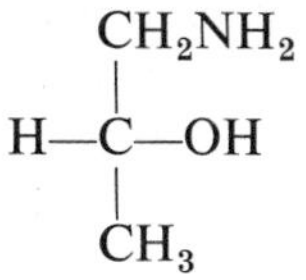

$$\begin{array}{c} CH_2NH_2 \\ | \\ H{-}C{-}OH \\ | \\ CH_3 \end{array}$$

(15)

33. E. A. Kaczka and K. Folkers, *J. Am. Chem. Soc.*, *75*, 6317 (1953).
34. C. Brink, D. C. Hodgkin, J. Lindsey, J. Pickworth, J. H. Robertson, and J. G. White, *Nature*, *174*, 1169 (1954).
35. B. Ellis, V. Petrow, and G. F. Snook, *J. Pharm. Pharmacol.*, *1*, 735 (1949).
36. B. Ellis, V. Petrow, and G. F. Snook, *J. Pharm. Pharmacol.*, *1*, 950 (1949).

This "ninhydrin-reacting" substance was isolated as a dibenzoate, and the substance itself was identified as D_g-1-amino-2-propanol (**15**) by degradation and synthesis.[37] Periodate oxidation of the purified free amine yielded acetaldehyde and formaldehyde which, considered in conjunction with the molecular formula, led to the conclusion that the "ninhydrin-reacting" product was 1-amino-2-propanol.

The structure of the "ninhydrin-reacting" product was confirmed by a synthesis which also elucidated the stereochemistry.[37] Resolution of *DL*-lactic acid (**16**) with morphine yielded D_g-lactic acid (**17**) which, in turn, was converted to ethyl D_g-lactate (**18**). Conversion of the latter to D_g-lactamide (**19**), followed by reduction with lithium aluminum hydride

$$\underset{(DL)\ (\mathbf{16})}{\begin{array}{c}COOH\\|\\CHOH\\|\\CH_3\end{array}} \longrightarrow \underset{(D_g)\ (\mathbf{17})}{\begin{array}{c}COOH\\|\\H—C—OH\\|\\CH_3\end{array}} \longrightarrow \underset{(D_g)\ (\mathbf{18})}{\begin{array}{c}COOC_2H_5\\|\\H—C—OH\\|\\CH_3\end{array}} \longrightarrow$$

$$\underset{(D_g)\ (\mathbf{19})}{\begin{array}{c}CONH_2\\|\\H—C—OH\\|\\CH_3\end{array}} \longrightarrow \underset{(D_g)\ (\mathbf{15})}{\begin{array}{c}CH_2NH_2\\|\\H—C—OH\\|\\CH_3\end{array}} \longrightarrow \underset{(D_g)\ (\mathbf{20})}{\begin{array}{c}CH_2NH\overset{O}{\overset{\|}{C}}C_6H_5\\|\\H—C—O\overset{O}{\overset{\|}{C}}C_6H_5\\|\\CH_3\end{array}}$$

yielded D_g-1-amino-2-propanol (**15**); benzoylation of (**15**) yielded the dibenzoate (**20**), identical with the product isolated from the hydrolyzate of cyanocobalamin.

Although there were some early discrepancies concerning the number of 1-amino-2-propanol moieties present in cyanocobalamin, it was demonstrated spectrophotometrically that one equivalent of 1-amino-2-propanol was obtained per mole of cyanocobalamin hydrolyzed.[38]

The generation of both 1-amino-2-propanol and 1-α-*D*-ribofuranosyl-5,6-dimethylbenzimidazole 3′-phosphate (**13**) on mild acid hydrolysis of cyanocobalamin suggested to some investigators that these two moieties were linked through the phosphate group in the intact molecule. The mode of linkage was deduced as follows. Crystalline *DL*-1-amino-2-propyl phosphate (**23**) was prepared by heating a mixture of *DL*-1-amino-2-propanol (**15**) and pyrophosphoric acid on the steam bath for thirty

37. D. E. Wolf, W. H. Jones, J. Valiant, and K. Folkers, *J. Am. Chem. Soc.*, 72, 2820 (1950).

minutes.[38] Its structure was established since it was found that 1-dibenzyl-amino-2-propanol (**21**) on phosphorylation with diphenylphosphoro-chloridate and pyridine, followed by catalytic hydrogenation, gave the same *DL*-1-amino-2-propyl phosphate.[38] Attempts to hydrolyze the phosphate ester (**23**) under the conditions which liberated 1-amino-2-

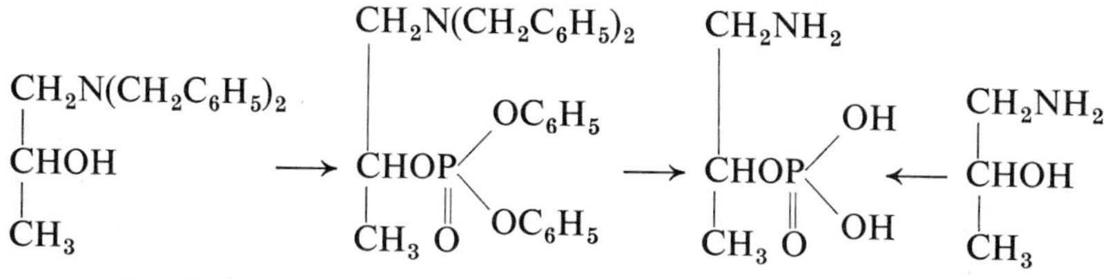

$CH_2N(CH_2C_6H_5)_2$–CHOH–CH_3 (DL) (**21**) → $CH_2N(CH_2C_6H_5)_2$–CHOP(O)(OC_6H_5)$_2$–CH_3 (DL) (**22**) → CH_2NH_2–CHOP(O)(OH)$_2$–CH_3 (DL) (**23**) ← CH_2NH_2–CHOH–CH_3 (**15**)

propanol from cyanocobalamin were unsuccessful, and the starting material was recovered. Since the monoesters of phosphoric acid are much more stable than the corresponding di- and trisubstituted esters, it was assumed that the phosphate ester in cyanocobalamin was one of the latter two types, and that the 1-amino-2-propanol moiety constituted one of the substituents of the ester. Furthermore, it was believed that the 1-amino-2-propanol moiety was joined to the rest of the molecule through an amide link.

On the basis of data accumulated to this stage,[33,38,39] the partial structure (**24**) was advanced for the cyanocobalamin molecule. When the

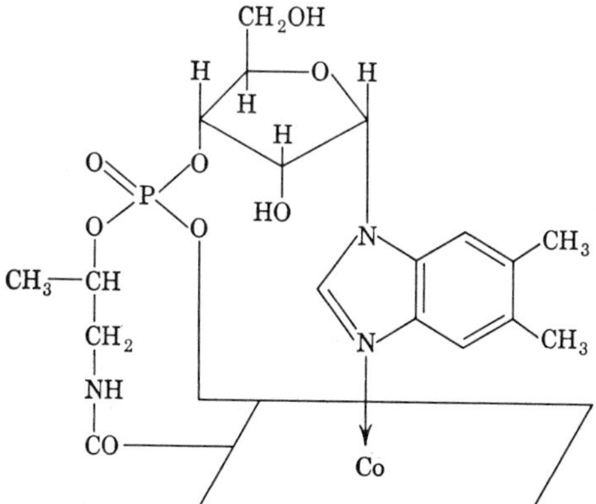

(**24**)

38. G. Cooley, M. T. Davies, B. Ellis, V. Petrow, and B. Sturgeon, *J. Pharm. Pharmacol.*, 5, 257 (1953).
39. J. B. Armitage, J. R. Cannon, A. W. Johnson, L. F. J. Parker, E. L. Smith, W. H. Stafford, and A. R. Todd, *J. Chem. Soc.*, 3849 (1953).

remaining studies, concerned especially with the detailed structure of the polycyclic nucleus surrounding the cobalt atom, were completed, only a minor modification of this partial structure was necessary.

D. The Corrin Moiety

1. THE PRIMARY AMIDE FUNCTIONS. Ammonia was recognized by all early investigators studying the hydrolytic degradation of cyanocobalamin, and in view of the presence of fourteen nitrogen atoms in the molecule, a quantitative determination of the ammonia liberated was of specific interest. Three determinations of the ammonia liberated after treating cyanocobalamin with 20% hydrochloric acid at 100° gave an average value of 5.74%.[38] This determination corresponded to six moles of ammonia per mole of cyanocobalamin. Hydrolysis of cyanocobalamin with barium hydroxide at 100° liberated five moles of ammonia,[39] and five to six moles of ammonia was generated from cyanocobalamin hydrolyzed in a mixture of dilute hydrochloric acid and butanol under reducing conditions.[40] Theoretically, the vitamin should yield seven moles of ammonia.

The nature of the moieties of cyanocobalamin that are susceptible to hydrolytic cleavage was investigated in a detailed study of the red cobalt-containing hydrolytic fragments of cyanocobalamin by electrophoresis and paper chromatography.[39] These experiments showed that alkaline or dilute acid hydrolysis of cyanocobalamin proceeded first with the release of the cyanide group and the evolution of ammonia. Next, the labile primary amide groups were converted to carboxyl groups. With cold dilute acid or alkaline hydrolysis, the nucleotide and 1-amino-2-propanol moieties were not liberated. If hot dilute acid or a mixture of dilute acid and nitrous acid was used, additional primary amide groups were hydrolyzed; under certain of the latter conditions the nucleotide moiety was liberated prior to or during the hydrolysis of these amide groups. Hydrolytic conditions were also found for the liberation of the nucleotide moiety without attacking the amide functions. For example, when cyanocobalamin was treated with concentrated hydrochloric acid at 65° for five minutes or at room temperature overnight, only the nucleotide moiety was liberated. There was little or no attack on the cyanide group or the amide linkages, and the 1-amino-2-propanol moiety was retained in the red cobalt-containing pigment. This hydrolytic product was identical with Factor B which was also recognized as a microbiologically active fecal component.[41]

40. H. Schmid, A. Ebnother, and P. Karrer, *Helv. Chim. Acta*, *36*, 65 (1953).
41. J. E. Ford and J. W. G. Porter, *Biochem. J.*, *51*, v (1952).

The hydrolysis products of most useful interest to elucidate the nature of the amide moieties of cyanocobalamin were those obtained by hydrolysis with either dilute or concentrated acid. Dilute acid hydrolyzates, composed of nucleotide-containing pigments, were separated by electrophoresis into five uniformly spaced red zones containing compounds of similar molecular weight but with no or one to four acidic groups. Each electrophoretic zone was purified by paper chromatography. The zones corresponding to a monocarboxylic acid fraction and a dicarboxylic acid fraction were purified by paper chromatography, and each yielded three distinct compounds. The zone corresponding to the tricarboxylic acid fraction appeared homogeneous on chromatography. In this way, three monobasic acids, three dibasic acids, and one tribasic acid were prepared, and it was postulated that the vitamin contained at least three labile primary amide groups.

This interpretation was confirmed by converting the isomeric carboxylic acids to cyanocobalamin through the intermediate formation of a mixed anhydride, followed by reaction with ammonia.[39,42] Infrared absorption bands corresponding to both substituted and unsubstituted amide functions were also apparent in the spectrum of cyanocobalamin; the complexity of the spectrum, however, relegated these data to a purely supportive role.

The corresponding mono-, di-, and tricarboxylic acids without the nucleotide moiety were isolated after dilute acid hydrolysis of Factor B. Resynthesis of Factor B through an intermediate mixed anhydride and ammonia was also accomplished.

Evidence for other nucleotide-free carboxylic acids was obtained as follows. Cyanocobalamin and many related substances and degradation products form purple complexes on treatment with aqueous potassium cyanide. These compounds have an additional negative charge due to the second cyanide group and, with the exception of the nucleotide-free compounds, are relatively unstable. By virtue of their apparently greater stability, hydrolysis mixtures containing nucleotide-free carboxylic acids gave, on electrophoresis in buffer solutions containing cyanide, a series of eight uniformly spaced zones corresponding to compounds having no or one to seven acidic groups.

Hydrolysis of cyanocobalamin with 30% sodium hydroxide solution at 150° yielded a mixture of compounds containing five and six acidic groups.

On the basis of all these hydrolytic data, it appeared that the vitamin

42. R. J. McConnel, B. G. Owerell, V. Petrow, and B. Sturgeon, *J. Pharm. Pharmacol.*, *5*, 179 (1953).

contains at least three labile primary amide groups and in addition, a secondary amide group containing the 1-amino-2-propanol moiety.

2. THE PYRROLE-LIKE RINGS OF THE CORRIN MOIETY. The elucidation of the remainder of the cyanocobalamin structure rested upon oxidation studies on the organochemical side, and on X-ray crystallographic studies on the physicochemical side. The latter contributed significantly to the details of the "macro ring" around the cobalt atom and to the stereochemistry of the entire molecule.

Early evidence supported the presence of pyrrole-like moieties in cyanocobalamin. Alkali fusion of the vitamin gave a distillate that showed pyrrole-type reactions,[17] and related evidence was derived from a study of cobalt coordination complexes of porphyrins.[42] When a mixed ester fraction derived from a hydrolysis mixture from cyanocobalamin was oxidized with potassium permanganate under alkaline conditions, eight acids were isolated and crystallized. Four of these acids were identified as oxalic, succinic, methylsuccinic, and dimethylmalonic acid.[40]

Oxidation of an acid hydrolyzate of cyanocobalamin with sodium chromate in acetic acid yielded two substituted succinimides that were identified by degradation and synthesis as *DL*-3,3-dimethyl-2,5-dioxo-4-hydroxypyrrolidine-4-propionic acid lactone (**25**) and *DL*-3,3-dimethyl-2,5-dioxopyrrolidine-4-propionic acid (**26**).[43] When cyanocobalamin

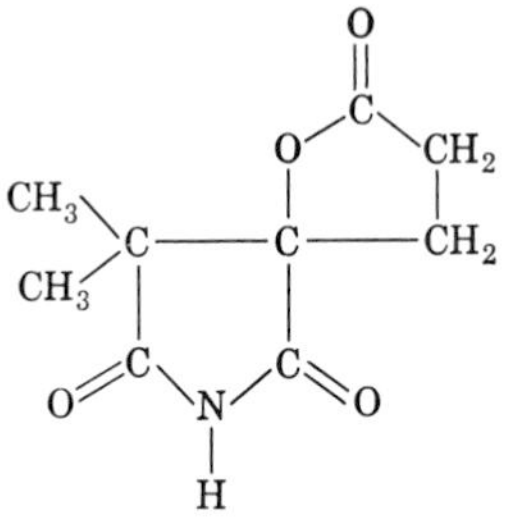

(25)

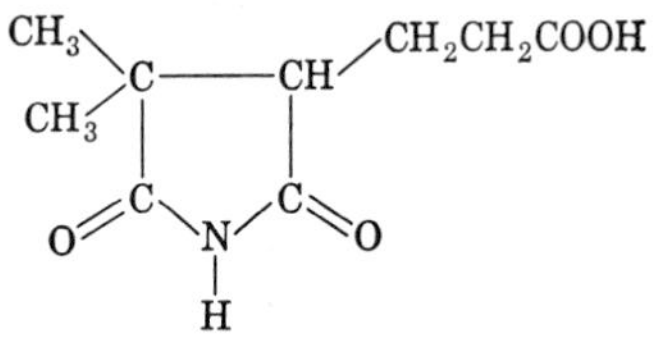

(26)

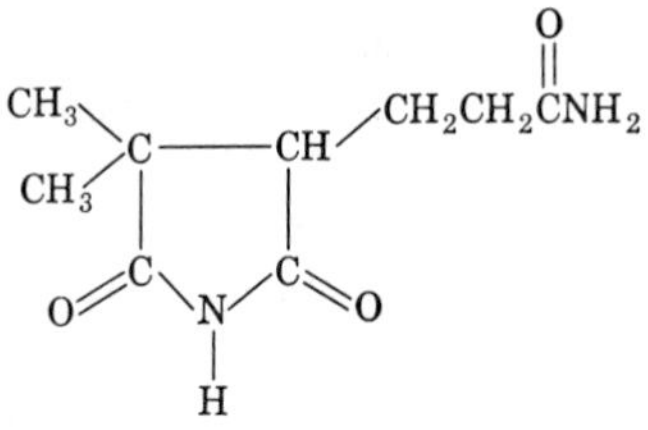

(27)

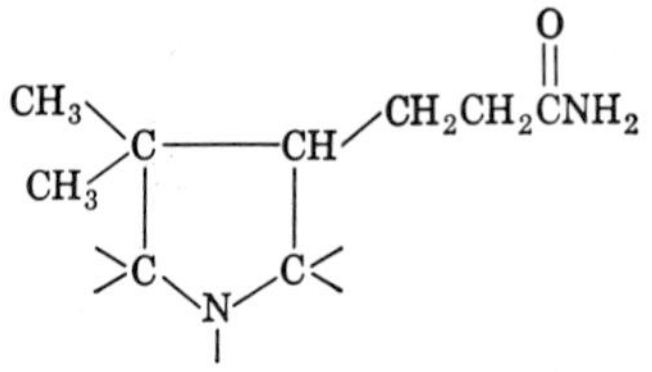

(28)

43. F. A. Kuehl, C. H. Shunk, and K. Folkers, *J. Am. Chem. Soc.*, *77*, 251 (1955).

itself was oxidized in acetic acid solution with sodium chromate, a third crystalline succinimide derivative was obtained and identified as 3,3-dimethyl-2,5-dioxopyrrolidine-4-propionamide (**27**).[44] The isolation of these succinimides constituted proof for the existence of a 3,3-dimethyl-pyrrolidine-4-propionamide-like moiety (**28**) in the vitamin, and provided the first detailed degradative evidence for the porphyrin-like character of the tetranuclear corrin moiety.

E. X-Ray Diffraction Data—The Coordination Complex

X-Ray crystallographic studies on cyanocobalamin[45,46] and a hexa-carboxylic acid degradation product[47,48] led to the clarification of the

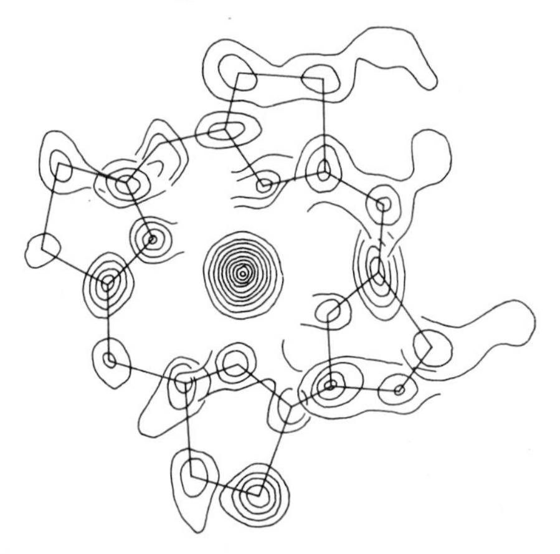

Fig. 1. Positions of the atoms in the "planar" group of cyanocobalamin. Reprinted through the courtesy of NATURE.

remaining features of the structure of the vitamin. Figure 1 shows the positions of the atoms in the "planar" or corrin ring.

Figure 2 shows the atomic positions in the entire cyanocobalamin molecule as determined by crystallographic studies. Additional details concerning this structure have been summarized.[16]

44. F. A. Kuehl, C. H. Shunk, M. V. Moore, and K. Folkers, *J. Am. Chem. Soc.*, *77*, 4418 (1955).
45. D. C. Hodgkin, J. Kamper, M. Mackay, J. Pickworth, K. N. Trueblood, and J. G. White, *Nature*, *178*, 64 (1956).
46. D. C. Hodgkin, J. Pickworth, J. H. Robertson, K. N. Trueblood, R. J. Prösen, J. G. White, R. Bonnett, J. R. Cannon, A. W. Johnson, I. Sutherland, A. R. Todd, and E. L. Smith, *Nature*, *176*, 325 (1955).
47. R. Bonnett, J. R. Cannon, A. W. Johnson, and A. R. Todd, *J. Chem. Soc.*, 1148 (1957).
48. J. R. Cannon, A. W. Johnson, and A. R. Todd, *Nature*, *174*, 1168 (1954).

Cyanocobalamin is a neutral cobalt coordination complex. The cobalt atom is in the trivalent state and has the coordination number six. The cyano group and one nitrogen atom in the corrin nucleus contribute two negative charges and satisfy two coordinate linkages. The remaining three nitrogen atoms of the corrin ring and *N*-3 of the benzimidazole nucleus

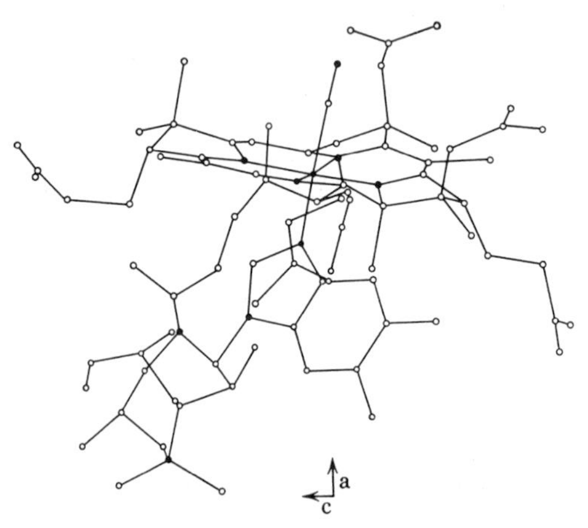

Fig. 2. Atomic positions in cyanocobalamin. Reprinted through the courtesy of NATURE.

contribute four neutral groups satisfying the remaining four coordination requirements. Since there are only two negative groups, the trivalent cobalt atom retains a positive charge that is neutralized by the phosphate anion giving a cyanocobalamin molecule that is neutral. The coordination complex has been depicted as in **(29)** in which the two minus signs and the

$$[\mathrm{Co}^{3+}\ 0000^{--}]^{+} > \overset{\overset{\displaystyle \mathrm{O}}{\|}}{\mathrm{P}}\text{—}\mathrm{O}^{-}$$

(29)

four ciphers denote the charged and neutral groups constituting the six coordinate linkages.

The cyanocobalamin molecule is built around the central cobalt atom in a compact arrangement. The benzimidazole nucleus is approximately perpendicular to the corrin nucleus; the ribofuranose ring is nearly perpendicular to the benzimidazole nucleus and nearly parallel with the corrin nucleus. The cyano group is depicted on one side, and the nucleotide moiety is depicted on the other side of the corrin nucleus. All of these groups compose the octahedron of the complex. The six groups which are linked coordinately to the cobalt atom are each approximately 1.9Å from the cobalt atom. The phosphate anion and the cobalt atom are approximately 9Å apart.

The three acetic acid and four propionic acid side chains, which are linked to the β-positions of the component rings of the corrin moiety, bear a close relationship in number and orientation to the four acetic acid and four propionic acid side chains in uroporphyrin-III (**30**). The

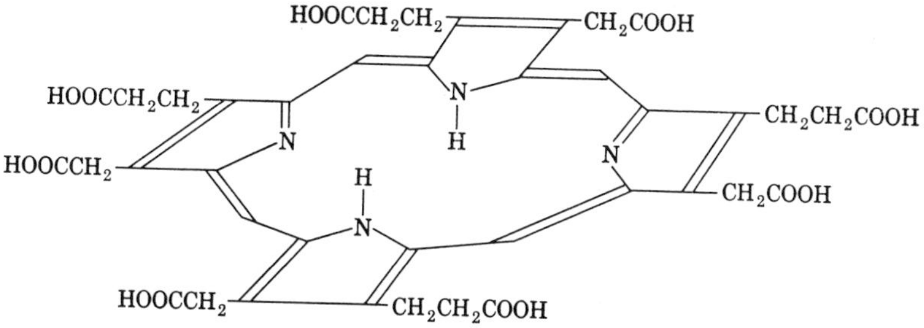

(30)

propionic acid side chains are on the same side of the corrin nucleus as the benzimidazole nucleus; the acetic acid chains are on the other side of the corrin nucleus with the cyano group. The propionic acid side chains and the propanolamine moiety have the expected staggered configurations.

The four rings of the corrin moiety constitute a nearly planar nucleus. Three of the linkages between the 5-membered rings are through bridge carbon atoms as in the porphyrins, but the fourth bond is a direct link between the α-position of two of these rings. All four nitrogen atoms and

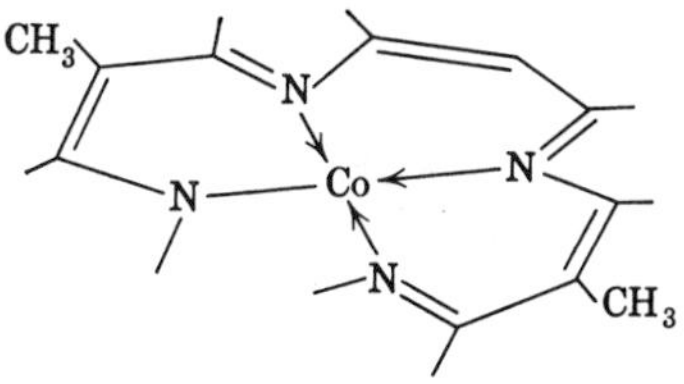

(31)

the nine carbon atoms which directly surround the cobalt atom, as well as the two methyl groups and the cobalt atom, are within 0.15Å of a single plane. The four nitrogen- and nine carbon atoms constituting the so-called "inner thirteen atoms" are, in essence, a nucleus containing six conjugated double bonds which with the cobalt atom forms the resonant chromaphore (**31**). The four nitrogen atoms of this system are nearly equivalent in two pairs.

4. Nomenclature

In view of the great array of degradation products that were characterized during the elucidation of structure of this vitamin, and especially the increasing number of modifications of the molecule that were prepared by synthesis and biosynthesis, it became apparent that a fundamental nomenclature system was required. A nomenclature committee submitted

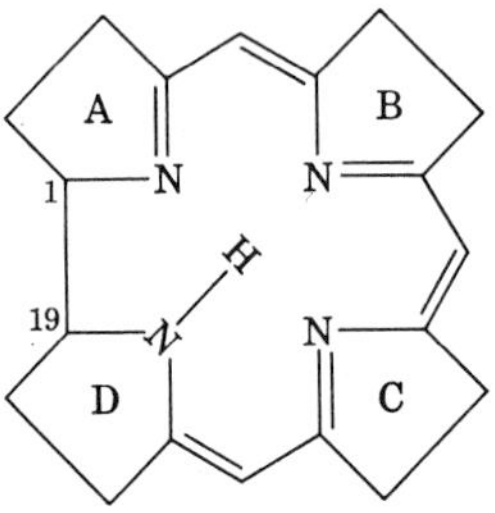

Corrin (32)

a basic proposal of "tentative" rules;[49] this nomenclature was published in 1960.[50]

The macro ring system (**32**) containing four nitrogen-containing 5-membered rings joined through three bridge carbon atoms is designated

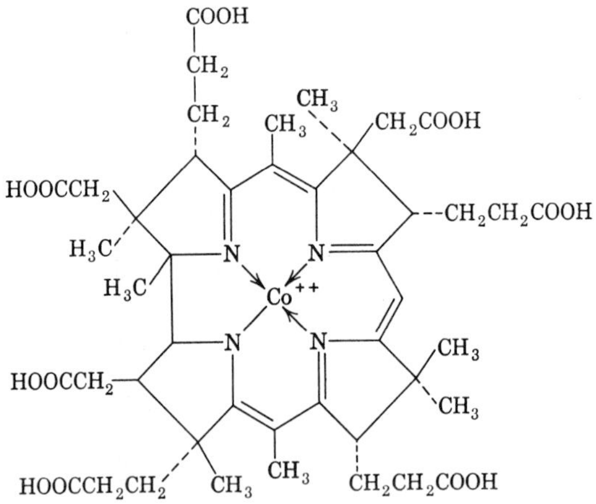

Cobyrinic acid (33)

49. E. L. Smith, in H. C. Heinrich, ed., *Vitamin B_{12} und Intrinsic Factor*, Ferdinand Enke Verlag, Stuttgart, 1957, p. 554.
50. IUPAC, *Commission on the Nomenclature of Biological Chemistry*, *J. Am. Chem. Soc.*, *82*, 5581 (1960).

corrin. The rings are lettered to correspond with the porphyrin series. Numbering of the carbon atoms proceeds clockwise, starting from the carbon atom of ring A involved in the direct α,α-link. Metal derivatives of this compound are designated with the corresponding prefix as in *cobalto-corrin*, *cobalti-corrin*, etc.

The heptacarboxylic acid (**33**), derived from cyanocobalamin by converting all the amide groups to carboxyl groups, is designated *cobyrinic acid.*

The nucleotide-free hexacarboxylic acid (**34**), in which all amide linkages but the propanolamide are converted to carboxyl groups, is designated *cobinic acid*; the corresponding nucleotide-free compound (**35**), in which all original amide groups are intact, is referred to as *cobinamide*.

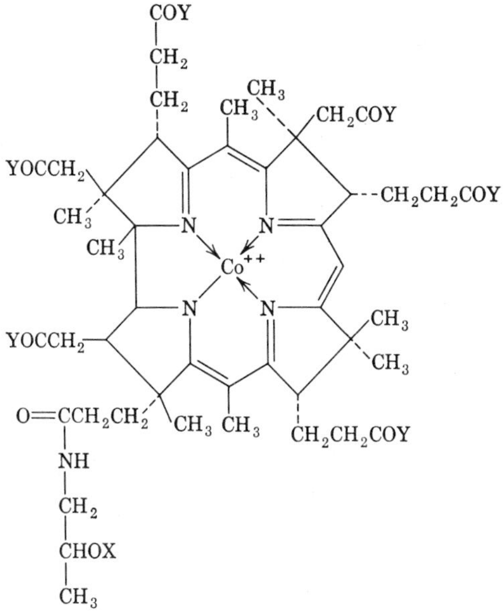

Cobinic acid (**34**): Y = OH, X = H
Cobinamide (**35**): Y = NH_2, X = H
Cobamic acid (**36**): Y = OH, X =

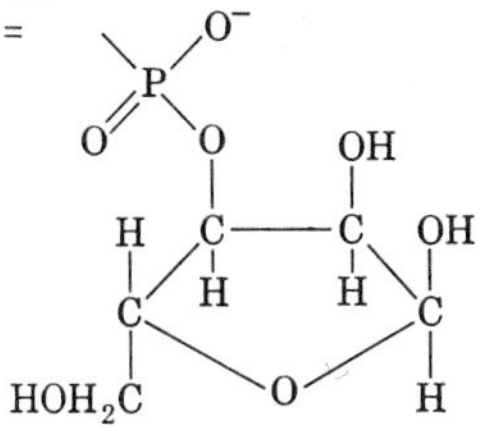

Cobamide (**37**): Y = NH_2, X as in (**36**)

The ribose 3-phosphate-containing hexacarboxylic acid (**36**), in which the primary amide groups are converted to carboxyl groups, is designated *cobamic acid.* The corresponding structure (**37**), in which the carboxyl groups are converted to carbamido groups, is designated *cobamide.*

The term cobalamin is reserved for its original meaning; namely, cyanocobalamin without the cyano group. Under this nomenclature system, cyanocobalamin is designated α-(5,6-dimethylbenzimidazolyl)-cobamide cyanide. By way of further illustration, the analogs of vitamin B_{12} in which the 5,6-dimethylbenzimidazole moiety is replaced by 5-hydroxybenzimidazole (Factor III) or by adenine (ψ-vitamin B_{12}) are designated α-(5-hydroxybenzimidazolyl)cobamide cyanide and α-adenylcobamide cyanide, respectively.

5. Modifications of Cyanocobalamin

A. Replacement of the Cyano Group

Early in the study of cyanocobalamin, it was found that other charged groups and neutral molecules could replace the cyano group.[51,52] For example, vitamin B_{12a} (also designated aquocobalamin and hydroxocobalamin) and other complexes such as chlorocobalamin, thiocyanatocobalamin, cyanatocobalamin, and nitritocobalamin were reported. The microbiological activity of many of these compounds was found to depend upon the conditions of the assay and varied from 30 to 100% of that of cyanocobalamin.

B. Controlled Oxidation Products

Controlled oxidation of cyanocobalamin yielded two interesting though biologically inactive modifications of the vitamin.[53] Air oxidation of cyanocobalamin under mild alkaline conditions yielded dehydrovitamin B_{12} (**38**) in which the acetamido group of the B-ring of the corrin moiety is cyclized, forming a fused γ-lactam ring. This product is practically identical to cyanocobalamin in its physical properties, but it is almost without biological activity. The corresponding γ-lactone form (**39**) was obtained after treating cyanocobalamin with one equivalent of *N*-chloroamides, bromine water, or iodine in alkaline solution. This lactone is biologically inactive.

51. E. A. Kaczka, D. E. Wolf, F. A. Kuehl, Jr., and K. Folkers, *Science*, *112*, 354 (1950).
52. E. A. Kaczka, D. E. Wolf, F. A. Kuehl, Jr., and K. Folkers, *J. Am. Chem. Soc.*, *73*, 3569 (1951).
53. R. Bonnett, J. R. Cannon, A. W. Johnson, L. F. J. Parker, E. L. Smith, and A. R. Todd, *J. Chem. Soc.*, 1158 (1957).

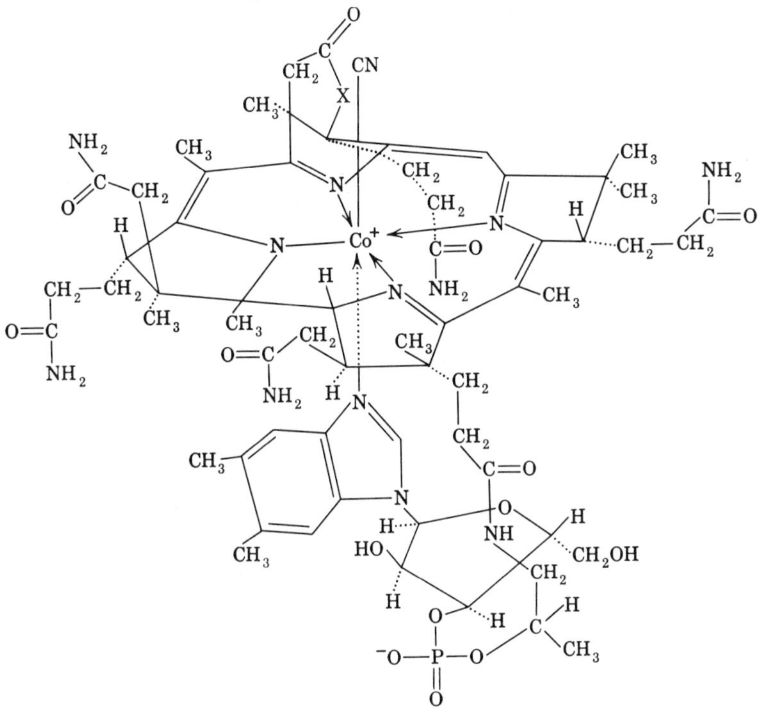

(38): X=NH
(39): X=O

C. *Replacement of the* 5,6-*Dimethylbenzimidazole Moiety*

Modifications of cyanocobalamin in which the 5,6-dimethylbenzimidazole moiety of the nucleotide is replaced by another nitrogen-containing base have been obtained from animal feces, from sewage, and by biosynthesis. The separation and identification of these complexes have been accomplished essentially by chromatography, electrophoresis, and solvent distribution. In each case, the total structure is identical with that of cyanocobalamin, except that the 5,6-dimethylbenzimidazole moiety (**40**) is replaced by a stereochemically corresponding group.

Examples of modifications in which the 5,6-dimethylbenzimidazole moiety is displaced by purine bases include pseudovitamin B_{12} (**41**), which is derived from adenine,[54] and Factor A (**42**), which contains the 2-methyladenine moiety.[55] The modifications designated Factors G and H (**43**

54. J. J. Pfiffner, H. W. Dion, and D. C. Calkins, *Proc. Soc. Exptl. Biol. Med.*, *11*, 269 (1952).
55. J. E. Ford, S. K. Kon, and J. W. G. Porter, *Biochem. J.*, *50*, ix (1951).

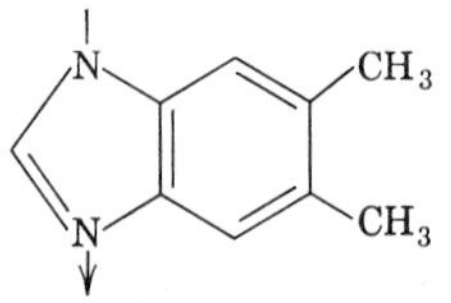

Cyanocobalamin
(40)

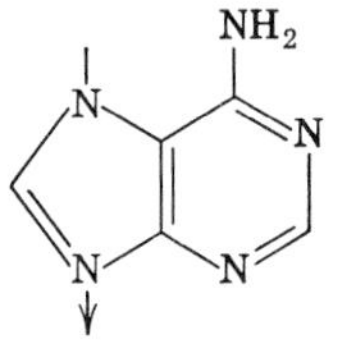

ψ-Vitamin B_{12}
(41)

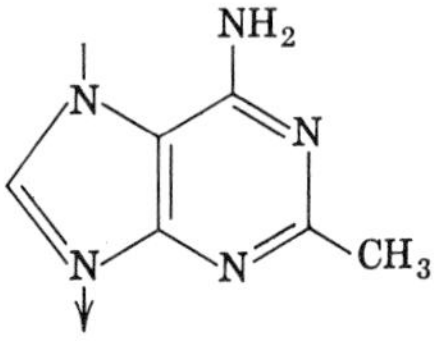

Factor A
(42)

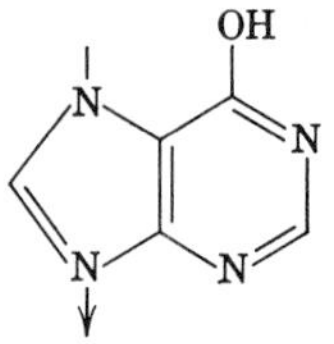

Factor G
(43)

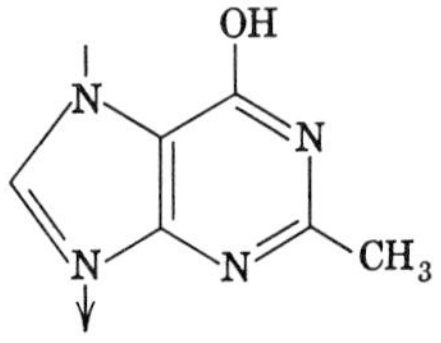

Factor H
(44)

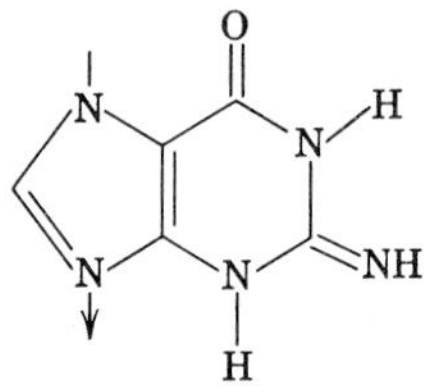

Guanine Analog
(45)

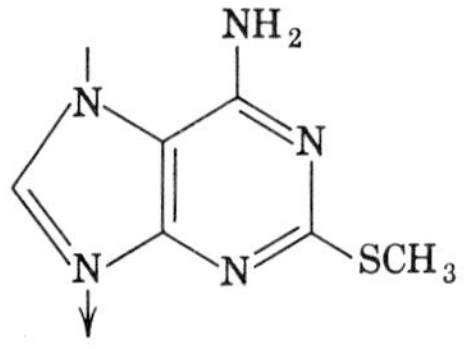

2-Methylmercaptoadenine Analog
(46)

and **44**) are derived from hypoxanthine and 2-methylhypoxanthine, either by direct biosynthesis or by chemical displacement of the 6-amino group of adenine or 2-methyladenine.[56] A guanine analog (**45**) and a 2-methylmercaptoadenine analog (**46**) are among the recent modifications of cyanocobalamin to be isolated from sewage sludge.[57,58]

56. F. B. Brown, J. C. Cain, D. E. Gant, L. F. J. Parker, and E. L. Smith, *Biochem. J.*, *59*, 82 (1955).
57. W. Friedrich and K. Bernhauer, *Angew. Chem.*, *71*, 311 (1959).
58. W. Friedrich and K. Bernhauer, *Ber.*, *90*, 1966 (1957).

With the exception of Factors G and H, these purine base analogs of cyanocobalamin possess significant microbiological activity. However, all such modifications exhibit slight, if any, activity for the growth of animals comparable to that of cyanocobalamin.

All of the aforementioned analogs of cyanocobalamin containing purine bases have N-7 ribosylpurines coordinately linked to the rest of the molecule through N-9. More recently, a new fermentation factor of the vitamin B_{12} group was obtained which is novel in several respects.[59,60] The compound, designated Factor 1, is a guanosine diphosphate derivative of Factor B. The ribose moiety is apparently linked to Factor B through a pyrophosphate bridge at one end and the ribosyl link is at N-9 rather than N-7 of the purine. The latter report is unique in the chemistry of cyanocobalamin analogs.

Analogs of cyanocobalamin in which the 5,6-dimethylbenzimidazole moiety is replaced by other benzimidazole derivatives are also known.

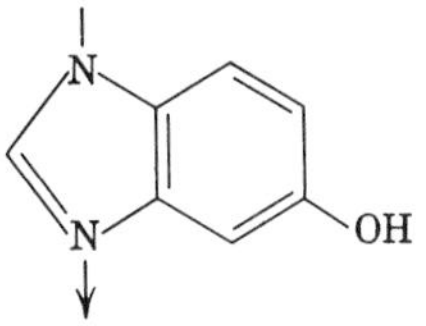

Factor III
(47)

Factor III, a benzimidazole analog which was isolated from sewage,[61] contains the 5-hydroxybenzimidazole moiety (**47**).[62] The majority of these analogs are readily obtained by biosynthetic incorporation during fermentation. At least fifteen to twenty benzimidazole analogs of cyanocobalamin have been obtained by biosynthetic incorporation.

When Factor B, the acid degradation product of cyanocobalamin possessing all of the structure except the nucleotide, and an appropriate purine or benzimidazole derivative were incorporated in a medium for the growth of *Escherichia coli* 113-3, the corresponding cobalt complex was formed.[63] Although biosynthesis with either resting or growing cells of *E. coli* required the addition of Factor B, it was possible to obtain similar

59. G. Boretti, A. DiMarco, L. Fuoco, M. P. Marnati, A. Migliacci, and C. Spalla, *Biochim. et Biophys. Acta*, *37*, 380 (1960).
60. R. Barchielli, G. Boretti, A. DiMarco, P. Julita, A. Migliacci, A. Minghetti, and C. Spalla, *Biochem. J.*, *74*, 382 (1960).
61. W. Friedrich and K. Bernhauer, *Angew. Chem.*, *65*, 627 (1953).
62. C. H. Shunk, F. M. Robinson, J. F. McPherson, M. M. Gasser, and K. Folkers, *J. Am. Chem. Soc.*, *78*, 3228 (1956).
63. J. E. Ford, E. S. Holdsworth, and S. K. Kon, *Biochem. J.*, *59*, 87 (1955).

cobalt complexes from *S. griseus* merely by incorporating the base into the medium.[64] In some cases evidence for the formation of the complex consisted only of an appropriately differentiated pink spot on a paper chromatogram; in other instances the fermentations were "scaled up," and the cobalt complexes were recovered in crystalline form. For example, crystalline cobalt complexes were obtained with nucleotide base moieties from benzimidazole (**48**), 5,6-dichlorobenzimidazole (**49**), 2,3-naphthimidazole (**50**), 5,6-diethylbenzimidazole (**51**), 5(6)-aminobenzimidazole (**52**), and 5(6)-trifluoromethylbenzimidazole (**53**).[65–68] A recent benzimid-

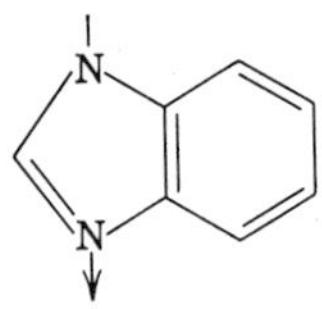

(48)

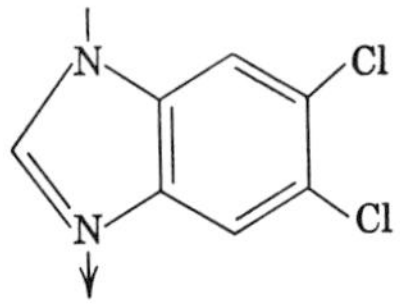

(49)

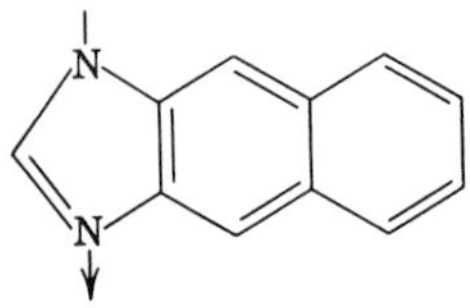

(50)

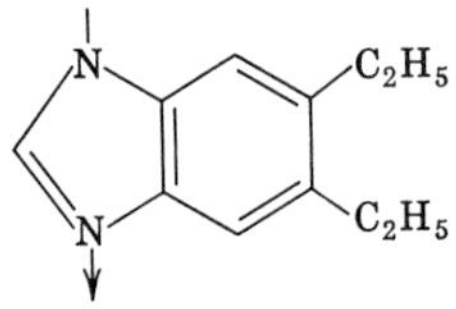

(51)

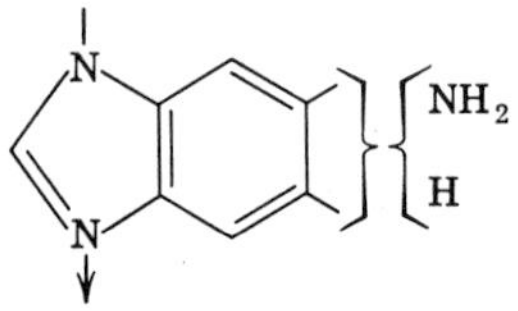

(52)

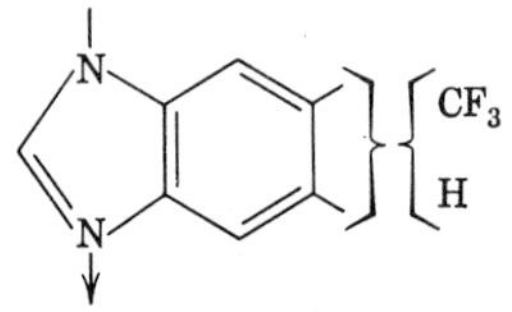

(53)

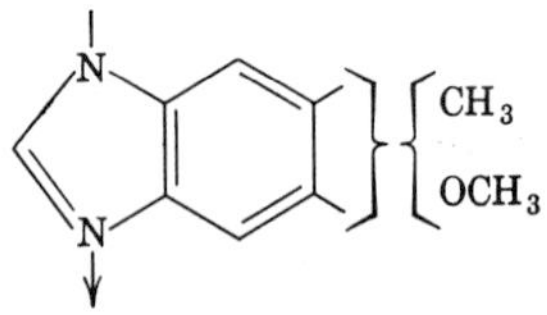

Factor S
(54)

64. K. H. Fantes and C. H. O'Callaghan, *Biochem. J.*, *58*, xxi (1954).
65. H. Dellweg, E. Becher, and K. Bernhauer, *Biochem. Z.*, *327*, 422 (1956).
66. K. H. Fantes and C. H. O'Callaghan, in H. Heinrich, ed., *Vitamin B_{12} und Intrinsic Factor*, Ferdinand Enke Verlag, Stuttgart, 1957, p. 60.
67. K. H. Fantes and C. H. O'Callaghan, *Biochem. J.*, *67*, 619 (1956).
68. K. H. Fantes and C. H. O'Callaghan, *Biochem. J.*, *59*, 87 (1955).

azole analog to be described is designated Factor S (**54**).[69] This biosynthetic product, obtained from a *Propionibacterium* fermentation using the 5-methyl-6-methoxybenzimidazole precursor, was from one-half to two-thirds as active as cyanocobalamin for the growth of *Ochromonas malhamensis*.

D. Replacement of the α-Ribazole Phosphate and 1-Amino-2-propanol Moieties

Analogs of cyanocobalamin in which the α-ribazole phosphate and 1-amino-2-propanol moieties are replaced by an alkanolamine moiety have been synthesized. The starting compound for the synthesis of these analogs is Factor V_{1a} (**55**); this factor was isolated from sewage sludge in 1960,[70] and its structure was established as dicyanocobyrinic acid-*abcdeg*-hexamide.[71]

The synthesis of these new analogs proceeds by the conversion of Factor V_{1a} (**55**) to the corresponding mixed anhydride at the *f*-carboxyl group, followed by reaction with an appropriately substituted alkanolamine.[72–78] In this manner, the *N*-(2-hydroxyethyl)-*f*-amide[72] (**56**), [*N*-(2-hydroxypropyl)-*f*-amide]-dihydrogen phosphate[73] (**57**), *N*-(1-carboxy-2-hydroxyethyl)-*f*-amide[74] (**58**), *N*-(1-carboxy-3-hydroxypropyl)-*f*-amide[75] (**59**), *N*-(1-carboxy-2-hydroxypropyl)-*f*-amide[74] (**60**), and *N*-(1-carboxy-2-hydroxy-2-phenethyl)-*f*-amide[75] (**61**) of Factor V_{1a} were synthesized. The corresponding dihydrogen phosphate esters (**62**) and (**63**) were synthesized by reacting the mixed anhydride of Factor V_{1a} with serine phosphate and threonine phosphate, respectively.[78]

The microbiological activity of these analogs was determined with *O. malhamensis* and *E. coli* 113-3, and on the basis of these studies,[77] it was concluded that the methyl group of the 1-amino-2-propanol moiety is important for the microbiological activity of cyanocobalamin and related compounds. Replacement of the methyl group by hydrogen resulted in a

69. I. Molnar and W. Taterka, *Chimia (Aarau)*, *13*, 292 (1959).
70. K. Bernhauer, H. Dellweg, W. Friedrich, G. Gross, F. Wagner, and P. Zeller, *Helv. Chim. Acta*, *43*, 693 (1960).
71. K. Bernhauer, F. Wagner, and P. Zeller, *Helv. Chim. Acta*, *43*, 696 (1960).
72. K. Bernhauer and F. Wagner, *Z. Physiol. Chem.*, *322*, 184 (1960).
73. K Bernhauer, F. Wagner, H. Dellweg, and P. Zeller, *Helv. Chim. Acta*, *43*, 700 (1960).
74. K. Bernhauer and H. Dellweg, *Z. Physiol. Chem.*, *322*, 190 (1960).
75. K. Bernhauer and F. Wagner, *Z. Physiol. Chem.*, *322*, 194 (1960).
76. W. Friedrich and H. C. Heinrich, *Biochem. Z.*, *333*, 550 (1961).
77. W. Friedrich, H. C. Heinrich, E. Gabbe, C. Nardin, and P. Riedel, *Biochem. Z.*, *333*, 554 (1961).
78. K. Bernhauer and F. Wagner, *Biochem. Z.*, *335*, 325 (1962).

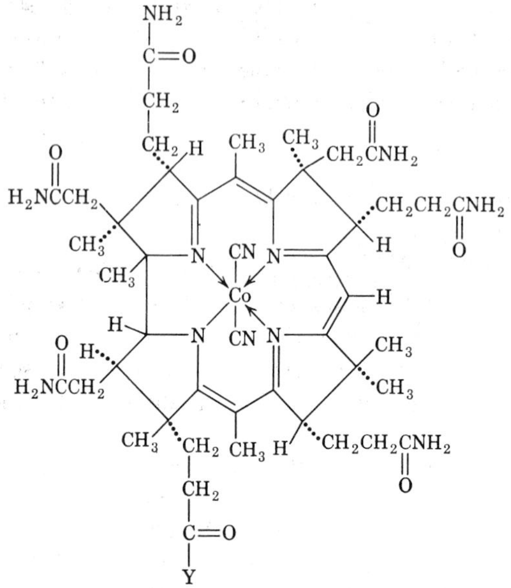

(55): Y=OH; Factor V_{1a} (Dicyanocobyrinic acid-*abcdeg*-hexamide)

(56): $Y{=}NHCH_2CH_2OH$

(57): $Y{=}NHCH_2CHOP(O)(OH)_2$, with CH_3 on CH

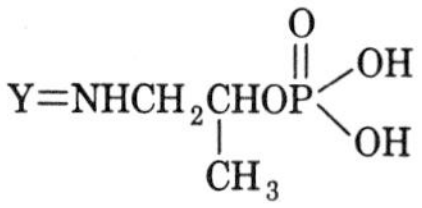

(58): $Y{=}NHCHCH_2OH$, with COOH on CH

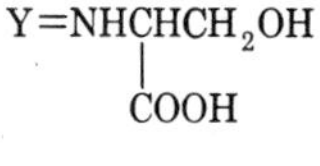

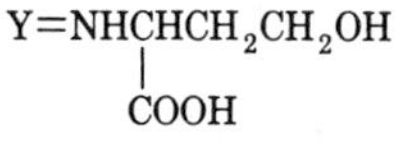

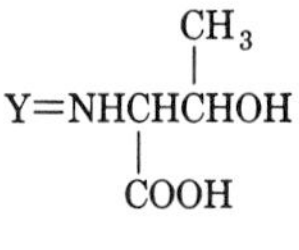

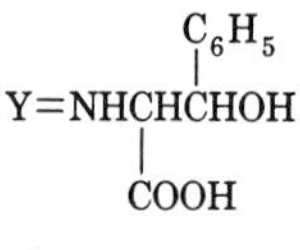

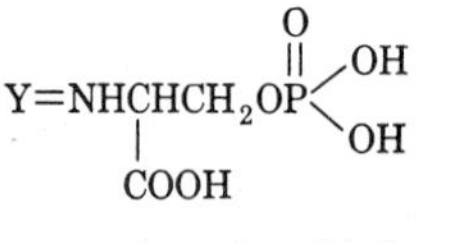

(59): $Y{=}NHCHCH_2CH_2OH$, with COOH on CH

(60): $Y{=}NHCHCHOH$, with COOH and CH_3

(61): $Y{=}NHCHCHOH$, with COOH and C_6H_5

(62): $Y{=}NHCHCH_2OP(O)(OH)_2$, with COOH on CH

(63): $Y{=}NHCHCHOP(O)(OH)_2$, with COOH and CH_3

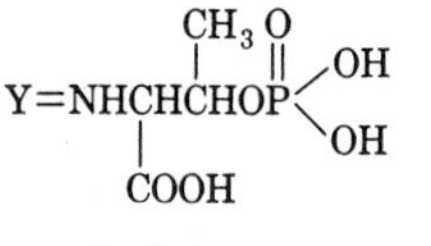

significant decrease in microbiological activity relative to cyanocobalamin; substitution of a phenyl or benzyl group for methyl in the 1-amino-2-propanol moiety produced a complete loss of activity. The configuration of the 1-amino-2-propanol moiety had no influence on microbiological activity.

6. Synthesis

Cyanocobalamin and its related analogs are produced commercially by fermentation for medical and other biological uses. Until recently, studies on synthesis were conducted almost exclusively for proof of structure of various degradation products and for the preparation of biosynthetic precursors.

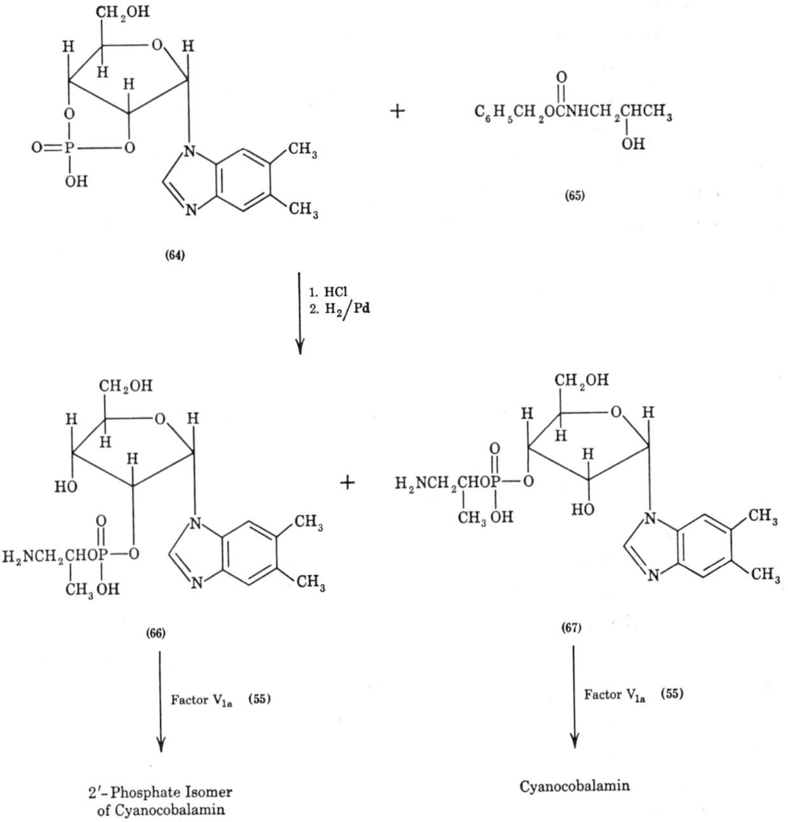

(64) + $C_6H_5CH_2OCONHCH_2CH(OH)CH_3$ (65)

1. HCl
2. H_2/Pd

(66) + (67)

(66) → Factor V_{1a} (55) → 2′-Phosphate Isomer of Cyanocobalamin

(67) → Factor V_{1a} (55) → Cyanocobalamin

The partial synthesis of cyanocobalamin from Factor V_{1a} (**55**) has been achieved.[79] For this synthesis, 1-α-*D*-ribofuranosyl-5,6-dimethylbenzimidazole (**6**) was converted to the corresponding 2′,3′-cyclic phosphate (**64**),

79. W. Friedrich, G. Gross, K. Bernhauer, and P. Zeller, *Helv. Chim. Acta*, *43*, 704 (1960).

which in turn was condensed with *D*-1-benzyloxycarbonylamino-2-propanol (**65**). After the carbobenzyloxy group was removed by hydrogenolysis, the reaction mixture was resolved by chromatography. Unreacted α-ribazole phosphate was separated from the mixture by ion exchange chromatography; the reaction mixture was further purified by chromatography on DEAE cellulose, and then the 2′- and 3′-ribazole-aminoalkyl-hydrogen phosphates (**66**) and (**67**) were separated by paper chromatography. The 3′-ribazole-aminoalkyl-hydrogen phosphate (**67**) was converted to the corresponding sodium salt and condensed with the mixed anhydride of Factor V_{1a} to yield cyanocobalamin. Similar treatment of the 2′-ribazole-aminoalkyl-hydrogen phosphate (**66**) with the mixed anhydride of Factor V_{1a} yielded the corresponding isomer of cyanocobalamin which contains a 2′-ribose phosphate moiety.

Extensive exploratory studies of possible synthetic routes for the preparation of the corrin nucleus (**32**) have been reported.[80–86] This nucleus, unknown in organic chemistry prior to the structural elucidation of cyanocobalamin, differs from the closely related porphyrin nucleus by existing in an oxidation state intermediate between that of a pyrrole and a 1-pyrroline, and by having a direct α,α-link between rings A and D. The ring

(68) (69) (70) (71)

system may be visualized as containing two types of bicyclic components. The A-D bicyclic component is related to 2,2′-dipyrrolidinyl (**68**) which may be formally regarded as a reductive dimerization product of a 1-pyrroline (**69**); the B-C bicyclic component is related to di-(pyrrolidin-2-yl)methane (**70**). The latter compound may be visualized as a reduction product of a mixed aldol-type compound formed from 2-methyl-1-pyrroline 1-oxide (**71**) and 1-pyrroline 1-oxide.

80. R. Bonnett, V. M. Clark, A. Giddey, and A. Todd, *J. Chem. Soc.*, 2087 (1959).
81. R. Bonnett, R. F. C. Brown, V. M. Clark, I. O. Sutherland, and A. Todd, *J. Chem. Soc.*, 2094 (1959).
82. R. Bonnett, V. M. Clark, and A. Todd, *J. Chem. Soc.*, 2102 (1959).
83. R. F. C. Brown, V. M. Clark, and A. Todd, *J. Chem. Soc.*, 2105 (1959).
84. R. F. C. Brown, V. M. Clark, I. O. Sutherland, and A. Todd, *J. Chem. Soc.*, 2109 (1959).
85. R. F. C. Brown, V. M. Clark, M. Lampchen, and A. Todd, *J. Chem. Soc.*, 2116 (1959).
86. V. M. Clark, B. Sklarz, and A. Todd, *J. Chem. Soc.*, 2123 (1959).

Several suitably substituted di-(pyrrolidin-2-yl)methane- and 2,2′-dipyrrolidinyl derivatives have been prepared from the corresponding 1-pyrroline 1-oxides. For example, base catalyzed addition of the nitrone 2,4,4-trimethyl-1-pyrroline 1-oxide (**72**) to the nitrone 4,5,5-trimethyl-1-pyrroline 1-oxide (**73**) yielded 2-(1-hydroxy-4,5,5-trimethylpyrrolidin-2-ylmethyl)-4,4-dimethyl-1-pyrroline 1-oxide (**74**).[84] Potassium borohydride

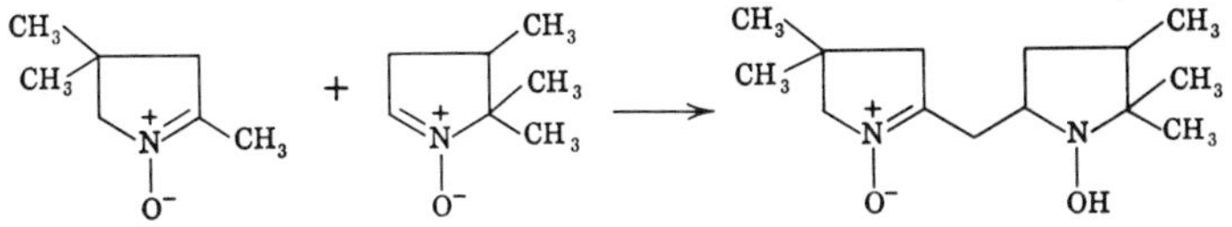

CH_3 CH_3 $\overset{+}{N}$ CH_3 O^- + CH_3 CH_3 CH_3 $\overset{+}{N}$ O^- → CH_3 CH_3 $\overset{+}{N}$ O^- CH_3 CH_3 CH_3 N OH

(72) (73) (74)

→ CH_3 CH_3 N OH CH_3 CH_3 CH_3 N OH → CH_3 CH_3 N H N CH_3 CH_3 CH_3

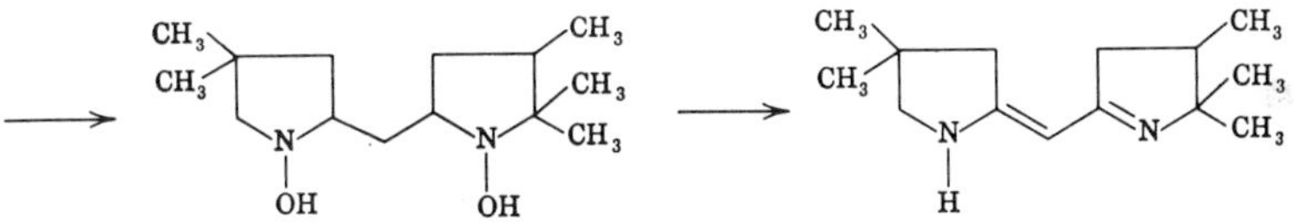

(75) (76)

reduction of the latter gave the corresponding *bis*-hydroxylamine (**75**), which on treatment with phosphorus oxychloride and triethylamine yielded 2-(4,4-dimethylpyrrolidin-2-ylidenemethyl)-4,5,5-trimethyl-1-pyrroline (**76**). The basicity and spectral characteristics of this product suggested that it existed as a vinylogous amidine.

Derivatives corresponding to the 2,2′-dipyrrolidinyl moiety (**68**) were synthesized by the catalytic dimerization of corresponding 1-pyrroline

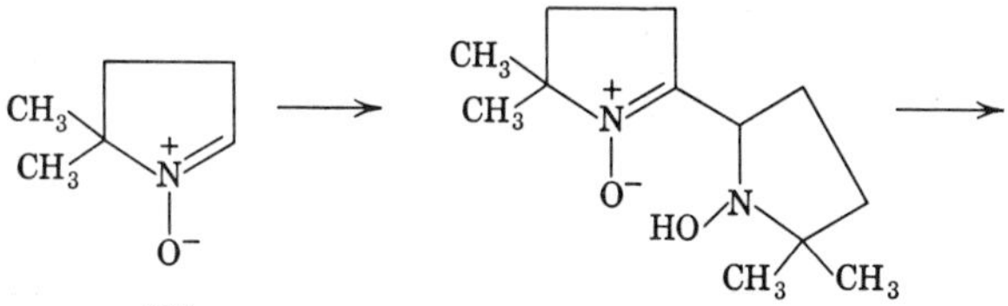

CH_3 CH_3 $\overset{+}{N}$ O^- → CH_3 CH_3 $\overset{+}{N}$ O^- HO N CH_3 CH_3 →

(77) (78)

CH_3 CH_3 N H H N CH_3 CH_3

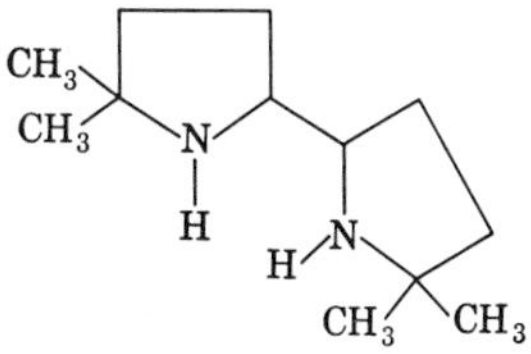

(79)

1-oxides. For example, dimerization of 5,5-dimethyl-1-pyrroline 1-oxide (**77**) yielded 2-(1-hydroxy-5,5-dimethylpyrrolidin-2-yl)-5,5-dimethyl-1-pyrroline 1-oxide (**78**).[85,86] Reduction of the latter yielded the corresponding *bis*-hydroxylamine, which on reduction with zinc and hydrochloric acid yielded 5,5,5′,5′-tetramethyl-2,2′-dipyrrolidinyl (**79**).

7. Metabolic Role

Although it is established that cyanocobalamin is required for the maintenance of growth, neural function, and blood formation, its effects cannot be explained in terms of specific metabolic functions. The direct or indirect intervention of the vitamin in the metabolism of protein, nucleic acid, carbohydrate, and fat has been demonstrated in the intact animal, and its effect on a number of reactions in intermediary metabolism has been elucidated. The function of cyanocobalamin in individual metabolic reactions in these areas has also been studied at the cellular and subcellular level.

A. Single-Carbon Unit Metabolism

A function for the vitamin in the metabolism of labile methyl groups was suggested when rats receiving cyanocobalamin continued to grow on choline- and methionine-free diets containing homocystine.[87] The prevention of a characteristic hemorrhagic kidney syndrome by the administration of cyanocobalamin to weanling rats fed choline-free diets constituted additional evidence for this function.[88] Further insight into this role was obtained from a study of the biosynthesis of labile methyl groups in vitamin B_{12}-deficient rats and baby pigs that were fed C^{14}-labeled methyl group precursors; in these studies, cyanocobalamin was shown to enhance the *in vivo* synthesis of choline- and methionine-methyl groups from formate, the β-carbon of serine, and the α-carbon of glycine.[89–91] From these and subsequent studies it was found that cyanocobalamin participates in the *de novo* synthesis of labile methyl groups but has no influence on the efficiency of transmethylation in methionine and choline

87. M. A. Bennett, *J. Biol. Chem.*, *187*, 751 (1950).
88. A. E. Schaefer, W. D. Salmon, and D. R. Strength, *Federation Proc.*, *9*, 369 (1950).
89. H. R V. Arnstein and A. Neuberger, *Biochem. J.*, *55*, 259 (1953).
90. B. C. Johnson, J. Firth, and S. P. Mistry, *Arch. Biochem. Biophys.*, *54*, 467 (1955).
91. I. Chang and B. C. Johnson, *Arch. Biochem. Biophys.*, *55*, 151 (1955).

metabolism. For example, a vitamin B_{12} deficiency had no effect on the transfer of preformed labile methyl groups to homocysteine in the chick; the deficient animal grew as well when homocystine and betaine were added to the methionine-free diet as when methionine itself was added.[92] In another study, perosis was prevented and growth was maintained in vitamin B_{12}-depleted chicks by using betaine and homocystine in place of dietary methionine or by using monomethylaminoethanol and betaine in place of dietary choline.[93] The failure of vitamin B_{12}-deficiency to influence the kidney-choline level or urinary excretion of choline in the pig that had been fed choline-free diets supplemented with methionine also confirmed the fact that the vitamin does not participate in the transmethylation reactions of choline biosynthesis.[94]

Studies of the effect of cyanocobalamin on the metabolism of formate, serine, and histidine in the rat led to the conclusion that the vitamin is required in methionine and choline biosynthesis for oxidation-reduction of the one-carbon unit in the active metabolites;[95] the latter are most likely derivatives of 5,6,7,8-tetrahydropteroylmonoglutamic acid (see Chapter VII). In addition it was established that the vitamin did not participate in the transfer reactions of the single-carbon unit.

Study of the biosynthesis of thymidine by *Lactobacillus leichmannii*[96] or in bone marrow cell suspensions suggested that cyanocobalamin is required for the reductive conversion of formate to the methyl group of thymine.[97,98] On the basis of studies with labeled formate, glycine, serine, and methionine in the bacterial system, it was concluded that the vitamin is essential for reductive incorporation of formate in thymidine biosynthesis by a pathway not involving methionine or a hydroxymethyl intermediate.[96] In bone marrow cell suspensions from vitamin B_{12}-deficient chicks, cyanocobalamin stimulated the conversion of C^{14}-formate to the methyl group of thymine,[97] but failed to effect the conversion of C^{14}-formaldehyde or 3-C^{14}-serine to thymine methyl.[98] On the basis of this observation, it was concluded that cyanocobalamin participates in thymidine biosynthesis solely by the reduction of one-carbon units at the oxidation state of formate.

92. M. B. Gillis and L. C. Norris, *Proc. Soc. Exptl. Biol. Med.*, *77*, 13 (1951).
93. R. J. Young, L. C. Norris, and G. F. Heuser, *J. Nutr.*, *53*, 233 (1954).
94. J. Firth, S. P. Mistry, M. F. James, and B. C. Johnson, *Proc. Soc. Exptl. Biol. Med.*, *85*, 307 (1954).
95. H. R. V. Arnstein, *Biochim. et Biophys. Acta*, *29*, 652 (1958); *Biochem. J.*, *73*, 23P (1959); *74*, 616 (1960).
96. J. S. Dinning, B. K. Allen, R. S. Young, and P. L. Day, *J. Biol. Chem.*, *233*, 674 (1958).
97. J. S. Dinning and R. S. Young, *J. Biol. Chem.*, *234*, 1199 (1959).
98. J. S. Dinning and R. S. Young, *J. Biol. Chem.*, *234*, 3241 (1959).

In another study with *L. leichmannii*, it was suggested that cyanocobalamin participates in the biosynthesis of thymidine by reductive conversion of uridine to 2′-deoxyuridine.[99] The decreased conversion of formate to the methyl group of thymine by this system in the absence of cyanocobalamin was visualized as resulting from a decreased concentration of the acceptor deoxyribonucleoside rather than decreased reduction of formate.

B. Amino Acid Biosynthesis

Nutritional studies with the pig appeared to indicate a role for cyanocobalamin in the biosynthetic incorporation of amino acids into protein; ultimately it was found that the biosynthesis of amino acids was the step affected. The vitamin appeared to have no effect on either ribonucleic acid or deoxyribonucleic acid synthesis in the pig,[100] but its participation in the *de novo* synthesis of methyl groups was well established.[90,91] Since the administration of methionine and choline had no effect on the course of this vitamin B_{12}-deficiency syndrome, it was apparent that these symptoms were unrelated to the failure of *de novo* methyl-group synthesis.[101,102]

According to a study of tissue components of vitamin B_{12}-deficient and normal pigs and rats following the injection of labeled glucose and serine,[101,103] the metabolic area related to the deficiency syndrome was seemingly restricted to the area of protein biosynthesis. Although the biosynthesis of body components such as nucleic acids, sterols, glycogen, and fat was not affected in the deficient animal, protein biosynthesis was decreased as evidenced by lowered labeling of protein. Extension of these studies at the *in vitro* level provided further support for the participation of the vitamin in this metabolic area.[104] Tissue preparations from vitamin B_{12}-deficient and normal rat liver and spleen were fractionated at the subcellular level by homogenization and differential centrifugation, and the supernatant phase containing the microsomal fraction was used to study the effects of vitamin deficiency on amino acid incorporation into protein. When labeled amino acids were added to the supernatant fraction, the preparations from the liver of rats on adequate vitamin B_{12}-diets were

99. K. W. Floyd and R. W. Whitehead, *Biochem. Biophys. Res. Commun.*, *3*, 220 (1960).
100. S. R. Wagle, D. A. Vaughan, S. P. Mistry, and B. C. Johnson, *J. Biol. Chem.*, *230*, 917 (1958).
101. S. R. Wagle and B. C. Johnson, *Arch. Biochem. Biophys.*, *70*, 617 (1957).
102. B. C. Johnson, in H. C. Heinrich, ed., *Vitamin B_{12} und Intrinsic Factor*, Ferdinand Enke Verlag, Stuttgart, 1957, p. 133.
103. B. C. Johnson, *Am. J. Clin. Nutr.*, *6*, 34 (1958).
104. S. R. Wagle, R. Mehta, and B. C. Johnson, *J. Biol. Chem.*, *230*, 137 (1958).

reported to incorporate about five times more amino acid into protein than preparations from vitamin B_{12}-deficient animals. The addition of cyanocobalamin to *in vitro* preparations from deficient animals resulted in a restoration of amino acid incorporation to about 60% of normal.

To establish that the administered cyanocobalamin was present principally in the system being used to study amino acid incorporation, Co^{60}-labeled cyanocobalamin was administered to a normal rat. A study of the distribution of the vitamin in the various liver fractions indicated that only 11% and 13% of the vitamin occurred in the nuclei and mitochondria respectively; the rest was found in the microsomes and supernatant fraction.[105] Since the subcellular distribution of the vitamin appeared to coincide with the location of the activity for amino acid incorporation, further fractionation of the combined supernatant and microsomal fraction was undertaken. When the pH of the supernatant phase was adjusted to 5.2, a crude mixture of enzymes precipitated; this material was designated pH-5-enzymes. The combined microsomal fraction and pH-5-enzyme system derived from the liver of vitamin B_{12}-deficient animals was only about 25% as efficient as that derived from normal animals for the incorporation of amino acids into protein; once again, the activity of the vitamin B_{12}-deficient system could be increased by the addition of cyanocobalamin *in vitro*.[106,107] It appeared likely that the effect of cyanocobalamin was primarily on the pH-5-enzymes since the incorporation was significantly less when the pH-5-enzymes from the vitamin B_{12}-deficient animal were added to a microsomal fraction from the normal animal; in contrast, the addition of pH-5-enzymes from the normal animal to microsomal material from the deficient animal appeared to stimulate amino acid incorporation about 3-fold. This deduction was supported when essentially all of the Co^{60}-labeled cyanocobalamin in the active fraction was precipitated with the pH-5-enzymes. Association of cyanocobalamin with the activity of the pH-5-enzymes was also indicated by selective precipitation. A fraction precipitating at 40–60% saturation with ammonium sulfate contained 90% of the radioactive cyanocobalamin and represented about 90% of the enzymic activity of the original enzyme fraction.[108] This evidence associating cyanocobalamin with enzymes required in protein biosynthesis was supported by two additional observations: firstly, the apparent incorporation of amino acids into protein by

105. S. R. Wagle, R. Mehta, and B. C. Johnson, *J. Am. Chem. Soc.*, *79*, 4249 (1957).
106. S. R. Wagle, R. Mehta, and B. C. Johnson, *Federation Proc.*, *17*, 330 (1958).
107. S. R. Wagle, R. Mehta, and B. C. Johnson, *J. Biol. Chem.*, *233*, 619 (1958).
108. S. R. Wagle, R. Mehta, and B. C. Johnson, *Biochim. et Biophys. Acta*, *28*, 215 (1958).

the combined microsomal fraction and pH-5-enzyme system from normal animals is markedly inhibited upon the addition of vitamin B_{12} antagonists such as the monoanilide, monoethylamide, and monomethylamide derived from a monocarboxylic acid of cyanocobalamin.[108] This effect was partially reversed upon the further addition of the vitamin B_{12}-containing pH-5-enzymes. Secondly, addition of cyanocobalamin to the microsomal and pH-5-enzyme system derived from a vitamin B_{12}-deficient animal never completely restored the amino acid incorporation activity; however, the addition of a coenzyme form of the vitamin to the deficient system restored the incorporation activity to the normal level.[109] The nature of this and other enzyme forms of the vitamin is the subject of the following section.

This initial research on cyanocobalamin and protein biosynthesis assumed that the vitamin is associated with an enzyme necessary for the incorporation of the intact amino acid into protein, and the data appeared to support this concept. There is later evidence, however, leading to the conclusion that decreased incorporation of amino acid into protein in the absence of cyanocobalamin is related to the biosynthesis of the amino acid and not to the incorporation reactions *per se*.[110] The protozoan *O. malhamensis* was used in this later study since it resembles animal tissue in having an absolute requirement for cyanocobalamin. Incubation of cell suspensions with C^{14}-labeled amino acids showed that cyanocobalamin increased the specific radioactivity of protein up to 3-fold. When the cells were incubated with labeled glucose, however, and the protein samples were hydrolyzed and resolved into component amino acids, the labeling of certain amino acids such as valine, methionine, phenylalanine, tyrosine, and to a lesser extent serine and glycine, was drastically reduced in the absence of cyanocobalamin. More significantly, the effect of the vitamin deficiency was far greater on the incorporation of radioactivity into the amino acid than it was on the incorporation of amino acid into protein.

C. Coenzyme Forms

A coenzyme form of vitamin B_{12} eventually designated adenylcobamide coenzyme was discovered, isolated, and crystallized in the course of investigating the metabolism of glutamate by cell-free extracts of *Clostridium tetanomorphum*. The reaction proceeds with the conversion of glutamate (**80**) to mesaconate (**82**) by cleavage of the bond between C-2 and C-3 of glutamate, followed by the formation of a new bond between

109. R. Mehta, S. R. Wagle, and B. C. Johnson, *Biochim. et Biophys. Acta*, *35*, 286 (1959).
110. H. R. V. Arnstein and A. M. White, *Biochim. et Biophys. Acta*, *36*, 286 (1959).

$$\begin{array}{c} {}^{1}COOH \\ | \\ {}^{2}CHNH_2 \\ | \\ {}^{3}CH_2 \\ | \\ {}^{4}CH_2 \\ | \\ {}^{5}COOH \\ \textbf{(80)} \end{array} \longrightarrow \begin{array}{l} {}^{1}COOH \\ | \\ {}^{2}CHNH_2 \\ | \\ {}^{4}CH{-}{}^{3}CH_3 \\ | \\ {}^{5}COOH \\ \textbf{(81)} \end{array} \longrightarrow$$

$$\begin{array}{l} {}^{1}COOH \\ | \\ {}^{2}CH \\ \| \\ {}^{4}C{-}{}^{3}CH_3 \\ | \\ {}^{5}COOH \\ \textbf{(82)} \end{array} \longrightarrow \overset{2}{C}H_3\overset{1}{C}OOH + \overset{3}{C}H_3\overset{4}{\underset{\underset{O}{\|}}{C}}\overset{5}{C}OOH$$

C-2 and C-4; consequently, the methyl carbon atom of mesaconate is derived from C-3 of glutamate.[111,112] Purification of the extract containing the factor(s) essential for the conversion of glutamate to mesaconate showed that the reaction occurred through the intermediate formation of an amino acid that was later identified as β-methylaspartic acid (**81**).[113] Since charcoal-treated extracts promoted the formation of β-methylaspartate from mesaconate and ammonia, but not the synthesis of mesaconate from glutamate, it was apparent that the charcoal adsorbate contained a coenzyme essential for the isomerization of glutamate to β-methylaspartate. After the factor was eluted from the charcoal and purified, it was characterized as a derivative of pseudovitamin B_{12} with at least one additional purine-containing moiety.[114,115]

When *C. tetanomorphum* was grown in the presence of either 5,6-dimethylbenzimidazole or benzimidazole, the corresponding 5,6-dimethylbenzimidazolylcobamide and benzimidazolylcobamide coenzymes were

111. J. T. Wachsman and H. A. Barker, *J. Biol. Chem.*, *217*, 695 (1955).
112. A. Munch-Petersen and H. A. Barker, *J. Biol. Chem.*, *230*, 649 (1958).
113. H. A. Barker, R. D. Smyth, E. J. Wawszkiewicz, N. N. Lee, and R. M. Wilson, *Arch. Biochem. Biophys.*, *78*, 468 (1958).
114. H. A. Barker, H. Weissbach, and R. D. Smyth, *Proc. Natl. Acad. Sci.* (*U.S.*), *44*, 1093 (1958).
115. H. A. Barker, R. D. Smyth, H. Weissbach, A. Munch-Petersen, J. I. Toohey, J. N. Ladd, B. E. Volcani, and R. M. Wilson, *J. Biol. Chem.*, *235*, 181 (1960).

produced.[116,117] All three coenzymes have been crystallized, and all are active, though apparently not equally, in catalyzing the interconversion of glutamate and β-methylaspartate. They have the same maximal activities, but differ significantly in their affinity for the apoenzyme.

Coenzyme forms of vitamin B_{12} have been isolated in moderate purity from the liver of the chicken, rabbit, sheep, and human;[118] on the basis of spectral data, the major cobamide-containing component of liver extracts from all four species appears to be a benzimidazolyl-containing cobamide coenzyme. In the purest preparations, which were obtained from extracts of sheep and human liver, the coenzyme was identified as the 5,6-dimethylbenzimidazolylcobamide coenzyme.

D. Structure of the Coenzymes

Initial structural observations were based upon cleavage of the coenzyme forms by cyanide ion and by photolysis. Treatment of the adenylcobamide coenzyme with potassium cyanide yielded adenine and adenylcobamide cyanide (pseudovitamin B_{12}); photolysis yielded two unidentified adenine nucleosides and adenylcobamide hydroxide.[119] Cyanide cleavage of the benzimidazolyl- and dimethylbenzimidazolylcobamide coenzymes yielded adenine and benzimidazolyl- and dimethylbenzimidazolylcobamide cyanide, respectively.[116,117] In addition to the corresponding benzimidazole-containing cobamide hydroxides, photolysis of the benzimidazolyl- and dimethylbenzimidazolylcobamide coenzymes yielded the same two unidentified adenine nucleosides that had been obtained earlier by the photochemical cleavage of the adenylcobamide coenzyme.[120] Consideration of these data in conjunction with other analytical data led to the conclusion that the cobamide-containing coenzymes possess all structural features of the corresponding vitamins except the cyano group which is replaced by an adenine-containing moiety.

Acid hydrolysis of the dimethylbenzimidazolylcobamide coenzyme provided some insight into the nature of the adenine-containing moiety. Among the products of this reaction were aquocobalamin, adenine, and a carbohydrate which was identified as *D-erythro*-2,3-dihydroxy-4-pentenal

116. H. Weissbach, J. Toohey, and H. A. Barker, *Proc. Natl. Acad. Sci.* (*U.S.*), *45*, 521 (1959).
117. H. A. Barker, R. D. Smyth, H. Weissbach, J. I. Toohey, J. N. Ladd, and B. E. Volcani, *J. Biol. Chem.*, *235*, 480 (1960).
118. J. I. Toohey and H. A. Barker, *J. Biol. Chem.*, *236*, 560 (1961).
119. H. Weissbach, J. N. Ladd, B. E. Volcani, R. D. Smyth, and H. A. Barker, *J. Biol. Chem.*, *235*, 1462 (1960).
120. J. N. Ladd, H. P. C. Hogenkamp, and H. A. Barker, *Biochem. Biophys. Res. Commun.*, *2*, 143 (1960).

(**83**).[121] The carbohydrate was established as an unbranched deoxyaldopentose with *cis* hydroxyl groups at the 2- and 3-position and a double bond at the 4-position since ozonolysis of the compound yielded formaldehyde and the dialdehyde (**84**); the latter compound was characterized on the basis of its reduction to erythritol (**85**). The *D*-configuration of the

CHO—(H—C—OH)—(H—C—OH)—CH=CH_2 (**83**) $\xrightarrow{O_3}$ CHO—(H—C—OH)—(H—C—OH)—CHO (**84**) $\xrightarrow{NaBH_4}$ CH_2OH—(H—C—OH)—(H—C—OH)—CH_2OH (**85**)

(**83**) $\xrightarrow{NaBH_4}$ CH_2OH—(H—C—OH)—(H—C—OH)—CH=CH_2 (**86**) $\xrightarrow{O_3}$ CH_2OH—(H—C—OH)—(H—C—OH)—CHO (**87**) + HCHO

(**83**) $\xrightarrow{OsO_4}$ CHO—(H—C—OH)—(H—C—OH)—(H—C—OH)—CH_2OH (**88**) + CHO—(H—C—OH)—(H—C—OH)—(HO—C—H)—CH_2OH (**89**)

hydrolysis product was established by reduction of the pentenal (**83**) to the pententriol (**86**), which on ozonolysis yielded *L*-erythrose (**87**) and formaldehyde. Evidence confirming the structure and configuration of the pentenal (**83**) was obtained by hydroxylating the double bond; two

121. H. P. C. Hogenkamp and H. A. Barker, *J. Biol. Chem.*, *236*, 3097 (1961).

aldopentoses were isolated from the reaction mixture and were identified as *D*-ribose (**88**) and *L*-lyxose (**89**).

Since earlier evidence indicated that *D-erythro*-2,3-dihydroxy-4-pentenal (**83**) was also obtained by acid hydrolysis of one of the adenine nucleosides formed by photolysis of the coenzymes,[120] it was concluded that the dihydroxypentenal was derived from the new adenine-containing moiety of the coenzymes. It was assumed that the double bond of the pentenal was not present in the intact coenzymes, but was introduced during acid cleavage of the adenine nucleoside moiety. Although the nature of the bond between the deoxypentose and purine moieties of this nucleoside was unknown, spectral evidence indicated that N-9 of adenine was bound to the deoxypentose moiety.

Elucidation of the structure of the adenine-containing moiety of the coenzymes was completed after

(a) investigating the mechanism of photochemical cleavage and discovering the role of oxygen in the photolysis reaction;

(b) selectively degrading the new adenine nucleosides isolated after photolysis; and

(c) X-ray crystallographic studies.

An investigation of the photolytic cleavage of the dimethylbenzimidazolylcobamide coenzyme revealed that the reaction occurs in two stages.[122] Photolytic cleavage *per se* converts this coenzyme quantitatively to a dimethylbenzimidazolylcobamide-containing moiety and an adenine-containing moiety, both of which exist momentarily as free radicals. Under anaerobic conditions, the final products of photolysis were identified spectrophotometrically as vitamin B_{12r} and a deoxyadenosine derivative that was eventually identified as a 5′,8-cyclic analog. Under aerobic conditions, the initial fragments of photochemical cleavage are oxidized; the final products under these conditions are aquocobalamin and deoxynucleosides which were later established as 5′-aldehyde and 5′-carboxylic acid derivatives of adenosine. An independent polarographic study of the mechanism of the photolytic cleavage also showed that the dimethylbenzimidazolylcobamide coenzyme is cleaved to vitamin B_{12r} under anaerobic conditions and to dimethylbenzimidazolylcobamide hydroxide under aerobic conditions.[123]

Anaerobic conversion of the dimethylbenzimidazolylcobamide coenzyme to vitamin B_{12r} indicated that the cobalt atom of the cobamide-containing coenzymes is bivalent.[122,123] The presence of bivalent cobalt in the coenzymes was also suggested on the basis of their electrophoretic

122. R. O. Brady and H. A. Barker, *Biochem. Biophys. Res. Commun.*, *4*, 373 (1961).
123. K. Bernhauer and O. Müller, *Biochem. Z.*, *334*, 199 (1961); *335*, 44 (1961).

behavior[124] and paramagnetic character.[124,125] On the other hand, the absence of a signal in electron-spin resonance studies with coenzyme B_{12} would indicate that the cobalt atom is in the trivalent state.[125a] According to these studies, the cobalt atom of the coenzyme is diamagnetic whereas that of the photolysis product is paramagnetic. The oxidation state of the cobalt atom of these coenzyme forms is not considered as established and is a subject of current research.

Three adenine nucleosides have been isolated after the photolytic cleavage of the cobamide-containing coenzymes, and all are more resistant to acid hydrolysis than adenosine and 2′-deoxyadenosine. One of the nucleosides, which was isolated by two groups of investigators,[116,117,119,126] was very resistant to acid hydrolysis and appeared to possess an unusual structural feature. This compound was identified as the 5′,8-cyclic analog (**90**) of 5′-deoxyadenosine.[127] The structural assignment was based on the following observations.

(a) Periodate oxidation of the compound required one equivalent of the reagent, but formaldehyde and formic acid were not detected among the oxidation products.

(b) Vigorous acid hydrolysis of the nucleoside yielded a new nucleoside which contained an aldehyde function but did not liberate a purine or carbohydrate.

(c) Periodic acid oxidation of the new aldehyde-containing nucleoside, derived by acid hydrolysis of the deoxynucleoside, yielded three equivalents of formic acid and no formaldehyde.

The structures of the other nucleosides isolated from the photolysis reactions were simpler in nature. One compound was characterized[126] as the 5′-carboxylic acid (**91**) derived from adenosine on the basis of periodate oxidation, electrophoresis, and comparison with an authentic synthetic specimen. The other was identified[127,128] as the 5′-aldehyde (**92**) derived from adenosine on the basis of its hydrolysis to adenine, reduction to adenosine, and oxidation to the corresponding 5′-carboxylic acid (**91**).

124. L. Nowicki and J. Pawelkiewicz, *Bull. Acad. Polon. Sci., Ser. Sci. Biol., 8*, 433 (1960).
125. K. Bernhauer, P. Gaiser, and O. Müller, *Biochem., Z., 333*, 560 (1961).
125a. H. P. C. Hogenkamp, H. A. Barker, and H. S. Mason, *Arch. Biochem. Biophys., 100*, 353 (1963).
126. A. W. Johnson and N. Shaw, *Proc. Chem. Soc.*, 420 (1960); 447 (1961); *J. Chem. Soc.*, 4608 (1962).
127. H. P. C. Hogenkamp and H. A. Barker, *Federation Proc., 21*, 470 (1962); H. P. C. Hogenkamp, *J. Biol. Chem., 238*, 477 (1963).
128. H. P. C. Hogenkamp, J. N. Ladd, and H. A. Barker, *J. Biol. Chem., 237*, 1950 (1962).

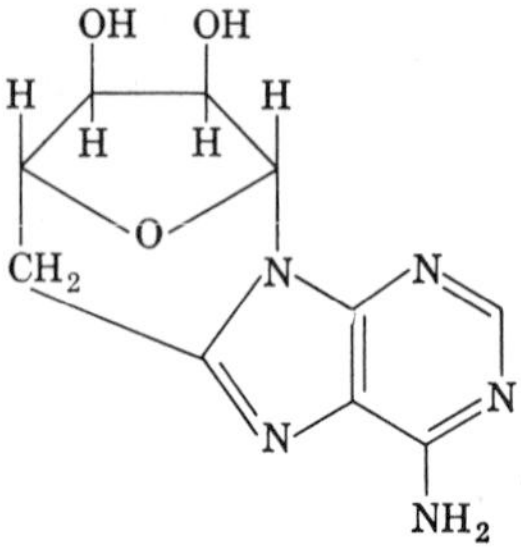

(90) 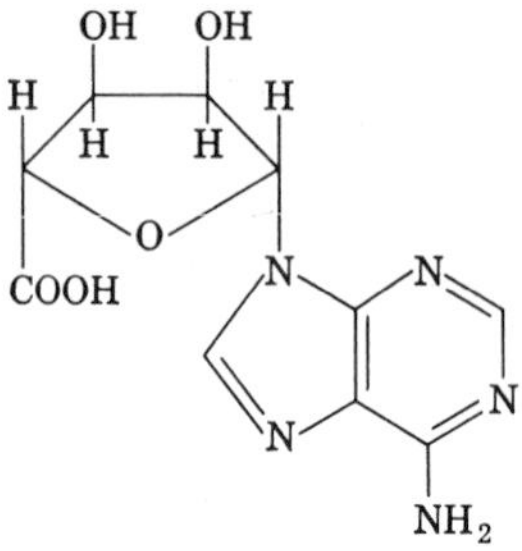 (91)

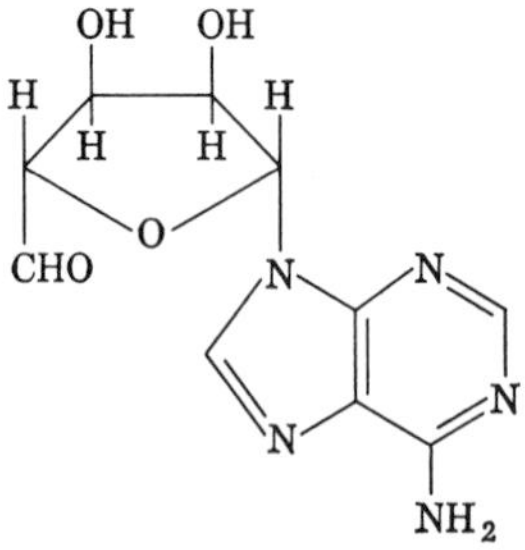

(92) 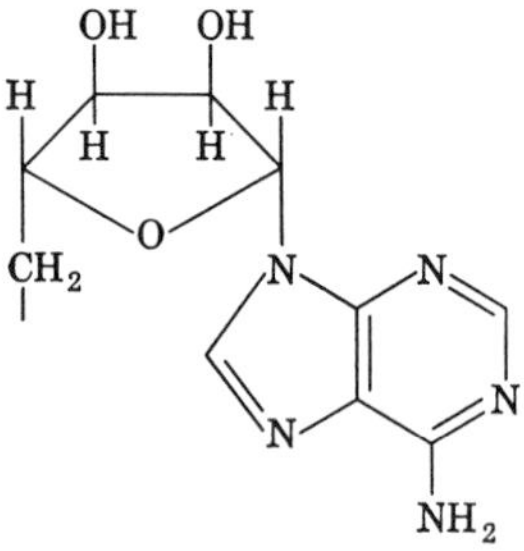 (93)

The isolation and identification of the adenine nucleosides obtained from the photolytic cleavage of the cobamide-containing coenzymes indicated that the new adenine-containing component of these coenzymes is the 5′-deoxyadenosine moiety (**93**) which is probably linked directly through its 5′-methylene group to the cobalt atom of the coenzyme.

During the same period in which the structures of the adenine nucleosides were being established, an X-ray crystallographic study of the dimethylbenzimidazolylcobamide coenzyme was completed, and the nucleoside moiety in the intact coenzyme was identified as a 5′-deoxyadenosine moiety, which is linked directly through the 5′-methylene group to the cobalt atom.[129] Except for an uncertainty regarding the oxidation state of the cobalt atom, the X-ray crystallographic studies established the structure of the dimethylbenzimidazolylcobamide coenzyme as shown in (**94**).

E. Partial Synthesis of the Coenzymes

The dimethylbenzimidazolylcobamide coenzyme (**94**) was synthesized by condensing a corresponding, fully reduced cobamide derivative with

129. P. G. Lenhert and D. C. Hodgkin, *Nature*, *192*, 937 (1961).

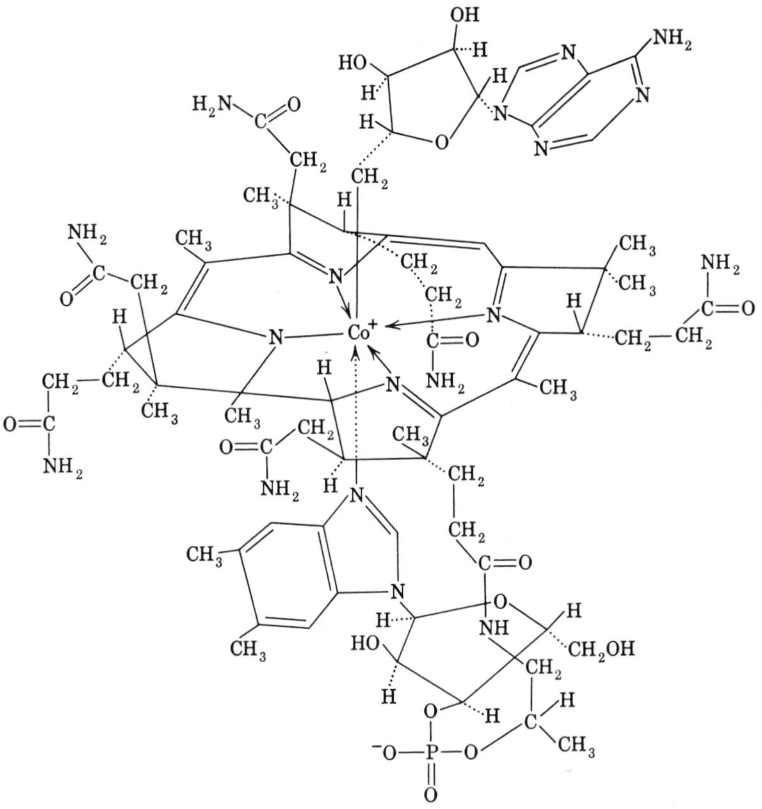

(94)

2′,3′-isopropylidene-5′-toluenesulfonyladenosine.[129a,129b] For the condensation reaction, cyanocobalamin or aquocobalamin is reduced to a gray-green intermediate in which the cobalt atom is at an oxidation level lower than Co^{2+}; vitamin B_{12r}, a reduced cobalamin intermediate containing Co^{2+}, is apparently unreactive under the conditions of the condensation reaction. After the reaction product was purified by extraction with phenol, followed by chromatography, the isopropylidene group was cleaved by mild acid hydrolysis to yield the dimethylbenzimidazolylcobamide coenzyme.

The 5′-deoxyinosine and 5′-deoxyuridine analogs of the cobamide coenzyme (**94**) were synthesized by analogous condensation reactions.[129a]

129a. E. L. Smith, L. Mervyn, A. W. Johnson, and N. Shaw, *Nature*, *194*, 1175 (1962).
129b. K. Bernhauer, K. O. Müller, and G. Müller, *Biochem. Z.*, *336*, 102 (1962).

The physical properties of these analogs were similar to those of the cobamide coenzymes. In the enzyme assay, however, the analogs were potent competitive inhibitors of the cobamide coenzymes.

F. Metabolic Role of the Coenzymes

The cobamide-containing coenzymes participate in microbial metabolism by catalyzing the isomerization of glutamate to β-methylaspartate. The role of the coenzymes in this metabolic area has been discussed in a preceding section describing the discovery of coenzyme forms of vitamin B_{12}.

The cobamide-containing coenzymes also participate in the microbial and mammalian metabolism of propionate. The inability to metabolize propionic acid was recognized as a basic mammalian metabolic lesion of vitamin B_{12} deficiency first in the ruminant[130] and later in the rat.[131] Earlier studies had shown that propionyl coenzyme A, methylmalonyl coenzyme A, and succinyl coenzyme A were intermediates in the mammalian metabolism of propionic acid, and the two enzymes required for these conversions were isolated and characterized.[132–135] The first, propionyl coenzyme A carboxylase, catalyzed the addition of carbon dioxide to propionyl coenzyme A, forming methylmalonyl coenzyme A. The participation of biotin in this step had been suggested on the basis of analogous biotin-dependent reactions such as transcarboxylation between methylmalonyl coenzyme A and pyruvate,[136] and the decarboxylation of β-methylglutaconyl coenzyme A to β-methylcrotonyl coenzyme A.[137]

The requirement for a cobamide-containing coenzyme in propionate metabolism to reversibly isomerize methylmalonyl coenzyme A to succinyl coenzyme A was suggested by the observation that the methylmalonyl isomerase activity of an enzyme from the liver of vitamin B_{12}-deficient rats was severely depressed.[131] The analogy between this isomerization and the glutamic acid-β-methylaspartic acid transformation also played an important role in directing attention to the cobamide-containing coenzymes.[131] The first direct experimental evidence for the participation of a coenzyme form of vitamin B_{12} in the methylmalonyl isomerase step of

130. H. R. Marston, *Med. J. Australia*, 105 (1959-II).
131. R. M. Smith and K. J. Monty, *Biochem. Biophys. Res. Commun.*, *1*, 105 (1959).
132. M. Flavin and S. Ochoa, *J. Biol. Chem.*, *229*, 965 (1957).
133. M. Flavin, H. Castro-Mendoza, and S. Ochoa, *J. Biol. Chem.*, *229*, 981 (1957).
134. W. S. Beck, M. Flavin, and S. Ochoa, *J. Biol. Chem.*, *229*, 997 (1957).
135. W. S. Beck and S. Ochoa, *J. Biol. Chem.*, *232*, 931 (1958).
136. E. R. Stadtman, P. Overath, H. Eggerer, and F. Lynen, *Biochem. Biophys. Res. Commun.*, *2*, 1 (1960).
137. F. Lynen, J. Knappe, E. Lorch, G. Jutting, and E. Ringelman, *Angew. Chem.*, *71*, 481 (1959).

propionate metabolism was obtained by converting methylmalonyl coenzyme A to succinyl coenzyme A in cell-free extracts of *Propionibacterium shermanii.*[136] From this observation, propionate metabolism was formulated as proceeding according to the following reaction sequence.

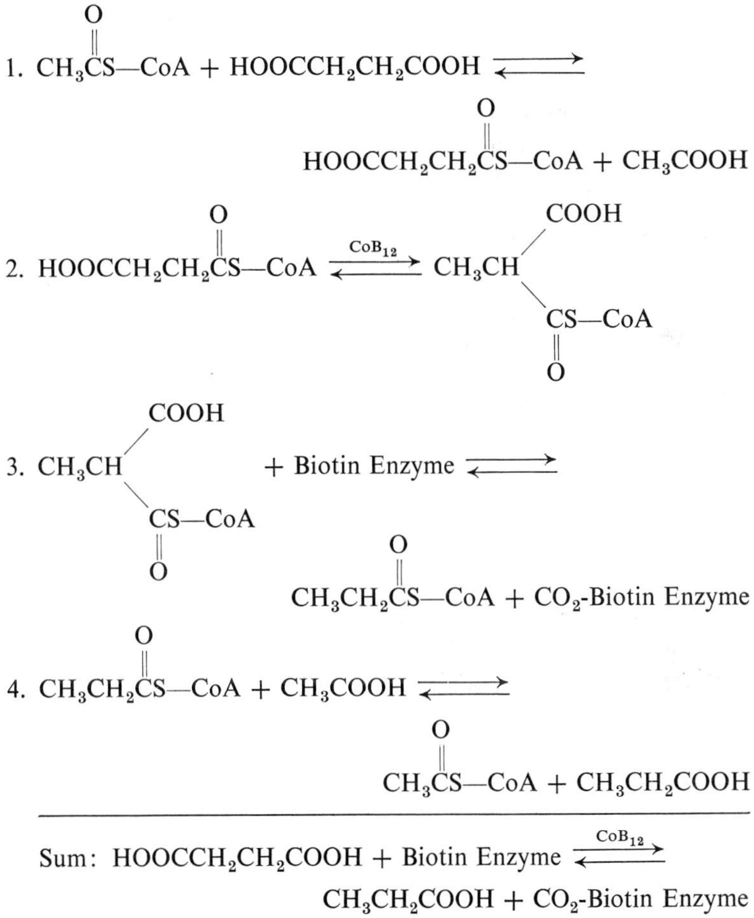

$$1.\quad CH_3\overset{\overset{O}{\|}}{C}S\text{—}CoA + HOOCCH_2CH_2COOH \rightleftharpoons HOOCCH_2CH_2\overset{\overset{O}{\|}}{C}S\text{—}CoA + CH_3COOH$$

$$2.\quad HOOCCH_2CH_2\overset{\overset{O}{\|}}{C}S\text{—}CoA \xrightleftharpoons{CoB_{12}} CH_3CH\begin{matrix} \diagup COOH \\ \diagdown \underset{\underset{O}{\|}}{C}S\text{—}CoA \end{matrix}$$

$$3.\quad CH_3CH\begin{matrix} \diagup COOH \\ \diagdown \underset{\underset{O}{\|}}{C}S\text{—}CoA \end{matrix} + \text{Biotin Enzyme} \rightleftharpoons CH_3CH_2\overset{\overset{O}{\|}}{C}S\text{—}CoA + CO_2\text{-Biotin Enzyme}$$

$$4.\quad CH_3CH_2\overset{\overset{O}{\|}}{C}S\text{—}CoA + CH_3COOH \rightleftharpoons CH_3\overset{\overset{O}{\|}}{C}S\text{—}CoA + CH_3CH_2COOH$$

$$\text{Sum:}\quad HOOCCH_2CH_2COOH + \text{Biotin Enzyme} \xrightleftharpoons{CoB_{12}} CH_3CH_2COOH + CO_2\text{-Biotin Enzyme}$$

Additional support for the participation of coenzyme forms of vitamin B_{12} in this area of metabolism was provided later by the observed stimulation of methylmalonyl coenzyme A isomerase in ox liver fractions[138] after the addition of the 5,6-dimethylbenzimidazolylcobamide coenzyme, and also by the restoration of isomerase activity to mitochondrial systems

138. J. R. Stern and D. L. Friedman, *Biochem. Biophys. Res. Commun.*, *2*, 82 (1960).

from the liver of vitamin B_{12}-deficient rats after the addition of the coenzyme form of vitamin B_{12}, but not vitamin B_{12} itself.[139] In another study, addition of the benzimidazolyl- or dimethylbenzimidazolylcobamide coenzyme to the methylmalonyl isomerase apoenzyme isolated from the kidney cortex of the sheep resulted in the restoration of isomerase activity.[140] Addition of the adenylcobamide coenzyme to the same system had little or no effect on the restoration of activity. All three coenzyme forms, however, were active in restoring activity to a methylmalonyl isomerase apoenzyme prepared from *P. shermanii.*

A mechanism has been suggested to depict the role of the cobamide-containing coenzymes in the isomerization of methylmalonyl coenzyme A to succinyl coenzyme A.[141,142] Since 80% of the 2-C^{14}-methylmalonyl coenzyme A added to an extract of *P. shermanii* was converted to 3-C^{14}-succinyl coenzyme A, the mechanism of isomerization is visualized as follows. The coenzyme produces the methylmalonyl radical (**95**) by a one-

$$\begin{array}{c} COOH \\ | \\ HC{-}CH_3 \\ | \\ C{=}O \\ | \\ SCoA \end{array} \underset{Co^{2+}}{\overset{Co^{3+}}{\rightleftharpoons}} \underset{\mathbf{(95)}}{\begin{array}{c} COOH \\ | \\ HC{-}CH_2\cdot \\ | \\ C{=}O \\ | \\ SCoA \end{array}} \rightleftharpoons \underset{\mathbf{(96)}}{\begin{array}{c} COOH \\ | \\ HC{-}CH_2 \\ \quad | \\ \quad C{=}O \\ \quad | \\ \quad SCoA \end{array}} \underset{Co^{3+}}{\overset{Co^{2+}}{\rightleftharpoons}} \begin{array}{c} COOH \\ | \\ CH_2 \\ | \\ CH_2 \\ | \\ C{=}O \\ | \\ SCoA \end{array}$$

electron oxidation of methylmalonyl coenzyme A; in this reaction the cobalt atom of the coenzyme is reduced to the bivalent state. The thiol ester group then migrates, most probably intramolecularly, to yield the succinyl radical (**96**). Reduction of this radical by the Co^{2+} of the coenzyme generated in the first stage yields succinyl coenzyme A.

Another reaction dependent upon the participation of a cobamide-containing coenzyme is the enzymic conversion of a 1,2-glycol to the corresponding saturated aldehyde. For example,[143,144] cell-free extracts of *Aerobacter aerogenes* lose their ability to catalyze the conversion of ethylene

139. S. Gurnani, S. P. Mistry, and B. C. Johnson, *Biochim. et Biophys. Acta, 38,* 187 (1960).
140. P. Lengyl, R. Mazumder, and S. Ochoa, *Proc. Natl. Acad. Sci.* (*U.S.*), *46,* 1312 (1960).
141. H. Eggerer, P. Overath, F. Lynen, and E. R. Stadtman, *J. Am. Chem. Soc., 82,* 2643 (1960).
142. H. Eggerer, E. R. Stadtman, P. Overath, and F. Lynen, *Biochem. Z., 333,* 1 (1960).
143. R. H. Abeles and H. A. Lee Jr., *J. Biol. Chem., 236,* PC1 (1961).
144. A. M. Brownstein and R. H. Abeles, *J. Biol. Chem., 236,* 1199 (1961).

glycol to acetaldehyde, and propanediol to propionaldehyde after treatment with charcoal; the addition of a cobamide-containing coenzyme to the charcoal-treated extract, however, restores full activity. Subsequent studies of this reaction revealed that the solvent does not participate, and it was suggested that the coenzyme mediates in the transfer of hydrogen from C-1 to C-2 of the diol in a manner analogous to that depicted in the methylmalonyl isomerase reaction.[145,146]

8. Nutritional and Therapeutic Role

A. In Animals

Vitamin B_{12} has been identified as the active principle in concentrates of the "animal protein factor" and is essential for the growing chick, rat, pig, dog, and calf and other ruminants.

Suboptimal growth is the most obvious sign of a vitamin B_{12}-deficiency in the chick, and the hatchability of eggs from hens decreases from about 80–30% of normal in the course of a six-month deprivation period.[147] Hatchability improves, however, almost immediately after supplementation of the diet with vitamin B_{12}. Because of the profound effect of a vitamin B_{12} deficiency upon hatchability and embryo mortality, most congenital abnormalities of the deficiency state in the chick have been studied at the embryonic stage. Among the manifestations of the deficiency is a myatrophy of the leg, malposition of the head, perosis, and hemorrhage. All embryos from vitamin B_{12}-deficient hens are smaller than normal, and edema and fatty heart, liver, and kidneys are usually observed.[148,149] About 10–20 μg. of vitamin B_{12} per kg. of diet promotes the growth of chicks on corn-soybean meal diets.[150,151]

The vitamin B_{12} requirement of growing-fattening pigs is about 10 μg./lb. of ration.[152] The vitamin is also essential for normal reproduction and lactation in swine. The effects on reproduction are evidenced especially by decreased litter size and smaller pigs.[153] In addition, the deficiency

145. R. H. Abeles and H. A. Lee, Jr., *J. Biol. Chem.*, *236*, 2347 (1961).
146. R. H. Abeles and H. A. Lee, Jr., *Federation Proc.*, *21*, 253 (1962).
147. D. J. G. Black, J. Getty, M. E. Coates, G. F. Harrison, and S. K. Kon, *Biochem. J.*, *46*, viii (1950).
148. O. Olcese, J. R. Couch, J. H. Quisenberry, and P. B. Pearson, *J. Nutr.*, *41*, 423 (1950).
149. T. M. Ferguson and J. R. Couch, *Federation Proc.*, *13*, 456 (1954); *J. Nutr.*, *54*, 361 (1954).
150. W. H. Ott, E. L. Rickes, and T. R. Wood, *J. Biol. Chem.*, *174*, 1047 (1948).
151. R. J. Lillie, C. A. Denton, and H. R. Bird, *J. Biol. Chem.*, *176*, 1477 (1948).
152. D. Catron and C. C. Culbertson, *Iowa Farm Sci.*, *3*, 3 (1949).
153. G. C. Anderson and A. G. Hogan, *Proc. Soc. Exptl. Biol. Med.*, *75*, 288 (1950).

state is characterized by hematological abnormalities and neuromuscular disorders.[154]

Although adult ruminants apparently do not require an exogenous source of vitamin B_{12}, their calves do.[155] There is also increasing evidence for a close relationship between the cobalt- and vitamin B_{12} requirement in ruminant nutrition.[156] Ruminants are the only class of animals for which a cobalt deficiency has been demonstrated to date, and the intimate relationship between a cobalt requirement and vitamin B_{12} has been demonstrated most clearly in sheep. Adult cobalt-deficient ewes carry their lambs to full term, but the lambs either succumb within a few days after birth or grow very slowly. Administration of liver fractions or crystalline vitamin B_{12} to these cobalt-deficient lambs produces a prompt improvement in appetite, weight, and hematopoiesis.

B. In the Human

Vitamin B_{12} is required for normal blood formation, maintenance of neural function, normal growth, and other fundamental metabolic processes. The deficiency syndrome in man is characterized by megaloblastic erythropoiesis with concurrent changes in leucopoiesis and thrombocyte production. The pathologic manifestations of the deficiency state are reported to be so closely related biochemically to those of a pteroylmonoglutamic acid deficiency that a clear-cut distinction between the two vitamin deficiencies cannot be made simply by studying hematopoietic disturbances leading to megaloblastic anemia. Distinctions can be made, however, between certain manifestations of vitamin B_{12} avitaminosis and pteroylmonoglutamic acid deficiency through the examination of metabolic processes in tissue other than that of the hematopoietic system. Detailed descriptions of the various manifestations of human vitamin B_{12} deficiency, which are summarized in the following paragraphs, may be found in several reviews.[157–159]

1. PERNICIOUS ANEMIA AND THE INTRINSIC FACTOR. Pernicious anemia is not a primary dietary deficiency, but rather a conditioned deficiency that occurs owing to a metabolic defect and results in a failure to assimilate the vitamin already present in the alimentary tract. This unique deficiency was

154. B. C. Johnson and A. L. Neumann, *J. Biol. Chem.*, *178*, 1001 (1949).
155. B. C. Johnson, W. B. Nevens, and H. H. Mitchell, *J. Dairy Sci.*, 34, 506 (1951).
156. J. P. Anderson and E. D. Andrews, *Nature*, *170*, 807 (1952).
157. F. H. Bethell, in W. H. Sebrell, Jr. and R. S. Harris, eds., *The Vitamins: Chemistry, Physiology, and Pathology*, *Vol. I*, Academic, N.Y., 1954, p. 491.
158. R. W. Vilter, in M. G. Wohl and R. S. Goodhart, eds., *Modern Nutrition in Health and Disease*, Lea and Febiger, Philadelphia, 1955, p. 330.
159. J. G. Heathcote and F. S. Mooney, *J. Pharm. Pharmacol.*, *10*, 593 (1958).

studied extensively[160] and it was established that a gastric secretory substance, designated the "intrinsic factor," is essential for the absorption of vitamin B_{12} from the alimentary tract. It has been aptly stated that pernicious anemia "would not develop if the patient could effect daily the transfer of one millionth of a gram of vitamin B_{12} the distance of a small fraction of a millimeter across the intestinal mucosa and into the blood stream."[161] It should be noted, however, that the presence of gastric intrinsic factor is essential for the absorption of vitamin B_{12} only when it is administered orally and at the μg.-dose level. Adequate remission of pernicious anemia sometimes occurs even in the absence of the intrinsic factor on oral administration if the dosage is in the mg.-range.

Research on the purification and identification of the intrinsic factor and its chemical nature has been interpreted on occasion in terms of the properties of a mucoprotein. It appears, however, that the absorption, transport, storage, and even the biological function of the vitamin may be accomplished by a vitamin B_{12}-peptide complex. Such bound forms were encountered in certain early studies of vitamin B_{12} activity[11] and their characterization is a topic of current interest.[162]

In its fully-developed state, pernicious anemia is characterized by macrocytosis, megaloblastic bone marrow, leucopenia, neurological and mental changes, and achlorhydria. Other disorders that are associated with the deficiency syndrome include atrophic gastritis, oral mucous membrane disorders, endocrine dysfunction, and disturbances in fat metabolism. Although daily parenteral administration of 1 μg. of the vitamin has been reported for the treatment of pernicious anemia in relapse, it is frequently reported as administered in 10–15 μg.-doses daily, and remisssions have been maintained by the monthly parenteral administration of 15–30 μg. of the vitamin. Oral administration of vitamin B_{12} is relatively ineffective at this dosage unless a concentrate of the intrinsic factor is also included in the formulation.

2. OTHER MEGALOBLASTIC ANEMIAS. Megaloblastic anemia following total gastrectomy appears to be due in part to the removal of the source of secretion of the intrinsic factor. Since oral absorption of dietary vitamin B_{12} is greatly impaired in the absence of this gastric factor, the administration of vitamin B_{12} is imperative for the remainder of the individual's life if pernicious anemia is to be prevented.

The megaloblastic anemia resulting in the human as a consequence of infestation with fish tapeworm (*Diphylloborthrium latum*) is apparently a

160. W. B. Castle, *Am. J. Med. Sci.*, *178*, 748 (1929).
161. W. B. Castle, *New Engl. J. Med.*, *249*, 603 (1953).
162. A. Hedbom, *Biochem. J.*, *74*, 307 (1960).

true vitamin B_{12} deficiency state. In this instance utilization of the available vitamin B_{12} in the intestinal contents by the tapeworm leads to a vitamin B_{12} deficiency in the host. Administration of the vitamin in amounts greater than the tapeworm's requirement leads to a therapeutic benefit for the host.

Other intestinal abnormalities may lead to megaloblastic anemia. The therapeutic responses to vitamin B_{12} in such cases have been variable since a given patient may be primarily deficient in either pteroylmonoglutamic acid or in vitamin B_{12}, or in both.

3. PREGNANCY. Although all degrees of reproductive failure have been demonstrated in vitamin B_{12}-deficient animals under both experimental and natural conditions, available data concerning the effect of vitamin B_{12}-deficiency on reproductive failure in the human fail to show the same dramatic effects. It has been reported that human pregnancy appears to increase the capacity for vitamin B_{12} absorption, but studies of serum vitamin B_{12} levels show that as pregnancy advances, the concentration of the vitamin falls progressively to levels well below those observed in nonpregnant women. Since the vitamin B_{12} level of maternal blood is considerably lower than that of nonpregnant women of comparable age in spite of increased absorption and decreased excretion of vitamin B_{12}, the fetus is apparently the main beneficiary of the increased absorption rate. The vitamin B_{12} reserve of the mother is restored to normal rapidly after delivery. In view of these observations and in view of the fact that a severe deficiency of the vitamin has been considered likely to induce a congenital abnormality during the early stages of pregnancy, supplementary administration of vitamin B_{12} is indicated throughout pregnancy.[163]

4. GROWTH. Vitamin B_{12} is considered by some investigators to be essential for the normal growth of children. Its stimulatory effect is especially evident among growth-retarded children, but cannot be demonstrated in clinically healthy full-term or premature infants. The growth-promoting effect of the vitamin has been demonstrated in chronically ill children whose diet consisted mainly of vegetable proteins, and in children under other nutritional stresses.[164–167] Although the large number of variables

163. R. E. L. Nesbitt, Jr. and B. F. Chow, *Obstetrical and Gynecological Survey*, *13*, 461 (1958).
164. N. C. Wetzel, H. H. Hopwood, M. E. Kuechle, and R. M. Grueninger, *Am. J. Clin. Nutr.*, *1*, 17 (1952).
165. B. F. Chow, *Southern Medical J.*, *45*, 604 (1952).
166. N. Jolliffe, R. Funaro, G. Frontali, G. Magioni, S. Carbo, and G. Lanciano, *Nutritional Symposium Series*, *7*, The Natl. Vitamin Foundation, New York, 1953, p. 119.
167. E. E. Howe, *Am. J. Clin. Nutr.*, *6*, 18 (1958).

influencing human growth render this aspect of clinical research in vitamin B_{12} exceedingly difficult, it appears reasonable that children, because of their relatively higher metabolic rate, may require relatively more vitamin B_{12} than adults.

5. GERIATRICS. Elderly people frequently have special nutritional problems because of physiologic changes accompanying old age. One such change is decreased production of gastric juice to bind vitamin B_{12}. Decreased absorption of orally-administered vitamin B_{12} in older persons has been noted, and assays of serum samples from randomly selected populations of different age groups show that the serum vitamin B_{12} level decreases with advancing age. Tissue levels as well as blood levels of the vitamin decrease with advancing age

6. NEUROPATHIES. A number of painful neuropathies associated with conditions such as malnutrition, chronic alcoholism, diabetes, tabes dorsalis, and trigeminal neuralgia have been reported to be therapeutically benefited by the administration of vitamin B_{12}. Since some of these conditions are of obscure etiology, any therapeutic effect of the vitamin has been considered to occur owing to a pharmacological action rather than the simple alleviation of a deficiency state. This apparent function of the vitamin for the maintenance of integrity of the neurons and its apparent usefulness in certain neuropathies is a challenge for further research.

7. REQUIREMENTS. Since data are considered insufficient to set a minimum daily requirement for vitamin B_{12}, the consumption of a small amount of animal protein daily is considered sufficient to provide an adequate dietary supply of the vitamin.[168] The fact that complete remission of pernicious anemia has been reported to occur upon the daily parenteral administration of 1 μg. of vitamin B_{12} has led to the inference that the normal daily requirement of the vitamin might be met by the absorption of 1 μg. from the alimentary tract. Nutritional megaloblastic anemias have been reported to respond to the daily oral administration of 10–50 μg. of the vitamin, and a dose of 10 μg. of vitamin B_{12} daily has been reported in the study of growth promotion in retarded children.

Among the best sources of the vitamin are liver, kidney, and certain seafoods. Fermented materials such as rumen contents and feces are particularly rich sources of the vitamin. Plant tissue contains little or no vitamin B_{12}.

168. *Recommended Dietary Allowances*, Natl. Acad. Sci., Natl. Res. Council Publ., 589, Washington, D.C., 1958, p. 23.

CHAPTER XI

Lipoic Acid

1. Introduction

Lipoic acid is one of the more recent factors encountered during studies of microbial growth and microbial metabolism. Its status as a vitamin in mammalian nutrition is uncertain today, and most organisms apparently synthesize the factor in sufficient quantity to satisfy their nutritional requirement. Its importance in carbohydrate metabolism has been established, but its exact role is a problem of immediate interest and an object of current research.

In 1941 it was found that crude liver extracts were necessary for the sustained growth of the protozoan *Tetrahymena geleii* in casein media,[1] and by 1944 this material was partially purified by fractional precipitation.[2] The precipitated fraction was designated Factor I, and the water-soluble fraction was named Factor II. Next it was shown that Factor I could be replaced by a purine and one of the pteroylglutamic acids;[3] then Factor II, which could not be identified with any of the known essential nutrients, was further purified and designated Factor IIA.[4] It was not recognized at the time, but the same activity was also discovered in yeast extracts.[5,6] A requirement for sodium acetate by growing *Lactobacillus casei* had been demonstrated,[7,8] but it was found that *L. casei* could be grown in acetate-free media provided a small amount of yeast extract was added.[5] The active component of this yeast extract was designated the acetate-replacing factor. Later, it was reported by others that resting cells of *Streptococcus faecalis* failed to metabolize pyruvate unless a factor in a yeast extract was present; in this study, the factor was referred to as the pyruvate-oxidation factor.[6] In the meantime, Factor IIA was

1. V. C. Dewey, *Proc. Soc. Exptl. Biol. Med.*, *46*, 482 (1941).
2. V. C. Dewey, *Biol. Bull.*, *87*, 107 (1944).
3. G. W. Kidder and V. C. Dewey, *Arch. Biochem.*, *8*, 293 (1945).
4. G. W. Kidder and V. C. Dewey, *Arch. Biochem.*, *20*, 433 (1949).
5. B. M. Guirard, E. E. Snell, and R. J. Williams, *Arch. Biochem.*, *9*, 361 (1946).
6. D. J. O'Kane and I. C. Gunsalus, *J. Bacteriol.*, *56*, 499 (1948).
7. E. E. Snell, F. M. Strong, and W. H. Peterson, *Biochem. J.*, *31*, 1789 (1937).
8. E. E. Snell, E. L. Tatum, and W. H. Peterson, *J. Bacteriol.*, *33*, 207 (1937).

concentrated and designated protogen.[9] By 1949 a precise comparison of the growth effect of these preparations led to the conclusion that the active factor in each was identical.[10]

The active substance has been referred to as Factor II, Factor IIA, the acetate-replacing factor, pyruvate-oxidation factor, protogen, α-lipoic acid, thioctic acid, and 6-thioctic acid. Of these, only lipoic acid and 6-thioctic acid are in current use and of the two, the American Society of Biological Chemists has adopted lipoic acid as the "official trivial" name.

2. Isolation

The isolation and characterization of lipoic acid was completed by several research groups at about the same time. The factor was liberated from yeast or liver by enzymic, acid, or alkaline hydrolysis and was first isolated in crystalline form from processed insoluble liver residues. It was designated α-lipoic acid to denote its fat-soluble and acidic characteristics[11] and was reportedly 250,000 times as active as yeast. Later in the same year, a monosulfoxide of the factor was isolated from papain digests of liver and designated protogen B.[12]

The existence of other forms of lipoic acid in cellular extracts was demonstrated by paper chromatography and by countercurrent distribution. Five distinct forms of lipoic acid activity were observed bioautographically on chromatographs of commercial liver and yeast extracts.[13] Other workers recognized five chromatographically distinct types of lipoic acid activity on the basis of partition between organic and aqueous solvents.[14] One form, which is widely distributed in nature, was referred to as a "bound-form." Another form, observed principally in tissue and cell extracts after enzymic digestion, was water-soluble. Three organic solvent-soluble forms, referred to as a weak acid, a strong acid, and a neutral substance, were observed mostly after hydrolysis with acid or alkali.

9. E. L. R. Stokstad, C. E. Hoffmann, M. A. Regan, D. Fordham, and T. H. Jukes, *Arch. Biochem.*, *20*, 75 (1949).
10. E. E. Snell and H. P. Broquist, *Arch. Biochem.*, *23*, 326 (1949).
11. L. J. Reed, B. G. DeBusk, I. C. Gunsalus, and C. S. Hornberger, *Science*, *114*, 93 (1951).
12. E. L. Patterson, J. A. Brockman, F. P. Day, J. V. Pierce, M. E. Macchi, C. E. Hoffmann, C. T. O. Fong, E. L. R. Stokstad, and T. H. Jukes, *J. Am. Chem. Soc.*, *73*, 5919 (1951).
13. L. J. Reed, B. G. DeBusk, P. M. Johnston, and M. E. Getzendaner, *J. Biol. Chem.*, *192*, 851 (1951).
14. I. C. Gunsalus, L. Struglia, and D. J. O'Kane, *J. Biol. Chem.*, *194*, 859 (1952).

Two forms of the activity encountered in yeast and liver are lipoic acid and its monosulfoxide, usually referred to as β-lipoic acid or protogen B. When it became evident that lipoic acid contained a disulfide linkage, it was suggested that some uncharacterized forms of lipoic acid activity might be mixed disulfides of lipoic acid formed by reaction with naturally occurring thiols.[15]

The isolation of lipoic acid from beef liver residues was facilitated by two developments. A manometric assay based on the oxidation of pyruvate by resting cell suspensions of *S. faecalis* was used to follow the concentration of activity,[16] and bioautographic[13] and countercurrent distribution[14] techniques were developed to distinguish between the different forms of the activity. The factor liberated from beef liver residues by hydrolysis with hot 6*N* sulfuric acid was extracted with benzene and removed by bicarbonate extraction. The acidic fraction was esterified with diazomethane and purified by chromatography on alumina. Methyl α-lipoate was eluted with benzene; methyl β-lipoate was eluted with ethyl acetate. Methyl α-lipoate was further purified by chromatography on alumina, and the most active fractions were chromatographed on Florisil to obtain a highly purified concentrate. Saponification of this concentrate under mild conditions yielded a yellow oil which was crystallized from petroleum ether to give pure α-lipoic acid.[17]

The monosulfoxide of lipoic acid was isolated as a crystalline *S*-benzylthiouronium salt.[12,18] The active components of a papain digest of beef and hog liver, after hydrolysis with hot alkali and acidification, were extracted into chloroform. A countercurrent distribution of the hydrolyzate between chloroform and a phosphate buffer revealed the presence of three types of activity. The predominant form, designated protogen A, corresponded to α-lipoic acid. A water-soluble form, designated protogen B, corresponded to β-lipoic acid; the third form was probably an ester of one or both of the acidic compounds. α- and β-Lipoic acid were each further purified by chromatography on silicic acid. Final purification of β-lipoic acid was accomplished by separation as a crystalline *S*-benzylthiouronium salt.

During these investigations, the oxidation-reduction relationship between α- and β-lipoic acid was established. Mild oxidizing agents such as

15. L. J. Reed, B. G. DeBusk, C. S. Hornberger, Jr., and I. C. Gunsalus, *J. Am. Chem. Soc.*, *75*, 1271 (1953).
16. I. C. Gunsalus, M. I. Dolin, and L. Struglia, *J. Biol. Chem.*, *194*, 849 (1952).
17. L. J. Reed, I. C. Gunsalus, G. H. F. Schnakenberg, Q. F. Soper, H. E. Boaz, S. F. Kern, and T. V. Parke, *J. Am. Chem. Soc.*, *75*, 1267 (1953).
18. E. L. Patterson, J. V. Pierce, E. L. R. Stokstad, C. E. Hoffmann, J. A. Brockman, Jr., F. P. Day, M. E. Macchi, and T. H. Jukes, *J. Am. Chem. Soc.*, *76*, 1823 (1954).

t-butyl hydroperoxide, air, or iodine, converted α-lipoic acid to β-lipoic acid; reduction of β-lipoic acid with sodium borohydride or zinc in acetic acid yielded α-lipoic acid.

3. Structure Determination

The structure of lipoic acid was established as 5-[3-(1,2-dithiolanyl)]-pentanoic acid on the basis of degradative[19,20] and synthetic[21] studies, and its configuration (**1**) was determined. The compound was deduced to be a cyclic disulfide of octanoic acid (pKa 5.0) since it

(a) gave octanoic acid on Raney nickel desulfurization;

(b) generated two sulfhydryl groups on mild reduction; and

(c) showed no *C*-methyl groups either in a Kuhn-Roth determination or in the infrared spectrum.

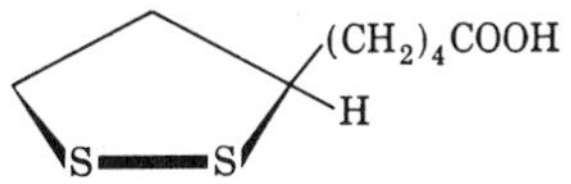

$(CH_2)_4COOH$
H
S—S

(1)

The absence of a *C*-methyl group in the molecule led to the conclusion that one of the sulfur atoms was linked to the terminal carbon atom of the skeleton. The second sulfur atom could not be located by usual degradation, but substitution on the carbon atoms α- and β- to the carboxyl group was eliminated on the basis of the pKa of the acid. From these data, it was postulated that the compound was either a 5-membered, a 6-membered, or a 7-membered cyclic disulfide bearing an ω-carboxyalkyl substituent on the carbon atom adjacent to the disulfide linkage. The disulfide ring, which was not elucidated by degradation, was shown to be 5-membered by synthesis.[21]

4. Synthesis

In one of the first syntheses of lipoic acid, δ-carbethoxyvaleryl chloride (**2**) was condensed with ethylene in the presence of aluminum chloride to yield the α,β-unsaturated ketone (**3**).[21] The addition of thioacetic acid to

19. J. A. Brockman, Jr., E. L. R. Stokstad, E. L. Patterson, J. V. Pierce, and M. E. Macchi, *J. Am. Chem. Soc.*, *76*, 1827 (1954).
20. J. A. Brockman, Jr., E. L. R. Stokstad, E. L. Patterson, J. V. Pierce, M. Macchi, and F. P. Day, *J. Am. Chem. Soc.*, *74*, 1868 (1952).
21. M. W. Bullock, J. A. Brockman, Jr., E. L. Patterson, J. V. Pierce, M. H. Von Saltza, F. Sanders, and E. L. R. Stokstad, *J. Am. Chem. Soc.*, *76*, 1828 (1954).

the α,β-unsaturated system of (**3**) gave the β-acetylmercaptoketone (**4**), which on sodium borohydride reduction yielded the β-acetylmercaptocarbinol (**5**). Alkaline hydrolysis of the ester functions in (**5**) yielded

$$\underset{(2)}{ClC(=O)(CH_2)_4COOC_2H_5} \xrightarrow[AlCl_3]{CH_2{=}CH_2} \underset{(3)}{CH_2{=}CHC(=O)(CH_2)_4COOC_2H_5} \xrightarrow{CH_3C(=O)SH}$$

$$\underset{(4)}{CH_3C(=O)SCH_2CH_2C(=O)(CH_2)_4COOC_2H_5} \xrightarrow{NaBH_4} \underset{(5)}{CH_3C(=O)SCH_2CH_2CH(OH)(CH_2)_4COOC_2H_5} \xrightarrow{NaOH}$$

$$\underset{(6)}{CH_2(SH)CH_2CH(OH)(CH_2)_4COOH} \xrightarrow[(H_2N)_2C{=}S]{HI} \underset{(7)}{HSCH_2CH_2CH(SH)(CH_2)_4COOH} \xrightarrow{KI_3} \text{Lipoic Acid}$$

6-hydroxy-8-mercaptooctanoic acid (**6**), which after treatment with hydrogen iodide and thiourea gave 6,8-dimercaptooctanoic acid (**7**). Oxidation of the dithiol (**7**) with iodine in potassium iodide solution yielded lipoic acid.

$$\underset{(8)}{\text{2-oxocyclohexyl-}CH_2COOC_2H_5} \xrightarrow{HOCH_2CH_2OH} \text{ethylene ketal, }CH_2COOC_2H_5 \xrightarrow{LiAlH_4} \text{ethylene ketal, }CH_2CH_2OH \xrightarrow{\text{Acetylate}}$$

$$\text{ethylene ketal, }CH_2CH_2OC(=O)CH_3 \xrightarrow{H_3O^+} \underset{(9)}{\text{2-oxocyclohexyl-}CH_2CH_2OC(=O)CH_3} \xrightarrow{CH_3C(=O)OOH} \underset{(10)}{\text{lactone, }CH_2CH_2OC(=O)CH_3} \xrightarrow{(H_2N)_2C{=}S}$$

$$\underset{(7)}{CH_2(SH)CH_2CH(SH)(CH_2)_4COOH} \xrightarrow{KI_3} \text{Lipoic acid}$$

Other syntheses of lipoic acid appeared during the ensuing years.[22–26] The key compound of one of the more recent syntheses of *DL*-lipoic acid is the 7-membered lactone (**10**) of 6-hydroxy-8-acetoxyoctanoic acid.[26] Ethyl cyclohexanone-2-acetate (**8**) was converted in several steps to 2-(2-acetoxyethyl)cyclohexanone (**9**). Oxidation of the cyclohexanone (**9**) with peracetic acid yielded the 6-lactone (**10**) of 6-hydroxy-8-acetoxyoctanoic acid, which on treatment with thiourea gave dihydrolipoic acid (**7**).

5. Resolution and Configuration

The resolution of racemic lipoic acid has been difficult up to date. There is one resolution by fractional crystallization of the cinchonidine salts of lipoic acid,[27] but the yields were very low (0.5–4.4%). This method gave the dextrorotatory isomer, but it did not yield a pure levorotatory isomer.

$$C_2H_5OOC(CH_2)_4CH{=}CHCOOH \xrightarrow{CH_3\overset{\overset{O}{\|}}{C}SH} C_2H_5OOC(CH_2)_4\underset{\underset{\underset{O}{\|}}{SCCH_3}}{|}{\!\!\!CHCH_2COOH} \xrightarrow{SOCl_2}$$

(11)

(Resolved into optical antipodes with *l*-ephedrine)

$$C_2H_5OOC(CH_2)_4\underset{\underset{\underset{O}{\|}}{SCCH_3}}{|}{\!\!\!CHCH_2\overset{\overset{O}{\|}}{C}Cl} \xrightarrow{NaBH_4} C_2H_5OOC(CH_2)_4\underset{\underset{\underset{O}{\|}}{SCCH_3}}{|}{\!\!\!CHCH_2CH_2OH} \xrightarrow{NaOH}$$

(12)

$$HOOC(CH_2)_4\underset{SH}{\underset{|}{C}}HCH_2CH_2OH \xrightarrow[(H_2N)_2C{=}S]{HBr} HOOC(CH_2)_4\underset{SH}{\underset{|}{C}}HCH_2\underset{SH}{\underset{|}{C}}H_2 \xrightarrow{KI_3} (+)\text{- and } (-)\text{-Lipoic acid}$$

(7)

22. C. S. Hornberger, Jr., R. F. Heitmiller, I. C. Gunsalus, G. H. F. Schnakenberg, and L. J. Reed, *J. Am. Chem. Soc.*, *75*, 1273 (1953).
23. Q. F. Soper, W. E. Buting, J. E. Cochran, Jr., and A. Pohland, *J. Am. Chem. Soc.*, *76*, 4109 (1954).
24. L. J. Reed and Ching-I Niu, *J. Am. Chem. Soc.*, *77*, 416 (1955).
25. E. Walton, A. F. Wagner, F. W. Bachelor, L. H. Peterson, F. W. Holly, and K. Folkers, *J. Am. Chem. Soc.*, *77*, 5144 (1955).
26. A. Segre, R. Viterbo, and G. Parisi, *J. Am. Chem. Soc.*, *79*, 3503 (1957).
27. D. S. Acker and W. J. Wayne, *J. Am. Chem. Soc.*, *79*, 6483 (1957).

Both optical antipodes have been synthesized directly in good yield by resolving intermediates in a reaction sequence and converting these stereoisomers to the pure optical antipodes of lipoic acid.[25,27,28] For example, *DL*-3-acetylthio-7-carbethoxyheptanoic acid (**11**) was synthesized and resolved.[25] The dextrorotatory isomer of (**11**) was converted to the corresponding acid chloride, which was reduced to ethyl 6-acetylthio-8-hydroxyoctanoate (**12**). Alkaline hydrolysis of (**12**), followed by treatment with hydrobromic acid and thiourea, yielded (−)-dihydrolipoic acid (**7**). Oxidation of the resulting (−)-dimercapto acid gave the naturally-occurring (+)-isomer of lipoic acid. (−)-3-Acetylthio-7-carbethoxyheptanoic acid was treated similarly to give (−)-lipoic acid.

Hydrolysis of the (+)- and (−)-3-acetylthio-7-carbethoxyheptanoic acid isomers (**11**) to (−)- and (+)-3-mercaptooctanedioic acid (**13**), respectively,

$$HOOC(CH_2)_4\underset{\displaystyle SH}{\underset{|}{C}}HCH_2COOH$$

(13)

led to the derivation of the absolute configuration of (+)- and (−)-lipoic acid.[29] The phase behavior of mixtures of (−)-3-mercaptooctanedioic acid and (+)-3-methyloctanedioic acid (**14**) was compared with that of

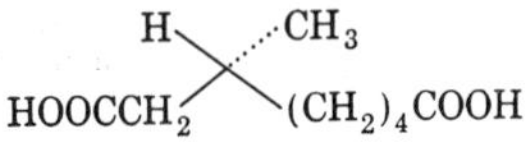

H, CH_3, $HOOCCH_2$, $(CH_2)_4COOH$

(14)

mixtures of (+)-3-mercaptooctanedioic acid and (+)-3-methyloctanedioic acid. Comparison of these melting point composition diagrams showed that (−)-3-mercaptooctanedioic acid (**13**) was sterically related to the configurationally known (+)-3-methyloctanedioic acid. Since the (−)-antipode of the mercaptodiacid (**13**) was derived from the (+)-intermediate (**11**) that gave (+)-lipoic acid, the order of substituents around the asymmetric center of (+)-lipoic acid, its precursors, and derivatives is represented as in (**1**).

6. Metabolic Role

A. Oxidative Decarboxylation

1. PARTICIPATION IN ACYL GENERATION AND ACYL TRANSFER. Lipoic acid is an essential factor for the enzymic oxidative decarboxylation of α-keto acids. On the basis of current evidence, the factor participates at one stage as the cyclic disulfide form and at other stages as the 6-*S*-acyldihydro

28. D. S. Acker, U.S. Pat., 2,792,406 (1957).
29. K. Mislow and W. C. Meluch, *J. Am. Chem. Soc.*, *78*, 5920 (1956).

and dihydro form. In the course of these transformations, the molecule is depicted as an acyl-generating, an acyl-transferring, and a hydrogen-transferring factor. The sequence of lipoic acid transformations during oxidative decarboxylation is based on studies using substrate amounts of free lipoic acid rather than catalytic amounts of lipoic acid in either a protein-bound or slightly dissociable form, which is typical of the physiological reactions. For this reason it was suggested that the proposed transformations of lipoic acid during the decarboxylation of an α-keto acid be regarded as tentative until the early stages of oxidative decarboxylation are fully elucidated, and the coenzyme or bound-form of lipoic acid is identified.[30]

The first association of lipoic acid with oxidative decarboxylation of α-keto acids stemmed from the observation that an unidentified factor, later shown to be lipoic acid, was required for the oxidation of pyruvate by *S. faecalis*;[6,31] the same requirement was also shown for *Escherichia coli*.[32–34] The presence of significant amounts of lipoic acid in purified pyruvate oxidase from pigeon breast muscle[35] and in α-ketoglutarate oxidase from pig heart muscle[36] also supported the concept that lipoic acid plays a role in α-keto acid metabolism. Recently, evidence was provided for the participation of lipoic acid in the pyruvate metabolism of rat heart mitochondria.[37,38]

The purification of a soluble pyruvate oxidase from *E. coli* marked a significant advance in establishing the site of lipoic acid participation in α-keto acid metabolism.[39] This system catalyzed the conversion of two molecules of pyruvate in the presence of phosphate to one molecule of acetyl phosphate, one molecule of lactate, and one molecule of carbon dioxide. When this complex enzyme system was resolved,[33] it was found to require the three known cofactors: thiamine pyrophosphate, coenzyme A, and diphosphopyridine nucleotide. In addition, it contained the enzymes phosphotransacetylase, lactic dehydrogenase, and two unknown systems designated A and B. Since the reactions catalyzed by phosphotransacetylase and lactic dehydrogenase were already established, it was concluded

30. S. Ochoa, *Advan. Enzymol.*, *15*, 183 (1954).
31. D. J. O'Kane and I. C. Gunsalus, *J. Bacteriol.*, *54*, 20 (1947).
32. L. P. Hager, J. D. Fortney, and I. C. Gunsalus, *Federation Proc.*, *12*, 213 (1953).
33. S. Korkes, A. del Campillo, and S. Ochoa, *J. Biol. Chem.*, *193*, 721 (1951).
34. L. J. Reed and B. G. DeBusk, *J. Am. Chem. Soc.*, *74*, 3457 (1952).
35. V. Jagannathan and R. S. Schweet, *J. Biol. Chem.*, *196*, 551 (1952).
36. D. R. Sanadi, J. W. Littlefield, and R. M. Bock, *J. Biol. Chem.*, *193*, 683 (1951).
37. O. K. Reiss and L. Hellerman, *J. Biol. Chem.*, *231*, 557 (1958).
38. O. K. Reiss, *J. Biol. Chem.*, *233*, 789 (1958).
39. S. Korkes, J. R. Stern, I. C. Gunsalus, and S. Ochoa, *Nature*, *166*, 439 (1950).

that the unknown enzyme fractions A and B catalyzed one of the reactions converting pyruvate and coenzyme A to acetyl coenzyme A and carbon dioxide. Because of the large number of enzymes and coenzymes operating

$$\text{Pyruvate} + \text{CoA—SH} + \text{DPN}^+ \xrightarrow{\text{TPP}} \underset{\underset{\text{O}}{\|}}{\text{CoA—SCCH}_3} + \text{CO}_2 + \text{DPNH} + \text{H}^+$$

in this soluble pyruvate system, it was proposed that several separate reactions were occurring sequentially.[40] The decarboxylation step was regarded as a reaction between pyruvate and thiamine pyrophosphate yielding an "active aldehyde"-thiamine pyrophosphate complex (Chapter III). It was assumed that this complex reacted with coenzyme A to yield an aldehyde-bound coenzyme A and thiamine pyrophosphate; the final step was visualized as the oxidation of aldehyde-bound coenzyme A to acetyl coenzyme A by diphosphopyridine nucleotide. Revision of this role for

$$\text{Pyruvate} + \text{TPP} \rightleftarrows \text{“acetaldehyde-TPP”} + \text{CO}_2$$

$$\text{“Acetaldehyde-TPP”} + \text{CoA—SH} \rightleftarrows \text{CoA-}S\text{-“acetaldehyde”} + \text{TPP}$$

$$\text{CoA-}S\text{-“acetaldehyde”} + \text{DPN}^+ \rightleftarrows \underset{\underset{\text{O}}{\|}}{\text{CoA—SCCH}_3} + \text{DPNH} + \text{H}^+$$

coenzyme A was necessitated by the observation that the pyruvate oxidase of pigeon breast muscle oxidized pyruvate to acetate and carbon dioxide in the absence of coenzyme A and DPN; if coenzyme A and an appropriate acetyl acceptor were added to this system, acetyl transfer occurred. Consequently, it was suggested that the "active acetaldehyde"-enzyme complex from pyruvate and thiamine pyrophosphate was converted to an acetyl-enzyme complex prior to the participation of coenzyme A.[41] The unknown fractions A and B of the *E. coli* system could, therefore, be required for this intermediate stage; after Fraction B was associated with known cofactors for hydrogen transport,[42] only Fraction A remained to account for a new factor intermediate between thiamine- and coenzyme A participation in oxidative decarboxylation.

40. S. Ochoa and J. R. Stern, *Ann. Rev. Biochem.*, *21*, 547 (1952).
41. R. S. Schweet, M. Fuld, K. Cheslock, and M. H. Paul, in W. D. McElroy and B. Glass, eds., *Phosphorus Metabolism*, Vol. I, Johns Hopkins Press, Baltimore, Md., 1951, p. 246.
42. L. P. Hager and I. C. Gunsalus, *J. Am. Chem. Soc.*, *75*, 5767 (1953).

2. (+)-6-*S*-ACETYLDIHYDROLIPOIC ACID. Since lipoic acid was known to function in α-keto acid metabolism, it was assumed that lipoic acid was associated with Fraction A, and it was proposed that an *S*-acyldihydrolipoic acid-enzyme complex intervened prior to the participation of coenzyme A.[43–45] In this scheme (Fig. 1) for lipoic acid participation in α-keto acid metabolism,[46] lipoic acid is believed to operate between thiamine pyrophosphate and coenzyme A, first for acyl-generation then as an acyl-transferring agent. The optical specificity of the three-stage process has been demonstrated; specific enzymes required at two stages of the cycle have been prepared, and the intermediate (+)-6-*S*-acetyldihydrolipoic acid has been obtained by enzymic synthesis.[47] The three forms of lipoic acid appearing at various stages during the oxidative decarboxylation of pyruvate are (+)-lipoic acid (**1**), (+)-6-*S*-acetyldihydrolipoic acid (**15**), and (−)-dihydrolipoic acid (**7**); all three forms have the same absolute configuration.

The enzymic oxidation of "active acetaldehyde" to "active acetyl" is specific for the dextrorotatory isomer of lipoic acid. It is not known whether the "active acetaldehyde" moiety of the thiamine pyrophosphate intermediate is transferred oxidatively to (+)-lipoic acid to yield (+)-6-*S*-acetyldihydrolipoic acid, or whether the "acetaldehyde-thiamine pyrophosphate" complex is first oxidized by lipoic acid to yield acetylthiamine pyrophosphate, which then transfers its "active acetyl" to the dihydrolipoic acid derivative generated during the oxidation of "active acetaldehyde." Recent data indicate that acylthiamine pyrophosphate derivatives participate in the oxidative decarboxylation of α-keto acids;[47a] these observations suggest that acyl generation proceeds by the latter of the two alternative mechanisms.

The transfer of "active acetyl" to coenzyme A is optically specific for (+)-6-*S*-acetyldihydrolipoic acid and (−)-dihydrolipoic acid (**7**). The enzyme system is dihydrolipoic transacetylase; acetyl coenzyme A and coenzyme A are acetyl donor and acceptor, respectively. The oxidation-reduction stage showing the return from dihydrolipoic acid to lipoic acid is mediated by the enzyme system dihydrolipoic dehydrogenase and is not optically specific.

43. I. C. Gunsalus, *J. Cellular Comp. Physiol.*, *41*, (Suppl. 1), 113 (1953).
44. L. J. Reed and B. G. DeBusk, *J. Am. Chem. Soc.*, *74*, 3964 (1952).
45. R. S. Schweet and K. Cheslock, *J. Biol. Chem.*, *199*, 749 (1952).
46. I. C. Gunsalus in W. D. McElroy and B. Glass, eds., *The Mechanism of Enzyme Action*, Johns Hopkins Press, Baltimore, Md., 1954, p. 553.
47. I. C. Gunsalus, L. S. Barton, and W. Gruber, *J. Am. Chem. Soc.*, *78*, 1763 (1956).
47a. M. L. Das, M. Koike, and L. J. Reed, *Proc. Natl. Acad. Sci. U.S.*, *47*, 753 (1961).

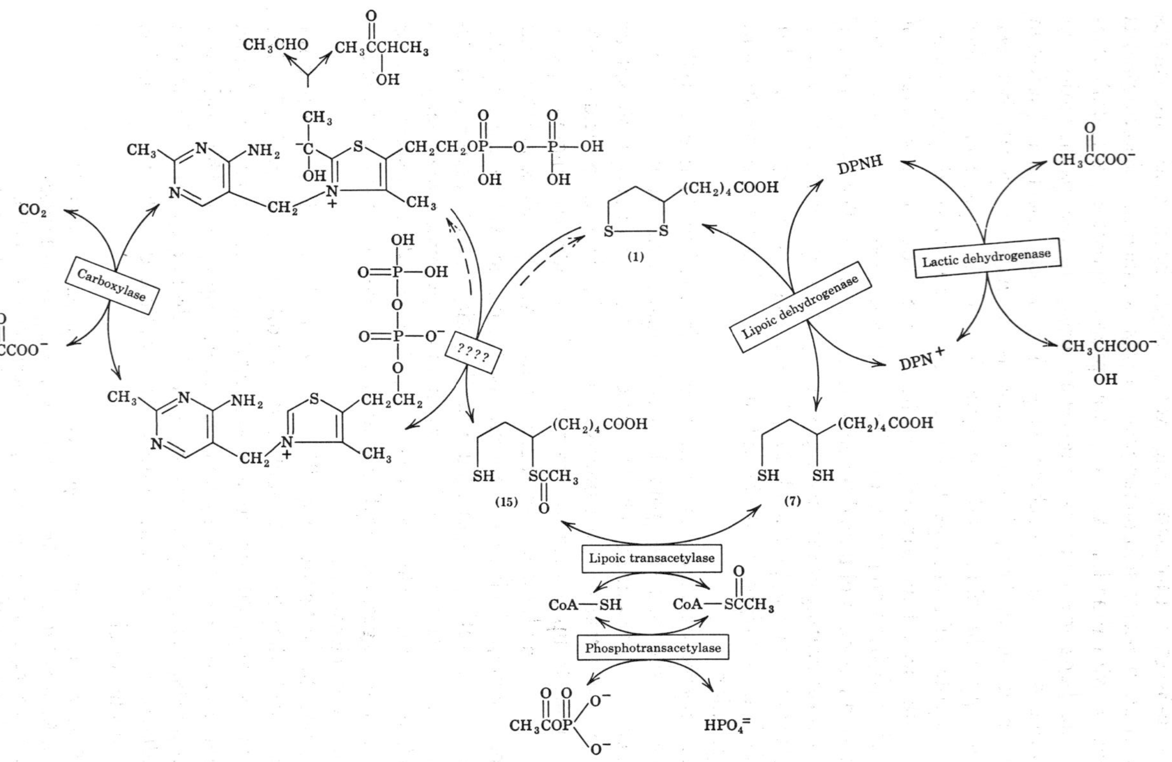

Fig. 1. Role of lipoic acid in oxidative decarboxylation based on studies with free-lipoic acid.[46,47]

3. "NATURAL FORM." Since the interpretations of the role of lipoic acid are based on reactions using substrate amounts of free lipoic acid, there has been an extended effort to isolate and identify a bound or coenzyme form of lipoic acid to verify the applicability of these transformations to the "natural system." A direct approach to the nature of the coenzyme form of lipoic acid using an *E. coli* mutant led to the tentative proposal that lipoic acid reacted with the 4-amino group of thiamine pyrophosphate to yield the amide lipothiamide pyrophosphate, which could function as a coenzyme form of lipoic acid in oxidative decarboxylation.[48] From a chemical point of view, acylation at the 4-amino group of the pyrimidine moiety seemed to be an unlikely reaction. In view of failures to confirm this interpretation and as a result of subsequent publications on the nature of lipoic acid binding in its coenzyme form, the lipothiamide formulation is no longer tenable.[49,50]

The present evidence supports the concept that enzymically active lipoic acid is bound through its carboxyl group to protein. Cell-free extracts of *S. faecalis* deficient in lipoic acid would catalyze the dismutation of pyruvate or α-ketobutyrate only when the extracts were pre-incubated with lipoic acid.[49] After incubation, the extract was dialyzed with only a slight loss of activity, suggesting that lipoic acid was converted to an enzymically active protein-bound form during incubation. Divalent metal ion and inorganic phosphate are also required for binding and for enzymic activity. The inhibition of pyruvate dismutation by arsenite, added either before or after pre-incubation of the *S. faecalis* extract with lipoic acid, suggests that the factor is not bound to protein through its sulfur-containing moiety. Thiamine pyrophosphate does not participate in the binding process since the amount of lipoic acid bound in the absence of thiamine pyrophosphate was essentially the same as that bound in its presence.

Fractionation of the *S. faecalis* extract yielded a lipoic acid activating system and an apopyruvate dehydrogenation system. Incorporation of lipoic acid into the *S. faecalis* apopyruvate oxidation system required incubation of this fraction with lipoic acid, adenosine triphosphate, and a divalent metal ion. Evidence was also found which showed that lipoic acid was converted to "lipoyl adenylate" by an ATP-dependent reaction prior to being bound covalently through its carboxyl group to protein.

Further support for the concept of a lipoyl enzyme was provided after

48. L. J. Reed and B. G. DeBusk, *J. Am. Chem. Soc.*, *74*, 3457, 3964, 4727 (1952); *Federation Proc.*, *13*, 723 (1954).
49. L. J. Reed, R. F. Leach, and M. Koike, *J. Biol. Chem.*, *232*, 123 (1958).
50. L. J. Reed, M. Koike, M. E. Levitch, and F. R. Leach, *J. Biol. Chem.*, *232*, 143 (1958)

the preparation of partially purified enzymes[50,51] which deactivate the pyruvate dehydrogenation system by liberating lipoic acid from the protein-bound form. The releasing enzyme, which apparently cleaves the covalent bond between lipoic acid and protein, is designated "lipoyl-*X*-hydrolase."[50] With the availability of this method to deactivate the pyruvate dehydrogenase systems from *S. faecalis* and *E. coli*, it was possible to determine whether free- or protein-bound lipoic acid participated in the over-all enzymic sequence and in each of its isolated component reactions.[50,52–54] The release of protein-bound lipoic acid from the enzyme complex resulted in the loss of activity to catalyze the conversion of pyruvate to acetyl phosphate; the isolated transacetylation and dehydrogenation reactions of this multistep sequence were unaffected by the release of protein-bound lipoic acid. From these observations, the early concept for the enzymic conversion of pyruvate to acetyl phosphate was modified to include:

(a) protein-bound lipoic acid participating in the oxidation of "active acetaldehyde" to yield protein-bound 6-*S*-acetyldihydrolipoic acid;

(b) protein-bound 6-*S*-acetyldihydrolipoic acid and protein-bound dihydrolipoic acid functioning as substrates, respectively, for the enzymes catalyzing acetyl transfer and dehydrogenation; and

(c) flavine-adenine dinucleotide participating in the dehydrogenase reaction.

In the over-all reaction sequence, electron transfer flows from pyruvate to protein-bound lipoic acid to flavine-adenine dinucleotide and finally to diphosphopyridine nucleotide.

The reaction sequence (Fig. 2) begins with the conversion of pyruvate to "active acetaldehyde" by thiamine pyrophosphate. The "active acetaldehyde" moiety is visualized as a bound stabilized acetyl carbanion (cf. Chapter III). The mechanism for the generation of an acetyl group from the acetyl carbanion has not been established. This step may proceed by the transfer of the stabilized acetyl carbanion from thiamine pyrophosphate to protein-bound lipoic acid with concomitant oxidation, or alternatively the "acetaldehyde-thiamine pyrophosphate" intermediate may be oxidized by protein-bound lipoic acid to yield acetylthiamine, which in turn acetylates the protein-bound lipoic acid derivative generated during the oxidation of "active acetaldehyde." Recent data appear to support the latter mechanism.[47a] By either mechanism, however, the "active acetyl" group

51. G. R. Seaman, *J. Biol. Chem.*, *234*, 161 (1959).
52. M. Koike, L. J. Reed, and W. R. Carroll, *J. Biol. Chem.*, *235*, 1924, (1960).
53. M. Koike and L. J. Reed, *J. Biol. Chem.*, *235*, 1931 (1960).
54. M. Koike, P. C. Shah, and L. J. Reed, *J. Biol. Chem.*, *235*, 1939 (1960).

$$CH_3\overset{O}{\overset{\|}{C}}COO^- + TPP \rightleftharpoons CH_3\overset{OH}{\overset{|}{\underline{C}}}—TPP + CO_2$$

$$\overline{S—S}\text{(ring)}—(CH_2)_4\overset{O}{\overset{\|}{C}}—\text{Protein} + CH_3\overset{OH}{\overset{|}{\underline{C}}}—TPP \rightleftharpoons \ddot{S}^-,\ S\overset{}{C}(=O)CH_3—(CH_2)_4\overset{O}{\overset{\|}{C}}—\text{Protein} + TPP$$

$$\ddot{S}^-,\ SC(=O)CH_3—(CH_2)_4\overset{O}{\overset{\|}{C}}—\text{Protein} + CoA—SH \rightleftharpoons \ddot{S}^-,\ SH—(CH_2)_4\overset{O}{\overset{\|}{C}}—\text{Protein} + CoA—S\overset{O}{\overset{\|}{C}}CH_3$$

$$\ddot{S}^-,\ SH—(CH_2)_4\overset{O}{\overset{\|}{C}}—\text{Protein} + FAD + H^+ \rightleftharpoons \overline{S—S}\text{(ring)}—(CH_2)_4\overset{O}{\overset{\|}{C}}—\text{Protein} + FADH_2$$

$$FADH_2 + DPN \rightleftharpoons FAD + DPNH + H^+$$

TPP = Thiamine Pyrophosphate
CoA—SH = Coenzyme A
FAD = Flavine-Adenine Dinucleotide
DPN = Diphosphopyridine Nucleotide

Fig. 2. Modified role of lipoic acid in oxidative decarboxylation.[50,52-54]

is ultimately visualized as protein-bound 6-*S*-acetyldihydrolipoic acid. The acetyl group of this protein-bound moiety is transferred to coenzyme A by a reaction in which the protein-bound *S*-acetyl derivative is converted to protein-bound dihydrolipoic acid by dihydrolipoic transacetylase.

Prior to the discovery(55,56) that flavine-adenine dinucleotide participated in the reaction sequence, it had been assumed that the dehydrogenation of protein-bound dihydrolipoic acid was accomplished by "disulfide interchange" between free lipoic acid and protein-bound dihydrolipoic acid.(50) The interchange reaction was postulated to account for the formation of free dihydrolipoic acid during the reaction. With the discovery of participation by flavine-adenine dinucleotide, the occurrence of free dihydrolipoic acid was explained on the basis of a side reaction between dihydroflavine-adenine dinucleotide and free lipoic acid rather than on "disulfide interchange." In the modified reaction sequence, a flavine-adenine dinucleotide system designated dihydrolipoic dehydrogenase oxidizes protein-bound dihydrolipoic acid to protein-bound lipoic acid. The resulting dihydroflavine-adenine dinucleotide is then reoxidized by reaction with diphosphopyridine nucleotide.

a. Lipoyl Lysine. It was considered likely that the lipoyl moiety of the enzyme is attached to a basic protein component after lipoamide (**16**) and dihydrolipoamide (**17**) proved to be more effective substrates in model reactions than lipoic acid, dihydrolipoic acid, or their corresponding

$(CH_2)_4CONH_2$ $(CH_2)_4CONH_2$

S—S   SH SH

(16)   (17)

methyl esters.(50,57,58) Further support for this concept was obtained by the degradation of enzymically produced bound-lipoic acid.(59) Pyruvate and α-ketoglutarate dehydrogenase were prepared by incubation with S_2^{35}-lipoic acid, and purified concentrates of these systems were partially degraded by performic acid oxidation followed by hydrolysis. One product of the degradation reaction was a ninhydrin-positive, radioactive

55. V. Massey, *Biochim. et Biophys. Acta*, *32*, 286 (1959).
56. M. Koike and L. J. Reed, *J. Am. Chem. Soc.*, *81*, 505 (1959).
57. D. R. Sanadi and R. L. Searis, *Federation Proc.*, *16*, 241 (1957); *Biochim. et Biophys. Acta*, *24*, 220 (1957).
58. V. Massey, *Biochim. et Biophys. Acta*, *30*, 205 (1958).
59. H. Nawa, W. T. Brady, M. Koike, and L. J. Reed, *J. Am. Chem. Soc.*, *81*, 2908 (1959); *82*, 896 (1960).

conjugate identified as ε-*N*-(6,8-disulfooctanoyl)-*L*-lysine (**18**) by degradation and synthesis. Partial hydrolysis of the oxidized pyruvate dehydrogenation complex under even milder conditions yielded three 6,8-disulfooctanoyl peptides. The nature of these products indicated that lipoic acid was joined through the carbonyl moiety of its carboxyl group to the ε-amino function of lysine in the Ala. Lys. Asp. or Asp. Lys. Ala. segment of the protein as in (**19**).

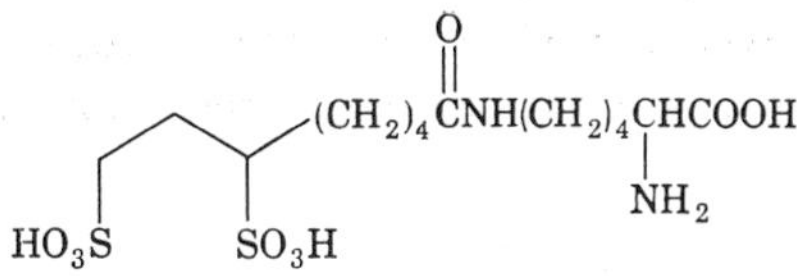

$(CH_2)_4C(=O)NH(CH_2)_4CH(NH_2)COOH$ with HO_3S and SO_3H on the chain

(18)

$(CH_2)_4C(=O)NH(CH_2)_4CH(NH—\cdots)—C(=O)—\cdots$ with S—S ring

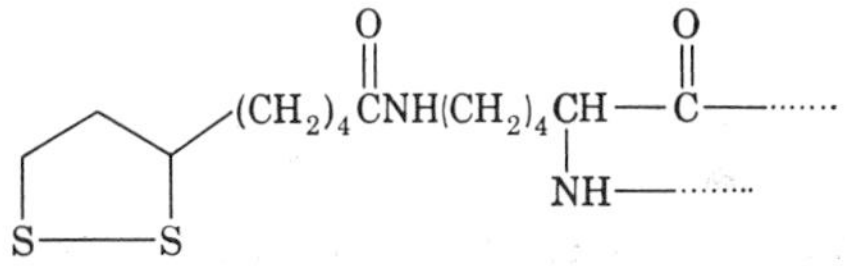

(19)

B. Possible Role in Photosynthesis

There has been increasing consideration that lipoic acid is a key agent in the primary quantum conversion step of photosynthesis. The term "primary quantum conversion" refers to a process in which electromagnetic energy of an excited molecule is transformed into chemical bond energy. In this instance, it refers to that stage of photosynthesis in which the excited chlorophyll molecule returns to its ground state, apparently transferring its electromagnetic energy through the labilization of the disulfide bond of lipoic acid. This role for lipoic acid was suggested after a study of the relative amounts of C^{14} introduced into products of the Krebs citric acid cycle by intermediates of the photosynthetic cycle during light and dark intervals.[60] In plants that were allowed to photosynthesize in the presence of $C^{14}O_2$, the conversion of photosynthetic intermediates to tricarboxylic acid intermediates occurred rapidly in the dark, but was completely inhibited during periods of illumination. To account for the rapid appearance of newly assimilated C^{14} in intermediates of the Krebs cycle, it was assumed that a direct pathway linked photosynthesis to the Krebs cycle and became blocked during illumination. Since lipoic acid was already known to generate and transfer acetyl groups in oxidative α-keto acid decarboxylation, it was suggested that this molecule is perhaps the

60. M. Calvin and P. Massini, *Experientia*, *8*, 445 (1952).

connecting link between the photosynthetic and Krebs cycles. Furthermore, it was suggested that the pathway linking these cycles was blocked by the photochemical conversion of the disulfide form of lipoic acid to the dithiol form; a direct transfer of electronic excitation energy from activated chlorophyll to lipoic acid could result in the formation of the dithiyl radical (**20**) which might then react with either a hydrogen carrier, water, or an oxygen carrier, forming either a dithiol, a thiolsulfenic acid, or a disulfide monoxide, respectively.[61,62] Such reactive species are incapable of participating in the oxidative decarboxylation of newly formed pyruvic acid to "active acetyl," but they could carry out the oxidation-reduction processes of natural photosynthesis.

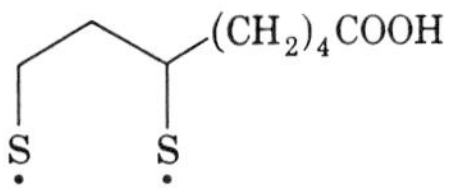

$(CH_2)_4COOH$

S· S·

(20)

A study of the effect of lipoic acid on the quantum efficiency of the Hill reaction resulted in some modification of this formulation.[63,64] Since the oxygen molecule evolved in photosynthesis has its proximate origin in the water molecule, the chlorophyll-induced photochemical reaction may be regarded as the cleavage of a water molecule to a reduced fragment capable of reducing carbon dioxide in the absence of light and an oxidized fragment which ultimately leads to molecular oxygen. The Hill reaction is a low energy photolytic cleavage of water to oxygen mediated by chloroplast suspensions.[65] Since these chloroplasts are unable to assimilate or reduce carbon dioxide, this reaction effectively separates the photochemical activation step from the carbon dioxide reduction step. The rate of oxygen evolution reflects the extent of the Hill reaction and since this would be restricted by recombination of the cleavage products of water, oxygen production is maintained by the addition of hydrogen acceptors with potentials below that of the oxygen electrode. The reaction is visualized as follows. Light-activated chlorophyll cleaves water into reduced and oxidized fragments. The oxidized fragments yield oxygen; the reduced fragments are removed by the reducible substrate, usually a quinone. The possible role of plastoquinone in photosynthesis is noted in Chapter XXI (Coenzyme Q).

61. M. Calvin and J. A. Barltrop, *J. Am. Chem. Soc.*, *74*, 6153 (1952).
62. J. A. Barltrop, P. M. Hayes, and M. Calvin, *J. Am. Chem. Soc.*, *76*, 4348 (1954).
63. D. F. Bradley and M. Calvin, *Arch. Biochem. Biophys.*, *53*, 99 (1954).
64. D. F. Bradley and M. Calvin, *Proc. Natl. Acad. Sci. U.S.*, *41*, 563 (1955).
65. R. Hill, *Nature*, *139*, 881 (1947); *Proc. Roy. Soc.* (*London*), *Ser. B*, *127*, 192 (1939).

Direct evidence is available for the effect of lipoic acid on the rate of quantum conversion in photosynthesis.[63,64] When the Hill reaction was performed under continuous illumination, conditions were found in which lipoic acid increased the quantum efficiency with the organism *Scenedesmus obliquus*. Although the rate of oxygen evolution increased, the final yield was the same as in control reactions without added lipoic acid. In these studies it was not possible to determine whether lipoic acid influenced the rate of oxygen evolution by increasing the rate at which water was cleaved or by decreasing the rate at which the cleavage products recombined.

To eliminate limitations in oxygen evolution produced by so-called dark chemical reactions, the effect of lipoic acid on the quantum efficiency of the Hill reaction was studied using intermittent light.[64] When the dark interval was of the order of 0.05 sec., the yield of oxygen was limited by the concentrations of both quinone and lipoic acid. With a dark interval of the order of 0.2 sec., the yield was subject to light limitation and equivalent to the total lipoic acid content of the plant calculated on a molecular basis. If the lifetime for thermal decay of photochemically active chlorophyll is assumed to be at least of the order of 0.2 sec. *in vivo*, these data would be consistent with the participation of lipoic acid in the quantum conversion process of photosynthesis. Thus, the photosynthetic process and the role of lipoic acid were depicted as follows. The absorption of light by chlorophyll leads to a metastable state visualized as a molecule with a trapped ion pair. The ion pair may be considered as a conduction electron and its corresponding hole. The hole is trapped or neutralized by the donation of electrons from water yielding oxygen. This reaction is assumed to be immediate and gives the conduction electron a relatively long life. Electron transfer to the primary acceptor is therefore considered the rate limiting step. The electron reacts with lipoic acid in the presence of a proton yielding dihydrolipoic acid, which serves as a reducing agent through the mediation of triphosphopyridine nucleotide for the conversion of carbon dioxide to carbohydrate.

There are data to contradict the possible participation of lipoic acid in photosynthetic processes. In some instances a sharp lipoic acid-induced stimulation of carbon dioxide uptake could not be established in *Scenedesmus* or *Chlorella*.[66] Even in the presence of quinone, low concentrations of lipoic acid barely promoted the photosynthetic reduction of carbon dioxide. When *Chlorella* was incubated with low concentrations of lipoic acid in light, there was no significant increase in the net $C^{14}O_2$ fixed, but rather greater activity of C^{14} in the Krebs cycle. The latter fact tends to

66. B. B. Biswas and S. P. Sen, *Nature*, *181*, 1219 (1958).

refute the possibility of photochemical generation of any significant amount of dihydrolipoic acid. Disputative evidence was also presented from another study. When *Chlorella* is incubated with radioactive lipoic acid, the major portion of the lipoic acid is found to be incorporated in the plastid fraction;[67] in studies of the Hill reaction with whole chloroplasts from spinach leaves, however, no inhibition was obtained with typical dimercaptan oxidants such as iodoacetamide, *p*-chloromercuribenzoate, or arsenite.[68] If dihydrolipoic acid were participating in the Hill reaction, inhibition by these reagents would be anticipated.

7. Nutritional and Therapeutic Studies

A. In Animals

There is no clear evidence for a deficiency of lipoic acid in mammalian nutrition. Lipoic acid is an essential nutrient for several microorganisms, but fails to produce a growth response in chicks or rats fed certain purified diets.[69] At first it was reported that good growth responses were obtained on the administration of lipoic acid to rats and chicks on purified diets,[70] but since that time there have been many reported failures to obtain growth response in chicks by lipoic acid supplementation.[71–75] Lipoic acid also has no effect on the growth of turkey poults.[76]

Contradictory results have been reported on the ability of lipoic acid to reduce cholesterol levels. Some investigators reported that lipoic acid treatment tended to limit the increase in plasma-, liver-, and aorta-lipid of rabbits maintained on high cholesterol diets;[77] others failed to observe decreased levels and reported increased atherosclerosis in the rabbits

67. R. C. Fuller, H. Grisebach, and M. Calvin, *J. Am. Chem. Soc.*, *77*, 2659 (1958).
68. D. I. Arnon, M. B. Allen, and F. R. Whatley, *Biochim. et. Biophys. Acta*, *20*, 449 (1956).
69. E. L. R. Stokstad, H. P. Broquist, and E. L. Patterson, *Federation Proc.*, *12*, 430 (1953).
70. B. G. DeBusk and R. J. Williams, *Arch. Biochem. Biophys.*, *55*, 587 (1955).
71. A. B. Morrison and L. C. Norris, *Poultry Sci.*, *35*, 739 (1956).
72. E. L. R. Stokstad, E. L. Patterson, A. M. Albrecht, and R. H. White-Stevens, *Proc. Soc. Exptl. Biol. Med.*, *92*, 88 (1956).
73. W. C. Supplee, G. F. Combs, and G. L. Romoser, *Arch. Biochem. Biophys.*, *61*, 140 (1956).
74. G. M. Briggs and M. R. Spivey Fox, *Poultry Sci.*, *36*, 657 (1957).
75. R. Dam, L. C. Norris, and F. W. Hill, *Poultry Sci.*, *36*, 1110 (1957).
76. F. H. Kratzer, P. Vohra, P. N. Davis, and R. L. Atkinson, *Poultry Sci.*, *37*, 955 (1958).
77. L. Angelucci and E. Mascitelli-Coriandoli, *Nature*, *181*, 911 (1958).

treated with lipoic acid.[78] This discrepancy might be explained on the basis of the amount of cholesterol fed and the amount of lipoic acid administered. The effect of lipoic acid on cholesterol levels in atherosclerosis requires further evaluation.

Treatment of experimental tumors with lipoic acid in rats and mice has resulted largely in negative results,[79,80] and it has been suggested that lipoic acid might even stimulate tumor growth.[80]

There has been one report of a reduction in voluntary alcohol consumption after the administration of lipoic acid to rats deficient in the vitamin B complex.[81]

At one time, it was proposed that lipoic acid might function in the process of vision.[82] The rod, retina, and choroid of the frog contain lipoic acid, but an injection of *DL*-lipoic acid into the eye failed to accelerate the regeneration of rhodopsin in the dark-adapted frog.[83]

B. In the Human

A limited number of tests with lipoic acid in the human have been reported. Lipoic acid has been administered during therapy of the human liver disease hepatic coma with reportedly beneficial results.[84–86]

78. D. Kritchevsky and A. W. Moyer, *Nature*, *182*, 396 (1958).
79. V. Di Carlo, G. Maimone, and G. Giordano, *Naturwissenschaften*, *45*, 44 (1958).
80. H. Lettré, *Naturwissenschaften*, *45*, 217 (1958).
81. J. Mardones, N. Segovia, F. Alcaino, and A. Hederra, *Science*, *119*, 735 (1954).
82. B. S. Strauss, *Science*, *118*, 330 (1953).
83. I. Hanawa, K. Kuge, and J. Saito, *Science*, *132*, 1668 (1960).
84. P. Boni, F. Reduzzi, G. Bile, and V. Galloro, *Clin. terap.*, *9*, 129 (1955); through *J. Am. Chem. Soc.*, *79*, 3503 (1957).
85. F. Rausch, *Klin. Wochschr.*, *34*, 737 (1956); through *J. Am. Chem. Soc.*, *79*, 3503 (1957).
86. F. Steigman and S. M. Canahuati, *Federation Proc.*, *15*, 497 (1956).

CHAPTER XII

Choline and Cytidinediphosphocholine

1. Introduction

Choline occurs in all plant and animal cells either as free choline (**1**), acetylcholine (**2**), or in phospholipids such as the lecithins (**3**). It is an important dietary factor because of its lipotropic activity.

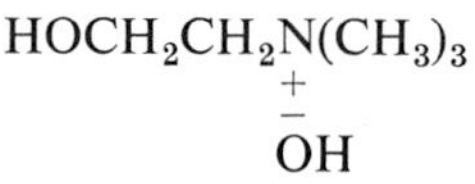

$$\underset{\textbf{(1)}}{HOCH_2CH_2\overset{+}{N}(CH_3)_3\ \bar{O}H} \qquad \underset{\textbf{(2)}}{CH_3\overset{O}{\overset{\|}{C}}OCH_2CH_2\overset{+}{N}(CH_3)_3\ \bar{O}H}$$

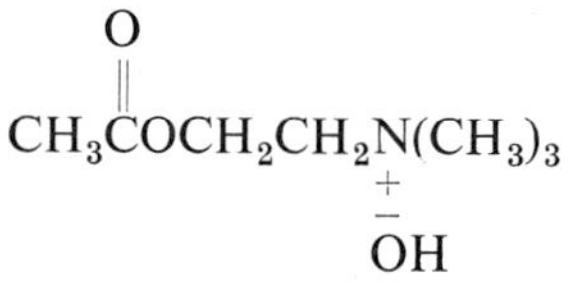

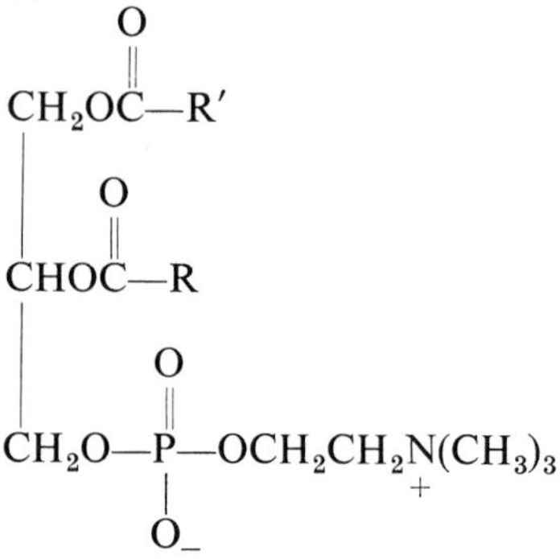

$$\underset{\textbf{(3)}}{\begin{array}{l} CH_2O\overset{O}{\overset{\|}{C}}—R' \\ | \\ CHO\overset{O}{\overset{\|}{C}}—R \\ | \\ CH_2O—\overset{O}{\overset{\|}{P}}(\underset{|}{}O^-)—OCH_2CH_2\overset{+}{N}(CH_3)_3 \end{array}}$$

Choline has been obtained from a large number of plant and animal tissues by extraction with methanol or water, and is usually precipitated from solution and purified in the form of salts such as phosphotungstates or reineckates. The structure of choline was established as β-hydroxyethyltrimethylammonium hydroxide by degradation[1] and by synthesis.

2. Syntheses

Various methods used to synthesize choline are summarized in Figure 1. One general method of synthesis consists of allowing trimethylamine to

1. A. Bayer, *Ann.*, *140*, 306 (1866); *142*, 322 (1867).

react with either ethylene oxide (**4**) or ethylene chlorohydrin (**5**).[2] Certain commercial syntheses of choline are based on these reactions.[3] The reaction with ethylene oxide is usually carried out in the presence of water and carbon dioxide. In the process with ethylene chlorohydrin, gaseous trimethylamine is passed through ethylene chlorohydrin at 80°, and choline chloride (**6**) is obtained.

$$\underset{(\mathbf{4})}{CH_2{-}CH_2 \text{ (epoxide, } {-}O{-})} \xrightarrow[H_2O]{(CH_3)_3N} \underset{(\mathbf{1})}{HOCH_2CH_2\overset{+}{N}(CH_3)_3\ \overset{-}{O}H}$$

$$\underset{(\mathbf{5})}{HOCH_2CH_2Cl} \xrightarrow{(CH_3)_3N} \underset{(\mathbf{6})}{HOCH_2CH_2\overset{+}{N}(CH_3)_3\ \overset{-}{Cl}}$$

$$\underset{(\mathbf{7})}{BrCH_2CH_2Br} \xrightarrow{(CH_3)_3N} \underset{(\mathbf{8})}{BrCH_2CH_2\overset{+}{N}(CH_3)_3\ \overset{-}{Br}} \longrightarrow (\mathbf{1})$$

$$\underset{(\mathbf{9})}{HOCH_2CH_2NH_2} \xrightarrow[KOH]{CH_3I} (\mathbf{1})$$

$$\underset{(\mathbf{10})}{C_2H_5OCH_2OCH_2CH_2N(CH_3)_2} \xrightarrow{HCOOCH_3}$$

$$\underset{(\mathbf{11})}{C_2H_5OCH_2OCH_2CH_2\overset{+}{N}(CH_3)_3\ HCOO^-} \xrightarrow{HCl} \underset{(\mathbf{6})}{HOCH_2CH_2\overset{+}{N}(CH_3)_3\ \overset{-}{Cl}}$$

Fig. 1. Syntheses of choline.[2–6]

Another method of synthesis allows trimethylamine to react with ethylene bromide (**7**) to form β-bromoethyltrimethylammonium bromide (**8**) which is then hydrolyzed to choline.[4] In another process, ethanolamine (**9**) is methylated with methyl iodide in methanolic potassium hydroxide solution.[5]

2. A. Wurtz, *Compt. Rend.*, *65*, 1015 (1867).
3. W. H. Griffith and J. F. Nyc, in W. H. Sebrell, Jr. and R. S. Harris, eds., *The Vitamins: Chemistry, Physiology, and Pathology*, Vol. II, Academic, N.Y., 1954, p. 14ff.
4. J. Bode, *Ann.*, *267*, 268 (1891).
5. G. Trier, *Z. Physiol. Chem.*, *80*, 409 (1912).
6. W. F. Gresham, U.S. Pat. 2,457,266 (1948); *Chem. Abstr.*, *43*, 2739f (1949).

Choline can also be prepared by heating [2-(ethoxymethoxy)ethyl]dimethylamine (**10**) at 140–150° and 25 p.s.i. with an excess of methyl formate;[6] the quaternary ammonium salt [2-(ethoxymethoxy)ethyl]trimethylammonium formate (**11**) is converted to choline chloride by refluxing in an ethanolic solution of hydrogen chloride. The crude choline chloride is purified by crystallization from isobutyl alcohol.

3. Biosynthesis

A. Origin of the Methyl Groups

The biosynthesis of choline and phospholipids proceeds from serine by decarboxylation and includes three successive methylation reactions. Two mechanisms have been suggested for the derivation of the methyl groups of biosynthetic choline.

In one mechanism, it is proposed that the first two methyl groups of biosynthetic choline are synthesized *de novo* and are transferred at the oxidation level of formaldehyde, presumably through the mediation of N^5,N^{10}-methylene-5,6,7,8-tetrahydropteroylmonoglutamic acid (Chapter VII);[7] the introduction of the third methyl group is visualized by transmethylation, presumably from activated methionine. Evidence for the *de novo* synthesis of two methyl groups of biosynthetic choline is based primarily on the observation that the biosynthesis of choline from dietary methionine is depressed in the rat that is deficient in pteroylmonoglutamic acid;[7,8] it has been suggested that this is a secondary effect that occurs owing to decreased biosynthesis of methionine in the absence of pteroylmonoglutamic acid.[9]

The second and currently favored mechanism suggests that all three methyl groups of biosynthetic choline are derived by transmethylation from activated methionine.[9,10] Evidence supporting this conclusion includes the following observations:

(a) About ninety per cent of the methyl groups in biosynthetic choline are deuterated after feeding rats CD_3-methionine over an extended period.[11]

7. J. A. Stekol, *Am. J. Clin. Nutr.*, *6*, 200 (1958).
8. J. A. Stekol, S. Weiss, P. Smith, and K. Weiss, *J. Biol. Chem.*, *201*, 299 (1953).
9. J. D. Wilson, K. D. Gibson, and S. Udenfriend, *J. Biol. Chem.*, *235*, 3213 (1960).
10. J. Bremer and D. M. Greenberg, *Biochim. et Biophys. Acta*, *35*, 287 (1959); *37*, 173 (1960).
11. V. du Vigneaud, M. Cohn, J. P. Chandler, J. R. Schenk, and S. Simmonds, *J. Biol. Chem.*, *140*, 625 (1940).

(b) Injected $C^{14}H_3$-methionine is about eight times more effective than C^{14}-formate as a precursor for choline in the rat.[8]

(c) With dietary C^{14}-formate, α-C^{14}-glycine, and α-C^{14}-serine, the incorporation of radioactivity into the methyl group of methionine is greater than that introduced into the methyl groups of choline.[12]

(d) *L*-methionine suppresses the incorporation of radioactivity into the methyl groups of choline by C^{14}-formate and C^{14}-formaldehyde.[9]

B. Biosynthesis of Choline and Phospholipids

There are at least two pathways for the biosynthesis of choline and phospholipids. By one pathway choline is biosynthesized from serine and then incorporated into the phospholipid fraction; in another pathway serine is converted to phosphatidylserine prior to decarboxylation and methylation. The two biosynthetic pathways apparently function in different systems of the cell. The incorporation of free choline into the phospholipid fraction occurs in the mitochondria; the biosynthesis of a phosphatidyl precursor of choline and subsequent methylation takes place in the microsomal fraction.

1. THE BIOSYNTHETIC PATHWAY FROM SERINE TO CHOLINE TO PHOSPHOLIPID. The biosynthesis of choline from serine and the subsequent incorporation of choline into the phospholipid fraction proceeds by the decarboxylation of serine to aminoethanol. Three successive transmethylation reactions convert aminoethanol to choline through the intermediate forms, mono- and dimethylaminoethanol. After phosphorylation, the phosphocholine moiety is incorporated into the phospholipid fraction; cytidinediphosphocholine (**15**) is the activated form which is essential for the incorporation of the choline moiety by the mitochondrial system from liver.[13–16]

a. Cytidinediphosphocholine. Stimulation of the biosynthesis of lecithin *in vitro* by cytidine triphosphate was the first clue to the requirement for cytidinediphosphocholine in phospholipid biosynthesis.[14] The requirement for cytidine triphosphate in this reaction was specific and is the first example demonstrating participation of a cytosine nucleotide in a coenzyme role.

The coenzyme (**15**) was synthesized by the condensation of cytidine 5′-phosphate (**12**) with phosphocholine (**13**) in the presence of dicyclohexylcarbodiimide (**14**).[13] The product was purified by ion exchange

12. H. R. V. Arnstein and A. Neuberger, *Biochem. J.*, *55*, 259 (1953).
13. E. P. Kennedy, *J. Am. Chem. Soc.*, *77*, 250 (1955); *J. Biol. Chem.*, *222*, 185 (1956).
14. E. P. Kennedy and S. B. Weiss, *J. Biol. Chem.*, *222*, 193 (1956).
15. E. P. Kennedy, *Federation Proc.*, *16*, 847 (1957).
16. E. P. Kennedy, *Am. J. Clin. Nutr.*, *6*, 216 (1958).

chromatography and was a more efficient precursor for lecithin than equivalent amounts of cytidine triphosphate and phosphocholine. The specificity of the coenzyme was evident since analogs in which adenosine, uridine, or guanosine replaced the cytidine moiety of the coenzyme were completely inactive.

$$\text{Cytidine-}CH_2OP(=O)(O^-)\text{—OH} \;(12) \quad + \quad HO\text{—}P(=O)(O^-)OCH_2CH_2\overset{+}{N}(CH_3)_3 \;(13)$$

$$\xrightarrow[]{C_6H_{11}\text{—}N{=}C{=}N\text{—}C_6H_{11}\;(14)} \text{Cytidine-}CH_2OP(=O)(O^-)\text{—O—}P(=O)(O^-)OCH_2CH_2\overset{+}{N}(CH_3)_3 \;(15)$$

Cytidinediphosphocholine is found in the liver, brain, and other tissues of various species, and is also present in yeast.

2. THE BIOSYNTHETIC PATHWAY FROM PHOSPHATIDYL DERIVATIVES. It now appears that the major pathway for the *de novo* synthesis of choline in the rat proceeds by way of phosphatidyl precursors.[17,18] This conclusion was reached from an *in vivo* study of the turnover rates and the specific activities of several potential intermediates in the biosynthesis of choline from labeled aminoethanol, methionine, and serine.[17] The role of phosphatidyl derivatives as the primary acceptors for transmethylation was confirmed by demonstrating the synthesis of methylated phosphatidylaminoethanol derivatives in an *in vitro* microsomal system.[17,18]

The biosynthesis (Fig. 2) of phospholipids and choline from serine in the microsomal system proceeds by the incorporation of serine (**16**) into the phospholipid fraction as phosphatidylserine (**17**).[17] The exact mechanism of incorporation is unknown, but it appears to be different from that

17. J. Bremer, P. H. Figard, and D. M. Greenberg, *Biochim. et Biophys. Acta*, *43*, 477 (1960).
18. K. D. Gibson, J. D. Wilson, and S. Udenfriend, *J. Biol. Chem.*, *236*, 673 (1961).

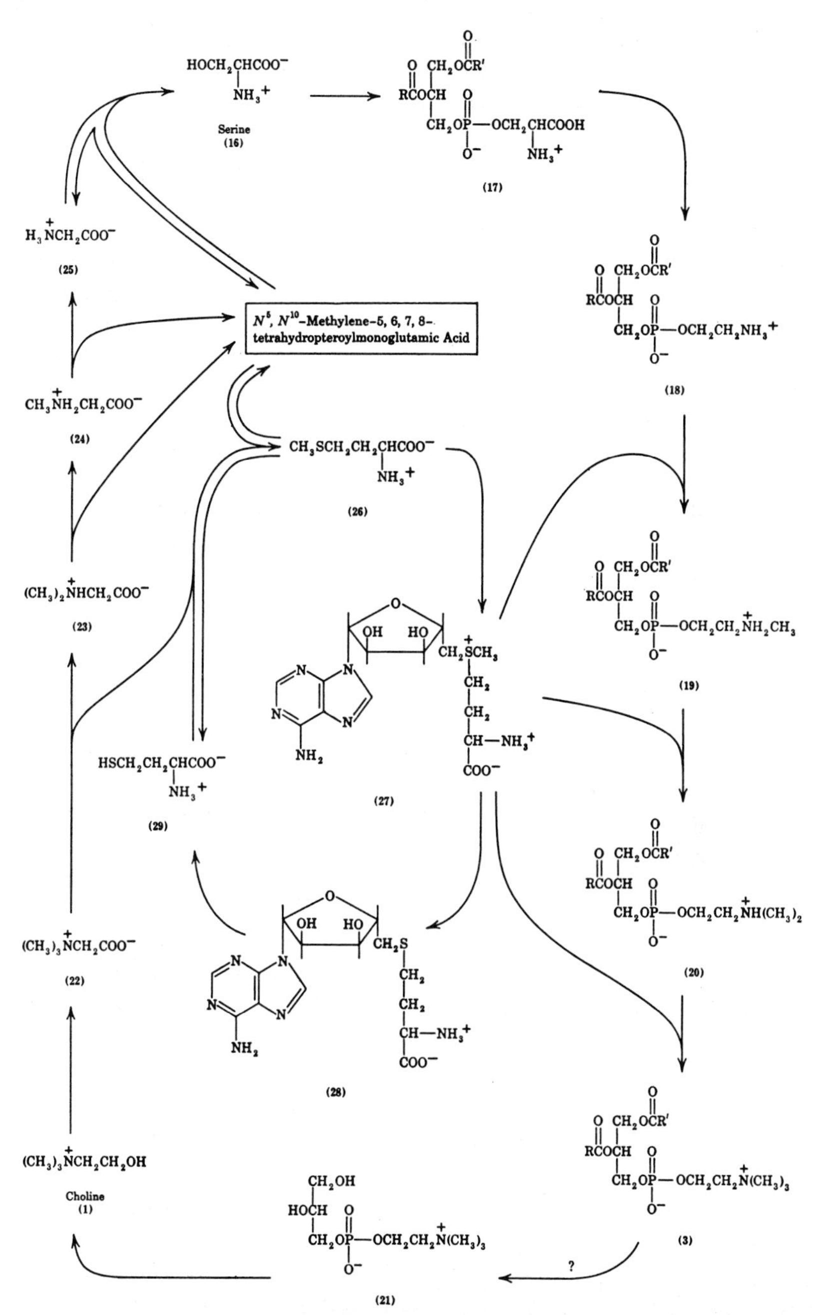

Fig. 2. A proposed pathway for the biosynthesis of phospholipids and choline.[17]

demonstrated for the incorporation of choline into phospholipids. Phosphatidylserine is then decarboxylated to phosphatidylaminoethanol (**18**), which is converted to phosphatidylmonomethylaminoethanol (**19**) by the transfer of a methyl group from the activated methionine derivative *S*-adenosylmethionine (**27**). The next two steps are also transmethylation reactions that require *S*-adenosylmethionine and yield phosphatidyldimethylaminoethanol (**20**) and phosphatidylcholine (lecithin) (**3**), respectively. A postulated hydrolysis of the acyl groups from lecithin would yield glycerophosphocholine (**21**), which in turn could yield choline.

The pathway for the conversion of choline to serine proceeds by the oxidation of choline to betaine (**22**). Betaine is then converted to dimethylglycine (**23**); in this step, the labile methyl group of betaine is transferred directly to homocysteine (**29**) yielding methionine (**26**). The two methyl groups of dimethylglycine are also contributed to single-carbon metabolism, but by stepwise oxidative degradation and through the mediation of N^5,N^{10}-methylene-5,6,7,8-tetrahydropteroylmonoglutamic acid ("active formaldehyde," Chapter VII). In these steps, dimethylglycine is converted to sarcosine (**24**), which in turn yields glycine (**25**). The final step of the cycle is the hydroxymethylation of glycine to serine; this reversible reaction is mediated by N^5,N^{10}-methylene-5,6,7,8-tetrahydropteroylmonoglutamic acid.

4. Nutritional Role

Fatty liver is perhaps the most common manifestation of choline deficiency in experimental animals, but dietary stores of essential amino acids, essential fatty acids, *meso*-inositol, etc., also play a role in fatty acid deposition. The deficiency state is less severe if pteroylmonoglutamic acid and cyanocobalamin are included in the diet and is largely alleviated by the addition of labile methyl groups in the form of betaine or methionine.

Symptoms of choline deficiency in animals vary with the species and are dependent in part on the presence or absence of other essential factors.[19–25] Choline deficiency in the rat leads to fatty liver, hemorrhagic

19. W. H. Griffith and J. F. Nyc, in W. H. Sebrell, Jr. and R. S. Harris, eds., *The Vitamins: Chemistry, Physiology, and Pathology*, Vol. II, Academic, N.Y., 1954, p. 63.
20. C. Artom, *Am. J. Clin. Nutr.*, *6*, 221 (1958).
21. D. B. Zilversmit and N. R. DiLuzio, *Am. J. Clin. Nutr.*, *6*, 235 (1958).
22. A. E. Harper, *Am. J. Clin. Nutr.*, *6*, 242 (1958).
23. I. C. Wells, *Am. J. Clin. Nutr.*, *6*, 254 (1958).
24. W. H. Griffith, *Am. J. Clin. Nutr.*, *6*, 263 (1958).
25. G. F. Wilgram, *Am. J. Clin. Nutr.*, *6*, 274 (1958).

degeneration of the kidney, and cardiovascular lesions. In the chick the deficiency is characterized by poor growth and perosis. A choline deficiency in the dog results in weight loss, anemia, dermal and peptic ulcers, and a fatty cirrhotic liver. The choline deficient pig has poor locomotor co-ordination and reproduces poorly.

Further studies of the role of choline and methionine in the pathogenesis and therapy of fatty liver disease in man are needed to provide evidence for their role in this metabolic area.

The daily human requirement of choline has been estimated to vary between 0.5 and 1 g.[26] The average mixed diet for an adult contains 300 to 600 mg. of choline.

26. H. Willstaedt, M. Borggard, and H. Lieck, *Z. Vitaminforsch.*, *18*, 25 (1946).

CHAPTER XIII

Meso-Inositol

1. Introduction

The first cyclohexitol (**1**) was isolated in 1850 from muscle tissue.[1] This compound, now known as *meso*-inositol, has been referred to as inositol, *myo*-inositol, or *i*-inositol. *Meso*-inositol is an essential nutrient for certain microorganisms and human cell lines, and deficiency symptoms in animals have been described.

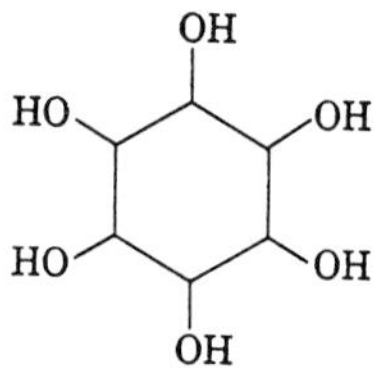

OH, HO, OH, HO, OH, OH

(1)

Meso-inositol occurs in plants as calcium and magnesium salts of the corresponding hexaphosphoric acid ester known as phytic acid; the salts are known as phytin. Plants are used as commercial sources of *meso*-inositol; phytic acid, isolated by extraction, is hydrolyzed to *meso*-inositol and inorganic phosphate, and the product is usually crystallized from water.

2. Configuration and Conformation

There are nine possible stereoisomeric forms of cyclohexitol, of which only two are optically active. As each of these isomeric compounds was identified, it was designated as an inositol and a distinguishing prefix was added. All nine stereoisomers of cyclohexitol are known, and their configurations and conformations have been assigned.[2,3] Two nomenclature systems have been suggested for the cyclohexitols, but neither system has been adopted officially.[3,4]

1. D. Scherer, *Ann.*, *73*, 322 (1850).
2. S. J. Angyal, *Quart. Revs.* (*London*), *11*, 212 (1957).
3. H. G. Fletcher, L. Anderson, and H. A. Lardy, *J. Org. Chem.*, *16*, 1238 (1951).
4. S. J. Angyal and C. G. MacDonald, *J. Chem. Soc.*, *686* (1952).

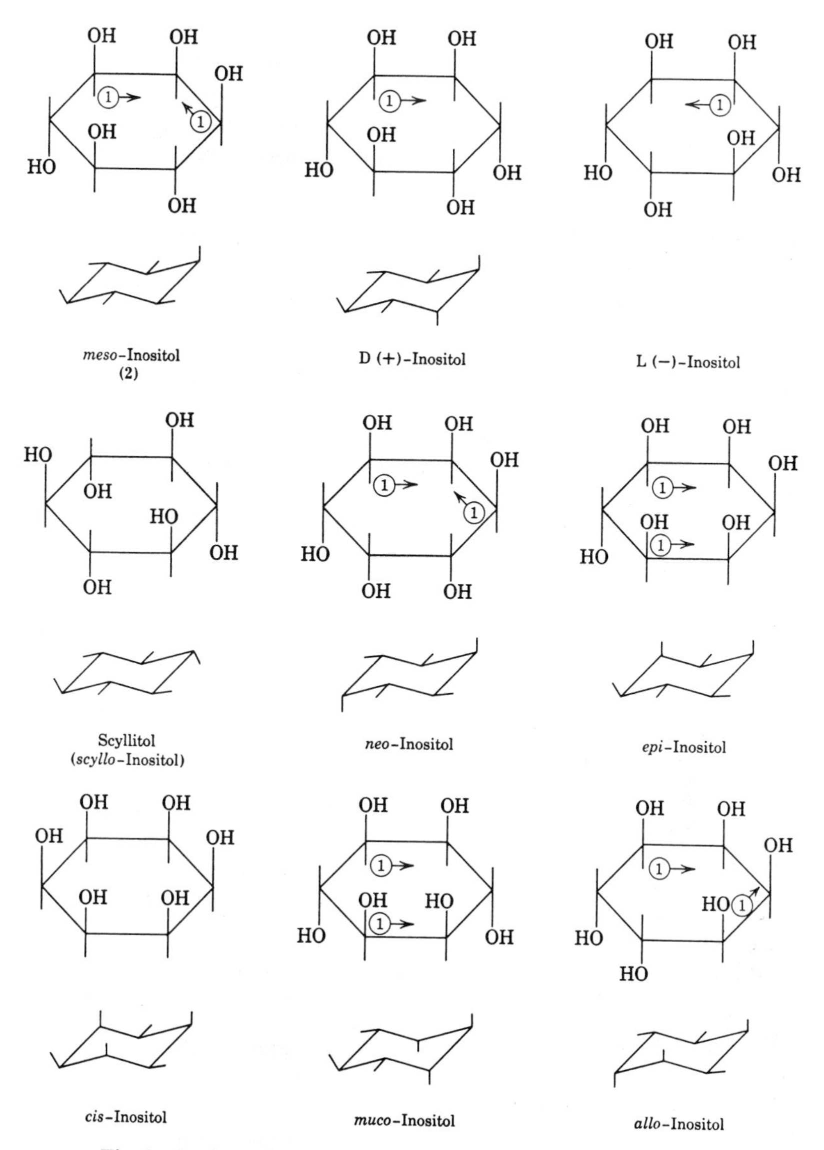

Fig. 1. Configurations and conformations of the cyclohexitols.[2,3]

The configurations and conformations of the nine cyclohexitols are shown in Figure 1. The first carbon atom is designated by the encircled arabic numeral, and the direction of counting is indicated by the arrow. The symmetry of *scyllo*- and *cis*-inositol are such that the first carbon atom need not be designated. Of all the isomeric forms of cyclohexitol, *meso*-inositol (**2**) is the most significant in current biological and nutritional interest. The conformations of the inositols have not been proved directly, but rather by analogy with other polysubstituted cyclohexanes and with sugars.[2] It is assumed that the inositols exist predominantly in the chair conformation with the smallest number of axial hydroxyl groups.

3. Structure Determination and Synthesis

The hexahydroxycyclohexane structure of the inositols was demonstrated by oxidation.[5] When inositol was oxidized with nitric acid, a mixture of hydroxy ketones was obtained. Isomerization and oxidation of the mixture in alkaline solution gave hexahydroxybenzene (**3**), tetrahydroxy-*p*-benzoquinone (**4**), and rhodizonic acid (**5**).

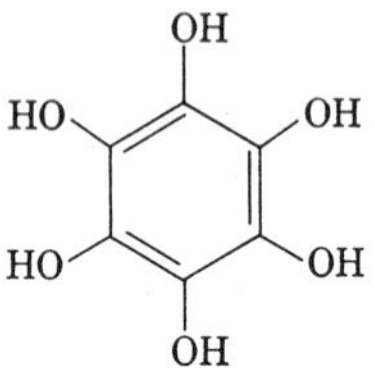

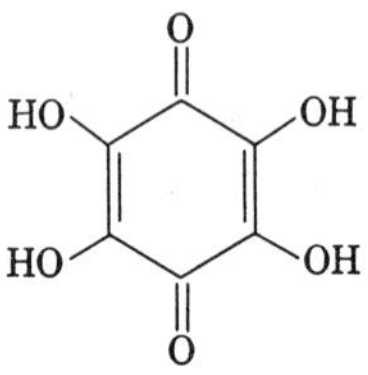

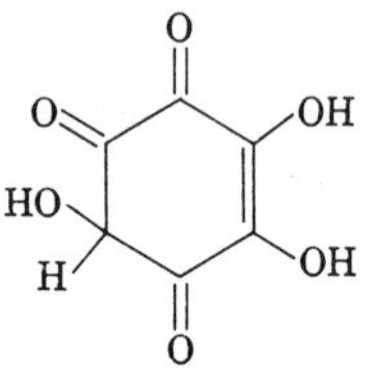

The configuration of *meso*-inositol was established by oxidation,[6,7] by selective enzymic dehydrogenation followed by oxidation,[8,9] and by selective acylation followed by oxidation.[10] When *meso*-inositol was oxidized, *DL*-glucosaccharic acid (**6**) and *DL*-talomucic acid (**7**) were isolated.[6,7] These data restricted the structure of *meso*-inositol to one of two possibilities; namely, the one assigned to *meso*-inositol or the one later assigned to *epi*-inositol (see Fig. 1). When *meso*-inositol was enzymically dehydrogenated at the 2-position, the compound known as Kluyver's

5. O. Gelormini and N. E. Artz, *J. Am. Chem. Soc.*, *52*, 2483 (1930).
6. T. Posternak, *Helv. Chim. Acta*, *24*, 1056 (1941); *25*, 746 (1942).
7. T. Posternak, *Helv. Chim. Acta*, *18*, 1284 (1935).
8. A. J. Kluyver and A. G. J. Boezaardt, *Rec. Trav. Chim.*, *58*, 956 (1939).
9. T. Posternak, *Helv. Chim. Acta*, *33*, 1597 (1950).
10. G. Dangschat and H. O. L. Fischer, *Naturwissenschaften*, *30*, 146 (1942).

inosose (**8**) was obtained.[8] Oxidation of this inosose with potassium permanganate gave *DL*-idosaccharic acid (**9**);[9] reduction of the inosose gave scyllitol (**10**) and *meso*-inositol (**2**).

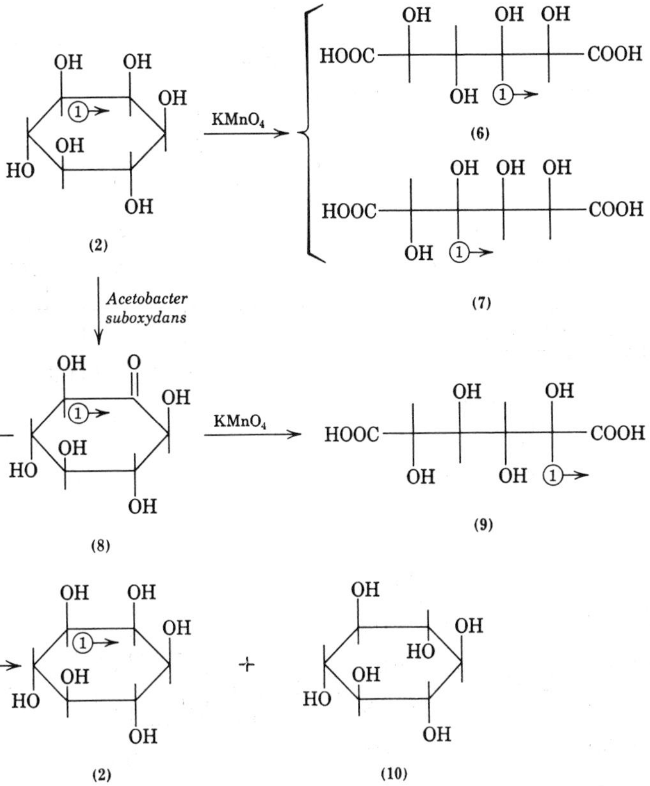

Independent studies leading to this same structure for *meso*-inositol were carried out as follows.[10] *Meso*-inositol was converted to the isopropylidene derivative (**11**) which was acetylated to the tetraacetyl-isopropylidene derivative (**12**). Removal of the isopropylidene group followed by oxidation of the intermediate product (**13**) with lead tetraacetate yielded tetraacetyl-*DL*-idosaccharic acid (**14**).

The synthesis of *meso*-inositol from *D*-glucose (**15**) proceeds through the intermediate formation of the nitro-6-deoxyglucose (**16**), the nitrodeoxyinositol (**17**), and the aminodeoxyinositol (**18**).[11]

11. S. Posternak and T. Posternak, *Helv. Chim. Acta*, *12*, 1165 (1929).

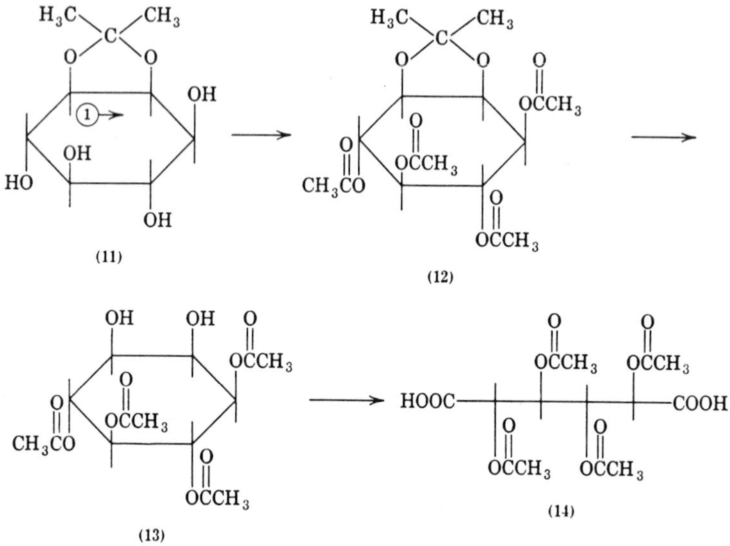

H_3C CH_3
C
O O
① →
OH
OH
HO
OH

(11)

→

H_3C CH_3
C
O O
O
‖
$OCCH_3$
O
‖
O $OCCH_3$
‖
CH_3CO
O
‖
$OCCH_3$

(12)

→

OH OH O
‖
$OCCH_3$
O
‖
O $OCCH_3$
‖
CH_3CO
O
‖
$OCCH_3$

(13)

→

O O
‖ ‖
$OCCH_3$ $OCCH_3$
HOOC— —COOH
O O
‖ ‖
$OCCH_3$ $OCCH_3$

(14)

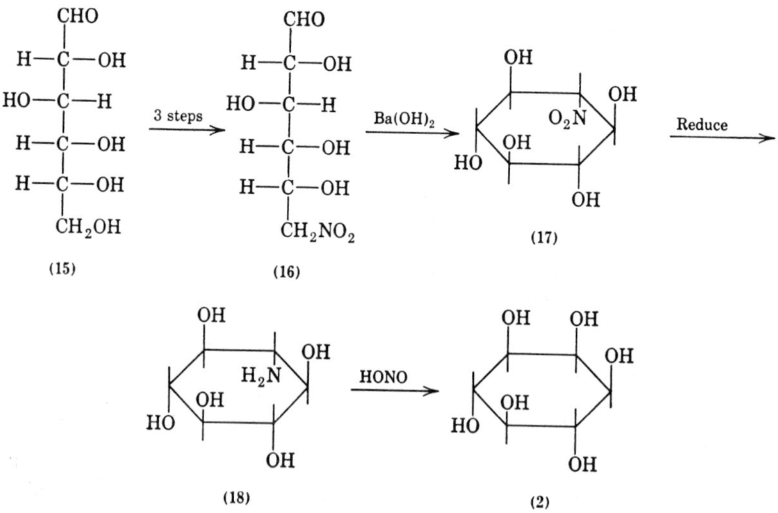

CHO
H—C—OH
HO—C—H
H—C—OH
H—C—OH
CH_2OH

(15)

3 steps →

CHO
H—C—OH
HO—C—H
H—C—OH
H—C—OH
CH_2NO_2

(16)

$Ba(OH)_2$ →

OH
OH
O_2N
OH
HO
OH

(17)

Reduce →

OH
OH
H_2N
OH
HO
OH

(18)

HONO →

OH OH
OH
OH
HO
OH

(2)

4. Nutritional Role

Meso-inositol is an essential nutrient for a number of microorganisms.[12–14] Although it is necessary for the growth and survival of certain yeasts and fungi, its metabolic role is unknown.

Symptoms that occur owing to a deficiency of *meso*-inositol in rats and mice include poor growth and a general loss of hair.[15] With hamsters, omission of both *meso*-inositol and *p*-aminobenzoic acid from the diet resulted in the death of some animals.[16]

A requirement for *meso*-inositol by a wide variety of human cell lines in tissue culture has been demonstrated,[17] but further study is required to establish whether the compound functions as a vitamin or a metabolite in human cell nutrition.

12. G. W. Beadle, *J. Biol. Chem.*, *156*, 683 (1944).
13. P. R. Burkholder, I. McVeigh, and D. Moyer, *J. Bacteriol.*, *48*, 385 (1944).
14. R. J. Williams, R. E. Eakin, and E. E. Snell, *J. Am. Chem. Soc.*, *62*, 1204 (1940).
15. D. W. Woolley, *Science*, *92*, 384 (1940); *J. Biol. Chem.*, *136*, 113 (1940).
16. J. M. Cooperman, H. A. Waisman, and C. A. Elvehjem, *Proc. Soc. Exptl. Biol. Med.*, *52*, 250 (1943).
17. H. Eagle, V. I. Oyama, M. Levy, and A. Freeman, *Science*, *123*, 845 (1956).

CHAPTER XIV

p-Aminobenzoic Acid

p-Aminobenzoic acid (**1**) emerged as an essential metabolite for certain microorganisms after the advent of sulfanilamide therapy. A deficiency of *p*-aminobenzoic acid has not been demonstrated conclusively in any vertebrate; therefore, it has been suggested that the compound no longer be considered as a vitamin, but rather a nutrilite.[1]

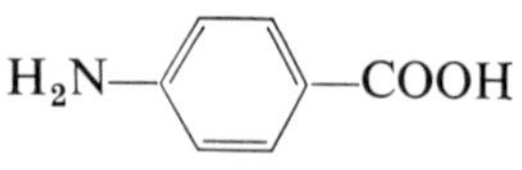

$H_2N-C_6H_4-COOH$ (**1**) $H_2N-C_6H_4-SO_2-NH_2$ (**2**)

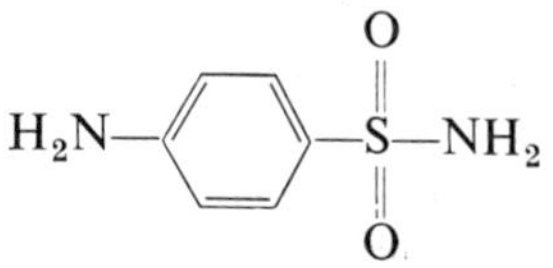

Soon after the discovery of sulfanilamide (**2**), it was found that some yeast or tissue extracts reversed the inhibitory effects of sulfanilamide for certain organisms. When these extracts were fractionated, *p*-aminobenzoic acid was isolated and identified as the active principle.[2] It was suggested that *p*-aminobenzoic acid is an essential metabolite for all organisms inhibited by sulfanilamide and that the sulfa drug owes its bacteriostatic activity to a competition with *p*-aminobenzoic acid for a position in a coenzyme necessary for bacterial reproduction.[3]

p-Aminobenzoic acid has been found to be an essential growth factor for *Clostridium acetobutylicum*,[4] *Streptobacterium plantarum*,[5] *Acetobacter suboxydans*,[6] *Lactobacillus arabinosus*,[6] *Lactobacillus helveticus*,[7] *Lactobacillus pentosus*,[7] and certain *Escherichia coli* mutants.[8]

p-Aminobenzoic acid is widely distributed in plant and animal cells, in both a free and a bound form. In yeast part of it is in a free form and part is bound in a conjugate form by a peptide linkage. In one conjugate

1. G. M. Briggs and F. S. Daft, *Ann. Rev. Biochem.*, *24*, 339 (1955).
2. D. D. Woods, *Brit. J. Exptl. Pathol.*, *21*, 74 (1940).
3. P. Fildes, *Lancet*, *1*, 956 (1940).
4. S. D. Rubbo and J. M. Gillespie, *Nature*, *146*, 838 (1940).
5. R. Kuhn and K. Schwartz, *Ber.*, *74*, 1617 (1941).
6. M. Landy and D. M. Dicken, *J. Biol. Chem.*, *146*, 109 (1942).
7. E. E. Snell and H. K. Mitchell, *Arch. Biochem.*, *1*, 93 (1942).
8. J. O. Lampen, R. R. Roepke, and M. J. Jones, *J. Biol. Chem.*, *164*, 789 (1946).

p-aminobenzoic acid is presumably bound through its amino group;[9] in a second conjugate, the amino group of *p*-aminobenzoic acid is presumably free and the carboxyl group is bound.[10] *p*-Aminobenzoic acid is also a moiety of pteroylmonoglutamic acid and can replace it in the nutrition of some, but not all microorganisms.

Although some investigators reported that *p*-aminobenzoic acid was effective in reversing an achromotrichia that was induced by hydroquinone or by diet alone in rats,[11–13] others failed to confirm this report.[14–16] Likewise, early reports[17–19] of a chromotrichial effect caused by administration of *p*-aminobenzoic acid to humans were not substantiated in later investigations.[20,21]

Large doses of *p*-aminobenzoic acid have been reported ameliorative for rickettsial infections such as typhus fever[22] and Rocky Mountain spotted fever.[23] Administration of *p*-aminobenzoic acid during the first week following the onset of infection is considered specific for the treatment of the typhus group of diseases.[24] Chloramphenicol and chlortetracycline, however, have replaced *p*-aminobenzoic acid as drugs for treating these infections.

9. K. C. Blanchard, *J. Biol. Chem., 140*, 919 (1941).
10. S. Ratner, M. Blanchard, and D. E. Green, *J. Biol. Chem., 164*, 691 (1946).
11. S. Ansbacher, *Science, 93*, 164 (1941).
12. G. J. Martin and S. Ansbacher, *J. Biol. Chem., 138*, 441 (1941).
13. G. J. Martin and S. Ansbacher, *Proc. Soc. Exptl. Biol. Med., 48*, 118 (1941).
14. G. Emerson, *Proc. Soc. Exptl. Biol. Med., 47*, 448 (1941).
15. L. M. Henderson, J. M. McIntire, H. A. Waisman, and C. A. Elvehjem, *J. Nutr., 23*, 47 (1942).
16. K. Unna, G. V. Richards, and W. L. Sampson, *J. Nutr., 22*, 553 (1941).
17. L. A. De Vilbiss, *Med. Women's J., 49*, 341 (1942).
18. J. J. Eller and L. A. Diaz, *N.Y. State J. Med., 43*, 1331 (1943).
19. B. F. Sieve, *Science, 94*, 257 (1941).
20. H. Brandaleone, E. Main, and J. M. Steele, *Am. J. Med. Sci., 208*, 315 (1944).
21. H. Brandaleone, E. Main, and J. M. Steele, *Proc. Soc. Exptl. Biol. Med., 53*, 47 (1943).
22. A. Yeomans, J. C Snyder, E. S. Murray, C. J. D. Zarafonetis, and R. S. Ecke, *J. Am. Med. Assoc., 126*, 349 (1944).
23. N. A. Tierney, *J. Am. Med. Assoc., 131*, 280 (1946).
24. E. C. Faust, *J. Am. Med. Assoc., 132*, 965 (1946).

CHAPTER XV

The Vitamin A Group

1. Introduction

The activity of vitamin A was discovered during investigations of the "accessory factors" in foods and not as a result of studies of a particular disease state. In 1913 it was reported that young rats did not grow to maturity on diets consisting solely of purified proteins, carbohydrates, lard, and salts; the addition of an ether extract of butter or eggs to such diets produced a prompt resumption of the normal growth pattern.[1] It was concluded, therefore, that accessory factors, which are essential for normal growth over an extended period, are present in certain foods. In a similar study, it was shown that growth depends upon nutritive conditions that are distinct from those required for maintenance.[2] Artificial diets consisting of protein, starch, lard, and "protein-free milk" sustained growth in rats for a limited time; if the lard in the diet were not replaced by butter or whole milk, growth eventually ceased and the animal died suddenly. With the passage of time, the unidentified fat-soluble growth factor was designated vitamin A.

Ocular disorders ascribed to "fat starvation" were eventually related to a deficiency of the unidentified fat-soluble growth factor. As early as 1904 a disproportionate number of children afflicted with xerosis of the conjunctiva and keratomalacia were found in populations subsisting principally on diets of vegetable origin.[3] "Fat starvation" was also designated as the cause of severe cases of necrosis of the cornea in children being fed fat-free skimmed milk.[4] The ophthalmologic syndrome, eventually designated xerophthalmia, is characterized by drying of ocular tissue and conjunctiva, which if allowed to go unchecked results in infection and permanent eye injury.[5,6] On the basis of animal studies, it was suggested

1. E. V. McCollum and M. Davis, *J. Biol. Chem.*, *15*, 167 (1913).
2. T. B. Osborne and L. B. Mendel, *J. Biol. Chem.*, *15*, 311 (1913).
3. M. Mori, *Jahrb. Kinderheilk.*, *59*, 175 (1904).
4. C. E. Bloch, *Ugeskrift Laeger*, *79*, 349 (1917); through *J. Am. Med. Assoc.*, *68*, 1516 (1917).
5. E. V. McCollum and N. Simmonds, *J. Biol. Chem.*, *32*, 181, 347 (1917).
6. S. Mori, *J. Am. Med. Assoc.*, *79*, 197 (1922).

that xerophthalmia resulted not from "fat starvation," but rather from a dietary deficiency of the fat-soluble growth factor.[5] Later, xerophthalmia in the human was related to an A-vitamin deficiency.[7]

The ancients recognized that the eating of liver benefited sight and minimized night blindness; in that early manner, nyctalopia was associated with a dietary deficiency centuries before the isolation of the A-vitamins. In 1925 vitamin A activity was related to the ability to see in subdued light; the relationship between visual dark adaptation and vitamin A was demonstrated in rats,[8] and later it was shown that the pigment, "visual purple," responsible for scotoptic vision was a protein complex of an A-vitamin.[9] Still later it was learned that the sensitive pigments of both photoreceptors of the retina were protein complexes of A-vitamins.

An important development in the history of the A-vitamins was the discovery of the provitamin relationship between the carotenes and the A-vitamins. In a series of animal feeding experiments, it was noted that vitamin A activity occurs predominantly in those plants containing a large amount of certain yellow pigments.[10,11] Others observed that the daily administration of as little as 5 μg. of carotene pigments produced a growth response in rats equivalent to that obtained with the A-vitamins.[12] Several investigators suggested that the vitamin A activity of the carotenes might be due to the presence of A-vitamins in these natural products, but it was shown conclusively that a carotene, or some part of the carotene molecule, behaves *in vivo* as a precursor for an A-vitamin.[13] The conclusion was based upon analyses of liver oil after the administration of large excesses of a carotene to rats deficient in the A-vitamins. After the rats were sacrificed, 99% of the specified chromogen in the liver oil was found to be an A-vitamin and only trace amounts of carotene pigment could be found. Furthermore, it was demonstrated that the color produced by carotenes in the antimony trichloride color reaction for the A-vitamins could not conceal a color response due solely to an A-vitamin. Negative color assays for the A-vitamins were obtained with the active carotene fractions and constituted further proof that the precursor relationship between the carotenes and the A-vitamins was valid.

Eventually, it was found that vitamin A activity is shared by a large group of structurally-related polyenes. The different forms of the polyenes

7. C. E. Bloch, *J. Hyg.*, *19*, 283 (1921).
8. L. S. Fridericia and E. Holm, *Am. J. Physiol.*, *73*, 63 (1925).
9. G. Wald, *J. Gen. Physiol.*, *19*, 351 (1935–1936).
10. H. Steenbock, *Science*, *50*, 352 (1919).
11. H. Steenbock and M. T. Sell, *J. Biol. Chem.*, *51*, 63 (1922).
12. B. von Euler, H. von Euler, and H. Hellström, *Biochem. Z.*, *203*, 370 (1928).
13. T. Moore, *Biochem. J.*, *24*, 692 (1930).

are either geometrical isomers of retinol, the first A-vitamin isolated, or functional group variants of this compound, each of which may also exist in several stereoisomeric forms. It was also shown that there are several forms of provitamin A, all structurally related to either α-, β-, or γ-carotene. The provitamin is converted *in vivo* to the corresponding A-vitamin in the intestinal tract and *in vitro* by cautious oxidation. The provitamins are generously distributed throughout the plant kingdom; the A-vitamins are found only in animals, especially in the liver and viscera of fish and mammals.

2. Isolation

Retinol, formerly designated vitamin A_1, is usually found in nature as an ester or bound to protein. High potency liver oils are the best source materials, but they must be saponified prior to the isolation of the vitamin. A typical procedure for the isolation of retinol from fish liver oil follows.[14–16]

A high potency fish liver oil was saponified with 10–12% alcoholic potassium hydroxide for one hour at 75°. The reaction was usually conducted in a nitrogen atmosphere, and the solution was allowed to concentrate to about one-half its original volume during the saponification reaction. The saponification mixture was diluted with ten volumes of water and extracted with ether. The ether extract was dried and concentrated *in vacuo*, and the residue was dissolved in hot methanol. The methanol solution was cooled, and the accompanying sterols were removed by precipitation. The filtrate was then concentrated and cooled from −10° to −50° to remove additional quantities of these steroids. After the filtrate was diluted with water, the A-vitamin was extracted into petroleum ether. The petroleum ether extract was dried and concentrated, yielding a pale yellow oil.

Attempted purification of the yellow oil by solvent extraction or adsorption on kieselguhr, kaolin, or calcium carbonate failed to achieve significant concentration of activity, but adsorption chromatography of the oil on alumina was sometimes used to increase the potency of various fractions. The vitamin was usually adsorbed from petroleum ether solution, and a broad band was obtained after development with petroleum ether. After the column of adsorbent was extruded, the broad band was divided

14. P. Karrer, R. Morf, and K. Schöpp, *Helv. Chim. Acta*, *14*, 1036 (1931).
15. H. von Euler and P. Karrer, *Helv. Chim. Acta*, *14*, 1040 (1931).
16. I. M. Heilbron, R. N. Heslop, R. A. Morton, E. T. Webster, J. L. Rea, and J. C. Drummond, *Biochem. J.*, *26*, 1178 (1932).

into three equal portions, and the material adsorbed on each section was eluted with petroleum ether–methanol. This step was usually repeated at least once.

Further purification of the retinol concentrate was achieved by distillation *in vacuo*. The best fractions distilled at 137–138° at pressures below 10 μ in a molecular still. Redistillation of this fraction achieved only a slight increase in potency. When the cyclic molecular still became available, the isolation of pure retinol was relatively simplified and the vitamin was eventually obtained in a crystalline form. Crystallization of highly purified concentrates from ethyl formate at −35° yielded pale yellow crystals of the vitamin melting at 63–64°.[17] If the vitamin is crystallized from methanol, the crystals contain methanol and melt at 5–6°.[18]

3. Structure Determination

The degradation reactions leading to the elucidation of the structure of retinol were carried out with highly active preparations that were obtained from the unsaponifiable portion of oil from either halibut or pike

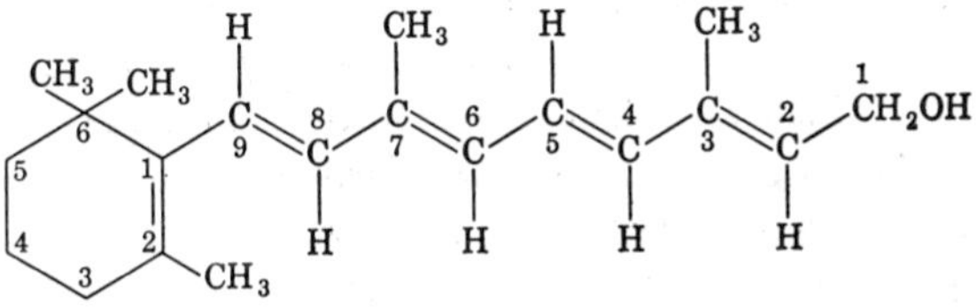

(1)

liver. On the basis of these studies, retinol (**1**) is designated 3,7-dimethyl-9-(2,6,6-trimethyl-1-cyclohexen-1-yl)-2,4,6,8-nonatetraen-1-ol.[14,16,19–21]

Retinol, $C_{20}H_{30}O$, contains a hydroxyl group which could be esterified; since the cautious oxidation of the carbinol function yielded an aldehyde, the vitamin was assumed to contain a primary hydroxyl group. Catalytic reduction of retinol indicated the presence of five double bonds in the molecule; the empirical formula of the reduction product was $C_{20}H_{40}O$

17. J. G. Baxter and C. D. Robeson, *Science*, *92*, 203 (1940).
18. H. N. Holmes, *Science*, *85*, 103 (1937).
19. P. Karrer, R. Morf, and K. Schöpp, *Helv. Chim. Acta*, *14*, 1036, 1431 (1931).
20. I. M. Heilbron, R. A. Morton, and E. T. Webster, *Biochem. J.*, *26*, 1194 (1932).
21. P. Karrer and R. Morf, *Helv. Chim. Acta*, *16*, 557, 625 (1933).

which indicated the presence of a ring structure in the molecule. Ozonolysis of retinol gave geronic acid (**2**). Since the same acid was also obtained by the ozonolysis of the known compounds β-ionone and β-carotene, the presence of the β-ionone ring system (**3**) in retinol was demonstrated.

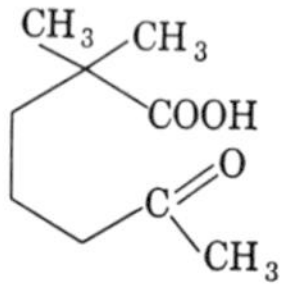

CH_3 CH_3 COOH C=O CH_3

(2)

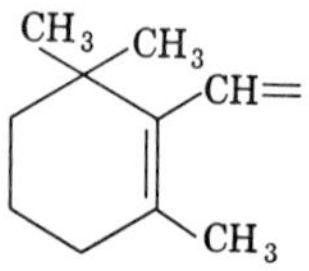

CH_3 CH_3 CH= CH_3

(3)

Oxidation of retinol with hot chromic acid gave three equivalents of acetic acid; milder oxidation with potassium permanganate gave two equivalents of acetic acid. These data indicated the presence of three *C*-methyl groups in the form of the moiety (**4**). Since a comparable group

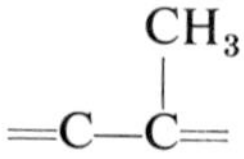

$$=\text{C}-\overset{\displaystyle CH_3}{\overset{|}{\text{C}}}=$$

(**4**)

could be accounted for in the β-ionone ring system, the side chain was considered to have two such moieties.

Treatment of retinol with alcoholic hydrogen chloride yielded an anhydro form, which on selenium dehydrogenation gave 1,6-dimethylnaphthalene. This reaction constituted further proof for the structural relationship between retinol and β-carotene. As a consequence of degradation data and knowledge of the precursor and structural relationships between β-carotene (**5**) and retinol, the structure of the vitamin was formulated as (**1**).[19]

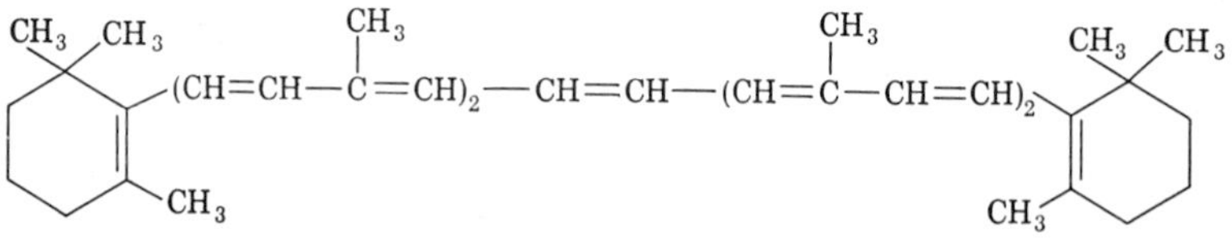

CH_3 CH_3 $(CH{=}CH{-}\overset{CH_3}{\overset{|}{C}}{=}CH)_2{-}CH{=}CH{-}(CH{=}\overset{CH_3}{\overset{|}{C}}{-}CH{=}CH)_2$ CH_3 CH_3 CH_3 CH_3

(5)

The basic carbon skeleton of retinol was confirmed by the synthesis (Fig. 1) of decahydroretinol (**7**) from β-ionone (**6**).[21] The positions of the double bonds and the stereochemistry of the side chain in the vitamin were based upon the derivation of retinol from β-carotene.

The preparations of decahydroretinol (7) obtained by synthesis from β-ionone and by the hydrogenation of naturally-occurring retinol were

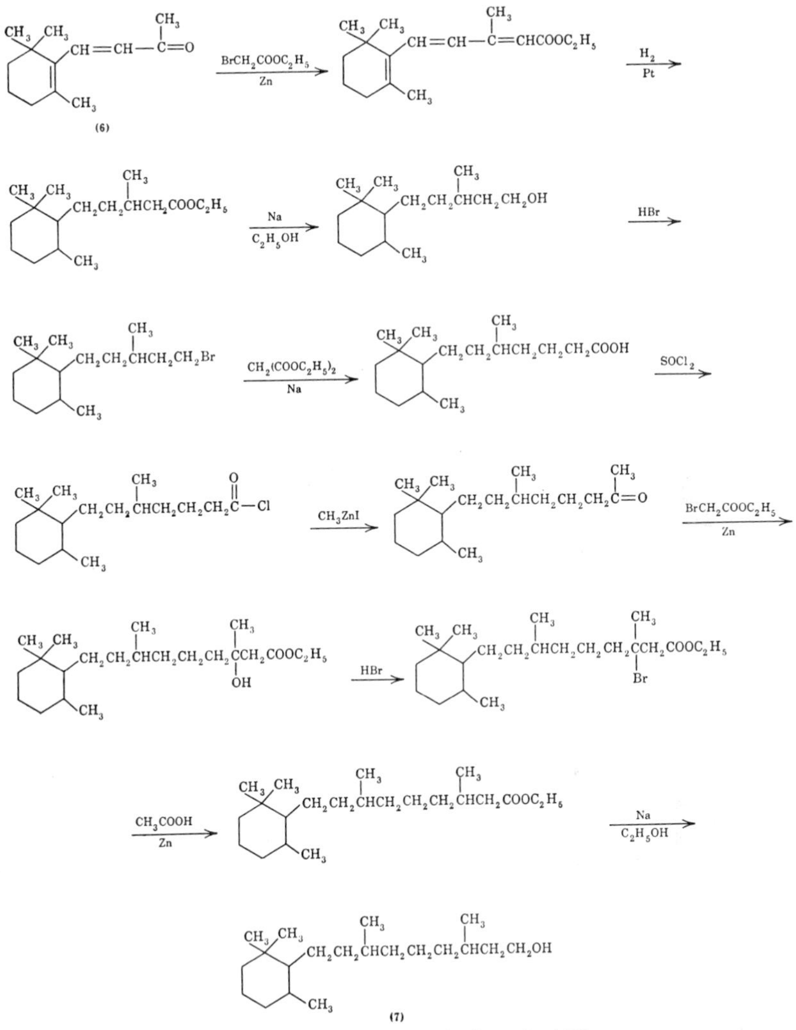

Fig. 1. Synthesis of decahydroretinol.[21]

oils that appeared to be identical. In order to obtain crystalline products for the purpose of further comparison, decahydroretinol was converted to the corresponding bromide which was condensed with malonic ester to yield the *bis*-homo acid (**8**). Conversion of the *bis*-homo acid to the corresponding acid chloride followed by reaction with methyl zinc iodide yielded the ketone (**9**). This same crystalline product was obtained from both synthetic and naturally-derived decahydroretinol.

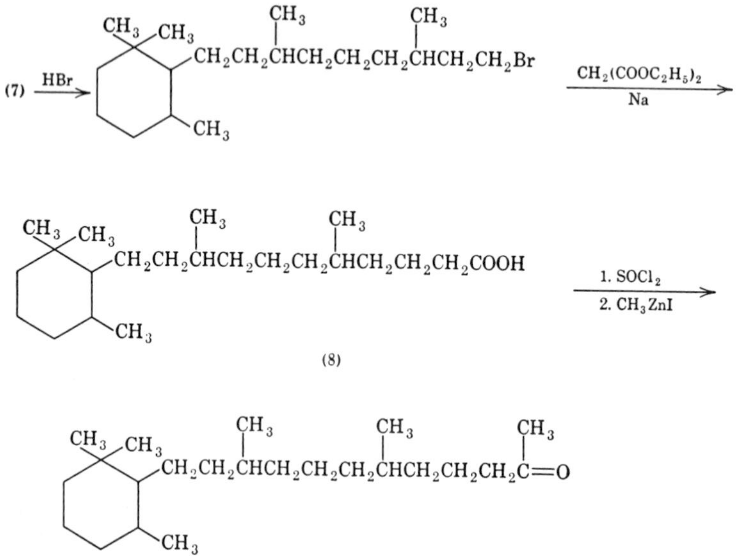

(7) $\xrightarrow{HBr}$ CH_3 CH_3 CH_3 CH_3 $CH_2CH_2CHCH_2CH_2CH_2CHCH_2CH_2Br$ CH_3 $\xrightarrow[Na]{CH_2(COOC_2H_5)_2}$

CH_3 CH_3 CH_3 CH_3 $CH_2CH_2CHCH_2CH_2CH_2CHCH_2CH_2CH_2COOH$ CH_3 $\xrightarrow[2.\ CH_3ZnI]{1.\ SOCl_2}$

(8)

CH_3 CH_3 CH_3 CH_3 CH_3 $CH_2CH_2CHCH_2CH_2CH_2CHCH_2CH_2CH_2C{=}O$ CH_3

(9)

4. Synthesis

Since the 1950's the A-vitamins of commerce have been almost exclusively synthetic products. Prior to this time the vitamin was isolated after the saponification of fish liver oils, and the concentrate was purified by molecular distillation. In some cases the distillate was crystallized from ethyl formate.[22] The vitamin is stabilized either by the addition of antioxidants such as hydroquinone or α-tocopherol, or by the conversion of the vitamin to the acetate. The acetate of retinol is one of the most stable crystalline esters of the vitamin prepared to date.[23]

The basic commercial method for the synthesis of retinol is the three-stage process outlined in Figure 2.[24–26] In the first stage, 4-(2,6,6-trimethyl-1-cyclohexen-1-yl)-2-methyl-2-buten-1-al (**13**) was synthesized from citral (**10**). The condensation of citral with acetone yielded ψ-ionone (**11**) which was isomerized with acid to yield β-ionone (**6**). The length of the β-ionone

22. J. G. Baxter and C. D. Robeson, *J. Am. Chem. Soc.*, *64*, 2411 (1942).
23. J. G. Baxter and C. D. Robeson, *J. Am. Chem. Soc.*, *64*, 2407 (1942).
24. N. A. Milas, *Science*, *103*, 581 (1946).
25. O. Isler, M. Koefler, W. Huber, and A. Ronco, *Experientia*, *2*, 31 (1946); *Helv. Chim. Acta*, *30*, 1911 (1947).
26. O. Isler, *Chem. Eng. News*, *29*, 3962 (1951).

side chain was increased by one carbon atom through a Darzens condensation; the reaction of (**6**) with ethyl chloroacetate, followed by treatment with sodium methylate, yielded the glycidic ester (**12**) which decarboxylated spontaneously upon treatment with alkali to yield the aldehyde (**13**).

In another stage of the synthesis, acetylene was condensed with methyl vinyl ketone in the presence of sodium and liquid ammonia. The product, 3-hydroxy-3-methyl-1-penten-4-yne (**14**), underwent an allylic rearrangement in the presence of sulfuric acid to yield 3-methyl-2-penten-4-yn-1-ol (**15**). Treatment of (**15**) with two equivalents of methyl magnesium bromide yielded the corresponding Grignard product (**16**).

(A)

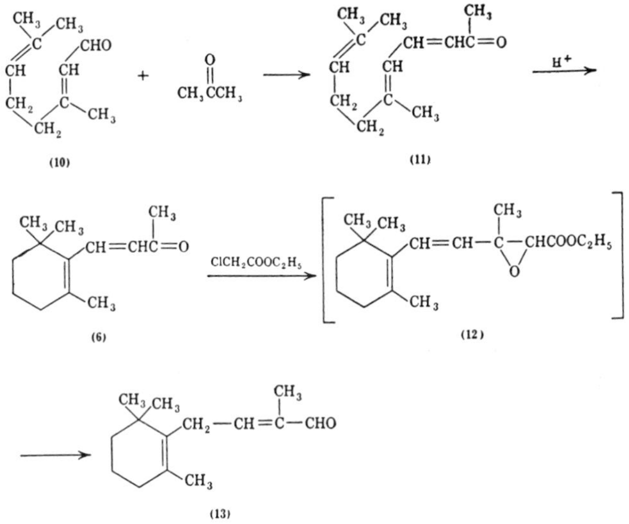

(10) + CH_3COCH_3 ⟶ (11) $\xrightarrow{H^+}$

(6) $\xrightarrow{ClCH_2COOC_2H_5}$ [(12)]

⟶ (13)

(B)

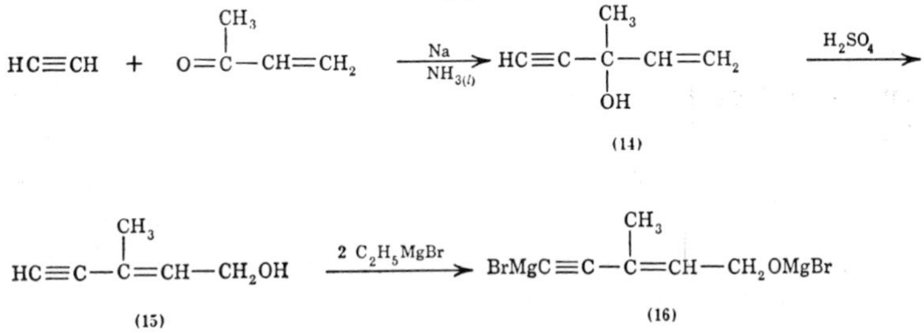

$$HC{\equiv}CH + O{=}C(CH_3){-}CH{=}CH_2 \xrightarrow[NH_{3(l)}]{Na} HC{\equiv}C{-}C(CH_3)(OH){-}CH{=}CH_2 \ (14) \xrightarrow{H_2SO_4}$$

$$HC{\equiv}C{-}C(CH_3){=}CH{-}CH_2OH \ (15) \xrightarrow{2\ C_2H_5MgBr} BrMgC{\equiv}C{-}C(CH_3){=}CH{-}CH_2OMgBr \ (16)$$

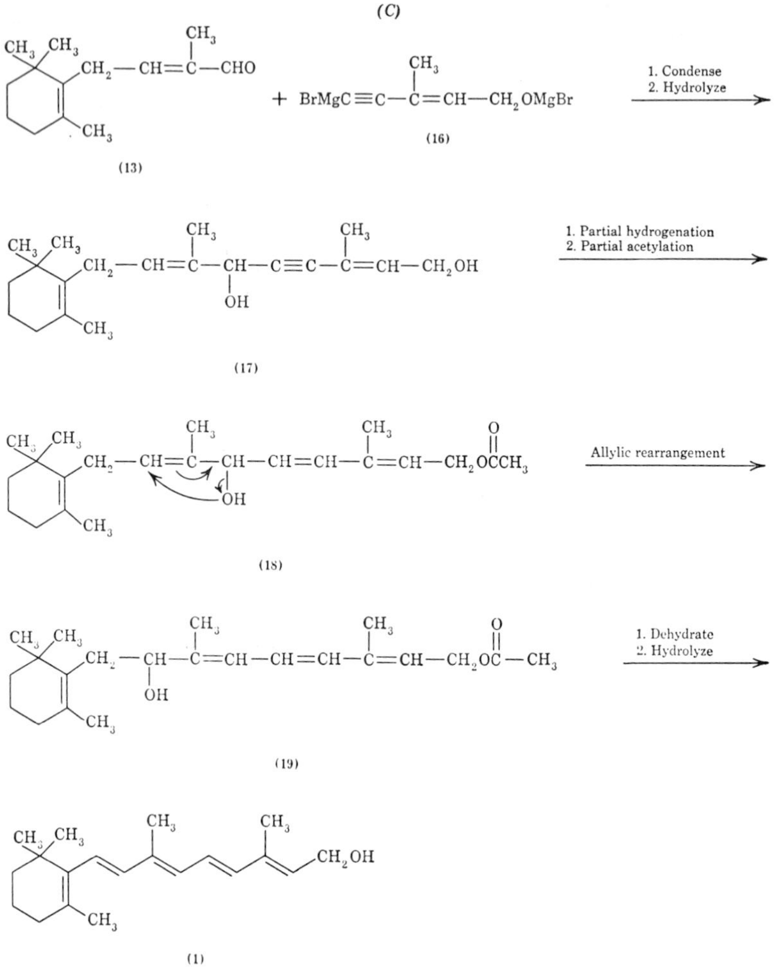

(C)

(13) + BrMgC≡C—C(CH_3)=CH—CH_2OMgBr (16) → 1. Condense 2. Hydrolyze

(17) [CH_2—CH=C(CH_3)—CH(OH)—C≡C—C(CH_3)=CH—CH_2OH] → 1. Partial hydrogenation 2. Partial acetylation

(18) [CH_2—CH=C(CH_3)—CH(OH)—CH=CH—C(CH_3)=CH—CH_2OCOCH_3] → Allylic rearrangement

(19) [CH_2—CH(OH)—C(CH_3)=CH—CH=CH—C(CH_3)=CH—$CH_2OC(O)$—CH_3] → 1. Dehydrate 2. Hydrolyze

(1) [CH_2OH]

Fig. 2. Synthesis of retinol.[24–26]

At the final stage, 4-(2,6,6-trimethyl-1-cyclohexen-1-yl)-2-methyl-2-buten-1-al (**13**) was condensed with the Grignard product (**16**) of 3-methyl-2-penten-4-yn-1-ol. The triple bond in the condensation product (**17**) was reduced to a double bond using a partially deactivated palladium on calcium carbonate catalyst; the primary hydroxyl group was selectively acetylated with acetyl chloride in the presence of dimethylaniline to yield the tetraenol (**18**). Allylic rearrangement of the intermediate (**18**) yielded (**19**) which was dehydrated by phosphorus oxychloride in pyridine and toluene. Alternatively, low temperature treatment of (**19**) with hydrogen bromide or phosphorus tribromide gave the bromo intermediate which eliminated hydrogen bromide on reaction with water to generate the final double bond. Saponification of the resulting acetate ester yielded retinol.

5. Nomenclature

In the IUPAC rules of 1957,[27] the Commission on the Nomenclature of Biological Chemistry recommended rule changes for naming the A-vitamins and their derivatives. The compound formerly known as vitamin A_1 is now designated retinol. The corresponding aldehyde and acid are designated retinal and retinoic acid, respectively. Before these rules were promulgated, derivatives and stereoisomers of vitamin A_1, vitamin A_1 aldehyde, and vitamin A_1 acid were designated by trivial names such as vitamin A_2, neovitamin A_1, retinene$_2$, isoretinene A, neovitamin A acid, etc. when they were discovered. According to the new rules, all such compounds are to be designated as a retinol, retinal, or retinoic acid whenever possible. Certain recommendations have also been made with regard to carotenoid nomenclature, and since the nomenclature of the A-vitamins is closely related to that of the carotenoids, changes in this latter field necessitated further changes with regard to vitamin A nomenclature. Beginning with volume 53 of *Chemical Abstracts*, the IUPAC numbering system for carotene is applied to the IUPAC-approved names for the A-vitamins and their derivatives. The "new" numbering system for retinol is depicted in (**20**).

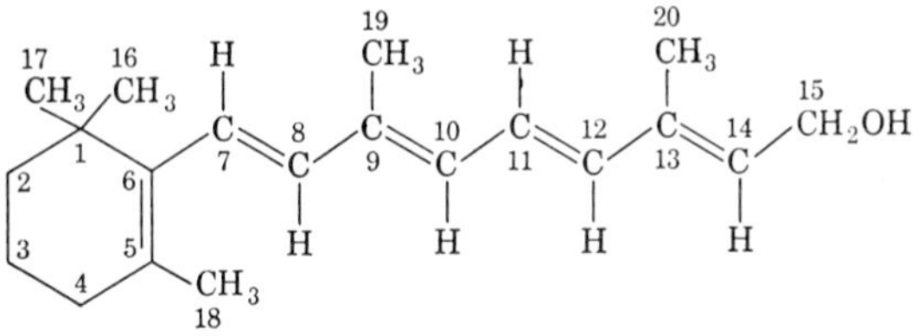

(**20**)

In the preceding sections dealing with isolation, structure determination, and synthesis, Geneva Convention names and numbering systems or trivial names have been used. Since the IUPAC-approved names and carotene numbering system are especially appropriate for a discussion of the stereoisomerism of retinol, retinal, and retinoic acid, the IUPAC rules

27. IUPAC Commission on the Nomenclature of Biological Chemistry, *J. Am. Chem. Soc.*, *82*, 5581, 5583 (1960).

of 1957 will be applied whenever possible in the succeeding sections. For certain derivatives of the retinols, trivial nomenclature and numbering systems are still being used in current literature and are retained in this chapter.

6. Stereochemistry

A. Theoretical Considerations

Retinol contains five carbon-carbon double bonds and could, disregarding other considerations, exist in thirty-two stereoisomeric forms. There are, however, theoretically prohibitive configurations along the carbon skeleton of retinol which restrict the number of geometrical isomers. Four unhindered isomers of retinol are known from nature and two hindered *cis* isomers of retinol have been synthesized; thus, six of the thirty-two possible stereoisomers of retinol are now known.

During the study of stereoisomerism in the carotene series, it became apparent that the number of *cis-trans* isomers in branched polyene chains is fewer than predictable on the basis of the number of unsaturated centers.[28,29] To account for such steric restriction in the carotenes, the distance of van der Waals' contact (distance between adjacent nuclei) of the 10- and 13-substituents in the *cis* double bond system in (**21**) and (**22**)

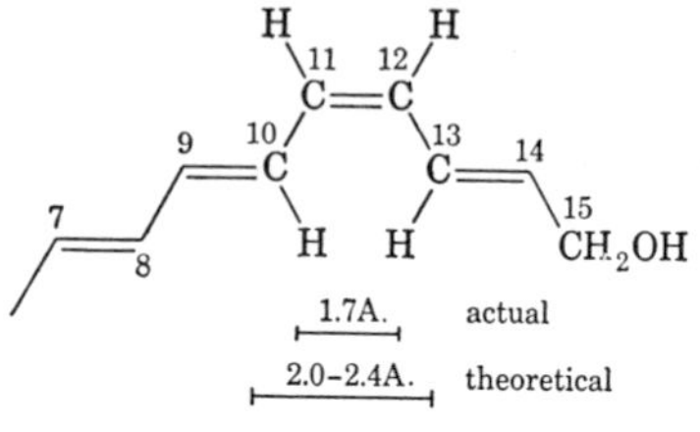

1.7A. actual
2.0–2.4A. theoretical

(21)

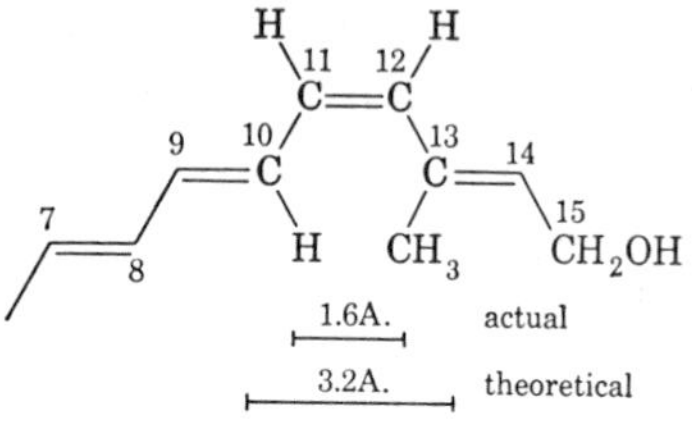

1.6A. actual
3.2A. theoretical

(22)

were considered.[28] At the *cis* configuration in (**21**) the distance (1.7A.) between the C-10 and C-13 hydrogen atoms is slightly less than the usual distance of van der Waals' contact (2.0–2.4A.), but the degree of strain is so minor that it can be relieved by a slight rotation of these substituents out of coplanarity. Such a system is labeled "stereochemically effective," so the C-11 double bond can exist in either an unhindered *cis* or *trans* configuration. In the *cis* configuration in (**22**), however, the distance of van der Waals' contact of the C-10 and C-13 substituents is only 1.6A. compared to a theoretical distance of 3.2A. Such a highly strained system is labeled "stereochemically ineffective," and only the *trans* form of such a substituted C-11 double bond is unhindered. From these considerations

28. L. Pauling, *Fortschr. Chem. Org. Naturstoffe*, *3*, 203 (1939).
29. L. Zechmeister, *Chem. Revs.*, *34*, 267 (1944).

it was predicted that in the isoprene units (**23**) of the carotenes, the α-double bond was the only "stereochemically effective" center.[28] This theory was applied effectively in the carotene series.

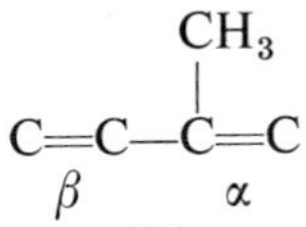

(**23**)

B. The Unhindered Stereoisomers of Retinol

Consideration of retinol on the basis of this theory led to the conclusion that only four unhindered stereoisomers were possible. The 5,6-double bond is restricted to a *cis* configuration because it is a ring component. *Cis* double bonds at C-7 and C-11 were prohibited on the assumption that these centers were "stereochemically ineffective" and therefore preferentially *trans* oriented. Only two "stereochemically effective" double bonds remained; these centers at C-9 and C-13 could give rise to four stereoisomeric forms.

The four unhindered geometrical isomers of retinol were formerly known as vitamin A_1 (**1**), isovitamin A_a (**24**), neovitamin A_a (**25**), and isovitamin A_b (**26**).[30] These compounds are now known as retinol, 9-*cis*-retinol, 13-*cis*-retinol, and 9,13-di*cis*-retinol, respectively.

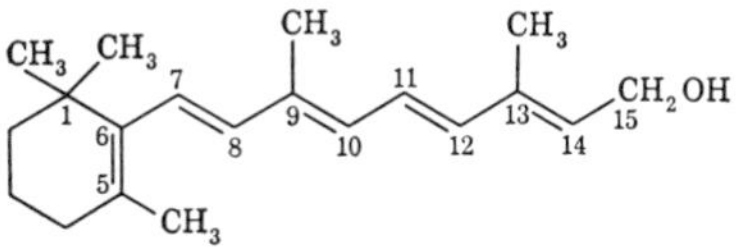

(1)
Retinol (all-*trans*)
(Vitamin A_1)

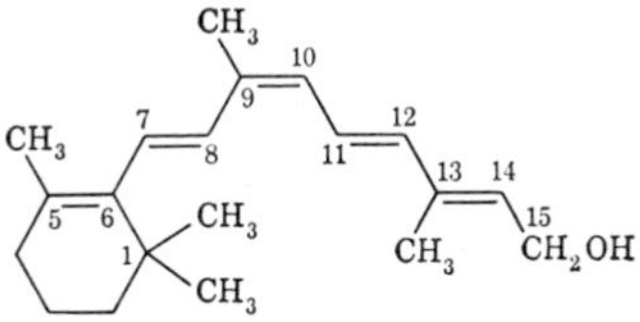

(24)
9-*cis*-Retinol
(Isovitamin A_a)

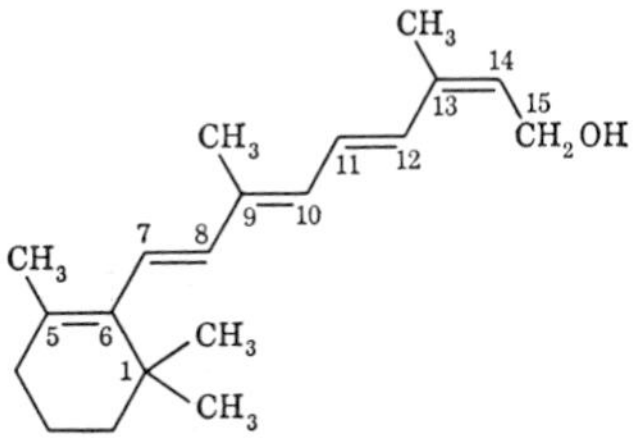

(25)
13-*cis*-Retinol
(Neovitamin A_a)

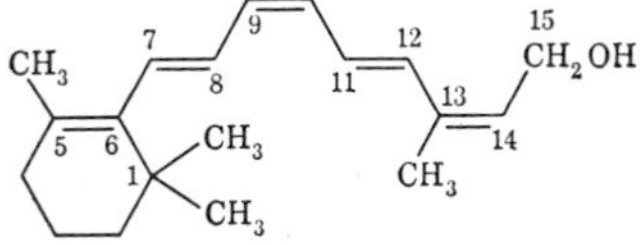

(26)
9, 13-di*cis*-Retinol
(Isovitamin A_b)

30. R. Hubbard and G. Wald, *Science*, *115*, 60 (1952).

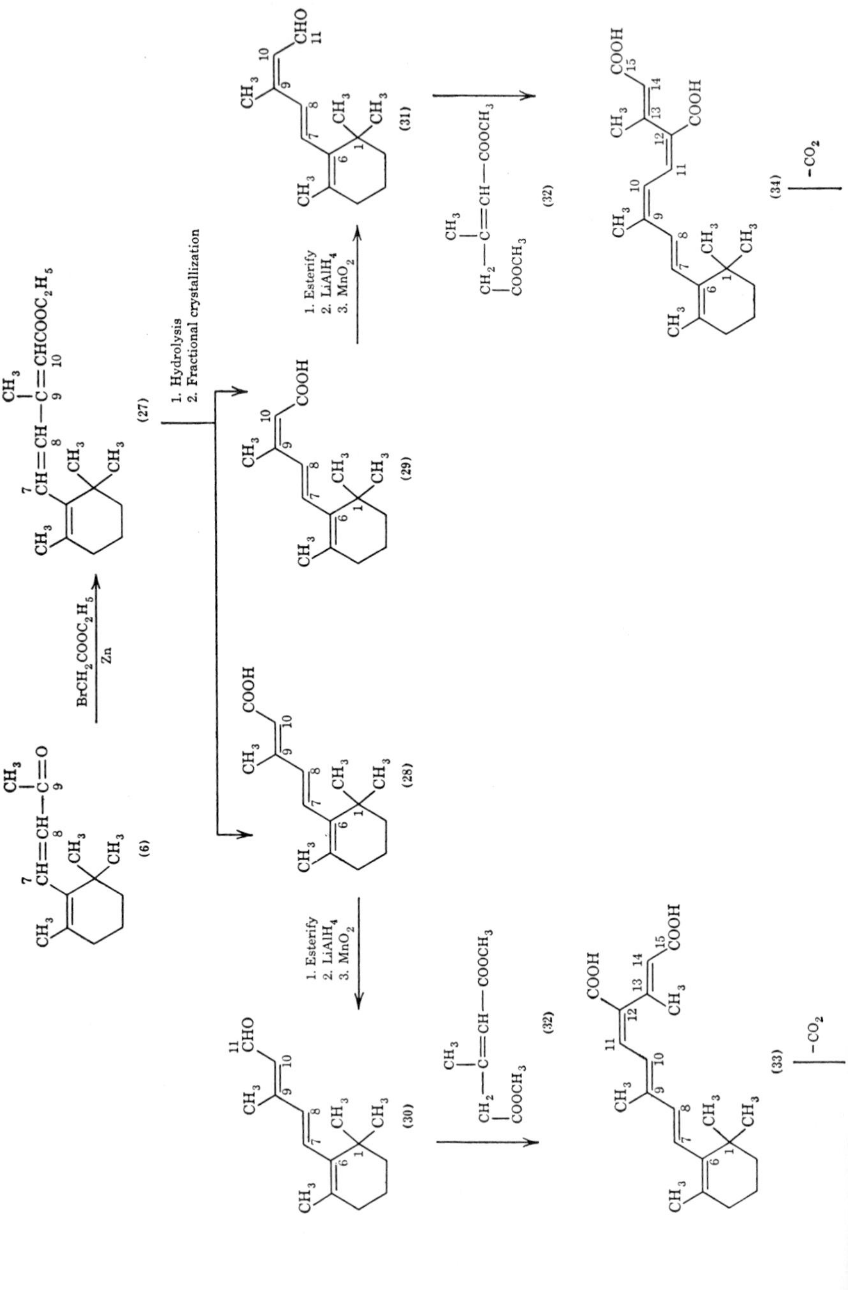

(6) $\xrightarrow[\text{Zn}]{BrCH_2COOC_2H_5}$ (27) $CH=CH-C(CH_3)=CHCOOC_2H_5$

1. Hydrolysis
2. Fractional crystallization

(28) (29)

1. Esterify
2. $LiAlH_4$
3. MnO_2

(30) (31)

$CH_2(COOCH_3)-C(CH_3)=CH-COOCH_3$ (32)

(33) $-CO_2$

(34) $-CO_2$

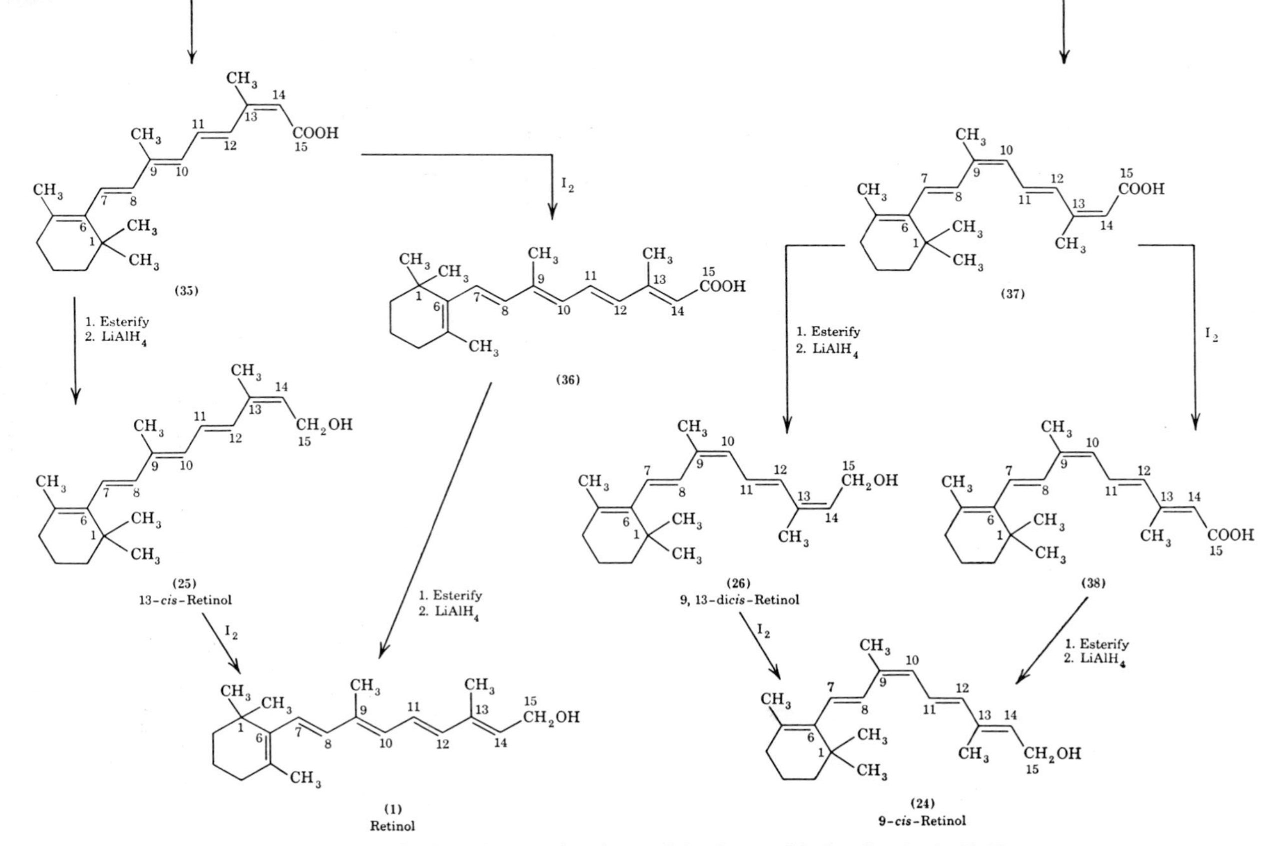

Fig. 3. Synthesis and stereochemistry of the four unhindered retinols.[31–33]

For the synthesis[31–33] and confirmation of the stereochemistry of the four unhindered isomers of retinol (Fig. 3), β-ionone (**6**) was condensed with ethyl bromoacetate to yield a mixture of *cis* and *trans* ethyl β-ionylideneacetate (**27**); hydrolysis followed by recrystallization of the products resulted in a separation of 9-*trans*-β-ionylideneacetic acid (**28**) from 9-*cis*-β-ionylideneacetic acid (**29**). Each of these compounds was converted to the corresponding aldehyde, 9-*trans*-β-ionylideneacetaldehyde (**30**) and 9-*cis*-β-ionylideneacetaldehyde (**31**), respectively.

When 9-*trans*-β-ionylideneacetaldehyde (**30**) was condensed with dimethyl β-methylglutaconate (**32**), the 7,9,13(?)-tri*trans*-11-*cis*-diacid (**33**) was obtained. The 11-*cis* configuration in this diacid is based on a study of the synthesis of γ-alkylidene- and γ-aralkylidene-β-methylglutaconic acids from glutaconic acid, and on a comparison of the ultraviolet absorption spectra of these model compounds with that of (**33**). Monodecarboxylation of (**33**) yielded 13-*cis*-retinoic acid (neovitamin A_a acid) (**35**), which on stepwise esterification and reduction with lithium aluminum hydride at low temperature yielded 13-*cis*-retinol (**25**). Isomerization of 13-*cis*-retinol with iodine yielded retinol (*all-trans*) (**1**). When 13-*cis*-retinoic acid (**35**) was treated with iodine, retinoic acid (*all-trans*) (**36**) was obtained. Esterification followed by lithium aluminum hydride reduction of the ester yielded retinol.

In an analogous manner, condensation of 9-*cis*-β-ionylideneacetaldehyde (**31**) with dimethyl β-methylglutaconate (**32**) gave the 7,13(?)-di*trans*-9,11-di*cis*-diacid (**34**). Its 11-*cis* configuration was deduced in the same manner as described for the diacid (**33**). By monodecarboxylation, 9,13-di*cis* retinoic acid (**37**) was obtained. Careful esterification of (**37**) followed by lithium aluminum hydride reduction of the ester yielded 9,13-di*cis*-retinol (**26**). 9,13-Di*cis*-retinol was isomerized to 9-*cis*-retinol (**24**) on treatment with iodine. Likewise,when 9,13-di*cis*-retinoic acid (**37**) was isomerized with iodine, 9-*cis*-retinoic acid (**38**) was obtained. Esterification followed by lithium aluminum hydride reduction of the ester yielded 9-*cis*-retinol (**24**).

The configurations assigned to these isomers were confirmed from a study of the rates of reaction of their *p*-phenylazobenzoate esters with maleic anhydride, and from the nature of the ultraviolet absorption spectra of the maleic anhydride adducts.

In the standard assay for vitamin A activity in the rat, the acetate of

31. J. D. Cawley, *J. Am. Chem. Soc.*, *77*, 4125 (1955).
32. J. D. Cawley and D. R. Nelan, *J. Am. Chem. Soc.*, *77*, 4130 (1955).
33. C. D. Robeson, J. D. Cawley, L. Weisler, H. M. Stern, C. C. Eddinger, and A. J. Checak, *J. Am. Chem. Soc.*, *77*, 4111 (1955).

13-*cis*-retinol was about 75% as active as the acetate of retinol. 9-*cis*-Retinol and 9,13-di*cis*-retinol were about 25% as active as the acetate of retinol in the same assay.[34]

C. The "Hindered" Retinols

Two isomers of retinol with a "hindered" *cis* configuration at the "stereochemically ineffective C-11 center" have been synthesized[35,36] by the condensation of *cis*- or *trans*-3-methyl-2-penten-4-yn-1-ol (**15**) with 4-(2,6,6-trimethyl-1-cyclohexen-1-yl)-2-methyl-2-buten-1-al (**13**) in a manner analogous to that described in Figure 2. 11-*cis*-Retinol (**39**) (neovitamin A_b) was obtained from *trans*-3-methyl-2-penten-4-yn-1-ol, and 11,13-di*cis*-retinol (**40**) (neovitamin A_c) was obtained from *cis*-3-methyl-2-penten-4-yn-1-ol. The configurations assigned to these isomers were

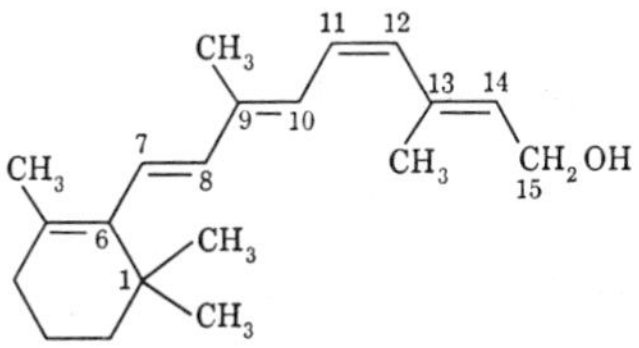

(39)

11-*cis*-Retinol
(Neovitamin A_b)

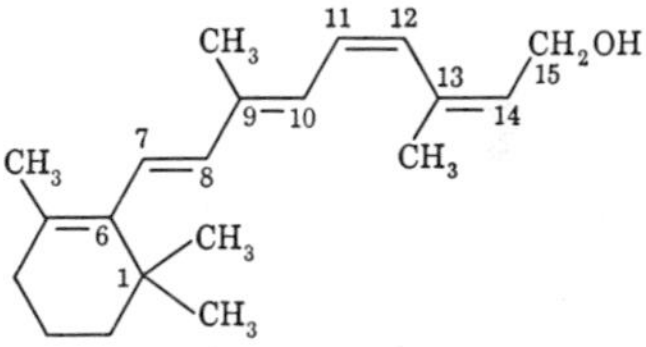

(40)

11, 13-di*cis*-Retinol
(Neovitamin A_c)

confirmed by a study of the rates of reaction of their *p*-phenylazobenzoate esters with maleic anhydride, and by the iodine isomerization of both isomers to retinol (*all-trans*). 11-*cis*-Retinol has about 25% of the activity of the acetate of retinol in the standard rat assay for vitamin A.[34]

Synthesis of the two isomers of retinol with a "hindered" *cis* configuration at the "stereochemically ineffective C-11 center" caused reconsideration of the applicability of this stereochemical theory for the retinols. Two points were considered in this reappraisal; first di*cis*-β-methylmuconic acid (**41**) had been synthesized, and second it was concluded that the concept of stereochemically ineffective centers was still valid for the carotenes.[37] It was predicted, therefore, that significant differences in stereochemical behavior could be expected between the long- and short-chain polyenes. Since the length of the polyene side chain of retinol is intermediate between β-carotene on one hand and β-methylmuconic acid on the other, the theoretical number of geometrical isomers

34. S. R. Ames, W. J. Swanson, and P. L. Harris, *J. Am. Chem. Soc.*, *77*, 4134 (1955).
35. R. Hubbard, *J. Am. Chem. Soc.*, *78*, 4662 (1956).
36. W. Oroshnik, *J. Am. Chem. Soc.*, *78*, 2651 (1956).
37. L. Pauling, *Helv. Chim. Acta*, *32*, 2241 (1949).

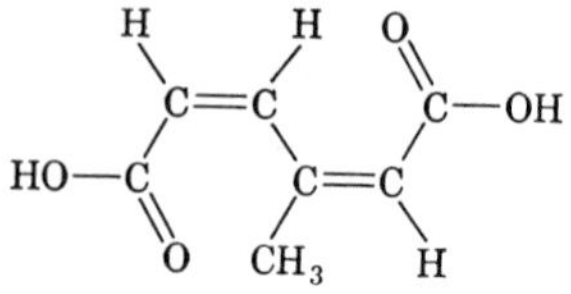

(41)

of retinol cannot be predicted with certainty. On the basis of this theory, however, it was concluded that isomers of retinol with a *cis* configuration at C-7 or C-11 cannot be synthesized from the corresponding *trans* isomers or provitamins by chemical or thermal methods.[37,38] This principle has been especially valuable in assigning configurations to the various geometrical isomers of retinol.

7. Functional Group Variants of Retinol

A. The Retinals and Retinoic Acids

In addition to the side chain geometrical isomers of retinol, there are compounds with vitamin A activity which are functional group variants of these isomers.

Retinal (**42**), formerly designated vitamin A aldehyde or retinene, was isolated from the retina.[9] Six stereoisomers of retinal are known and have

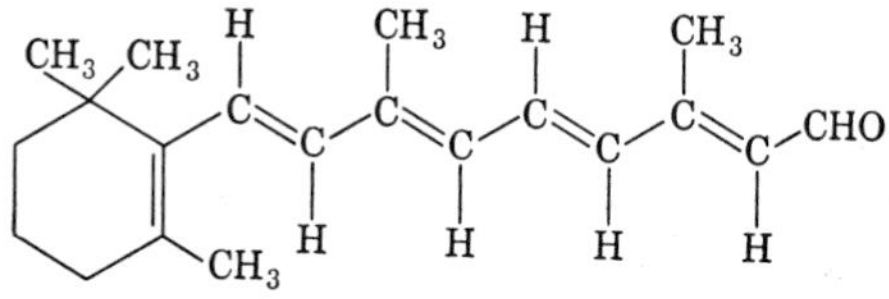

(42)

been synthesized from the corresponding alcohols by oxidation with manganese dioxide.[35,36,39] These known isomers are:

Retinal (*all-trans*) (Retinene$_1$)
9-*cis*-Retinal (Isoretinene$_a$)
9,13-di*cis*-Retinal (Isoretinene$_b$)
13-*cis*-Retinal (Neoretinene$_a$)
11-*cis*-Retinal (Neoretinene$_b$)
11,13-di*cis*-Retinal (Neoretinene$_c$)

38. L. Zechmeister and F. J. Petracek, *J. Am. Chem. Soc.*, *74*, 282 (1952).
39. C. D. Robeson, W. P. Bloom, J. M. Dieterle, J. D. Cawley, and J. G. Baxter, *J. Am. Chem. Soc.*, *77*, 4120 (1955).

The activity of these isomers has been measured relative to retinol in the standard rat assay.[40] Retinal and 13-*cis*-retinal have about 90% of the molar activity of the acetate of retinol. 11-*cis*-Retinal is about 50% as active as the acetate of retinol. Both 9-*cis*- and 9,13-di*cis*-retinal are about 20% as active as the acetate of retinol.

Retinoic acid (**36**) has not been isolated from natural sources. In the course of synthesis of the retinol isomers, however, four stereoisomeric forms of retinoic acid have been identified (see Fig. 3). Retinoic acid has about 60% of the activity of retinol in the rat assay.

B. The α-Vitamins A

3,7-Dimethyl-9-(2,6,6-trimethyl-2-cyclohexen-1-yl)-2,4,6,8-nonatetraenoic acid (α-vitamin A_1 acid) and 3,7-dimethyl-9-(2,6,6-trimethyl-2-cyclohexen-1-yl)-2,4,6,8-nonatetraen-1-ol (**44**) (α-vitamin A_1) have been synthesized from α-ionone (**43**).[33] The products contained a substantial

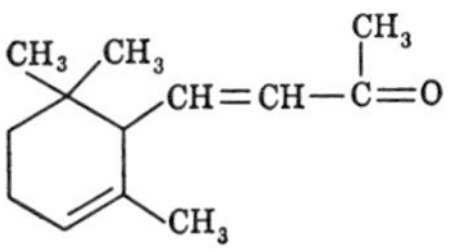

(43)

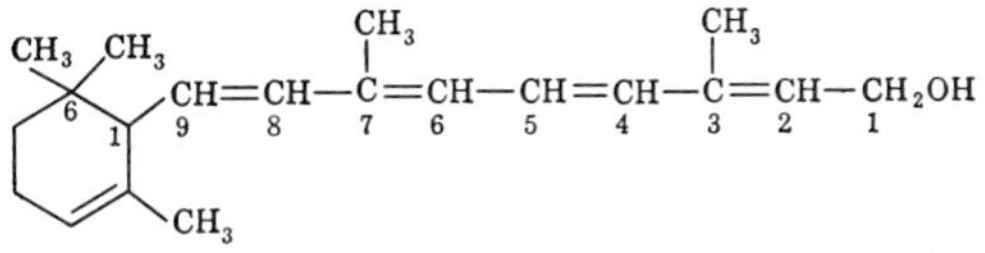

(44)

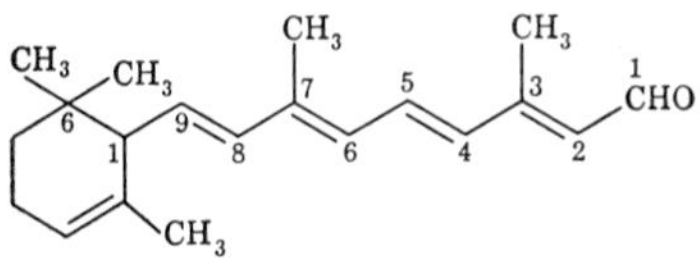

(45)

amount of the *all-trans* isomers. The *all-trans* form of 3,7-dimethyl-9-(2,6,6-trimethyl-2-cyclohexen-1-yl)-2,4,6,8-nonatetraenal (**45**) (*all-trans-α*-vitamin A aldehyde) has also been synthesized from α-ionone.

C. Anhydro- and Rehydrovitamin A_1

When retinol was heated with anhydrous ethanolic hydrogen chloride, a compound designated anhydrovitamin A_1 was obtained.[41] This compound has also been isolated from natural sources. Its structure has been

40. S. R. Ames, W. J. Swanson, and P. L. Harris, *J. Am. Chem. Soc.*, *77*, 4136 (1955).
41. E. M. Shantz, J. D. Cawley, and N. D. Embree, *J. Am. Chem. Soc.*, *65*, 901 (1943).

formulated as the retropolyene (**46**) and has been confirmed by a study of spectral relationships in a series of retroionylidene compounds.[42]

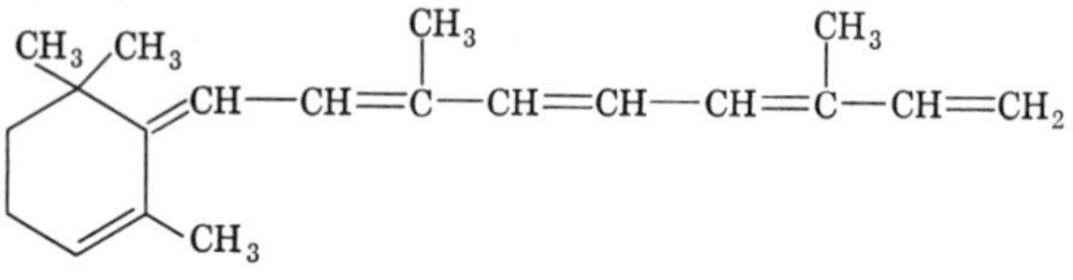

CH_3 CH_3 CH_3 CH_3

$=CH—CH=\overset{|}{C}—CH=CH—CH=\overset{|}{C}—CH=CH_2$

CH_3

(46)

Rehydrovitamin A_1, a compound apparently formed by the hydration of anhydrovitamin A_1, was isolated from the liver of rats fed anhydrovitamin A_1.[43] The structure of this derivative has not been proved, but it

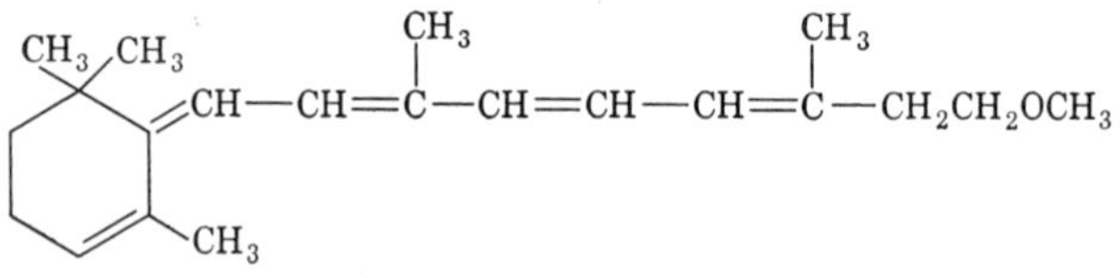

CH_3 CH_3 CH_3 CH_3

$=CH—CH=\overset{|}{C}—CH=CH—CH=\overset{|}{C}—CH_2CH_2OCH_3$

CH_3

(47)

too is assumed to have a retroionylidene-conjugated system. The methyl ether (**47**) of rehydrovitamin A_1 has been synthesized.[42]

D. 3-*Dehydroretinol*

3-Dehydroretinol (**48**), formerly designated vitamin A_2, was isolated from fish liver oil, and its structure was confirmed by synthesis.[44] The configuration of the side chain was assumed to be *all-trans* on the basis of the method of synthesis and starting materials. 3-Dehydroretinol is more

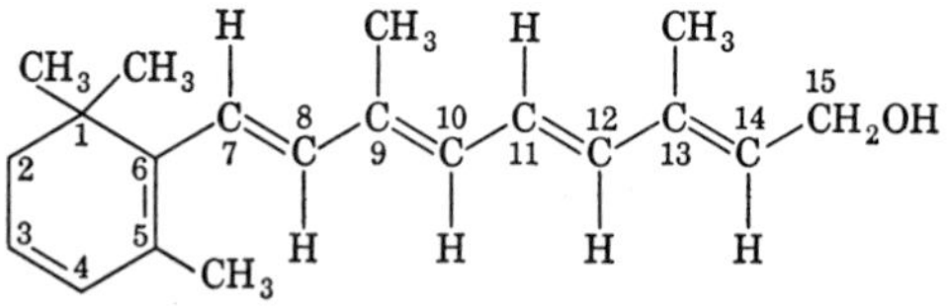

H CH_3 H CH_3

CH_3 CH_3 15

C 8 C 10 C 12 C 14 CH_2OH

1 7 C 9 C 11 C 13 C

2 6

3 5 H H H H

4 CH_3

(48)

sensitive to oxidation than retinol, and its behavior on treatment with acid differs from that of retinol. Treatment of 3-dehydroretinol with anhydrous ethanolic hydrogen chloride yielded a compound formerly designated anhydrovitamin A_2. This compound, like anhydrovitamin A_1, is a member

42. W. Oroshnik, G. Karmas, and A. D. Mebane, *J. Am. Chem. Soc.*, *74*, 295 (1952).
43. E. M. Schantz, *J. Biol. Chem.*, *182*, 515 (1950).
44. K. R. Farrer, J. C. Hamlet, H. B. Henbest, and E. R. H. Jones, *J. Chem. Soc.*, 2657 (1952).

of the retro-vitamin A series in which the conjugated system is moved back one carbon atom toward the ring. Structural studies have shown that anhydrovitamin A_2 is 4′-ethoxy-anhydrovitamin A_1 (**49**).[45] If this conversion of 3-dehydroretinol is carried out in methanol rather than ethanol solution, the vitamin is converted to the corresponding 4′-methoxy derivative. In recent studies it was reported that anhydrovitamin A_2 (**49**)

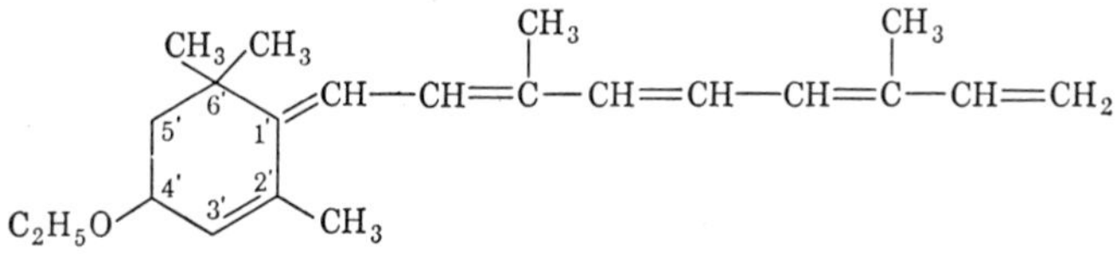

$$CH_3\;CH_3 \quad\quad CH_3 \quad\quad CH_3$$
$$=CH—CH=C—CH=CH—CH=C—CH=CH_2$$
$$C_2H_5O \quad\quad CH_3$$

(49)

occurs naturally in the liver oil of the fresh water fish *Wallago attu.*[46] It was also reported that anhydrovitamin A_2 was not formed as a result of heat treatment of the liver oil during extraction, and that the compound when fed to rats is transformed into a new compound designated rehydrovitamin A_2, which is stored in the liver.

8. Metabolic Role

A. In the Visual Process

Of all the facets of metabolic participation by the A-vitamins, their role in the visual process is the most clearly defined at this time. In the visual process the photoreceptors of the eye transmit the initial photostimulation to the optic nerve. These receptors are located in the retina and are classified as cones or rods, according to their shape. The cones are responsible for vision in bright light (photoptic vision), the rods for vision in dim light (scotoptic vision). The critical function of the A-vitamins in the initial photochemical process of both photoptic and scotoptic vision has been reviewed in detail.[47]

The cones and rods of the retina each contain a light-sensitive pigment which is bleached on exposure to light. The bleached pigment then goes through several thermally induced intermediate stages before a retinal and a protein are liberated. Although the transmission of the photochemically-induced impulse to the optic nerve has not been associated with a specific

45. H. B. Henbest, E. R. H. Jones, T. C. Owen, and V. Thaller, *J. Chem. Soc.*, 2763 (1955).
46. S. Balasundaram, M. S. Bamji, H. R. Cama, P. R. Sundaresan, and T. N. R. Varma, *J. Biol. Chem.*, *233*, 827 (1958).
47. G. Wald, *Ann. Rev. Biochem.*, *22*, 497 (1953); *Exptl. Cell Res., Suppl. 5*, 389 (1958).

stage in this biochemical process, the reaction resulting in the liberation of a retinal and a protein has been eliminated from consideration. This conclusion was reached solely on the basis of the time lag between the transmission of the impulse and the generation of a retinal.

The rods of the retina are known to contain one of two photosensitive pigments, rhodopsin (formerly designated "visual purple") or porphyropsin; the cones contain the light-sensitive pigment iodopsin. All of these pigments are protein complexes of an A-vitamin. The composition of the pigments is known, and the visual reactions have been separated and identified. The enzymes that facilitate these reactions have also been purified, and many of the reactions have been carried out *in vitro*. To illustrate the participation of the A-vitamins in the visual process, the classical research leading to the elucidation of the role of rhodopsin in the scotoptic visual process is outlined below.

The deleterious effects of an A-vitamin deficiency on scotoptic vision in rats was first demonstrated by the impeded regeneration of "visual purple" in the retina.[8,48] Later, retinol was isolated from the eye tissue and from the retina of frogs, sheep, pigs, and cattle.[49–51] After the pigments from both light- and dark-adapted retina of frogs were isolated and studied,[9,50,52] a three-stage scotoptic visual cycle was postulated. In the first stage rhodopsin is bleached by light to yield a mixture of retinal, originally designated "retinene," and a protein. This mixture was designated "visual yellow." In the second stage retinal is converted to retinol. The mixture of retinol and protein is referred to as "visual white." In the third stage the cycle is completed when a retinal combines with the protein to regenerate rhodopsin. This basic scheme was refined to account for a stereospecificity that was observed after the various processes were separated and observed in the isolated retina of frogs, and in some instances *in vitro*. Only the first two stages of the cycle occur in the isolated retina as well as in the eye. The third stage of the process goes to completion only in the intact eye.

The first indication of the stereospecificity of these reactions appeared after rhodopsin was isolated from the dark-adapted retina.[53] With this material available, the photochemical bleaching process was studied *in vitro*. Rhodopsin was converted to the intermediate lumirhodopsin by the

48. E. Holm, *Am. J. Physiol.*, *73*, 79 (1925).
49. G. Wald, *Nature*, *132*, 316 (1933).
50. G. Wald, *Nature*, *134*, 65 (1934).
51. G. Wald, *J. Gen. Physiol.*, *18*, 905 (1934–1935).
52. G. Wald, *J. Gen. Physiol.*, *19*, 781 (1935–1936).
53. G. Wald, J. Durell, and R. C. C. St. George, *Science*, *111*, 179 (1950).

absorption of light; two thermally induced transformations followed the initial photochemical reaction. In the dark, lumirhodopsin was converted to metarhodopsin, which in the presence of water was converted to retinal and a protein designated opsin. Retinal was structurally identified as the *all-trans* isomer (**42**) after it was synthesized from retinol by manganese dioxide oxidation.[54] The next stage of the process, namely the conversion of retinal to retinol, is an enzymic reaction. *In vitro* the final products of the bleaching process were retinal and opsin; in the retina the final products were retinol and opsin. The enzyme system responsible for the reduction of retinal to retinol was isolated from the retina[55] and was designated retinene reductase. The enzyme system is the same as the known alcohol dehydrogenase system,[56] and its coenzyme is the nicotinamide-adenine dinucleotide, coenzyme I. This stage of the process is, therefore, an oxidation-reduction step mediated by DPN. The final stage of the process, namely recombination of a retinal and opsin to form rhodopsin, consists of at least two steps. It was known that rhodopsin was regenerated completely from its photodegradation products in the intact eye, but in the isolated retina there was little, if any, regeneration of "visual purple."[57] This apparent anomaly was resolved by the following *in vitro* studies.[56] When a solution of an A-vitamin concentrate from fish liver, opsin, and alcohol dehydrogenase was allowed to stand in the dark, rhodopsin was formed; this biosynthetic rhodopsin had the same photochemical properties as naturally-occurring rhodopsin. When crystalline retinol (*all-trans*) was substituted for the A-vitamin mixture in a similar experiment, no rhodopsin was synthesized. This observation led to the conclusion that isomeric forms of retinol and retinal were participating in the resynthesis of rhodopsin. After the various known isomers of retinal were tested in the *in vitro* synthesis of rhodopsin from opsin, 11-*cis*-retinal was found to be the immediate precursor for rhodopsin.[58] In view of the facile regeneration of rhodopsin in the intact eye but not in the isolated retina, it was apparent that the intact eye had a mechanism to obtain the 11-*cis* isomer which was absent in the isolated retina. To account for this, it is assumed that the retina in the intact eye obtains the 11-*cis* isomer initially from the blood circulating through the pigment epithelium. In the eyes of some animals, the pigment epithelium also participates in the isomerization of the *all-trans* to the 11-*cis* isomer. This reaction is accomplished by the

54. S. Ball, T. W. Goodwin, and R. A. Morton, *Biochem. J.*, *42*, 516 (1948).
55. G. Wald and R. Hubbard, *J. Gen. Physiol.*, *32*, 367 (1948–1949).
56. R. Hubbard and G. Wald, *Proc. Natl. Acad. Sci.* (*U.S.*), *37*, 69 (1951).
57. G. Wald and P. K. Brown, *Proc. Natl. Acad. Sci.* (*U.S.*), *36*, 84 (1950).
58. R. Hubbard and G. Wald, *J. Gen. Physiol.*, *36*, 269 (1952–1953).

enzyme retinene isomerase,[59] which is found principally in the pigment epithelium of some animals and predominantly in the retina of others.

The cyclic process of scotoptic vision involving rhodopsin can be summarized as follows. The initial photochemical impulse results in the ultimate decomposition of rhodopsin to retinal (*all-trans*) and opsin. During some stage of the over-all process the impulse is transmitted to the optic nerve. Retinal is then converted to retinol by a nicotinamide-adenine dinucleotide enzyme system. During visual activity, it is assumed that retinol diffuses out of the retina into the pigment epithelium; some is eventually released into the bloodstream. The retina then selectively reabsorbs 11-*cis*-retinol which is enzymically oxidized to 11-*cis*-retinal. Recombination of 11-*cis*-retinal with opsin regenerates rhodopsin.

The rods of certain fresh-water fish and some amphibians have the light-sensitive pigment porphyropsin in the place of rhodopsin. This pigment functions exactly as rhodopsin does in the rods of other animals. The only difference between the pigments is that 3-dehydroretinol and 3-dehydroretinal function in the porphyropsin system in a manner analogous to the functions of retinol and retinal in the rhodopsin system.[60] The protein opsin is common to both systems and both have the same enzyme system for oxidation-reduction.

The light-sensitive pigment of the cones, iodopsin, has been isolated from the retina of chicks.[61] Retinol and retinal and their stereoisomers function in this system, but the protein opsin is replaced by another protein designated photopsin.

B. *In Other Metabolic Processes*

Vitamin A deficiency exerts a profound influence on glycogen neogenesis. This effect of the vitamin deficiency was ultimately related to the degeneration of certain cells and tissues including those of the adrenal cortex, rather than to a direct effect of the vitamin on glucose biosynthesis or glucocorticoid hormone biosynthesis. The vitamin A deficiency in this case may be considered a "chemical adrenalectomy."

The first indication of a vitamin A activity in the area of glycogen biosynthesis was demonstrated by the severe reduction in the incorporation of labeled acetate, lactate, and glycerol into the liver glycogen of the vitamin A-deficient rat.[62] The incorporation of glucose into liver glycogen occurred to the same extent in both the normal and vitamin A-deficient

59. R. Hubbard, *J. Gen. Physiol.*, *39*, 935 (1955–1956).
60. G. Wald, *J. Gen. Physiol.*, *22*, 775 (1938–1939).
61. G. Wald, P. K. Brown, and P. H. Smith, *Federation Proc.*, *11*, 304 (1952).
62. G. Wolf, M. D. Lane, and B. C. Johnson, *J. Biol. Chem.*, *225*, 995 (1957).

rat. It was shown that no enzyme system for glucose biosynthesis from triose was affected by the vitamin deficiency, and there appeared to be no deficiency of high energy phosphate. Since the injection of cortisone into the vitamin A-deficient rat four days prior to the injection of labeled acetate eliminated these differences in glycogen activity,[63,64] it was suggested that the A-vitamins exerted an indirect influence on glycogen biosynthesis through an effect on adrenal hormone biosynthesis. The independent observation that the adrenal gland of the rat showed a greater concentration of radioactivity than other organs after the oral administration of labeled β-carotene was further evidence for this consideration.[65] When ACTH failed to restore glycogen neogenesis to normal in the vitamin A-deficient rat,[64] it was concluded that the vitamin deficiency was indirectly influencing hormone biosynthesis by causing a degeneration of the cells and tissue of the adrenal cortex; otherwise ACTH would have caused increased secretion of the glucocorticoid hormones in the intact adrenal. This "chemical adrenalectomy" effect of vitamin A deficiency was confirmed by histological examinations that demonstrated a disturbance in those adrenal cortex cells which produce glucocorticoid hormones well before the depression of glycogen neogenesis occurred.

When cholesterol-4-C^{14} was used as an adrenal steroid precursor with adrenal tissue from a severely vitamin A-deficient pig or rat, there was a decrease in the biosynthesis of the three steroids: corticosterone, deoxycorticosterone, and progesterone.[66] When tissue from animals only "mildly deficient" in vitamin A were used, the corticosterone level was the only one affected.[66,67] The addition of retinol or retinoic acid to the *in vitro* system restored, at least partially, the biosynthesis of corticosterone from cholesterol. Consequently, it was concluded that the activity of an 11-β-hydroxylase of the adrenal is lower in vitamin A-deficient animals.

The earliest known manifestation of a vitamin A deficiency is the drying and hardening of mucous-secreting tissue. This observation suggested that the vitamin regulates the formation of mucopolysaccharides; an excess of the vitamin would lead to an increase in the biosynthesis of the mucous type of mucopolysaccharides, a deficiency to an increase in the connective-tissue type. *In vitro* studies using rat colon segments and colon homogenates clearly demonstrated a direct role for the A-vitamins in the

63. G. Wolf, S. R. Wagle, and B. C. Johnson, *Federation Proc.*, *16*, 272 (1957).
64. G. Wolf, S. R. Wagle, R. A. Van Dyke, and B. C. Johnson, *J. Biol. Chem.*, *230*, 979 (1958).
65. J. S. Willmer and D. H. Laughland, *Can. J. Biochem. Physiol.*, *35*, 819 (1957).
66. R. A. Van Dyke, *Dissertation Abstr.*, *21*, 450 (1960).
67. R. A. Van Dyke, G. Wolf, and B. C. Johnson, *Biochem. Biophys. Res. Commun.*, *3*, 123 (1960).

biosynthesis of colon mucopolysaccharide.[68,69] Vitamin A deficiency decreases the incorporation of S^{35}-sulfate into the mucopolysaccharide of the rat colon; the addition of retinol to the *in vitro* system restored activity to normal. Recent evidence indicates that the vitamin participates at the sulfate activation step in which 3′-phosphoadenosine 5′-phosphosulfate is biosynthesized.[69]

9. Nutritional and Therapeutic Role

A. In Animals

All vertebrates require an exogenous source of an A-vitamin or provitamin for vision, maintenance of epithelial tissue, and normal bone development. Epithelia most commonly affected are those which perform mucous-secreting functions. When these tissues are deprived of the A-vitamins, they begin to dry out and keratinize resulting ultimately in metaplasia. When such tissue is hyperkeratinized, it is more susceptible to bacterial invasion which may then result in permanent damage to the surface. The integrity of epiphyseal cartilage, the precursor of bone, is also affected by a deficiency of the vitamin. The effect of the deficiency state on epiphyseal cartilage is reflected in retarded skeletal growth and possibly in damage to the growing central nervous system. Over-all, the pathologic features of the vitamin deficiency result largely from an accumulation of keratinized epithelial cells in the various glands and organs of the animal.

The ability of the A-vitamins to suppress tissue keratinization was clearly demonstrated by the tissue culture technique.[70] When chick ectoderm explants were cultivated *in vitro* in normal fowl plasma, keratinization proceeded normally. Keratinization was suppressed, however, in those explants cultivated in plasma containing abnormally high concentrations of the A-vitamins. Under these conditions, the ectoderm was transformed into a mucous-secreting epithelium. The process was reversible, however, when the explants cultivated at high vitamin A concentrations were transferred to normal plasma.

Hyperkeratinization induced by a vitamin A deficiency is manifest in the condition of the eye termed xerophthalmia and by epithelial lesions in the respiratory tract, intestinal tract, and genitourinary tract of vitamin A-deficient animals. Other manifestations of epithelial lesions are a thick,

68. G. Wolf and P. T. Varandani, *Biochim. et Biophys. Acta*, *43*, 501 (1960).
69. P. T. Varandani, G. Wolf, and B. C. Johnson, *Biochem. Biophys. Res. Commun.*, *3*, 97 (1960).
70. H. B. Fell and E. Mellanby, *J. Physiol.*, *119*, 470 (1953).

dry and scaly epidermis, enlarged hair follicles, and abnormal development of enamel-forming cells in teeth.[71]

In the rat, the first histological change leading to xerophthalmia and keratomalacia is the keratinization of the cornea and conjunctival epithelium. Next the mucous cells of the conjunctiva are overlaid with keratinized cells. Then metaplasia of the ducts and atrophy of the lacrimal glands leads to a complete loss of secretory ability; at this stage the eye is most susceptible to bacterial invasion. Ultimately, the cornea may be destroyed by infection leading to blindness.[71]

In vitamin A deficiency, there is little or no coordination between the bone deposition and bone resorption processes necessary for normal bone modelling. Observed changes in bone structure due to a vitamin A deficiency have been restricted to animals in the prenatal and growing postnatal state; once normal skeletal growth has been completed, the deficiency state produces no lasting structural defect. In the prenatal and growing postnatal state, vitamin A is regarded as controlling the shape and texture of bones by controlling the location and activity of osteoclasts and osteoblasts.[72] Retarded bone growth induced by a vitamin A deficiency is regarded by some as the primary cause of the nerve lesions which are encountered in the deficient animal, since nerve tissue continues to enlarge even in the deficiency state and cannot be accommodated by the retarded skeleton.[73] Studies attempting to correlate the appearance of bone and nerve lesions were carried out with rabbits, rats, dogs, cattle, and fowl. In view of the conflicting results obtained with the various animal species, the interdependence of bone and nerve lesions in the vitamin A deficiency state has not been rigidly established.[74]

A vitamin A deficiency may also be manifest in a defective reproduction cycle. Acute vitamin A deficiency causes fetal resorption in the rat. In contrast to the vitamin E deficiency state, the placenta is affected before the fetus.[75] Acutely deficient animals that succeeded in carrying young to full term either died just before delivery, suffered difficult labor, or died during delivery. An incomplete pregnancy, however, was more usual. Congenital malformation has also been observed in the fetuses of the vitamin A-deficient rat[76] and pig.[77] Ocular deformities, retarded sex development, displaced kidneys, and retarded myocardial development

71. S. B. Wolbach and P. R. Howe, *J. Exptl. Med.*, *42*, 753 (1925).
72. E. Mellanby, *J. Physiol.*, *105*, 382 (1947).
73. S. B. Wolbach and O. A. Bessey, *Physiol. Revs.*, *22*, 233 (1942).
74. T. Moore, *Vitamin A*, Van Nostrand, Princeton, N.J., 1957, p. 314.
75. K. E. Mason, *Am. J. Anat.*, *57*, 303 (1935).
76. J. G. Wilson and J. Warkany, *Am. J. Anat.*, *83*, 357 (1948); *85*, 113 (1949).
77. F. Hale, *Heredity*, *24*, 105 (1933).

were often observed in the progeny of the vitamin A-deficient rat. Ocular abnormalities and deformities such as "accessory ears," harelip, cleft palate, and displaced kidneys were observed in piglets of the A-deficient gilt.

The hypervitaminosis A syndrome has also been demonstrated in animals. The most prominent features of massive overdoses (300,000 I.U./kilo daily) of the A-vitamins in animals have been attributed to the acceleration of bone resorption in the modelling process.[78] Bone fragility and spontaneous bone fractures observed in rats[79] are particularly impressive manifestations of the hypervitaminosis. Progeny of rats suffering hypervitaminosis A are born with congenital skeletal malformations that are particularly prominent in the skull.[80]

B. *In the Human*

Epithelial damage, especially with respect to eye tissue, is the most important clinical manifestation of the human avitaminosis A syndrome.[81] Although the failure of visual dark adaptation was one of the first manifestations of the A-vitamin deficiency to be recognized, clinical determination of this faculty is of little practical value for the early detection of a vitamin A deficiency. Ocular manifestations of the human avitaminosis A syndrome encountered in the clinic range from xerophthalmia, characterized by a drying and thickening of the conjunctiva and sometimes by chronic conjunctivities, to keratomalacia and sometimes permanent eye damage.

Although a severe primary deficiency of vitamin A is considered rare in the Western world, the problem of hypervitaminosis A is a subject of increasing interest.[82] Human hypervitaminosis A is characterized by loss of appetite, hyperirritability, appearance of sensitive lumps in the extremities, cortical thickening of bones, loss of scalp hair, and jaundice. Symptoms of acute intoxication in the human usually appear within hours after an overdosage and include central nervous system manifestations apparently related to a marked increase in spinal fluid pressure.

Experimentally induced hypervitaminosis A in the human was characterized by a prompt rise in the blood level of vitamin A and by clinical indications such as severe headaches, polyarthralgia, and skin changes.[83]

78. C. L. Maddock, S. B. Wolbach, and S. Maddock, *J. Nutr.*, *39*, 117 (1949).
79. T. Moore and Y. L. Wang, *Biochem. J.*, *39*, 222 (1945).
80. S. Q. Cohlan, *Science*, *117*, 535 (1953).
81. W. R. Aykroyd, *Federation Proc.*, *17*, *Suppl. 2*, 103 (1958).
82. H. Jeghers and H. Marraro, *Am. J. Clin. Nutr.*, *6*, 335 (1958).
83. R. W. Hillman, *Am. J. Clin. Nutr.*, *4*, 603 (1956).

Recovery from hypervitaminosis A is usually rapid and complete within a week after the administration of the vitamin is discontinued.

The human requirement for vitamin A is proportional to body weight; minimal requirements are met by the daily intake of 20 I.U. (6 mcg.) of preformed vitamin A per kilogram of body weight or 40 I.U. (24 mcg.) of β-carotene per kilogram of body weight.[84] The recommended daily dietary vitamin A allowance has been set at 5000 I.U. as provided by 4000 I.U. of carotene and 1000 I.U. of vitamin A. This allowance would be totally met by 6000 I.U. or 3600 mcg. of β-carotene. If the sole source were preformed vitamin A, 3000 I.U. or 900 mcg. would be required.

Among the best dietary sources of the preformed A-vitamins are milk, cheese, butter, eggs, liver, kidney, and heart. Important sources of pro-vitamin A include carrots, parsley, spinach, kale, and broccoli.

84. *Recommended Dietary Allowances*, Natl. Acad. Sci., Natl. Res. Council Publication 589, Washington, D.C., 1958, p. 10.

CHAPTER XVI

L-Ascorbic Acid

1. Introduction

The serious consequence of scurvy for mankind has been known for centuries. About 1700 it was shown that scurvy could be cured or prevented by providing fresh fruits and vegetables in the diet, and a relationship between the disease and nutritional deficiency was recognized gradually in the course of about 200 years. A significant stride was made when scurvy was induced experimentally, and quite unintentionally, in the guinea pig.[1,2] With this discovery, it was possible to determine which foods contain the protective and curative factor, and to initiate isolation of the active principle under the guidance of animal assays.

The antiscorbutic principle was designated vitamin C, and studies were undertaken to isolate the active substance from lemon juice. By 1925 a concentration of activity was achieved by precipitating the active principle as a basic lead complex and then regenerating the antiscorbutic factor by treating the complex with hydrogen sulfide.[3] In the period 1927–1932, the following critical contributions facilitated the identification and characterization of the antiscorbutic vitamin. In a study of oxidation-reduction systems,[4] a crystalline compound designated hexuronic acid was isolated from orange juice, cabbage juice, and the adrenal cortex. This compound was eventually identified as the antiscorbutic principle, but for a time there was little reason to suspect its relevancy to the search for the antiscorbutic vitamin. In other studies, the reducing capacities of the vitamin C concentrates were correlated with their physiological activities.[5,6] This observation provided a simple *in vitro* method of evaluating the enrichment of concentrates at various stages of the

1. A. Holst, *J. Hyg.*, *7*, 619 (1907).
2. A. Holst and T. Frölich, *J. Hyg.*, *7*, 634 (1907); *Z. Hyg. Infektionskrankh.*, *72*, 1 (1912).
3. S. S. Zilva, *Biochem. J.*, *17*, 416 (1923); *18*, 182, 186, 632 (1924); *19*, 589 (1925).
4. A. Szent-Györgyi, *Biochem. J.*, *22*, 1387 (1928).
5. S. S. Zilva, *Biochem, J.*, *21*, 689 (1927); *22*, 779 (1928); *24*, 1687 (1930).
6. J. Tillmans and P. Hirsch, *Biochem. Z.*, *250*, 312 (1932).

isolation process. Other investigators isolated the crystalline antiscorbutic principle from lemon juice under the guidance of the animal assay.[7]

There were early indications that hexuronic acid possessed antiscorbutic activity, and it was suggested that hexuronic acid and vitamin C are identical. This identity was established when the chemical and biological properties of the crystalline compound from the adrenal cortex were compared with those of the crystalline antiscorbutic factor from lemon juice,[7–9] and it was proposed that the name ascorbic acid be used to designate the antiscorbutic principle.[10]

2. Isolation

A. L-Ascorbic Acid From The Adrenal Cortex

In the first step for the isolation of *L*-ascorbic acid from the adrenal gland,[4] frozen ox adrenals were minced and extracted with cold methanol that was saturated with carbon dioxide and contained a trace of sodium cyanide. The extract was partially purified by diluting the methanol extract with sufficient 50% aqueous barium acetate to produce a barium acetate concentration of 0.5% in the diluted extract. Certain impurities precipitated as barium salts and were removed by filtration. Next the aqueous-methanol filtrate was diluted with a volume of hot saturated aqueous lead acetate sufficient to produce a lead acetate concentration of 5% in the diluted extract. The active principle was precipitated in a mixture of lead salts; after the mixture had been cooled, the precipitate was collected by filtration and washed with methanol.

An aqueous solution of the purified factor was prepared by suspending the mixture of lead salts in water and treating the suspension with sulfuric acid. Lead sulfate was removed by filtration, and the filtrate was concentrated *in vacuo*. The factor was extracted from the residue with methanol, and the extract was diluted with five volumes of anhydrous ether and filtered. Next the active principle was precipitated from solution by adding anhydrous ammonia to the cold methanol-ether extract, and the precipitate was isolated by filtration.

Further purification of the vitamin was accomplished by its selective precipitation as a lead complex. The precipitate from the anhydrous

7. W. A. Waugh and C. G. King, *Science*, *75*, 357 (1932); *J. Biol. Chem.*, *97*, 325 (1932).
8. W. A. Waugh and C. G. King, *Science*, *76*, 630 (1932).
9. J. L. Svirbely and A. Szent-Györgyi, *Nature*, *129*, 576 (1932); *Biochem. J.*, *26*, 865 (1932).
10. A. Szent-Györgyi and W. N. Haworth, *Nature*, *131*, 24 (1933).

ammonia treatment was dissolved in water and neutralized with acetic acid. An excess of saturated aqueous lead acetate was added to the aqueous solution, and certain impurities precipitated. After the mixture was filtered, the lead complex of the factor was precipitated by diluting the aqueous filtrate with three volumes of ethanol. The lead complex of the factor was isolated by filtration and dried *in vacuo*.

The active factor was regenerated from the lead complex by suspending the precipitate in acetone and treating the suspension with hydrogen sulfide. After the mixture was concentrated to a small volume, ether and petroleum ether were added, and the solvent phase was decanted from the precipitated oil. This residue solidified on drying *in vacuo*. The solid was extracted with anhydrous acetone and the extract was concentrated. The residue was dissolved in a small volume of methanol, and the solution was diluted with five volumes of ether and filtered. The methanol-ether filtrate was diluted with ten volumes of petroleum ether and the solution was cooled. The product precipitated, but with a small amount of oily contaminant. After the solvent was decanted, the contaminating oil was extracted by washing the mixture with a small volume of cold acetone. The *L*-ascorbic acid was then isolated in crystalline form by suspending the precipitate in a small volume of anhydrous ether and filtering.

In the isolation of *L*-ascorbic acid from the adrenal gland, approximately 300 mg. was obtained per kg. of ox adrenals. This corresponded to about 50% of the total *L*-ascorbic acid present in the glands.

B. L-Ascorbic Acid From Lemon Juice

In the first step for the isolation of *L*-ascorbic acid from lemon juice, the source material was decitrated by treatment with excess neutral lead acetate.[7,11–13] The pH of the decitrated solution was adjusted to 7.4–7.6 by the addition of dilute ammonium hydroxide. The active principle precipitated as a basic lead complex that was isolated by centrifugation and dissolved in dilute acetic acid. The active principle was precipitated from solution once again as the yellow basic lead complex by adding dilute ammonium hydroxide until the pH of the solution was 7.4–7.6. After the precipitate had been isolated by centrifugation, it was dissolved in dilute acetic acid, and the lead was precipitated from solution by the addition of 10% aqueous phosphoric acid.

After the aqueous solution was treated with butanol to remove colored impurities, it was concentrated *in vacuo* at low temperature. The residue

11. H. L. Sipple and C. G. King, *J. Am. Chem. Soc.*, *52*, 420 (1930).
12. F. L. Smith, 2nd and C. G. King, *J. Biol. Chem.*, *94*, 491 (1931–1932).
13. J. L. Svirbely and C. G. King, *J. Biol. Chem.*, *94*, 483 (1931–1932).

was dissolved in a small volume of ethanol, and the solution was diluted with anhydrous acetone and then concentrated to dryness. Next the purified concentrate was extracted with anhydrous acetone.

At the final stage of the isolation, the acetone solution was concentrated and the residue was dissolved in propanol. The solution was diluted with an equal volume of petroleum ether, and the precipitate was isolated by centrifugation and discarded. The solution was concentrated and the active compound was extracted with ethyl acetate. After the ethyl acetate solution was concentrated, diluted with an equal volume of petroleum ether, and cooled, the factor crystallized. After several crystallizations from ethyl acetate-petroleum ether, pure crystalline *L*-ascorbic acid was obtained.

On further investigation it was found that the vitamin could be crystallized from butanol, acetone, ethanol, or methanol after the addition of an equal volume of petroleum ether.

3. Structure Determination

On the basis of degradation data, the structure of *L*-ascorbic acid was established as *L-threo*-2,3,4,5,6-pentahydroxy-2-hexenoic acid-4-lactone (**1**).

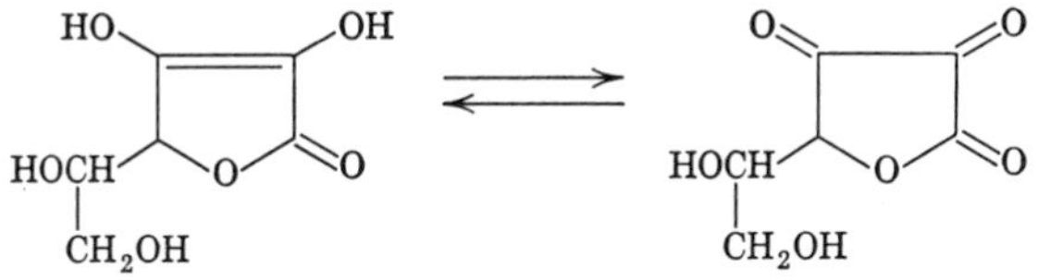

(1) (2)

L-Ascorbic acid has the molecular composition $C_6H_8O_6$. It reacts as a monobasic acid and is a strong reducing agent. In addition to its capacity to reduce Fehling's solution and ammoniacal silver nitrate,[(4)] *L*-ascorbic acid reduces two equivalents of iodine in aqueous solution.[(14)] In this reaction, iodine is reduced to hydrogen iodide and *L*-ascorbic acid is oxidized to dehydroascorbic acid (**2**). The oxidation is reversible since the reduction of dehydroascorbic acid to *L*-ascorbic acid was readily accomplished chemically with hydrogen iodide or hydrogen sulfide. Both *L*-ascorbic acid and dehydroascorbic acid have antiscorbutic activity; from the biological viewpoint, this redox system constitutes the most prominent feature of the chemistry of the vitamin.

14. R. W. Herbert, E. L. Hirst, E. G. V. Percival, R. J. W. Reynolds, and F. Smith, *J. Chem. Soc.*, 1270 (1933).

The carbohydrate nature of *L*-ascorbic acid and the absence of branching in the carbon skeleton were established promptly. Treatment of *L*-ascorbic acid with strong acids yielded furfural; this reaction serves as a basis for several characteristic color reactions of the carbohydrates. The absence of branching in the carbon skeleton was established by the catalytic reduction of *L*-ascorbic acid to *L*-idonic acid.[15]

Four of the oxygen atoms of *L*-ascorbic acid were established (Fig. 1) in the form of hydroxyl groups—two of which are "normal" and vicinal, and two of which are enolic and vicinal. Acetic anhydride in the presence

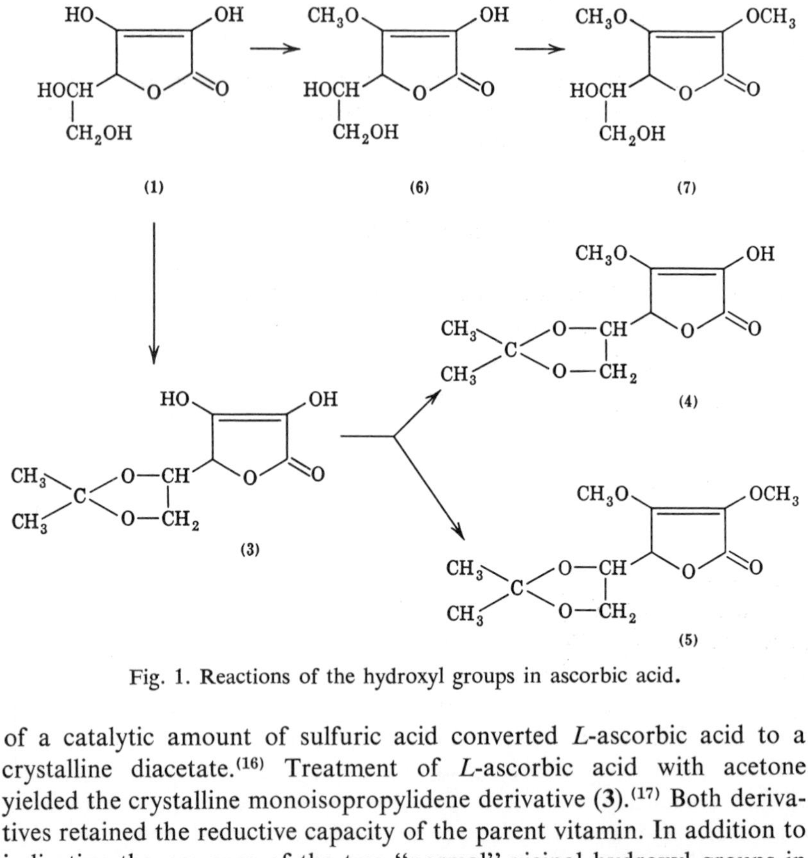

Fig. 1. Reactions of the hydroxyl groups in ascorbic acid.

of a catalytic amount of sulfuric acid converted *L*-ascorbic acid to a crystalline diacetate.[16] Treatment of *L*-ascorbic acid with acetone yielded the crystalline monoisopropylidene derivative (**3**).[17] Both derivatives retained the reductive capacity of the parent vitamin. In addition to indicating the presence of the two "normal" vicinal hydroxyl groups in

15. F. Micheel and K. Kraft, *Z. Physiol. Chem.*, *218*, 280 (1933).
16. M. Creighton, W. Wenner, and H. M. Wuest, *J. Org. Chem.*, *13*, 613 (1948).
17. L. von Vargha, *Nature*, *130*, 847 (1932).

the molecule, these reactions showed that the reductive capacity of the vitamin is not associated with the "normal" hydroxyl functions.

The isopropylidene derivative (**3**) reacted with diazomethane to yield the corresponding monomethyl[18] (**4**) and dimethyl[19] (**5**) derivatives which no longer possessed a reductive capability. Treatment of *L*-ascorbic acid with diazomethane yielded the monomethyl[18] (**6**) and dimethyl[19,20] (**7**) derivatives which also lacked a reductive capability. On the basis of these data, the reducing property of *L*-ascorbic acid was associated with the enolic functions.

The dimethyl derivative (**7**) was also a useful intermediate in establishing the nature of one of the "normal" hydroxyl groups. When this intermediate was titrated with lead tetraacetate, formaldehyde was formed in about seventy per cent of the theoretical yield.[21] Consequently, it was concluded that the hydroxyl groups are vicinal and that one must be primary.

Of the eight hydrogen atoms in the molecule, four are assigned to the hydroxyl groups, and only four are available to saturate the six unsatisfied valences of carbon in the skeleton. On this basis, it was assumed that the vitamin has one carbon-carbon double bond. The presence of this unsaturated center was demonstrated by catalytic reduction and by a color reaction with tetranitromethane.[19,20] Further evidence was obtained by comparing the reactions and spectral properties of *L*-ascorbic acid with those of the known compound, dihydroxymaleic acid (**8**).[14] In acid

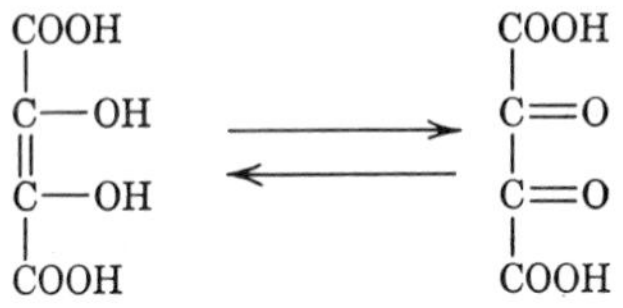

$$\begin{array}{l} \mathrm{COOH} \\ | \\ \mathrm{C{-}OH} \\ \| \\ \mathrm{C{-}OH} \\ | \\ \mathrm{COOH} \end{array} \quad \rightleftarrows \quad \begin{array}{l} \mathrm{COOH} \\ | \\ \mathrm{C{=}O} \\ | \\ \mathrm{C{=}O} \\ | \\ \mathrm{COOH} \end{array}$$

(**8**) (**9**)

solution the ultraviolet absorption spectra of *L*-ascorbic acid and dihydroxymaleic acid are characterized by a maximum at 245 mμ; in neutral solution both are characterized by a maximum at 265 mμ. Mild oxidation of each compound eliminated the chromophore. In addition to spectral similarities, dihydroxymaleic acid reacted with iodine and diazomethane in a manner identical to that found for *L*-ascorbic acid.

18. T. Reichstein, A. Grüssner, and R. Oppenauer, *Helv. Chim. Acta*, *17*, 510 (1934).
19. P. Karrer, H. Salomon, R. Morph, and K. Schöpp, *Biochem. Z.*, *258*, 4 (1933).
20. P. Karrer, H. Salomon, K. Schöpp, and R. Morph, *Helv. Chim. Acta*, *16*, 181 (1933).
21. F. Micheel and K. Kraft, *Z. Physiol. Chem.*, *222*, 235 (1933).

With iodine, dihydroxymaleic acid yielded the diketo compound (**9**); with diazomethane, the corresponding dimethyl derivative was obtained. When these similarities were considered in conjunction with the acidic properties of *L*-ascorbic acid, it was concluded that an α-keto ene-diol moiety is present in the vitamin.[14]

The ene-diol moiety in *L*-ascorbic acid was established at the 2,3-positions, and the configuration of the optically active centers was elucidated by oxidative degradation. Oxidation of the vitamin with sodium

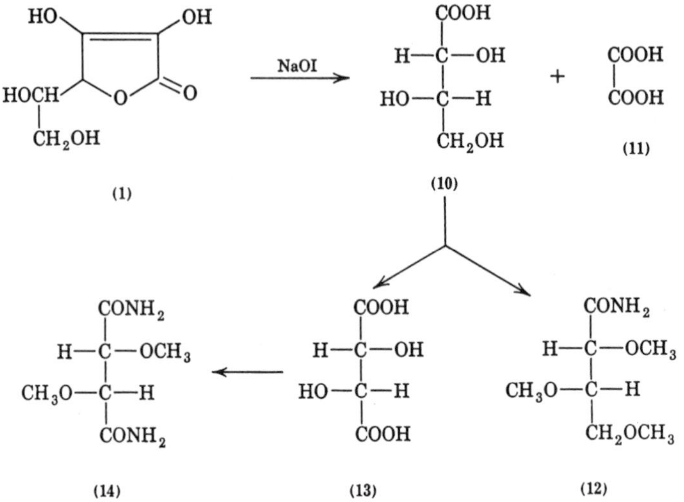

HO OH
HOCH O O
CH_2OH
(1)
NaOI
COOH
H—C—OH
HO—C—H
CH_2OH
(10)
+
COOH
COOH
(11)

$CONH_2$
H—C—OCH_3
CH_3O—C—H
$CONH_2$
(14)

COOH
H—C—OH
HO—C—H
COOH
(13)

$CONH_2$
H—C—OCH_3
CH_3O—C—H
CH_2OCH_3
(12)

hypoiodite gave a quantitative yield of *L*-threonic acid (**10**) and oxalic acid (**11**).[22] The *L*-threonic acid was identified by its conversion to trimethyl-*L*-threonamide (**12**) or alternatively by oxidation to *D*-tartaric acid (**13**), which in turn was converted to 2,3-dimethoxy-*D*-succinamide (**14**).

Ozonolysis of the di(*p*-nitrobenzoyl)-dimethyl derivative (**15**) of *L*-ascorbic acid also established the ene-diol moiety at the 2,3-positions and suggested the presence of a γ-lactone moiety in the molecule.[23] Treatment of the intermediate (**15**) with ozone in acetic acid solution yielded the tetraester (**16**) without the loss of carbon. On hydrolysis with alkali, the intermediate oxidation product (**16**) was cleaved to yield 3,4-di(*p*-nitrobenzoyl)-*L*-threonic acid (**17**) and oxalic acid (**11**).

22. E. L. Hirst, *J. Soc. Chem. Ind.*, *52*, 221 (1933).
23. F. Micheel and K. Kraft, *Z. Physiol. Chem.*, *215*, 215 (1933).

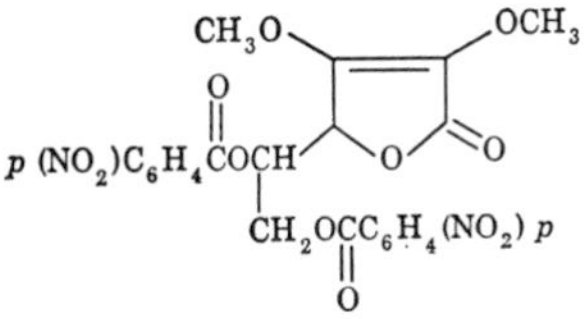

CH_3O OCH_3
$p\,(NO_2)C_6H_4COCH$ (C=O) … O … =O
$CH_2OCC_6H_4(NO_2)\,p$ (C=O)

(15)

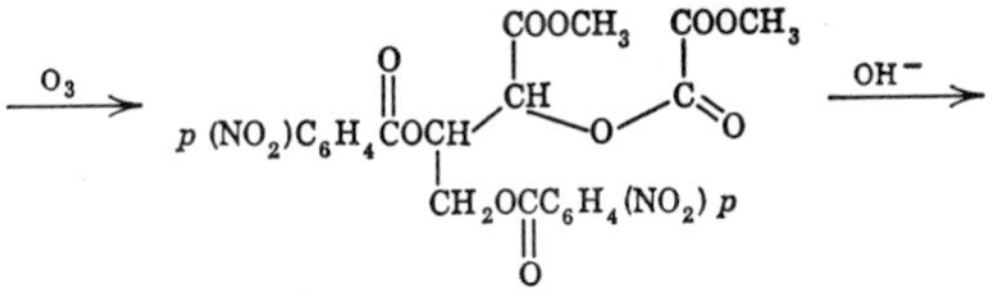

$\xrightarrow{O_3}$

$COOCH_3$ $COOCH_3$
$p\,(NO_2)C_6H_4COCH$ (C=O) — CH — O — C=O
$CH_2OCC_6H_4(NO_2)\,p$ (C=O)

(16)

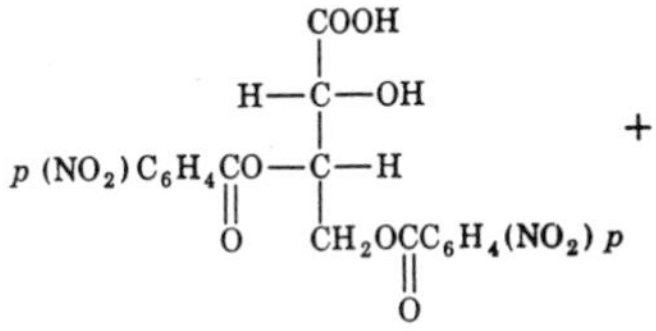

$\xrightarrow{OH^-}$

COOH
H—C—OH
$p\,(NO_2)C_6H_4CO$—C—H
$CH_2OCC_6H_4(NO_2)\,p$ (C=O)

(17)

+ COOH
COOH

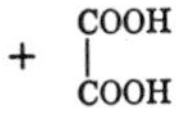

(11)

The presence of a γ-lactone moiety in the molecule was established by the oxidation of tetramethyl-*L*-ascorbic acid (**18**).[14,24] Ozonolysis of this intermediate yielded the diester (**19**), which on ammonolysis yielded 3,4-dimethyl-*L*-threonamide (**20**) and oxamide (**21**). The establishment of a hydroxyl group at the 2-position of the threonamide derivative (**20**) conclusively demonstrated that in *L*-ascorbic acid, C-1 and C-4 of the hexenoic acid chain are linked through the oxygen atom in the lactone moiety.

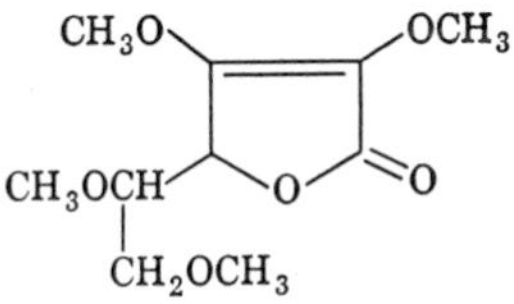

CH_3O OCH_3
CH_3OCH … O … =O
CH_2OCH_3

(18)

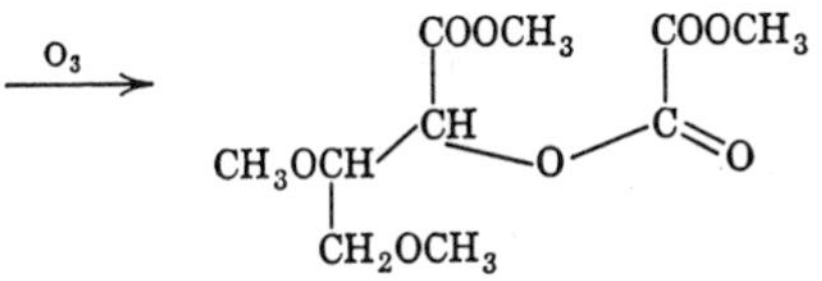

$\xrightarrow{O_3}$

$COOCH_3$ $COOCH_3$
CH_3OCH — CH — O — C=O
CH_2OCH_3

(19)

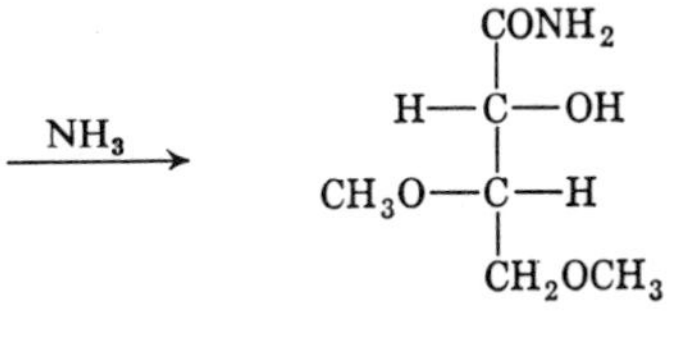

$\xrightarrow{NH_3}$

$CONH_2$
H—C—OH
CH_3O—C—H
CH_2OCH_3

(20)

+ $CONH_2$
$CONH_2$

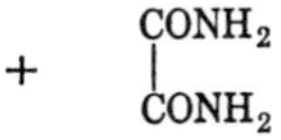

(21)

24. E. L. Hirst, E. G. V. Percival, and F. Smith, *Nature*, *131*, 617 (1933).

At this stage, the structure of *L*-ascorbic acid was established as the ene-diol γ-lactone (**1**).

4. Synthesis

The structure assigned to *L*-ascorbic acid on the basis of degradation was confirmed by a synthesis starting from *L*-xylosone.[25–27] In the first step *L*-xylosone (**22**) was treated with an aqueous solution of potassium cyanide in the presence of calcium chloride. The addition of hydrogen cyanide to the formyl group was completed rapidly, and the labile cyano-

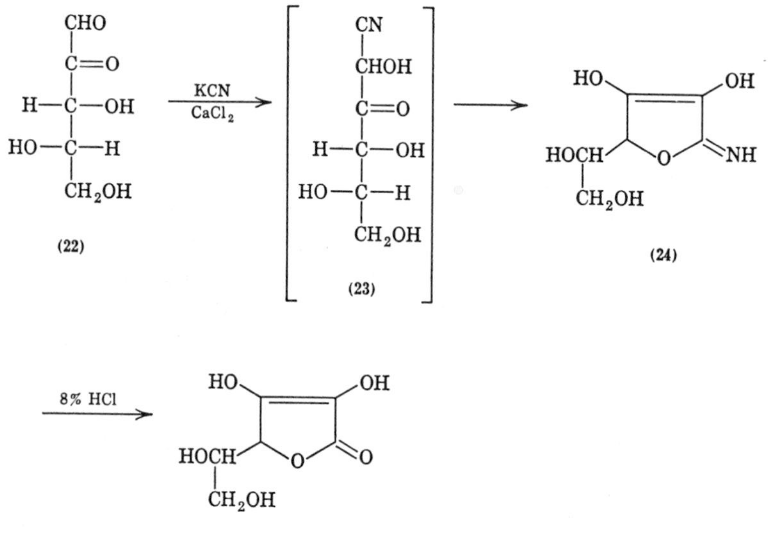

CHO
C=O
H—C—OH
HO—C—H
CH_2OH

(22)

KCN, $CaCl_2$ →

CN
CHOH
C=O
H—C—OH
HO—C—H
CH_2OH

(23)

→

HO, OH, HOCH, O, NH, CH_2OH

(24)

8% HCl →

HO, OH, HOCH, O, O, CH_2OH

(1)

hydrin intermediate (**23**) reacted further to yield a strongly reducing compound which was initially and erroneously formulated as the open chain ene-diol related to *L*-ascorbic acid.[25,26] At that time the product was designated ψ-*L*-ascorbic acid. Shortly thereafter, it was shown that the ultimate product of the cyanohydrin reaction was not the open chain ene-diol but imino-*L*-ascorbic acid (**24**).[27] In the final step of the synthesis,

25. W. N. Haworth and E. L. Hirst, *J. Soc. Chem. Ind.*, *52*, 645 (1933).
26. R. G. Ault, D. K. Baird, H. C. Corrington, W. N. Haworth, R. Herbert, E. L. Hirst, E. G. V. Percival, F. Smith, and M. Stacey, *J. Chem. Soc.*, 1419 (1933).
27. W. N. Haworth, E. L. Hirst, J. K. N. Jones, and F. Smith, *J. Chem. Soc.*, 1192 (1934).

imino-*L*-ascorbic acid was hydrolyzed by very dilute acid to yield *L*-ascorbic acid which was identical with the naturally occurring vitamin.

The addition of cyanide to an osone was applied to the synthesis of *D*-ascorbic acid by other investigators. Xylosone was reacted with liquid hydrogen cyanide in the presence of potassium cyanide at an elevated temperature; after acid hydrolysis the product was treated with acetone, and the crystalline acetonide (**3**) of *D*-ascorbic acid was isolated.[28]

The simultaneous isomerization and lactonization of certain 2-ketohexanoic acids to yield *L*-ascorbic acid is a key step in several commercial syntheses of the vitamin.[29] Of the eight possible isomeric 2-ketohexanoic acids, only *L*-xylo-2-ketohexanoic acid (**25**) and *L*-lyxo-2-ketohexanoic acid (**26**) yield *L*-ascorbic acid by this method because they have the

COOH
|
C=O
|
HO—C—H
|
H—C—OH
|
HO—C—H
|
CH_2OH
(**25**)

COOH
|
C=O
|
H—C—OH
|
H—C—OH
|
HO—C—H
|
CH_2OH
(**26**)

required *D*-configuration at the 4-position and the necessary *L*-configuration at the 5-position. The configuration at the 3-position may be either *D* or *L* since asymmetry at this position is lost by isomerization to the ene-diol moiety. Of the two, the *L*-xylo compound (**25**) is the one most commonly used because it can be synthesized from glucose.

Most commercial syntheses of *L*-ascorbic acid employ a combination of chemical and microbial transformations starting from *D*-glucose and proceed through the intermediate formation of either *L*-sorbose or *L*-idonic acid. For example, *D*-glucose (**27**) was catalytically reduced to *D*-sorbitol (**28**), which in turn was oxidized to *L*-sorbose (**29**) by submerged cultures of *Acetobacter suboxydans*.[30] The chemical conversion of *L*-sorbose to *L*-ascorbic acid proceeds with the reaction of *L*-sorbose and acetone to yield the diisopropylidene derivative (**30**), followed by oxidation to yield the diisopropylidene derivative (**31**) of *L*-xylo-2-ketohexanoic

28. T. Reichstein, A. Grüssner, and R. Oppenauer, *Helv. Chim. Acta*, *16*, 561 (1933).
29. T. Reichstein and A. Grüssner, *Helv. Chim. Acta*, *17*, 311 (1934).
30. P. A. Wells, J. J. Stubbs, L. B. Lockwood, and E. T. Roe, *Ind. Eng. Chem.*, *29*, 1385 (1937).

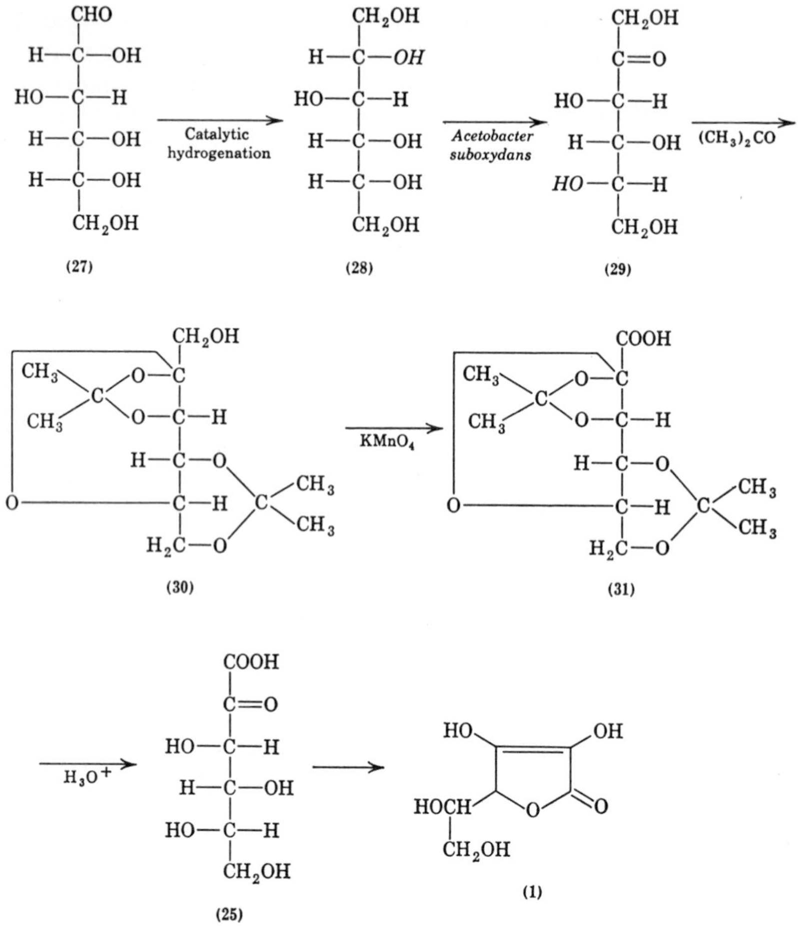

(27) $\xrightarrow{\text{Catalytic hydrogenation}}$ (28) $\xrightarrow{\textit{Acetobacter suboxydans}}$ (29) $\xrightarrow{(CH_3)_2CO}$ (30) $\xrightarrow{KMnO_4}$ (31) $\xrightarrow{H_3O^+}$ (25) $\longrightarrow$ (1)

acid.[29] Acid cleavage of the isopropylidene groups yielded the *L*-xylo intermediate (**25**), which was simultaneously isomerized and lactonized to yield *L*-ascorbic acid.

Another commercial method utilizes two microbiological oxidations in a process for the conversion of *D*-glucose to *L*-ascorbic acid.[31] The synthesis proceeds with the oxidation of *D*-glucose (**27**) to 5-ketogluconic acid (**32**) by *A. suboxydans*. The 5-keto intermediate (**32**) is then stereospecifically reduced by hydrogenation over Raney nickel to yield *L*-idonic acid (**33**).[32] This intermediate on microbiological oxidation yields *L*-xylo-

31. I. Hori and T. Nakatani, *Hakko Kogaku Zasshi*, *31*, 72 (1953).
32. T. Miki, T. Hasegawa, and Y. Sahashi, *J. Vitaminol.* (*Kyoto*), *6*, 205 (1960).

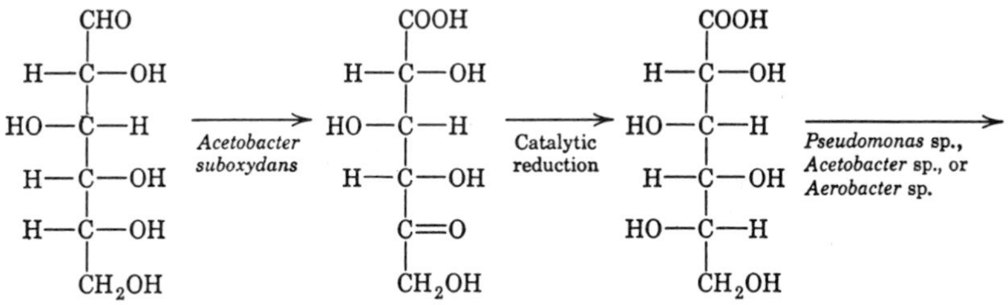

(27) → *Acetobacter suboxydans* → (32) → Catalytic reduction → (33) → *Pseudomonas* sp., *Acetobacter* sp., or *Aerobacter* sp. → (25) → (1)

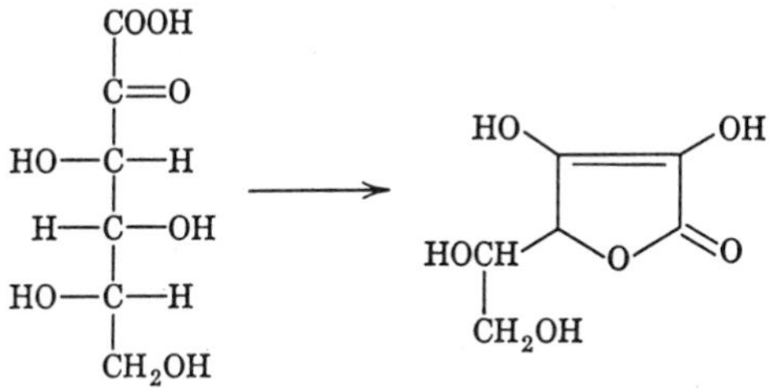

2-ketohexanoic acid (**25**) which is isomerized and lactonized by acid to yield *L*-ascorbic acid.

5. Biosynthesis

L-Ascorbic acid is biosynthesized by a wide variety of plant and animal species. Man, the other primates, and the guinea pig are notable exceptions among the mammals since they are unable to biosynthesize this compound. Because of this metabolic insufficiency, *L*-ascorbic acid is classified as a vitamin for these species.

A. In Animals

In the earliest studies, various hexoses and derived compounds were tested as dietary precursors for the biosynthesis of *L*-ascorbic acid in animals. The carbohydrates were selected as potential precursors solely on the basis of their structural similarity to *L*-ascorbic acid. The results from these early studies were at times conflicting, and conclusive evidence was never obtained to establish the direct transformation *in vivo* of such precursors to *L*-ascorbic acid.

Studies with the starved or narcotized rat provided the first indication that the biosynthesis of *L*-ascorbic acid in animals proceeded through intermediates of carbohydrate metabolism. When cyclic terpenoid ketones or cyclic terpenols were added to the diet of the starved rat, the excretion of *L*-ascorbic acid in the urine was increased significantly.[33,34] Simple ketones such as cyclopentanone, cyclohexanone, and acetophenone produced a similar effect. It was apparent that the carbinols and ketones were not participating as precursors of *L*-ascorbic acid, and it was suggested that *L*-ascorbic acid and *D*-glucuronic acid were related metabolically, possibly through a common biosynthetic precursor. The latter suggestion was made since *D*-glucuronic acid was known to participate in the mechanism of detoxification following the administration of cyclic alcohols and ketones to animals. The increased biosynthesis of *L*-ascorbic acid in these animals was consequently visualized as resulting from an increase in the concentration of a precursor for the biosynthesis of *D*-glucuronic acid which was needed to counteract the metabolic stress.

The observation that nerve depressant drugs cause increased excretion of *D*-glucuronic acid in some animals, and of *L*-ascorbic acid or both in other animals also suggested that the biosynthesis of *L*-ascorbic acid proceeded through intermediates of carbohydrate metabolism. Barbiturates, and hypnotic and antipyretic drugs were found to produce a marked increase in the urinary excretion of *L*-ascorbic acid by the rat.[35] The amount of *L*-ascorbic acid excreted was far in excess of the amount normally biosynthesized, but it was concluded that the drugs did not function as metabolic precursors. The increased rate of biosynthesis of *L*-ascorbic acid produced by such drugs *in vivo* was also demonstrated *in vitro* with liver, kidney, or brain slices.[36] *L*-Ascorbic acid was synthesized *in vitro* by tissue from the narcotized rat; with tissue from normal animals, the *in vitro* biosynthesis proceeded at a substantially diminished rate. Of the large number of substrates tested in the *in vitro* system, a mixture of pyruvate, glyceraldehyde, and hexose diphosphate produced the maximum biosynthesis; glucose, mannose, and *L*-ketogulonic acid were reported to be ineffective precursors for the biosynthesis of *L*-ascorbic acid by the *in vitro* system.

Up to this stage the evidence relating the biosynthesis of *L*-ascorbic acid to hexose metabolism was only suggestive. The first direct evidence establishing this relationship was obtained by the intraperitoneal administration of uniformly labeled C^{14}-*D*-glucose to the narcotized rat.[37] When

33. R. R. Musulin, R. H. Tully, 3rd, and C. G. King, *J. Biol. Chem.*, *129*, 437 (1939).
34. H. E. Longenecker, R. R. Musulin, R. H. Tully, 3rd, and C. G. King, *J. Biol. Chem.*, *129*, 445 (1939).
35. H. E. Longenecker, H. H. Fricke, and C. G. King, *J. Biol. Chem.*, *135*, 497 (1940).
36. C. V. Smythe and C. G. King, *J. Biol. Chem.*, *142*, 529 (1942).
37. S. S. Jackel, E. H. Mosbach, J. J. Burns, and C. G. King, *J. Biol. Chem.*, *186*, 569 (1950).

uniformly labeled *L*-ascorbic acid was isolated from the urine of these animals, the precursor relationship was established, and it was suggested that the carbon skeleton of *D*-glucose was not cleaved in the metabolic sequence which resulted in the biosynthesis of *L*-ascorbic acid.

The conversion of *D*-glucose *in vivo* to *L*-ascorbic acid without cleavage of the carbon chain was demonstrated by administering 1-C^{14}- or 6-C^{14}-*D*-glucose to the narcotized rat.[38,39] When 1-C^{14}-*D*-glucose was administered intraperitoneally, 6-C^{14}-*L*-ascorbic acid was isolated from the urine;[38] administration of 6-C^{14}-*D*-glucose resulted in the isolation of 1-C^{14}-*L*-ascorbic acid from the urine of the narcotized rat.[39] In the normal rat, 1-C^{14}- or 6-C^{14}-*L*-ascorbic acid was isolated from the urine following the administration of 6-C^{14}- or 1-C^{14}-glucose, respectively.[40] These data from normal and narcotized rats showed that inversion of configuration occurred during the biosynthetic conversion of *D*-glucose to *L*-ascorbic acid without cleavage of the carbon skeleton.

In the rat, 1-C^{14}-*D*-galactose is an efficient precursor of 6-C^{14}-*L*-ascorbic acid.[41] On the basis of efficiency of C^{14}-incorporation, it was suggested that *D*-galactose is converted to *L*-ascorbic acid without the preliminary formation of *D*-glucose.

Identification of intermediates on the biosynthetic pathway between *D*-glucose or *D*-galactose and *L*-ascorbic acid was achieved by administering potential intermediates to the narcotized rat. In one study, the injection of *L*-gulono-γ-lactone, *L*-galactono-γ-lactone, *D*-glucurono-γ-lactone, or methyl *D*-galacturonate produced significant increases in the biosynthesis of *L*-ascorbic acid by the rat.[42] *D*-Manno-γ-lactone was converted to *D*-araboascorbic acid, but *L*-idono-γ-lactone and *L*-talono-γ-lactone were without effect on biosynthesis in the rat. In other studies it was shown that

(a) Administration of uniformly labeled C^{14}-*D*-glucurono-γ-lactone to the narcotized rat yielded uniformly labeled C^{14}-*L*-ascorbic acid;[43]

(b) 6-C^{14}-*D*-Glucurono-γ-lactone and 1-C^{14}-*L*-gulono-γ-lactone yielded 1-C^{14}-*L*-ascorbic acid in both normal and narcotized rats; the corresponding free acids, however, were ineffective;[44] and

38. H. H. Horowitz, A. P. Doerschuk, and C. G. King, *J. Biol. Chem.*, *199*, 193 (1952).
39. H. H. Horowitz and C. G. King, *J. Biol. Chem.*, *200*, 125 (1953).
40. J. J. Burns and E. H. Mosbach, *J. Biol. Chem.*, *221*, 107 (1955).
41. C. Evans, A. H. Conney, N. Trousof, and J. J. Burns, *Federation Proc.*, *18*, 223 (1959).
42. F. A. Isherwood, Y. T. Chen, and L. W. Mapson, *Biochem. J.*, *56*, 1 (1954).
43. H. H. Horowitz and C. G. King, *J. Biol. Chem.*, *205*, 815 (1953).
44. J. J. Burns and C. Evans, *J. Biol. Chem.*, *223*, 897 (1956).

(c) Labeled *D*-glucose was converted to correspondingly labeled *D*-glucuronic acid and *L*-gulonic acid as well as *L*-ascorbic acid in the narcotized rat.[45–47]

The identification of intermediates on the biosynthetic pathway was also studied *in vitro*. A mitochondrial and microsomal fraction from rat liver converted *L*-gulono-γ-lactone and *L*-galactono-γ-lactone to *L*-ascorbic acid.[48,49] The corresponding free acids were not converted to *L*-ascorbic acid by the particulate system; however, both *L*-gulonic acid and *L*-galactonic acid were converted to *L*-ascorbic acid by a combined supernatant and particulate fraction from rat liver.[49,50] Extracts of rat liver also catalyzed the conversion of *D*-glucuronic acid, *D*-galacturonic acid, and their corresponding γ-lactones to *L*-ascorbic acid.[50]

On the basis of these data and studies of the enzyme requirements for particular steps of the biosynthesis, the pathway from *D*-glucose or *D*-galactose to *L*-ascorbic acid in animals proceeds according to Figure 2. In this sequence, *D*-glucose (**27**) is converted to uridinediphospho-*D*-glucose (**35**) through the intermediate formation of *D*-glucose 1-phosphate; starting from *D*-galactose (**34**), the sequence proceeds through the intermediate formation of *D*-galactose 1-phosphate and uridinediphospho-*D*-galactose, which is then isomerized to uridinediphospho-*D*-glucose.[51–53] Next uridinediphospho-*D*-glucose (**35**) is oxidized to uridinediphospho-*D*-glucuronic acid (**36**), which in turn is converted to *D*-glucuronic acid (**37**) after the intermediate formation of *D*-glucuronic acid 1-phosphate.[54] *D*-Glucuronic acid is then reversibly reduced to *L*-gulonic acid (**38**),[50,55,56] which in turn is cyclized to *L*-gulono-γ-lactone (**39**).[57] At the final stage, *L*-gulono-γ-lactone is oxidized to 2-keto-*L*-gulono-γ-lactone (**40**), which then isomerizes to *L*-ascorbic acid (**1**).[58]

45. J. J. Burns, E. H. Mosbach, S. Schulenberg, *J. Biol. Chem.*, *207*, 679 (1954).
46. J. J. Burns, *J. Am. Chem. Soc.*, *79*, 1257 (1957).
47. J. J. Burns, C. Evans, and N. Trousof, *J. Biol. Chem.*, *227*, 785 (1957).
48. F. A. Isherwood, *Proc. Nutr. Soc.* (*Engl.*, *Scot.*), *12*, 335 (1953).
49. F. A. Isherwood, L. W. Mapson, and Y. T. Chen, *Biochem. J.*, *76*, 157 (1960).
50. M. Ul Hassan and A. L. Lehninger, *J. Biol. Chem.*, *223*, 123 (1956).
51. J. Strominger, H. M. Kalckar, J. Axelrod, and E. S. Maxwell, *J. Am. Chem. Soc.*, *76*, 6411 (1954).
52. I. D. E. Storey and G. J. Dutton, *Biochem. J.*, *59*, 279 (1955).
53. H. M. Kalckar and E. S. Maxwell, *Physiol. Revs.*, *38*, 77 (1958).
54. V. Ginsburg, A. Weissbach, and E. S. Maxwell, *Biochim. et Biophys. Acta*, *28*, 649 (1958).
55. S. Ishikawa and K. Noguchi, *J. Biochem.* (*Japan*), *44*, 465 (1957).
56. G. Ashwell, *Federation Proc.*, *16*, 146 (1957).
57. J. Winkelman and A. L. Lehninger, *J. Biol. Chem.*, *233*, 794 (1958).
58. J. Kanfer, J. J. Burns, and G. Ashwell, *Biochim. et Biophys. Acta*, *31*, 556 (1959).

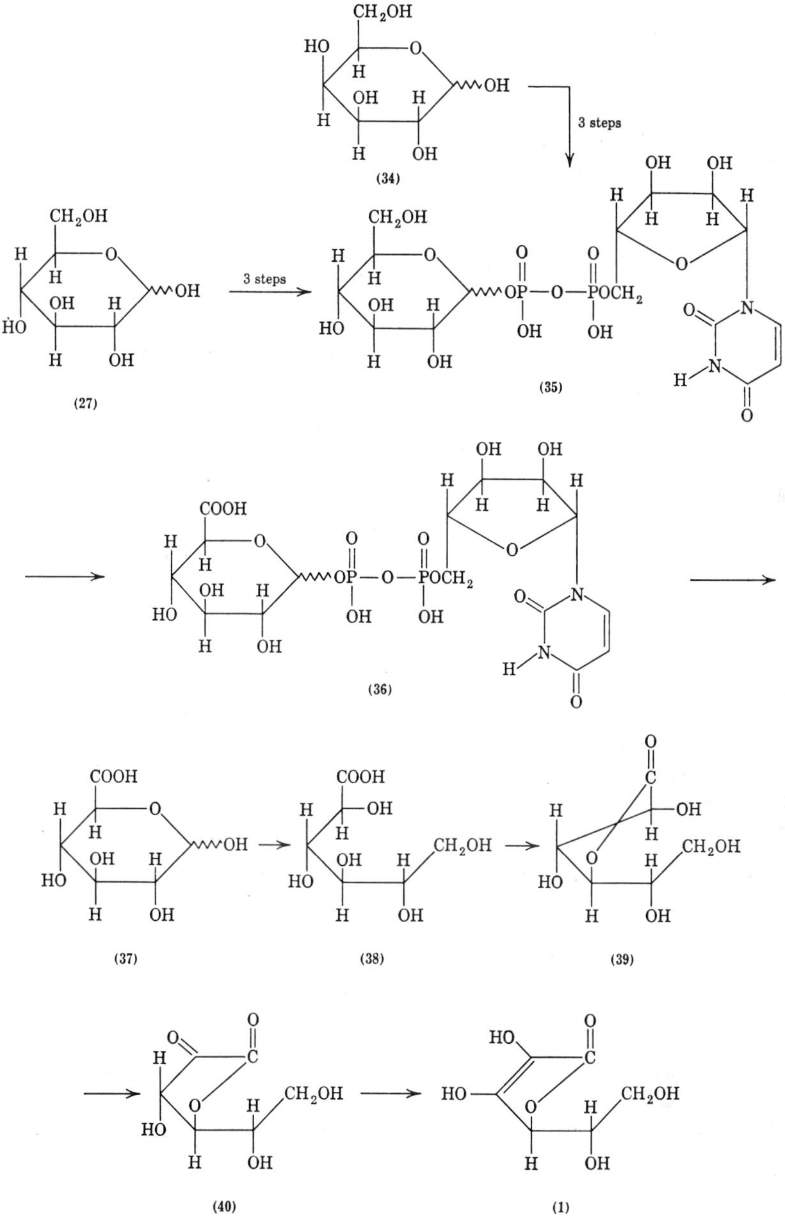

(34)

(27)

3 steps

(35)

(36)

(37) (38) (39)

(40) (1)

Fig. 2. Biosynthesis of *L*-ascorbic acid in animals.

B. In Plants

Two distinct pathways have been demonstrated for the biosynthesis of *L*-ascorbic acid in higher plants. One proceeds from *D*-glucose or *D*-galactose but in contrast to the results from animal studies, the carbon sequence is not inverted during the metabolic conversion.[59,60] For example, 1-C^{14}-*L*-ascorbic acid was isolated from the ripening strawberry after the injection of 1-C^{14}-*D*-glucose. The second pathway starts from *D*-glucurono-γ-lactone or *D*-galacturono-γ-lactone; inversion of configuration during biosynthesis by this path is achieved by inverting the carbon sequence.[60,61] Thus, 1-C^{14}-*D*-glucurono-γ-lactone is converted to 6-C^{14}-*L*-ascorbic acid.

It is not known whether the glucose or glucurono-γ-lactone pathway represents the actual metabolic sequence in the intact plant. At the present time the former pathway is favored,[62] but there is no indication of the mechanism for the conversion of a *D*- to *L*-configuration during the metabolic transformation.

6. Metabolic Studies

Tyrosine metabolism is abnormal in an animal deficient in *L*-ascorbic acid. In the scorbutic guinea pig, incomplete catabolism of tyrosine is manifest by the excretion of homogentisic acid, *p*-hydroxyphenylpyruvic acid, and *p*-hydroxyphenyllactic acid.[63] Abnormal excretion of tyrosine metabolites is also evident in the premature deficient infant, and can be arrested by the administration of *L*-ascorbic acid.[64] Later studies showed that the vitamin is required for tyrosine metabolism only when unusually large quantities of the amino acid are being ingested;[65] the amount of *L*-ascorbic acid required under these circumstances is far in excess of that necessary to prevent scurvy.

In the first step of tyrosine metabolism, the amino acid is converted to *p*-hydroxyphenylpyruvic acid; the reaction proceeds by transamination

59. F. A. Loewus, R. Jang, and C. G. Seegmiller, *J. Biol. Chem.*, *222*, 649 (1956).
60. F. A. Loewus, B. J. Finkle, and R. Jang, *Biochim. et Biophys. Acta*, *30*, 629 (1958).
61. B. J. Finkle, S. Kelly, and F. A. Loewus, *Biochim. et Biophys. Acta*, *38*, 332 (1960).
62. F. A. Loewus, *Ann. N.Y. Acad. Sci.*, *92*, 57 (1961).
63. R. R. Sealock and H. E. Silberstein, *Science*, *90*, 517 (1939); *J. Biol. Chem.*, *135*, 251 (1940).
64. S. Z. Levine, E. Marples, and H. H. Gordon, *Science*, *90*, 620 (1939); *J. Clin. Invest.*, *20*, 199, 209 (1941).
65. H. A. Painter and S. S. Zilva, *Biochem. J.*, *41*, 511 (1947).

and is mediated by pyridoxal phosphate (Chapter IX). Next *p*-hydroxyphenylpyruvic acid is oxidized to homogentisic acid by the enzyme, *p*-hydroxyphenylpyruvic acid oxidase. *In vitro*[66] and *in vivo*[67,68] studies of this system revealed that the enzyme was inhibited by an abnormally large concentration of substrate. The mechanism for such an unusual inhibition is unknown, but it was shown that reducing agents such as *L*-ascorbic acid and 2,6-dichlorophenolindophenol prevent inhibition of the enzyme in the *in vitro* system[66] and *in vivo*.[67,68]

On the basis of all the evidence, *L*-ascorbic acid is not considered to be an essential factor for tyrosine metabolism, and abnormal tyrosine metabolism is not regarded as part of the scurvy syndrome. However, the vitamin appears to play an effective role in protecting an oxidase of tyrosine metabolism when unusually large quantities of the amino acid are being ingested. This activity is not restricted to *L*-ascorbic acid but is shared by several common biological reducing agents.

Abnormal connective tissue is a primary lesion of *L*-ascorbic acid deficiency; this observation led to studies of the role of *L*-ascorbic acid in the biosynthesis of collagen and mucopolysaccharides. Collagen is the most abundant protein in the body. The turnover of collagen is considered to be negligible; therefore, the concentration of newly-formed collagen in normal tissue is invariably low. In contrast, a high concentration of newly-formed collagen is found in the fibrous tissue being formed during the healing of wounds or in response to the subcutaneous injection of a foreign body. For this reason, the effect of *L*-ascorbic acid on the biosynthesis of collagen was investigated in guinea pigs bearing wounds or artificial implants. The repair tissue of scorbutic animals consistently contained far less collagen than that from normal animals,[69–71] and it was concluded that *L*-ascorbic acid was required for the biosynthesis of collagen in response to wounds or foreign bodies.

Although it is generally agreed that *L*-ascorbic acid is required for the biosynthesis of collagen to repair damaged tissue, there is conflicting evidence regarding the requirement of the vitamin for the biosynthesis of collagen to support normal growth. Data from some studies indicate that *L*-ascorbic acid is required for the maximum biosynthesis of collagen in the skin, bone, and liver of uninjured animals, and it was concluded that

66. V. G. Zannoni and B. N. LaDu, *J. Biol. Chem.*, *234*, 2925 (1959).
67. V. G. Zannoni and B. N. LaDu, *J. Biol. Chem.*, *235*, 2667 (1960).
68. W. E. Knox and M. N. D. Goswami, *J. Biol. Chem.*, *235*, 2662 (1960).
69. W. van B. Robertson and B. Schwartz, *J. Biol. Chem.*, *201*, 689 (1953).
70. B. S. Gould and J. F. Woessner, *J. Biol. Chem.*, *226*, 289 (1957).
71. J. E. Dunphy and K. N. Udupa, *New Engl. J. Med.*, *253*, 847 (1955).

the vitamin is required for the biosynthesis of collagen to support both growth and tissue repair.[72] Others suggested that collagen was biosynthesized by more than one pathway. The biosynthesis of collagen for normal growth was visualized as slow and independent of *L*-ascorbic acid; that for tissue repair was envisioned as rapid and dependent on the vitamin. Two observations formed the basis for this conclusion. Firstly, the biosynthesis of collagen by chick embryo fibroblasts in tissue culture is independent of *L*-ascorbic acid.[73] Secondly, collagen is formed extensively in the skin and carcass, but not in the repair tissue of skin wounds of the growing guinea pig being fed a scorbutogenic diet.[74]

The mechanism by which *L*-ascorbic acid promotes the biosynthesis of collagen for tissue repair is largely unknown, but it appears that the vitamin participates directly at the site of biosynthesis rather than indirectly through the release of other activating substances.[72–75] According to one idea monodehydroascorbic acid, a partially oxidized radical form of the vitamin, participates in collagen biosynthesis.[72] A specific reaction of the biosynthetic sequence receiving considerable attention for possible mediation by the vitamin is the conversion of proline to hydroxyproline prior to incorporation into the protein precursor of collagen.

A hydroxylation reaction requiring *L*-ascorbic acid or a closely related derivative is the enzymic conversion of tryptophan to 5-hydroxytryptophan.[76] This reaction is part of the pathway for the biosynthesis of serotonin from tryptophan. The hydroxylating enzyme was isolated from normal tissue of the rat or guinea pig, and required both *L*-ascorbic acid and cupric ion for activity. Other derivatives of *L*-ascorbic acid such as dehydroascorbic acid or isoascorbic acid activated the apoenzyme, but the flavine nucleotides or pyridine nucleotides were without effect.

L-Ascorbic acid participates between DPNH and cytochrome b_5 in the electron transport chain of mammalian microsomes,[77–79] and it has been suggested that this reaction sequence may be coupled with hydroxylation. In microsomal systems derived from the liver or kidney of the rat, transport is depicted as proceeding from DPNH to monodehydroascorbic acid, a partially oxidized form of the vitamin which exists as a radical.[77–79]

72. W. van B. Robertson, *Ann. N. Y. Acad. Sci.*, *92*, 159 (1961).
73. J. F. Woessner and B. S. Gould, *J. Biophys. Biochem. Cytol.*, *3*, 685 (1957).
74. B. S. Gould, *Ann. N. Y. Acad. Sci.*, *92*, 168 (1961).
75. B. S. Gould, *J. Biol. Chem.*, *232*, 637 (1958).
76. J. R. Cooper, *Ann. N. Y. Acad. Sci.*, *92*, 208 (1961).
77. W. Kersten, H. Schmidt, and H. Staudinger, *Biochem. Z.*, *326*, 469 (1955).
78. H. Kersten, W. Kersten, and H. Staudinger, *Biochim. et Biophys. Acta*, *24*, 222 (1957); *27*, 598 (1958).
79. H. Staudinger, K. Krisch, and S. Leonhäuser, *Ann. N. Y. Acad. Sci.*, *92*, 195 (1961).

The transfer is mediated by a flavine transhydrogenase, and monodehydroascorbic acid is reduced to *L*-ascorbic acid. Next *L*-ascorbic acid is oxidized to monodehydroascorbic acid by cytochrome b_5. In the final stages of the sequence, the transfer proceeds from reduced cytochrome b_5 through the remaining members of the transport chain to oxygen. The final product from oxygen has the properties of a hydroxyl radical and may participate in enzymic hydroxylation.

A high concentration of *L*-ascorbic acid is present in the adrenal gland, and it is generally believed that the vitamin influences the biosynthesis of adrenocortical hormones. The role of *L*-ascorbic acid in this metabolic area is largely unknown, and contradictory results have been reported from *in vitro* studies. The vitamin promotes the biosynthesis *in vitro* of corticosterone and 17-hydroxycorticosterone from deoxycorticosterone in adrenal homogenates.[80–82] Some investigators observed a marked increase in the rate of hydroxylation of deoxycorticosterone at the 11β-position after adding *L*-ascorbic acid to an *in vitro* system;[81–83] in other studies, addition of the vitamin to an *in vitro* system failed to stimulate the rate of 11β-hydroxylation.[79,84,85] The rate of hydroxylation of deoxycorticosterone at the 21-position is also reported to increase following the addition of *L*-ascorbic acid to an *in vitro* system.[79]

The rate of cleavage of certain glucosinolates by an enzyme preparation from yellow mustard seed is increased significantly by *L*-ascorbic acid. On the basis of rate studies of the cleavage reaction,[86] *L*-ascorbic acid appears to be the coenzyme of a specific thioglucosidase isolated from the seed of *Sinapis alba*. For its role as a coenzyme, the vitamin apparently functions as a nucleophile to facilitate removal of the electron-withdrawing group from the 1-position of the glucosyl moiety.

7. Nutritional and Therapeutic Role

A. In Animals

L-Ascorbic acid is an essential nutrient for the guinea pig and primates. A severe deficiency of the vitamin in these animals produces scurvy. In this state the animal is liable to intramuscular and subcutaneous hemorrhage,

80. H. Hofmann and H. Staudinger, *Arzneimittel-Forsch.*, *1*, 416 (1951).
81. F. W. Kahnt and A. Wettstein, *Helv. Chim. Acta*, *34*, 1790 (1951).
82. H. Baccus, *Am. J. Physiol.*, *188*, 297 (1957).
83. H. Kersten, S. Leonhäuser, and H. Staudinger, *Biochim. et Biophys. Acta*, *29*, 350 (1958).
84. J. A. Nissim, *J. Endocrinol.*, *8*, 257 (1952).
85. O. Hechter and G. Pincus, *Physiol. Revs.*, *34*, 459 (1954).
86. M. G. Ettlinger, G. P. Dateo, Jr., B. W. Harrison, T. J. Mabry, and C. P. Thompson, *Proc. Natl. Acad. Sci. (U.S.)*, *47*, 1875 (1961).

tenderness of joints, and a general weakening of collagenous tissue; other manifestations of the deficiency include lethargy, loss of appetite, anemia, and rough lusterless fur. Scurvy is prevented in the guinea pig by a daily dose of 0.5 mg. of *L*-ascorbic acid per 100 g. of body weight.[87]

The vitamin is essential for the formation of repair tissue and adequate capillary invasion of healing wounds in animals.[88] *L*-Ascorbic acid accumulates in the scar tissue immediately after wounding, and there is a direct correlation between the amount of the vitamin in the diet and the strength of the healed wound.

The administration of large doses of *L*-ascorbic acid to the rat, guinea pig, and monkey increases the animal's capacity to tolerate a cold environment.[89–91] The amount of the vitamin required for survival increases as the temperature of exposure decreases. Little is known of the mechanism by which *L*-ascorbic acid conditions an animal for survival at low temperatures, but it has been shown that the beneficial effect is mediated through the thyroid hormones.[92]

B. In the Human

An acute, severe deficiency of *L*-ascorbic acid in the human produces scurvy. The early symptoms of the disease include weakness, listlessness, aching in the bones and joints, and a dry rough skin. As the disease progresses, typical hemorrhagic symptoms usually appear in the mouth. The gums become swollen, spongy, and friable, and the teeth become loose. Gangrene and infection of the devitalized tissue may occur; in the more severe cases, old scar tissue may break down and new wounds fail to heal.

L-Ascorbic acid is prescribed primarily for the prevention and treatment of clinical and subclinical scurvy. It is also prescribed during pregnancy and lactation to meet increased metabolic demands. There is considerable evidence that the requirement for *L*-ascorbic acid is increased significantly by trauma, infection, and other physiological stresses, and it is considered desirable to provide sufficient *L*-ascorbic acid (60–100 mg. daily) in the diet at all times to ensure approximate saturation of the tissue.[93] Therapy with *L*-ascorbic acid has been studied in connection with the treatment of metabolic stresses created by burns, injury, infection, and rheumatic

87. M. Dann and G. R. Cowgill, *J. Nutr.*, *9*, 507 (1935).
88. A. F. Abt, S. van Schuching, and J. N. Roe, *J. Nutr.*, *70*, 427 (1960).
89. L. P. Dugal and M. Thérien, *Can. J. Research*, *25*, 111 (1947).
90. L. P. Dugal and G. Fortier, *J. Appl. Physiol.*, *5*, 143 (1952).
91. L. P. Dugal, *Ann. N. Y. Acad. Sci.*, *92*, 307 (1961).
92. A. Des Marais, *Rev. Can. Biol.*, *16*, 189 (1957).
93. G. Goldsmith, *Ann. N. Y. Acad. Sci.*, *92*, 230 (1961).

disease. The vitamin has been used as an adjunct in the treatment of allergies, and has been administered postoperatively and pre-operatively to accelerate healing after surgery. Ascorbic acid has also been reported to be important for the prevention of the megaloblastic anemia of infancy and has been used for the treatment of other macrocytic anemias. When administered in large doses, the vitamin increases the absorption of iron from the intestinal tract.

The recommended minimum daily dietary allowance of *L*-ascorbic acid to prevent scurvy and maintain optimal health is 30 mg. for infants, 35–75 mg. for children, 75 mg. for adult men, and 70 mg. for women.[94] Increased allowances (100–150 mg.) are indicated during pregnancy. The richest dietary sources of the vitamin include raw liver, raw milk, fruits, and vegetables.

94. *Recommended Dietary Allowances*, Natl. Acad. Sci., Natl. Res. Council Publication 589, Wash., D.C., 1958, pg. 15.

CHAPTER XVII

The Vitamin D Group

1. Introduction

Rickets, the childhood disease identified by faulty bone formation, was associated with a dietary deficiency before the turn of the twentieth century. The ameliorative effect of sunlight was recognized in the early 1800's, and the use of natural oils such as cod liver oil in the therapy of rickets was begun in the early 1870's. By 1922 it was concluded that the beneficial effect of either sunlight or natural oils on rickets was due to the same activity or factor.[1]

The antirachitic activity of cod liver oil was concentrated in the unsaponifiable fraction, and it was suggested that the factor might be related to a cholesterol derivative.[2] Vitamin A may be concentrated in the same fraction, but the antirachitic activity of these natural oils was recognized as not due to vitamin A since activity was retained after the vitamin A had been destroyed by oxidation.[3] In close succession it was found that the irradiation of certain foods produced antirachitic activity,[4–6] and that this activity was due to the activation of sterol provitamins in these foods.[6–8] The antirachitic active substance in natural oils was designated vitamin D in 1925,[9] and its multiple chemical nature was realized promptly.

The provitamins D are 3(β)-hydroxy-$\Delta^{5,7}$-steroids (**1**), which differ only in the nature of the C-17 side chain. The precursor has no antirachitic activity until the B-ring is opened between the 9- and 10-positions by

1. A. F. Hess and M. G. Gutman, *J. Am. Med. Assoc.*, *78*, 29 (1922).
2. T. F. Zucker, A. M. Pappenheimer, and M. Barnett, *Proc. Soc. Exptl. Biol. Med.*, *19*, 167 (1922).
3. E. V. McCollum, N. Simmonds, J. E. Becker, and P. G. Shipley, *J. Biol. Chem.*, *53*, 253 (1922).
4. H. Steenbock, *Science*, *60*, 224 (1924).
5. A. F. Hess, *Am. J. Diseases Children*, *28*, 517 (1924).
6. A. F. Hess, M. Weinstock, and F. D. Helman, *J. Biol. Chem.*, *63*, 305 (1925).
7. O. Rosenheim and T. A. Webster, *Lancet*, 1025 (1925).
8. H. Steenbock and A. Block, *J. Biol. Chem.*, *64*, 263 (1925).
9. E. V. McCollum, N. Simmonds, J. E. Becker, and P. G. Shipley, *J. Biol. Chem.*, *65*, 97 (1925).

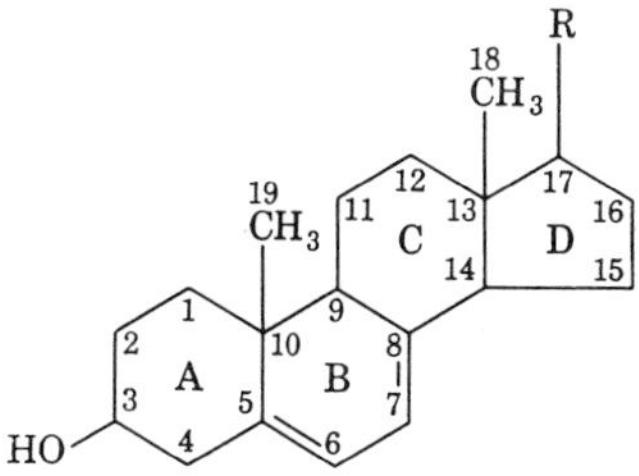

(1)

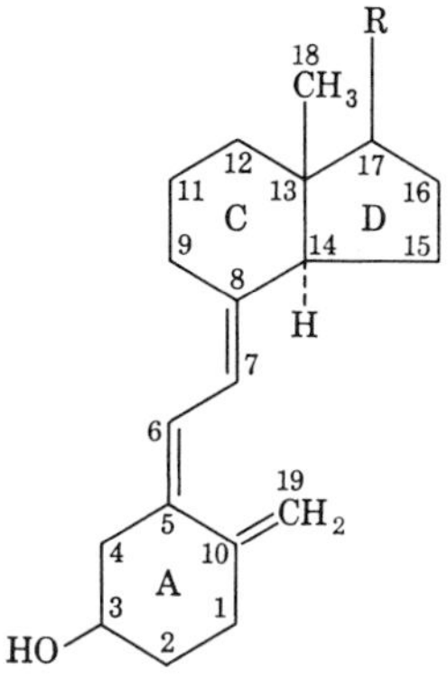

(2)

irradiation and a double bond is formed between the carbon atoms at the 10- and 19-positions; the resulting triene (**2**) is the vitamin D nucleus. The isolation and structure determination of the provitamins (e.g., ergosterol, 7-dehydrocholesterol, and the 7-dehydrositosterols) are described in treatises on steroids[10,11] and will not be reviewed.

2. Nomenclature

As each of the D-vitamins was discovered, it was designated with a numerical subscript; as forms "intermediate" between the provitamin and vitamin were isolated, the same numerical subscript was used. The term vitamin D_1 is no longer used since it was shown that the material originally designated vitamin D_1 was a molecular compound of vitamin D_2 and a photochemical product later identified as lumisterol$_2$.[12,13]

The D-vitamins are also described in terms of steroid nomenclature and numbering. To use the steroid name, the 9,10-*seco* prefix must be added to denote cleavage of the 9,10-bond of the cyclopentanoperhydrophenanthrene nucleus. The stereochemistry of the hydroxyl group is denoted relative to the position of the C-10 and C-13 methyl groups in the provitamin; the β-configuration denotes a *cis* relationship. The C-6 hydrogen atom is designated as "*cis*" or "*trans*" to indicate that the substituent is on

10. L. F. Fieser and M. Fieser, *Steroids*, Rheinhold, N.Y., 1959.
11. W. H. Strain, in H. Gilman, ed., *Organic Chemistry*, Vol. II, Wiley, N.Y., 1947, p. 1341.
12. F. A. Askew, H. M. Bruce, R. K. Callow, J. St. L. Philpot, and T. A. Webster, *Nature*, *128*, 758 (1931).
13. A. Windaus, O. Linsert, A. Lüttringhaus, and G. Weidlich, *Ann.*, *492*, 226 (1932).

the same or opposite side, respectively, as the C-4—C-5 bond in ring A. These 9,10-*seco*-5,7,10(19)-triene derivatives exist in a preferred configuration about the C-6—C-7 single bond. Such stabilization is referred to as atropic isomerism[14] and is usually denoted by the letter *s*. preceding the term *cis* or *trans*.

Generic names are also used for the various D-vitamins. For example, vitamin D_2 is designated ergocalciferol and vitamin D_3 is named cholecalciferol.[15]

3. Isolation

For the isolation of the pure D-vitamins, the various steps are conducted in an inert atmosphere, and solvents are saturated with inert gases such as nitrogen and carbon dioxide. The sequence for isolation consists of

(a) saponifying the natural oil and separating the unsaponifiable fraction;

(b) separating vitamin A from vitamin D by partition;

(c) concentrating the vitamin D fraction by adsorption chromatography;

(d) removing sterols by fractional crystallization or precipitation with digitonin;

(e) converting vitamin D to the 3,5-dinitrobenzoate or allophanate and purifying the ester by crystallization; and finally

(f) saponifying the purified ester and subsequently crystallizing the free vitamin.

A. Cholecalciferol

The isolation of crystalline cholecalciferol from the liver oil of tuna demonstrates the applicability of the general procedure.[16,17] The unsaponifiable fraction from the liver oil of the tuna was distributed between the phases of a mixture comprised of 10% petroleum ether and 90% methanol. The petroleum ether phase was separated, and the residue from distillation was extracted with boiling 98% ethanol. After five such treatments, the major portion of the antirachitic vitamin had been

14. W. Klyne, *Progress in Stereochemistry*, Academic, London, 1954, p. 137.
15. IUPAC Commission on the Nomenclature of Biological Chemistry, *J. Am. Chem. Soc.*, *82*, 5581 (1960).
16. H. Brockmann, *Z. Physiol. Chem.*, *241*, 104 (1936).
17. H. Brockmann and A. Busse, *Z. Physiol. Chem.*, *256*, 252 (1938); *Naturwissenschaften*, *26*, 122 (1938).

extracted into the alcohol. The ethanol was removed by distillation, and the residue was purified by chromatography on alumina. The factor was adsorbed on alumina from solution in benzene-petroleum ether, and the column was developed using the same solvent system. Column development was observed with the aid of selective dyes. After development, the adsorbent was extruded and the adsorbed material in a specific zone was eluted. After three purifications by adsorption, the best fractions were esterified with 3,5-dinitrobenzoyl chloride in pyridine solution. The ester mixture was purified by adsorption on alumina, and a selected adsorption band was eluted and crystallized from benzene-methanol. The crystalline 3,5-dinitrobenzoate was hydrolyzed under nitrogen with 5% methanolic potassium hydroxide, and the product was obtained as a colorless oil. Crystallization of this product from acetone-water yielded crystalline cholecalciferol melting at 83–85°.

B. Ergocalciferol

The irradiation of ergosterol (**3**) with ultraviolet light gave a mixture of products from which pure ergocalciferol (**4**) was obtained in 1932.[13,18]

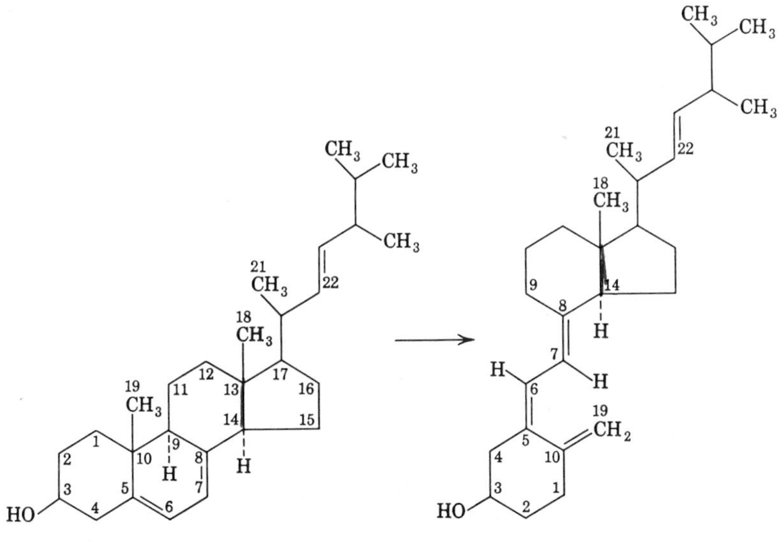

(3) (4)

18. F. A. Askew, R. B. Bourdillon, H. M. Bruce, R. K. Callow, J. St. L. Philpot, and T. A. Webster, *Proc. Roy. Soc. (London), Ser.B, 109*, 488 (1932).

4. Structure Determination

A. Ergocalciferol

The structure of ergocalciferol (**4**) was established as 3(*β*)-hydroxy-9,10-*seco*-6("*cis*")-6,7-*s.-trans*-ergosta-5,7,10(19),22-tetraene as follows. Catalytic reduction of ergocalciferol resulted in the consumption of four moles of hydrogen.[19] Reduction of ergocalciferol with sodium and alcohol yielded dihydroergocalciferol (**5**); the latter reacted with three equivalents of perbenzoic acid to give the trioxide (**6**).[20] These data showed that an additional unsaturated center was introduced during the conversion of ergosterol (**3**) to ergocalciferol, and since the elemental analysis showed no loss in either carbon or hydrogen during the conversion, it was assumed that the unsaturated center was introduced by photochemical cleavage of one of the rings of ergosterol.

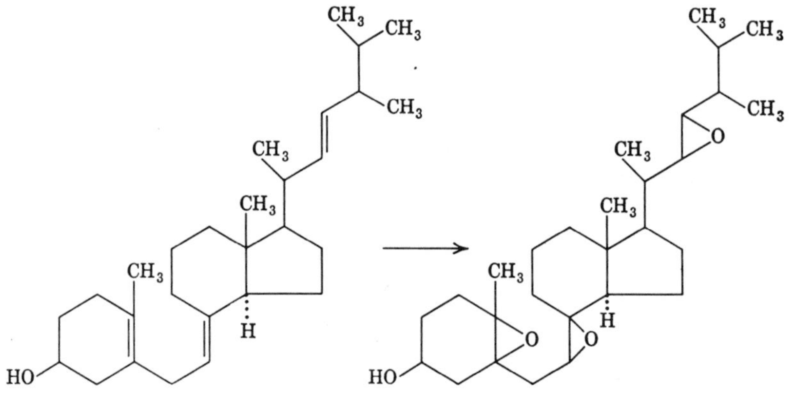

(5) (6)

The newly formed double bond was established between the 10- and 19-positions, and the three remaining centers of unsaturation were determined to be the same as in ergosterol.[21–24] Careful oxidation of ergocalciferol by chromic acid or potassium permanganate gave the *α*,*β*-unsaturated aldehyde (**7**), the ketone (**8**), and formic acid. Ozonolysis of

19. R. Kuhn and E. F. Möller, *Angew. Chem.*, *47*, 145 (1934).
20. S. Von Reichel and M. Deppe, *Z. Physiol. Chem.*, *239*, 143 (1936).
21. I. M. Heilbron and F. S. Spring, *Chem. & Ind.*, *54*, 795 (1935).
22. I. M. Heilbron, K. M. Samant, and F. S. Spring, *Nature*, *135*, 1072 (1935).
23. A. Windaus and W. Grundmann, *Ann.*, *524*, 295 (1936).
24. I. M. Heilbron, R. N. Jones, K. M. Samant, and F. S. Spring, *J. Chem. Soc.*, 905 (1936).

ergocalciferol gave the keto acid (**9**), 2,3-dimethylbutyraldehyde, and formaldehyde. Isolation of the aldehyde (**7**) showed unsaturation between the 5- and 6-positions and the 7- and 8-positions of the nucleus; isolation of the ketone (**8**) also showed unsaturation between the 7- and 8-positions.

Ergocalciferol $\xrightarrow[KMnO_4]{CrO_3 \text{ or}}$ (7) + (8) + HCOOH

Ergocalciferol $\xrightarrow{O_3}$ (9) + $(CH_3)_2CHCH(CH_3)CHO$ + HCHO

The results of ozonolysis confirmed the carbon–carbon unsaturation between the 7- and 8-positions and established unsaturation in the side chain between the 22- and 23-positions.

The structures of the bicyclic products from oxidative degradation, the formation of formic acid from permanganate oxidation, and the generation of formaldehyde from ozonolysis constituted strong evidence that the C-10 methyl group of ergosterol was converted to a methylene group in ergocalciferol.

The conclusions with respect to the location of the double bonds in ergocalciferol were also confirmed by the conversion of ergocalciferyl acetate to the corresponding maleic anhydride adduct (**10**), which in turn was converted to the dicarboxylic acid (**11**) and the corresponding dimethyl ester (**12**).[25] Platinum dehydrogenation of the diacid (**11**) gave naphthalene and β-naphthoic acid. Selenium dehydrogenation of the

25. A. Windaus and W. Thiele, *Ann.*, *521*, 160 (1936).

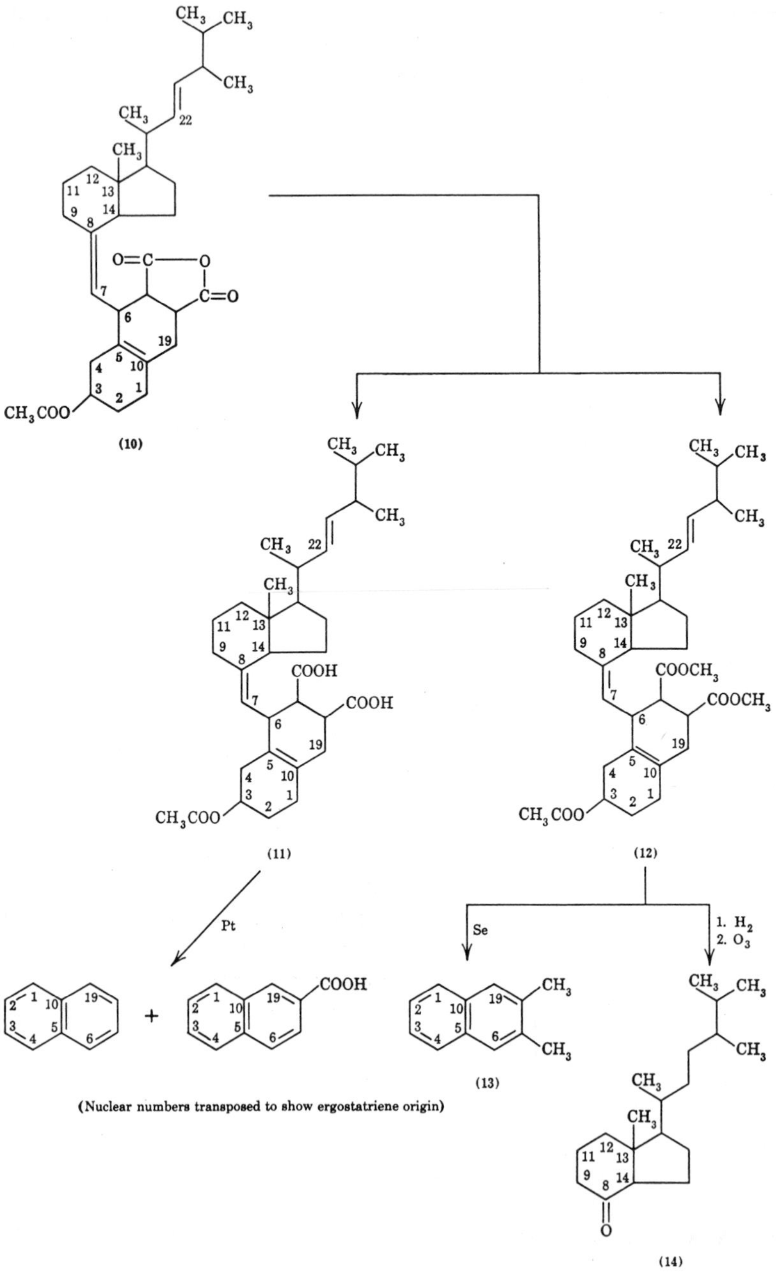

(10)

(11)

(12)

Pt

Se

1. H_2
2. O_3

(13)

(Nuclear numbers transposed to show ergostatriene origin)

(14)

diester (**12**) yielded the dimethylnaphthalene (**13**); partial hydrogenation of the diester (**12**), followed by ozonolysis, gave the saturated ketone (**14**). The only arrangement of double bonds in a triene system which would account for the formation of the perhydronaphthalene derivative (**10**) and its corresponding degradation products is the 9,10-*seco*-5,7,10(19)-ergostatriene nucleus (**2**).

The stereochemistry of ergocalciferol has been elucidated mainly by X-ray crystallography.[26] The molecule exists in an extended rather than a folded form in the crystalline state; since the C-17 side chain of ergocalciferol exists in the extended form, the side chains of the other compounds are also shown in this configuration, although it has not been demonstrated for all of them.

B. *The Other Calciferols*

Once the structure of ergocalciferol was established, the structures of the other D-vitamins were deduced from the structures of their provitamins.

5. Synthesis

A. *Partial Synthesis of Ergocalciferol*

The aldehyde (**7**), an oxidation product of ergocalciferol, was the starting compound for the partial synthesis of the 6("*trans*")- and 6("*cis*")-isomers of ergocalciferol and epi-ergocalciferol. Condensation of 4-acetoxy- or 4-hydroxycyclohexanone with the α,β-unsaturated aldehyde (**7**) yielded a mixture of the C-3 epimers of the trienolone (**15**);[27,28] the 3(β)-hydroxytrienolone (**16**) was separated from the 3(α)-epimer (**17**) by chromatography on alumina.[29] Treatment of each epimeric carbinol (**16** and **17**) with methylenetriphenylphosphorane yielded the corresponding C-10 methylene derivatives.

A 6("*trans*")-configuration was established[28] in the synthetic hydroxytetraenes (**18**) and (**19**) from the ultraviolet absorption spectra and also by Oppenauer oxidation. Both epimers and 6("*cis*")-ergocalciferol yielded the same α,β-unsaturated ketone upon Oppenauer oxidation. In this reaction, the 3-hydroxyl group was converted to a carbonyl group and the

26. D. Crowfoot and J. D. Dunitz, *Nature*, *162*, 608 (1948).
27. H. H. Inhoffen, J. F. Kath, and K. Brückner, *Angew. Chem.*, *67*, 276 (1955).
28. H. H. Inhoffen, J. Kath, W. Sticherling, and K. Brückner, *Ann.*, *603*, 25 (1957).
29. H. H. Inhoffen, K. Irmscher, H. Hirschfeld, U. Stache, and A. Kreutzler, *Ber.*, *91*, 2309 (1958).

5,6-double bond migrated to the 4,5-position in the ring; thus, the elimination of asymmetry at the 3-position and *cis-trans* isomerism at the 5,6-position in each of the three compounds removed all steric differences between them. Although one of the two epimeric hydroxytetraenes has the same configuration as 6("*cis*")-ergocalciferol at the 3-position, neither epimer was identical to the naturally occurring vitamin. Thus, it was

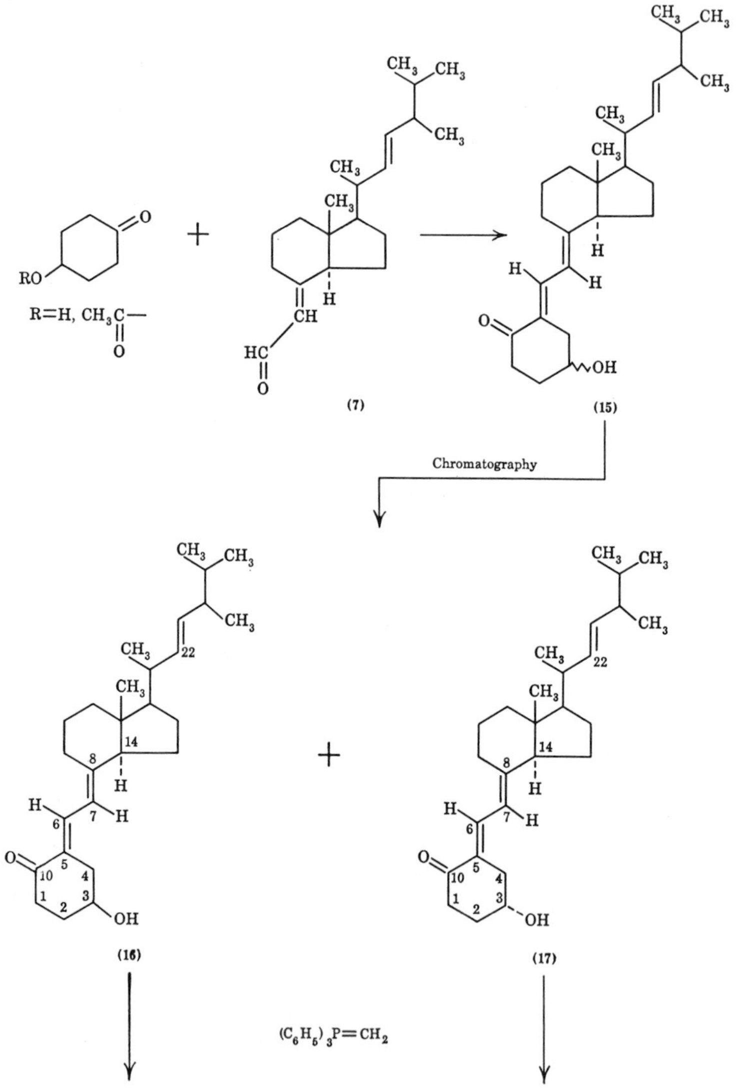

$R{=}H, CH_3C(=O)—$

(7)

(15)

Chromatography

(16)

(17)

$(C_6H_5)_3P{=}CH_2$

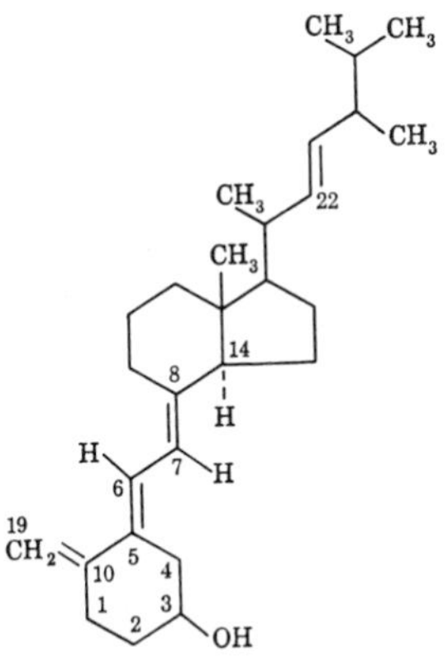

(18) 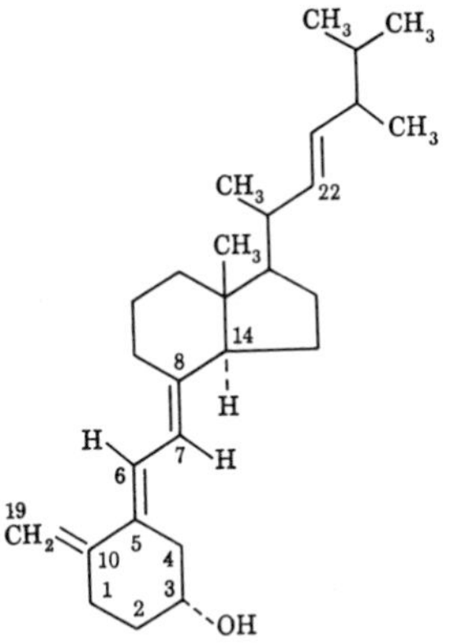 (19)

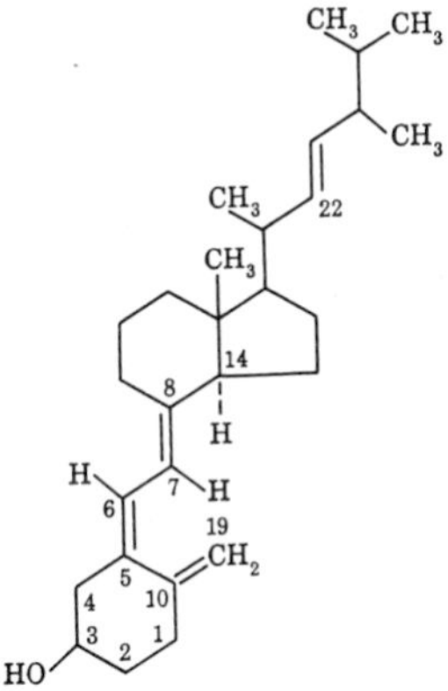

(4) 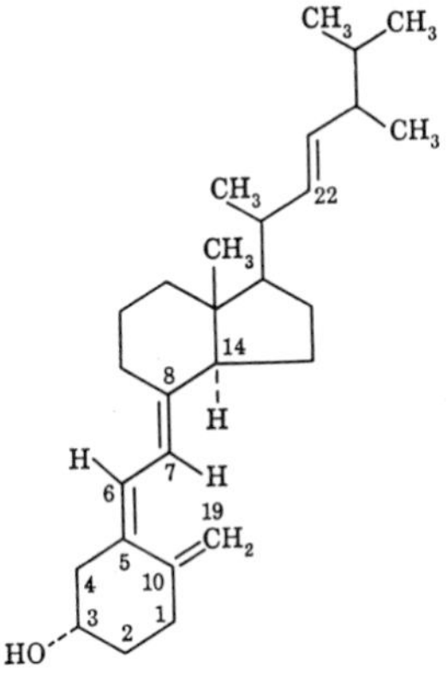 (20)

deduced that the synthetic products differed from the natural product in the configuration at the 5,6-position. The 3(β)-hydroxy epimer **(18)** was designated 6("*trans*")-ergocalciferol, and its configuration was confirmed by its identity with 3(β)-hydroxy-9,10-*seco*-6("*trans*")-6,7-*s.-trans*-ergosta-5,7,10(19),22-tetraene; the latter was obtained from the iodine-catalyzed photoisomerization of ergocalciferol.[30] The 3(α)-hydroxy epimer **(19)** was designated 6("*trans*")-epi-ergocalciferol.

In the final step of the synthesis, the 6("*trans*")-isomers were photoisomerized to the 6("*cis*")-isomers;[31] the use of glass filters permitted the

30. A. Verloop, A. L. Koevoet, and E. Havinga, *Rec. Trav. Chim.*, *74*, 1125 (1955).
31. H. H. Inhoffen, G. Quinkert, H.-J. Hess, and H. Hirschfeld, *Ber.*, *90*, 2544 (1957).

transmission of light necessary for isomerization but prevented the photochemical decomposition of the resulting 6("*cis*")-isomers. Under these conditions, the 3(β)-isomer (**18**) yielded ergocalciferol (**4**); similar treatment of the 3(α)-isomer (**19**) yielded a new compound designated epi-ergocalciferol (**20**).[32]

Other investigators completed the partial synthesis of ergocalciferol and epi-ergocalciferol from the aldehyde (**7**) by using the same reactions but varying the stages at which photoisomerization and epimer separation were accomplished.[33] The mixture of epimeric trienolones (**15**) was photo-isomerized to a mixture of the corresponding 6("*cis*")-trienolones prior to the introduction of the C-10 methylene group. After the introduction of this functional group, the epimers were converted to the corresponding 3,5-dinitrobenzoates, and the isomers were separated by chromatography. Hydrolysis of the 3,5-dinitrobenzoate of the 3(β)-isomer yielded ergocalciferol; saponification of the 3,5-dinitrobenzoate of the 3(α)-epimer yielded epi-ergocalciferol.

1. ISO-ERGOCALCIFEROL. During the early studies on the partial synthesis of ergocalciferol, the 3-hydroxyl group of the trienolone (**15**) was protected as a tetrahydropyranyloxy group.[27] After the introduction of the methylene group at C-10, the protecting group at C-3 was removed by acid hydrolysis. During this treatment, however, the exocyclic 10,19-double bond migrated into the ring to yield the isomer, 3(β)-hydroxy-9,10-*seco*-6("*trans*")-6,7-*s.-trans*-ergosta-1(10),5,7,22-tetraene (**21**) (see p. 346). This isomer has been designated iso-ergocalciferol.

B. Total Syntheses of Cholecalciferol

Formal total syntheses of cholecalciferol have been achieved by two groups of investigators. One synthesis (Fig. 1) was accomplished through the preparation of methyl 3-oxo-etiochola-4,9(11),16-trienate (**22**) and cholestanol (**23**);[34] the other (Fig. 2) was achieved through the synthesis of the 3(β)-acetoxyetioallobilianic acid methyl ester (**24**) and cholestanol (**23**).[35]

32. H. H. Inhoffen, K. Irmscher, H. Hirschfeld, U. Stache, and A. Kreutzer, *J. Chem. Soc.*, 385 (1959).
33. I. T. Harrison and B. Lythgoe, *J. Chem. Soc.*, 837 (1958).
34. R. B. Woodward, F. Sondheimer, D. Taub, K. Heusler, and W. M. MacLamore, *J. Am. Chem. Soc.*, *74*, 4223 (1952).
35. H. M. E. Cardwell, J. W. Cornforth, S. R. Duff, H. Holtermann, and R. Robinson, *J. Chem. Soc.*, 361 (1953).

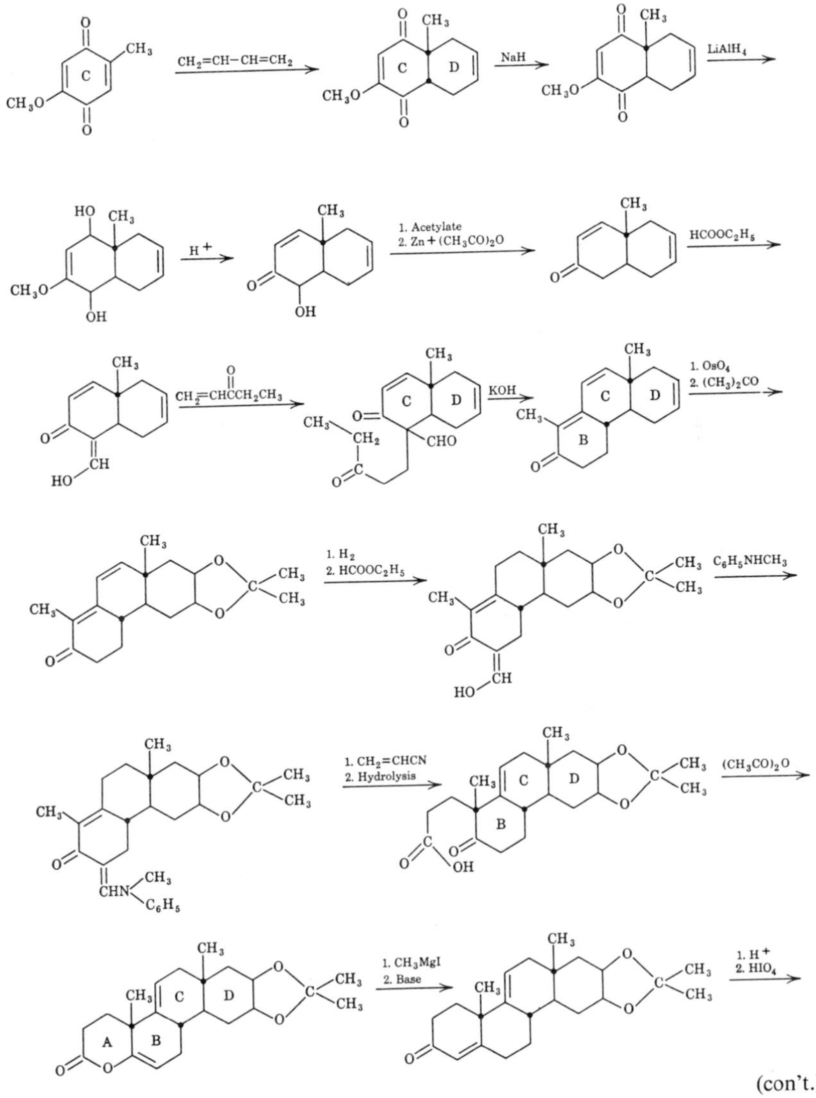

O
CH$_3$
C
CH$_3$O
O
CH_2=CH–CH=CH_2
O CH$_3$
C D
CH$_3$O
O
NaH
O CH$_3$
CH$_3$O
O
LiAlH$_4$

HO CH$_3$
CH$_3$O
OH
H$^+$
CH$_3$
O
OH
1. Acetylate
2. Zn + $(CH_3CO)_2O$
CH$_3$
O
$HCOOC_2H_5$

CH$_3$
O
CH
HO
O
CH_2=CHCCH$_2$CH$_3$
CH$_3$
C D
O
CH$_3$ CH$_2$ CHO
O C
KOH
CH$_3$
C D
CH$_3$
B
O
1. OsO_4
2. $(CH_3)_2CO$

CH$_3$
O
C CH$_3$
CH$_3$
CH$_3$
O
O
1. H_2
2. $HCOOC_2H_5$
CH$_3$
O
C CH$_3$
CH$_3$
CH$_3$
O
O
CH
HO
$C_6H_5NHCH_3$

CH$_3$
O
C CH$_3$
CH$_3$
CH$_3$
O
O
CHN CH$_3$
C$_6$H$_5$
1. CH_2=CHCN
2. Hydrolysis
CH$_3$
O
C CH$_3$
CH$_3$
CH$_3$ C D
B
O
O C O
OH
$(CH_3CO)_2O$

CH$_3$
O
C CH$_3$
CH$_3$
CH$_3$ C D
A B
O
O O
1. CH$_3$MgI
2. Base
CH$_3$
O
C CH$_3$
CH$_3$
CH$_3$
O
O
1. H$^+$
2. HIO_4

(con't.)

Fig. 1. Formal total synthesis of cholecalciferol.[34]

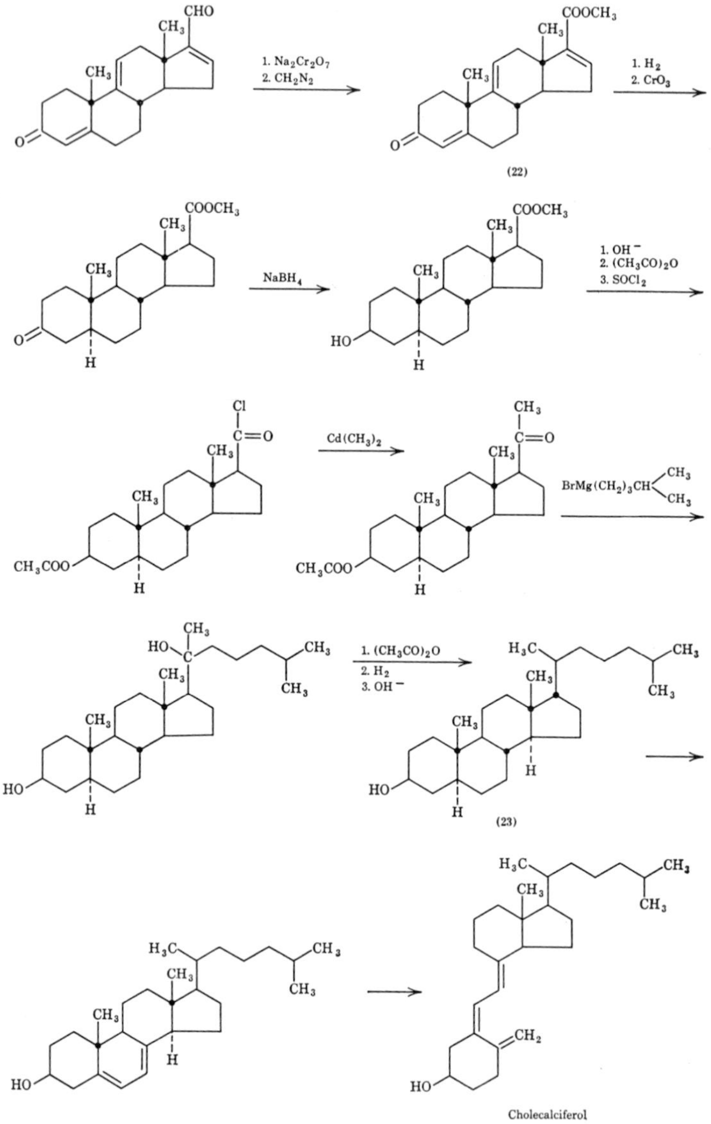

1. $Na_2Cr_2O_7$
2. CH_2N_2

(22)

1. H_2
2. CrO_3

$NaBH_4$

1. OH^-
2. $(CH_3CO)_2O$
3. $SOCl_2$

$Cd(CH_3)_2$

$BrMg(CH_2)_3CH(CH_3)_2$

1. $(CH_3CO)_2O$
2. H_2
3. OH^-

(23)

Cholecalciferol

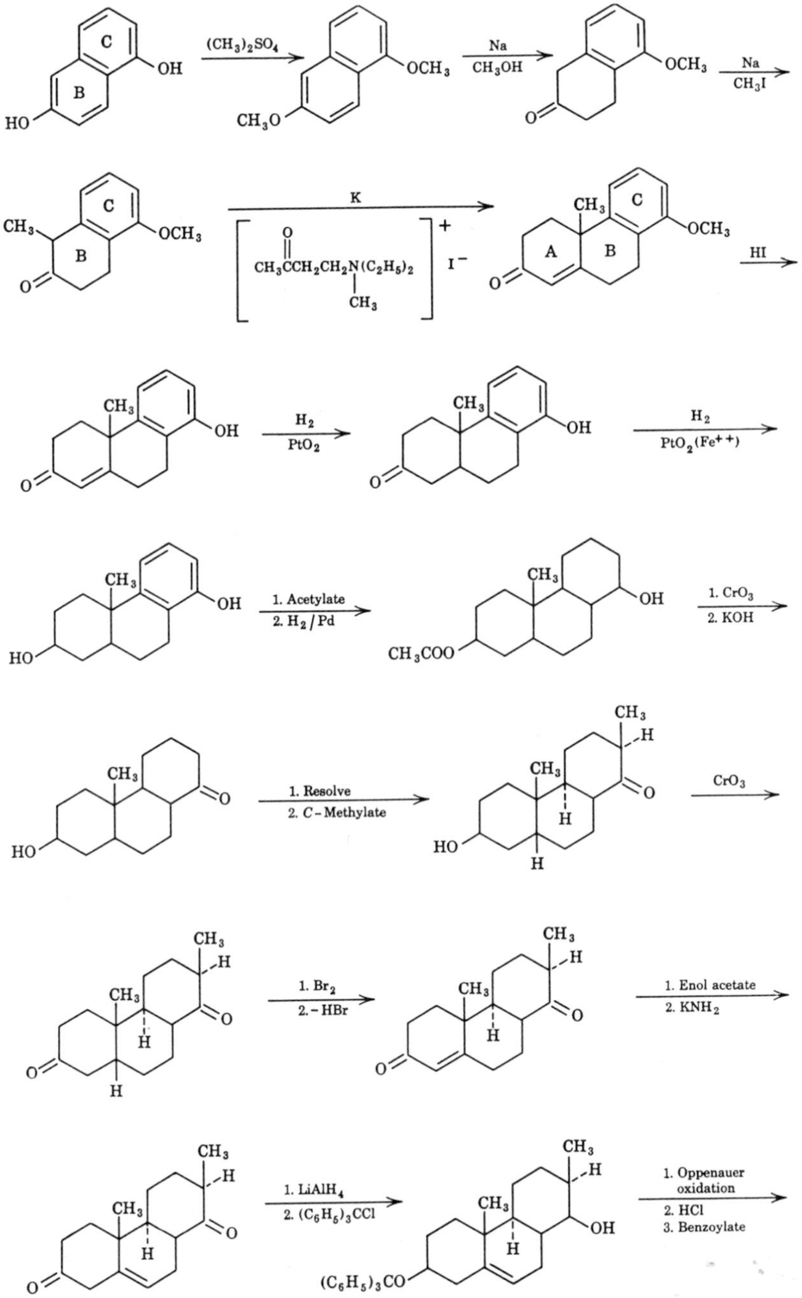

$(CH_3)_2SO_4$ — Na, CH_3OH — Na, CH_3I

K, $[CH_3COCH_2CH_2N(C_2H_5)_2CH_3]^+ I^-$ — HI

H_2, PtO_2 — H_2, $PtO_2(Fe^{++})$

1. Acetylate 2. H_2/Pd — 1. CrO_3 2. KOH

1. Resolve 2. *C*-Methylate — CrO_3

1. Br_2 2. $-HBr$ — 1. Enol acetate 2. KNH_2

1. $LiAlH_4$ 2. $(C_6H_5)_3CCl$ — 1. Oppenauer oxidation 2. HCl 3. Benzoylate

(con't.)

Fig. 2. A second formal total synthesis of cholecalciferol.[35]

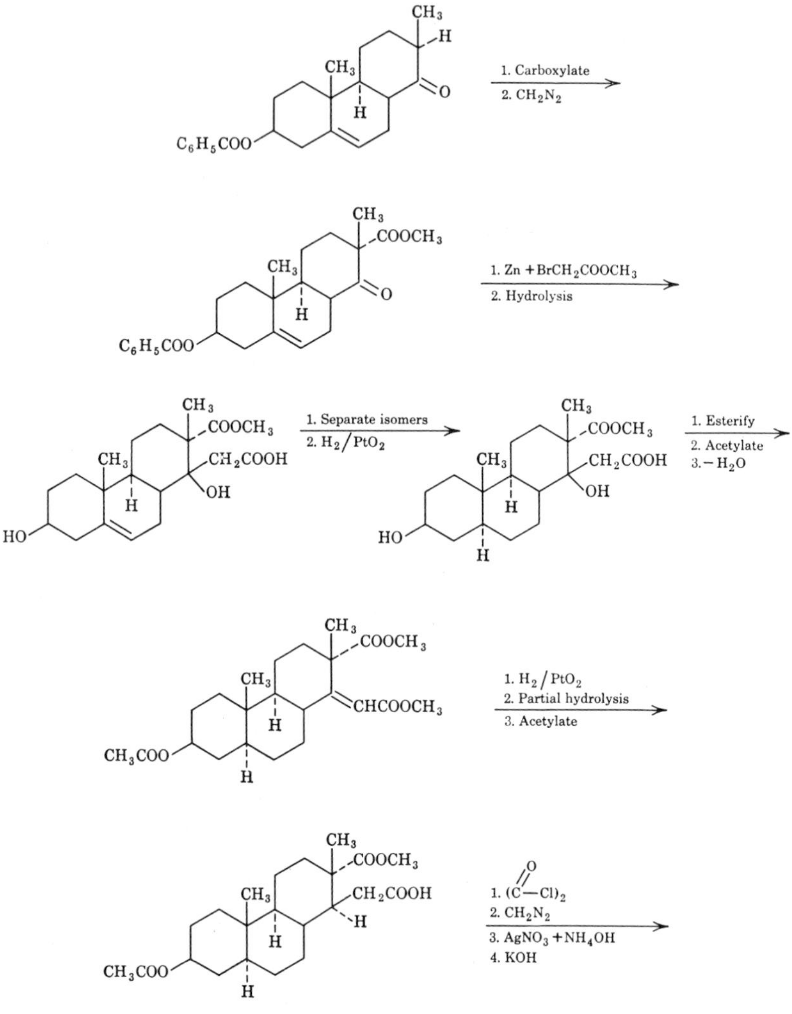

1. Carboxylate
2. CH_2N_2

1. Zn + $BrCH_2COOCH_3$
2. Hydrolysis

1. Separate isomers
2. H_2/PtO_2

1. Esterify
2. Acetylate
3. $-H_2O$

1. H_2/PtO_2
2. Partial hydrolysis
3. Acetylate

(24)

1. $(COCl)_2$
2. CH_2N_2
3. $AgNO_3 + NH_4OH$
4. KOH

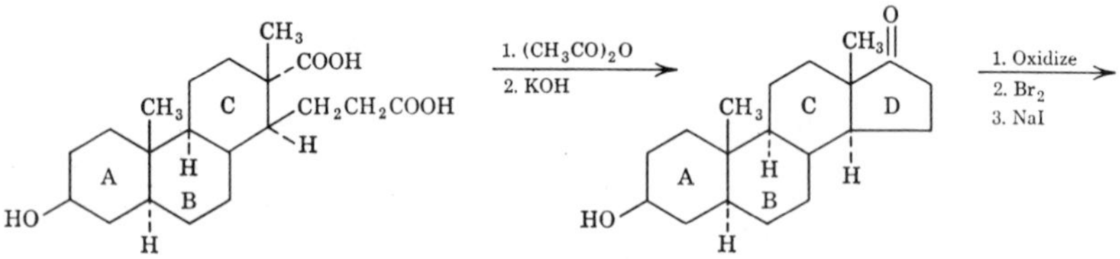

1. $(CH_3CO)_2O$
2. KOH

1. Oxidize
2. Br_2
3. NaI

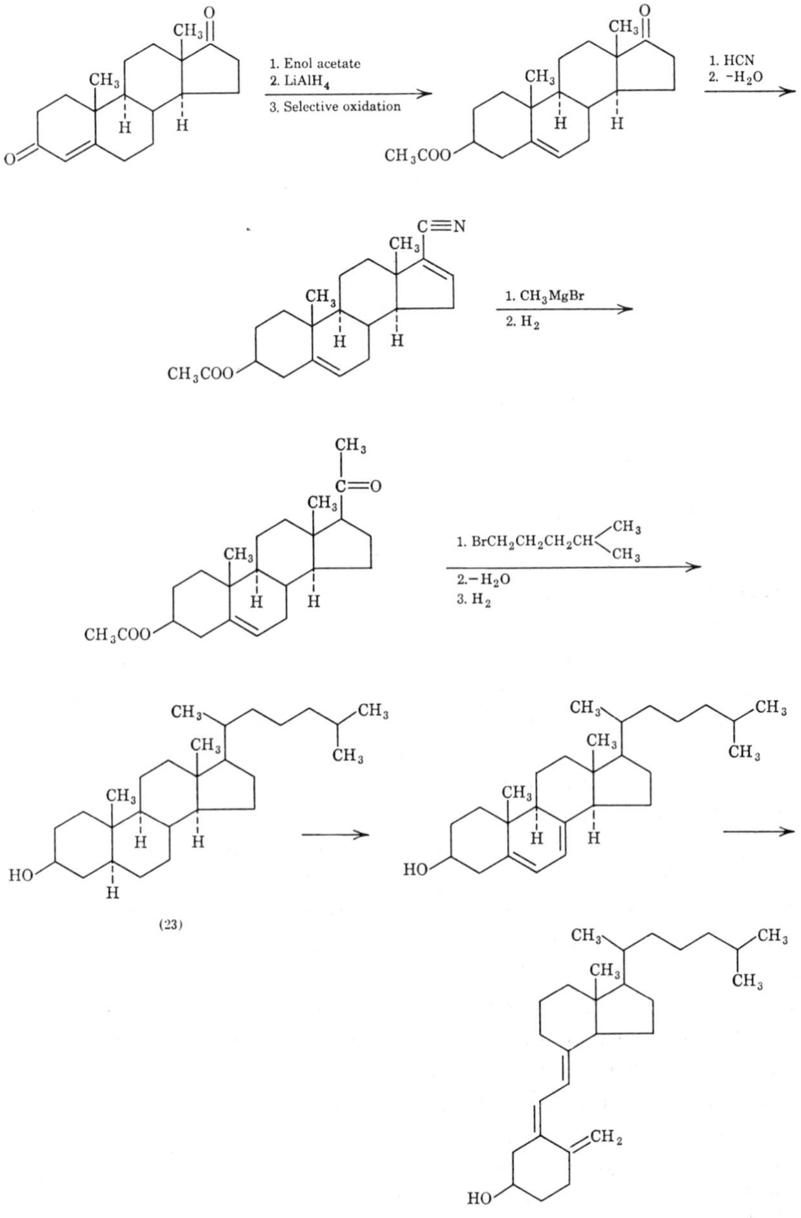

1. Enol acetate
2. $LiAlH_4$
3. Selective oxidation

1. HCN
2. $-H_2O$

1. CH_3MgBr
2. H_2

1. $BrCH_2CH_2CH_2CH(CH_3)_2$
2. $-H_2O$
3. H_2

(23)

Cholecalciferol

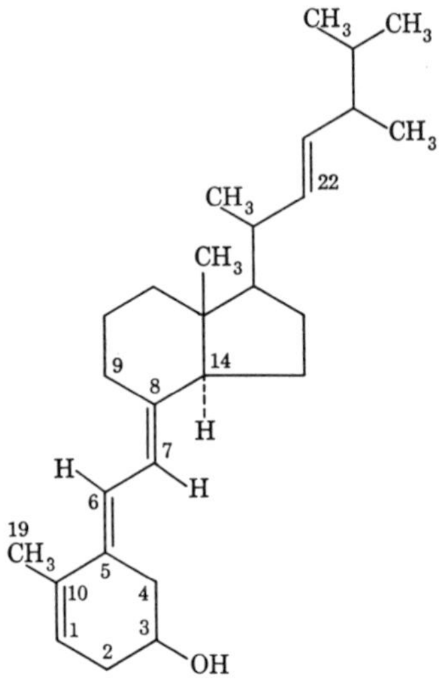

(21)

1. TOTAL SYNTHESES OF CHOLECALCIFEROL. Cholecalciferol and epi-cholecalciferol have been synthesized from 3-methyl-2-(2-carboxyethyl)-2-cyclohexenone (**25**).[36–39] The 1,4-addition of potassium cyanide to the cyclohexenone (**25**), followed by acid hydrolysis, yielded the intermediate tricyclic imide (**26**). Hydrolytic cleavage of the tricyclic intermediate (**26**) yielded a mixture of keto *trans*-dicarboxylic acids; the *trans*-diacid (**27**) was isolated and esterified, and its carbonyl function was reduced to yield the hydroxy *trans*-diester (**28**). Ring closure of the hydroxy *trans*-diester (**28**) under Dieckmann conditions, followed by hydrolysis and decarboxylation, yielded the 4-hydroxy-8-methyl-*trans*-hydrindanone (**29**).

Introduction of the side chain was initiated by the allylic addition of 2-butenyl magnesium bromide to the carbonyl function of the methyl-*trans*-hydrindanolone (**29**); conversion of the vinyl group in the resulting tertiary carbinol (**30**) to a glycol function, followed by treatment with periodate, yielded the β-hydroxyaldehyde (**31**). The β-hydroxyaldehyde was dehydrated to a mixture of *cis-trans* isomers from which the *cis*-α,β-unsaturated aldehyde (**32**) was isolated by chromatography. The remaining carbon atoms of the side chain were then introduced by a Wittig

36. H. H. Inhoffen, S. Schütz, P. Rossberg, O. Berges, K.-H. Nordsiek, H. Plenio, and E. Höroldt, *Ber.*, *91*, 2626 (1958).
37. H. H. Inhoffen, H. Burkhardt, and G. Quinkert, *Ber.*, *92*, 1564 (1959).
38. H. H. Inhoffen, K. Irmscher, G. Friedrich, D. Kampe, and O. Berges, *Ber.*, *92*, 1772 (1959).
39. H. H. Inhoffen, *Angew. Chem.*, *72*, 875 (1960).

CH_3 COOH O (25) $\xrightarrow{KCN}$ [CH_3 CN COOH O $\longrightarrow$ CH_3 CNH_2 O COOH O]

$\xrightarrow{H_3O^+}$ CH_3 C O NH O H O O (26) $\xrightarrow{H_3O^+}$ CH_3 COOH COOH O H (27)

$\xrightarrow[\text{2. NaBH}_4]{\text{1. Esterify}}$ CH_3 $COOCH_3$ $COOCH_3$ HO H (28) $\longrightarrow$ O CH_3 OH (29)

$\xrightarrow{CH_3CH{=}CHCH_2MgBr}$ CH_3 $CH{=}CH_2$ CH CH_3 OH OH (30) $\xrightarrow[\text{2. HIO}_4]{\text{1. OsO}_4}$ CH_3 CHO CH CH_3 OH OH (31)

(con't.)

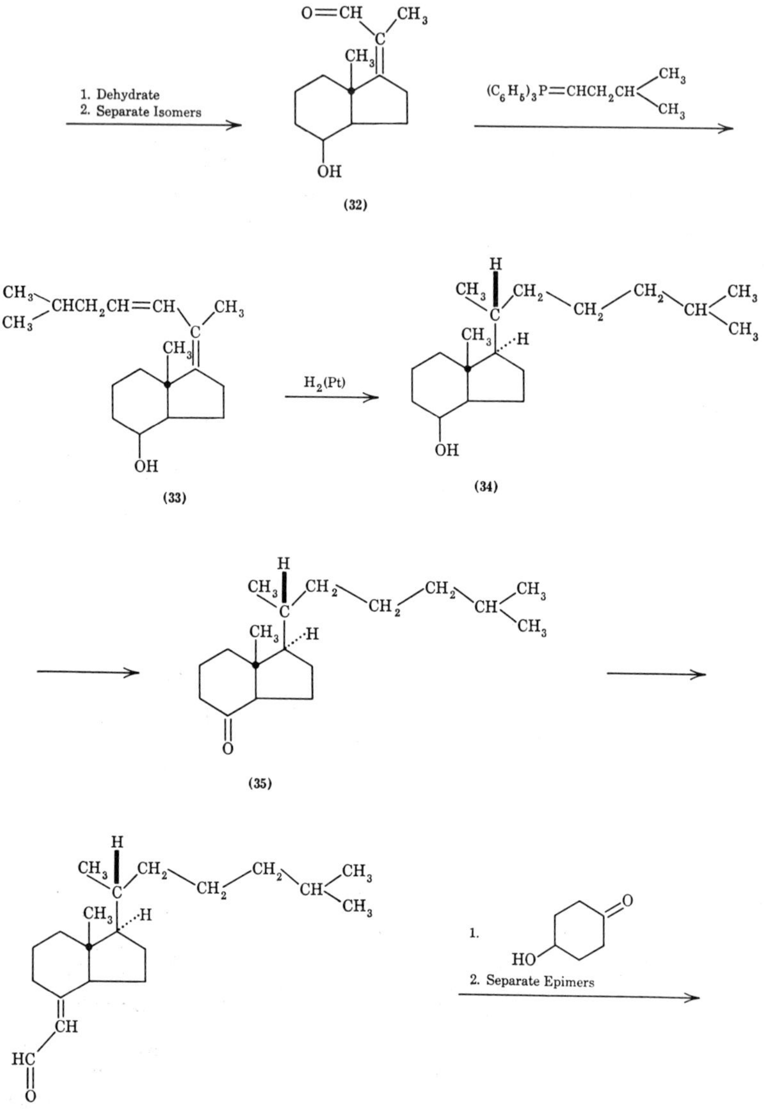

1. Dehydrate
2. Separate Isomers

O=CH CH$_3$ C CH$_3$ OH

(32)

$(C_6H_5)_3P{=}CHCH_2CH(CH_3)_2$

$(CH_3)_2CHCH_2CH{=}CH$ C CH$_3$ CH$_3$ OH

(33)

H_2(Pt)

H CH$_3$ C CH$_2$ CH$_2$ CH$_2$ CH CH$_3$ CH$_3$ CH$_3$ H OH

(34)

H CH$_3$ C CH$_2$ CH$_2$ CH$_2$ CH CH$_3$ CH$_3$ CH$_3$ H O

(35)

H CH$_3$ C CH$_2$ CH$_2$ CH$_2$ CH CH$_3$ CH$_3$ CH$_3$ H CH HC O

(36)

1. HO O
2. Separate Epimers

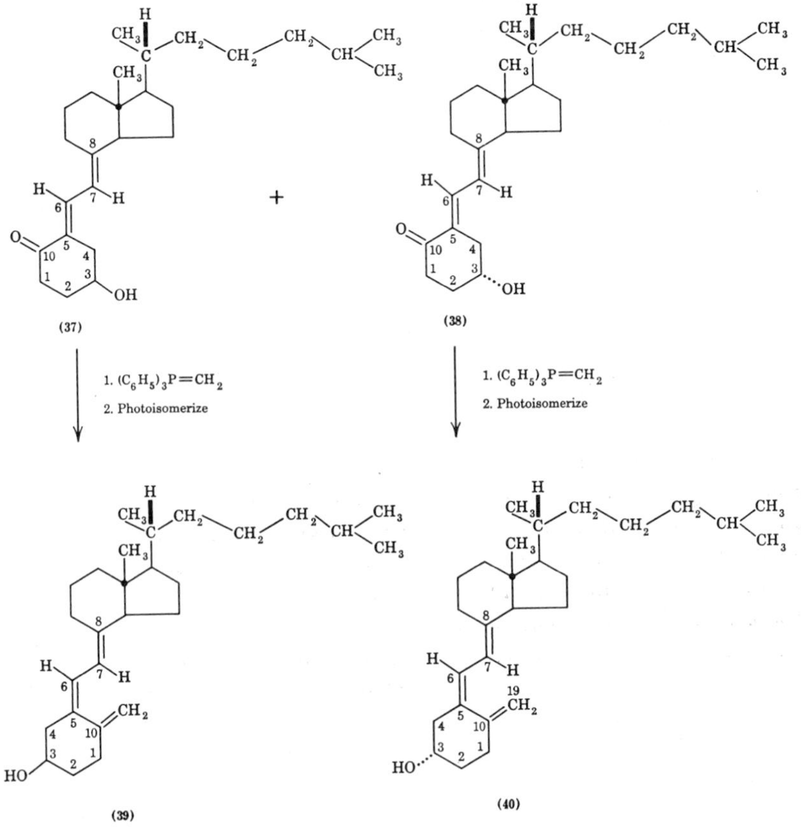

(37) + (38)

1. $(C_6H_5)_3P{=}CH_2$
2. Photoisomerize

1. $(C_6H_5)_3P{=}CH_2$
2. Photoisomerize

(39) (40)

(con't)

condensation of the *cis*-α,β-unsaturated aldehyde (**32**) with 3-methylbutylidenetriphenylphosphorane, and the resulting 1,3-diene (**33**) was catalytically reduced to the hydrindanol (**34**). Alternatively, the hydrindanol (**34**) was synthesized by catalytic reduction of the *cis*-α,β-unsaturated aldehyde (**32**) prior to the Wittig condensation or by the 1,4-reduction of the *trans* isomer of the α,β-unsaturated aldehyde (**32**) prior to the Wittig reaction.

The hydrindanol (**34**) was oxidized to the corresponding hydrindanone (**35**), and the latter was converted in two steps to the α,β-unsaturated aldehyde (**36**). First the carbonyl function in the hydrindanone (**35**) was converted to a *trans*-butadienyl function by a Wittig condensation with the *ylid* from allyl bromide; then the butadienyl function, in turn, was partially degraded by ozonolysis to yield the α,β-unsaturated aldehyde (**36**).

At this stage of the synthesis, the reaction sequence parallels that previously outlined for the synthesis of ergocalciferol and epi-ergocalciferol. The α,β-unsaturated aldehyde (**36**) was condensed with 4-hydroxycyclohexanone, and the C-3 epimers (**37**) and (**38**) were separated from the reaction mixture by chromatography. After the introduction of the C-10 methylene group and photoisomerization of the 5,6-double bond, the 6("*cis*")-isomers cholecalciferol (**39**) and epi-cholecalciferol (**40**) were obtained.

6. Irradiation Products of Ergosterol

A. Early Studies

During the early studies of the irradiation of ergosterol, several products were isolated in addition to ergocalciferol. Some of these products were assumed to be "intermediates" in the irradiation pathway from ergosterol to ergocalciferol; others were assumed to be over-irradiation products of ergosterol. The formation of these products is a function of the wavelength and duration of irradiation. As these compounds were discovered, they were designated as lumisterols, protachysterols, tachysterols, and suprasterols. A subscript is usually added to the name of the compound to relate it to the corresponding D-vitamin, and steroid nomenclature and numbering are applied to describe the structure of the product.

The pathway from a provitamin D to a vitamin D in the irradiation process was assumed to require the stepwise formation of the "intermediates" lumisterol, protachysterol, and tachysterol.[40] The over-all structural features of these compounds have been known for years, but the details of configuration and conformation have been elucidated only recently. In the early concept of the irradiation pathway (Fig. 3), the first intermediate to be encountered is lumisterol$_2$ (**41**).[41] The structure of this compound has been a subject of recent study;[42,43] as a result of these investigations, lumisterol$_2$ is now known to be a 3(β)-hydroxyergosta-5,7,22-triene which differs from ergosterol only in the α-orientation of its C-10 methyl group and the β-orientation of the C-9 hydrogen atom. The second product isolated[44] was the metastable protachysterol$_2$ which was converted readily to tachysterol$_2$ (**42**).[40] This compound is 3(β)-hydroxy-9,10-*seco*-ergosta-5(10),6-*trans*,8,22-tetraene; the 6-*trans*-configuration was

40. A. Windaus, F. Von Werder, and A. Lüttringhaus, *Ann.*, *499*, 188 (1932).
41. A. Windaus, K. Dithmar, and E. Fernholz, *Ann.*, *493*, 259 (1932).
42. J. Castells, E. R. H. Jones, and R. W. J. Williams, *Proc. Chem. Soc.*, 7 (1958).
43. J. Castells, E. R. H. Jones, G. D. Meakins, and R. W. J. Williams, *J. Chem. Soc.*, 1159 (1959).
44. A. Windaus and E. Auhagen, *Z. Physiol. Chem.*, *196*, 108 (1931).

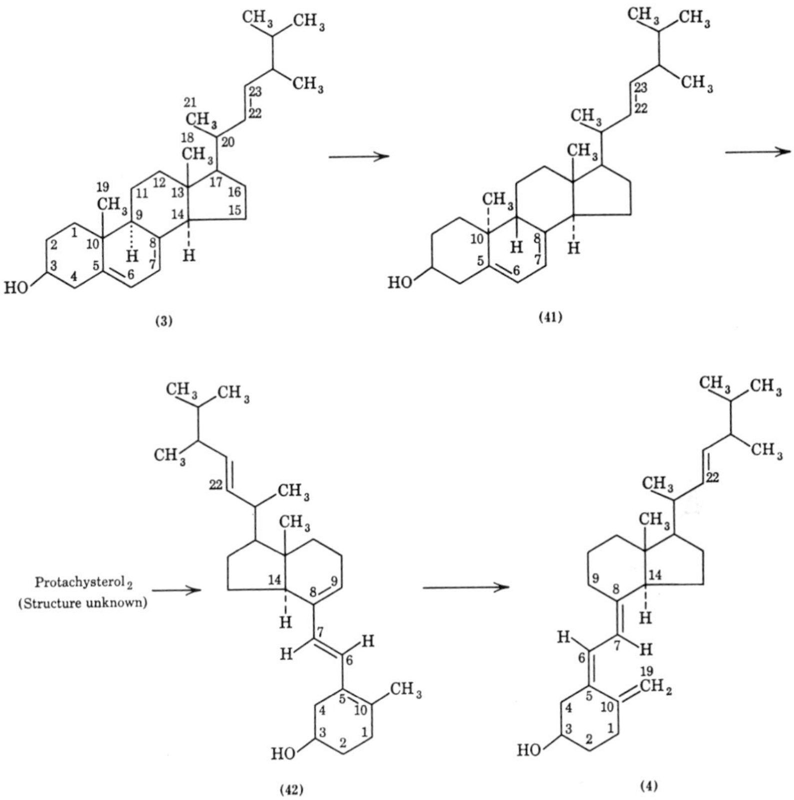

(3) (41)

Protachysterol$_2$
(Structure unknown)

(42) (4)

Fig. 3. Early concept of irradiation pathway from ergosterol to ergocalciferol.

assigned[45,46] on the basis of certain chemical reactions and on evidence derived from the infrared absorption spectrum.

The discovery and isolation of pre-ergocalciferol (**43**) marked the beginning of the current concept of the irradiation pathway from provitamin to vitamin.[47] When it was first discovered, the previtamin was assumed to be an intermediate between tachysterol$_2$ and ergocalciferol. Once its structure was established, it was apparent that the early concept was no longer valid. Pre-ergocalciferol differs from the compounds previously isolated from the irradiation mixture in two respects: it is the only product with a folded or *cis* structure, and it is converted to ergocalciferol by thermal means and in the absence of light. Structural studies

45. H. H. Inhoffen, K. Brückner, R. Grundel, and G. Quinkert, *Ber.*, *87*, 1407 (1954).
46. H. H. Inhoffen, K. Brückner, K. Irmscher, and G. Quinkert, *Ber.*, *88*, 1424 (1955).
47. L. Velluz, G. Amiard, and A. Pettit, *Bull. Soc. Chim. France*, 501 (1949).

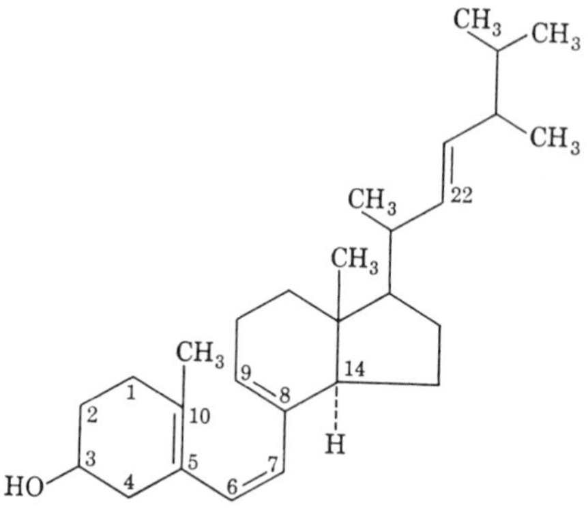

(43)

showed that pre-ergocalciferol is 3(β)-hydroxy-9,10-*seco*-ergosta-5(10),6-*cis*,8,22-tetraene.[48]

B. The Provitamin-Previtamin-Vitamin Pathway in the Irradiation Process

Since 1955 the problem of elucidating the main reaction and side reactions in the irradiation pathway from a provitamin D to a vitamin D has been studied with the aid of tracer techniques, kinetic measurements, and determination of quantum efficiencies.[48–56] According to this evidence, the synthesis of a D-vitamin from its provitamin by irradiation proceeds from the provitamin to the previtamin and finally to the vitamin.[48–50] Compounds such as the lumisterols and tachysterols are assumed to arise from side reactions of either the previtamin[48,49] or the activated provitamin.[50,53]

The first step of the main reaction (Fig. 4) is the photochemical conversion of ergosterol to pre-ergocalciferol; this reversible reaction proceeds in yields up to 85%.[48] The next and final step is accomplished by the thermal conversion of pre-ergocalciferol to ergocalciferol.[47] The formation of tachysterol$_2$ and lumisterol$_2$ in the irradiation reaction proceeds

48. L. Velluz, G. Amiard, and B. Goffinet, *Bull. Soc. Chim. France*, 1341 (1955).
49. L. Velluz, G. Amiard, and B. Goffinet, *Compt. Rend.*, *240*, 2326 (1955).
50. E. Havinga, A. L. Koevoet, and A. Verloop, *Rec. Trav. Chim.*, *74*, 1230 (1955).
51. L. Verloop, G. Amiard, and B. Goffinet, *Compt. Rend.*, *240*, 2156 (1955).
52. A. Verloop, A. L. Koevoet, and E. Havinga, *Rec. Trav. Chim.*, *76*, 689 (1957).
53. M. P. Rappoldt, J. A. K. Buisman, and E. Havinga, *Rec. Trav. Chim.*, *77*, 327 (1958).
54. M. P. Rappoldt, *Rec. Trav. Chim.*, *79*, 392 (1960).
55. M. P. Rappoldt and E. Havinga, *Rec. Trav. Chim.*, *79*, 369 (1960).
56. M. P. Rappoldt, *Rec. Trav. Chim.*, *79*, 1012 (1960).

from a reversible photochemical side reaction of pre-ergocalciferol. The quantum yield in the reversible photochemical conversion of pre-ergocalciferol to tachysterol$_2$ is especially high during irradiation with ultra-

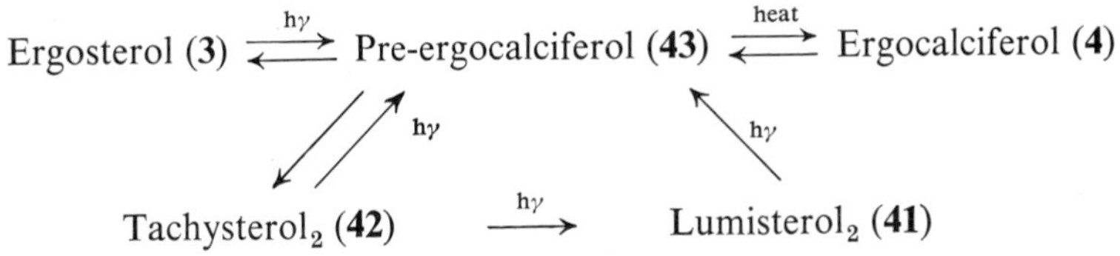

Ergosterol (**3**) $\underset{}{\overset{h\gamma}{\rightleftharpoons}}$ Pre-ergocalciferol (**43**) $\overset{heat}{\rightleftharpoons}$ Ergocalciferol (**4**)

Tachysterol$_2$ (**42**) $\overset{h\gamma}{\longrightarrow}$ Lumisterol$_2$ (**41**)

Fig. 4. The main and side reactions in the irradiation of ergosterol to ergocalciferol.[48,56]

violet light at a wavelength of 254 mμ;[55] tachysterol$_2$ is not formed from ergosterol but originates exclusively from pre-ergocalciferol. The origin of lumisterol$_2$ is less certain, but it appears to be formed irreversibly from tachysterol$_2$ and is converted exclusively and irreversibly to pre-ergocalciferol.[55,56]

C. Over-Irradiation Products

Over-irradiation of ergosterol yields biologically inactive products. These irradiation products of ergocalciferol are designated toxisterol$_2$, suprasterol$_2$I and suprasterol$_2$II.[57] It is assumed[58] that toxisterol$_2$ is

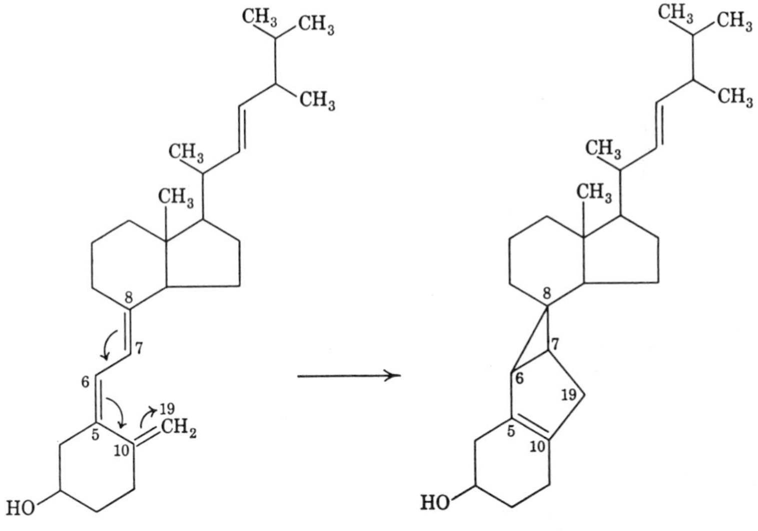

(**44**)

57. A. Windaus, I. Gaede, J. Köser, and G. Stein, *Ann.*, *483*, 17 (1930).
58. C. E. Bills, *Physiol. Revs.*, *15*, 1 (1935).

formed prior to the suprasterols$_2$ and that the suprasterols arise by ring closure of the conjugated triene system.[59]

The structure of suprasterol$_2$II was assigned on the basis of nuclear magnetic resonance, ultraviolet, and infrared spectra of suprasterol$_2$II, dihydrosuprasterol$_2$II, tetrahydrosuprasterol$_2$II, and their oxidation products.[60] Suprasterol$_2$II is depicted as the 8-*spiro*-pentacyclic compound (**44**) containing a 6,8-cyclopropane ring in conjugation with the tetra-substituted 5,10-double bond. The formation of the compound is visualized as arising from the migration of electrons in the conjugated triene system, followed by condensation between the 6- and 8-positions and the 7- and 19-positions.

7. Thermally-Induced Isomerization of Ergocalciferol

The biologically inactive isomers pyro-ergocalciferol (**45**) and isopyro-ergocalciferol (**46**) are obtained by heating ergocalciferol at 190° in the absence of air.[61] Early structural studies indicated that these compounds

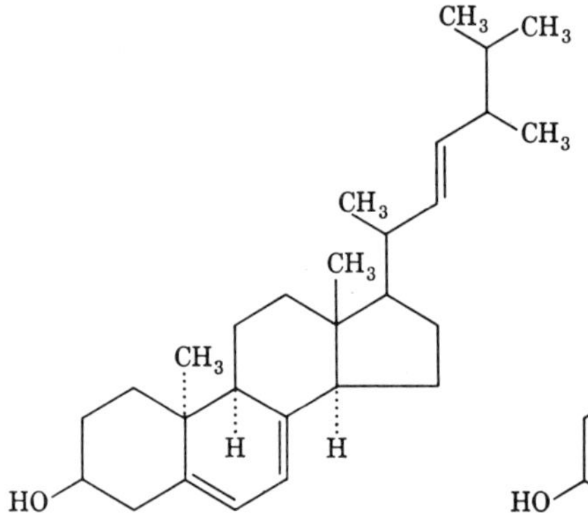

(**45**) 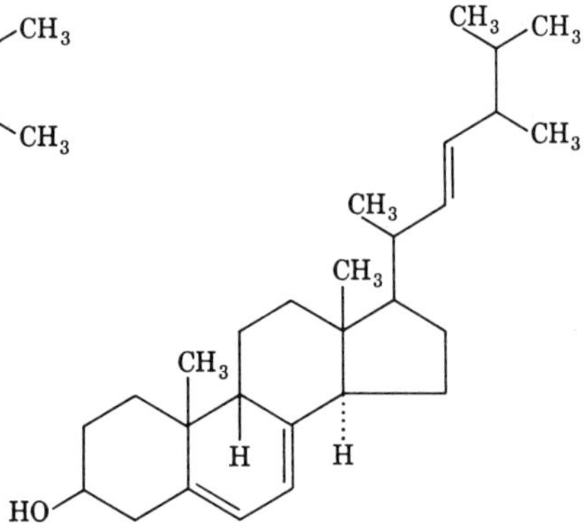 (**46**)

were tetracyclic 5,7,22-trienols which were isomeric with ergosterol and lumisterol$_2$.[62–64] On the basis of more recent studies,[42,43] pyro-ergo-calciferol was shown to have the 9(α)-H,10(α)-CH_3 configuration (**45**) and

59. H. Muller, *Z. Physiol. Chem.*, *233*, 223 (1935).
60. W. G. Dauben, I. Bell, T. W. Hutton, G. F. Laws, A. Rheiner, Jr., and H. Urscheler, *J. Am. Chem. Soc.*, *80*, 4117 (1958).
61. P. Busse, *Z. Physiol. Chem.*, *214*, 211 (1933).
62. K. Dimroth, *Ber.*, *69*, 1123 (1936).
63. A. Windaus and K. Dimroth, *Ber.*, *70*, 376 (1937).
64. T. Kennedy and F. S. Spring, *J. Chem. Soc.*, 250 (1939).

is designated 9(α)-lumisterol$_2$; isopyro-ergocalciferol has the 9(β)-H,10(β)-CH_3 configuration (**46**) and is referred to as 9(β)-ergosterol.

8. The Vitamin D Group

There are about ten provitamins which on irradiation yield compounds having antirachitic activity. All of the vitamins are 3(β)-hydroxy-9,10-*seco*-5,7,10(19)-triene derivatives (**2**) which differ only in the nature of the C-17 side chain. The various side chains of the vitamins showing antirachitic properties are represented by (**2a–2f**).[65]

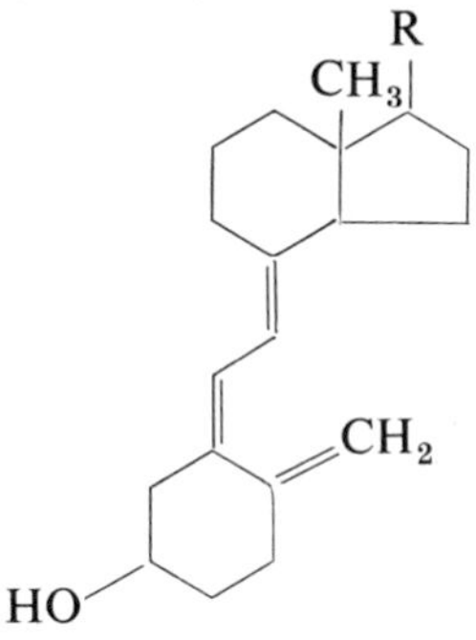

R, CH_3, CH_2, HO

(**2**)

Vitamin D_2 (**2a**) $R = CH(CH_3)CH{=}CHCH(CH_3)CH(CH_3)_2$

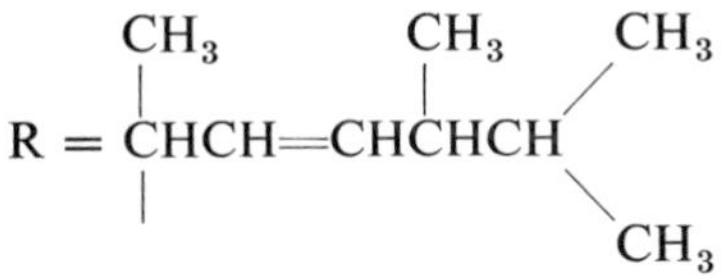

Vitamin D_3 (**2b**) $R = CH(CH_3)CH_2CH_2CH_2CH(CH_3)_2$

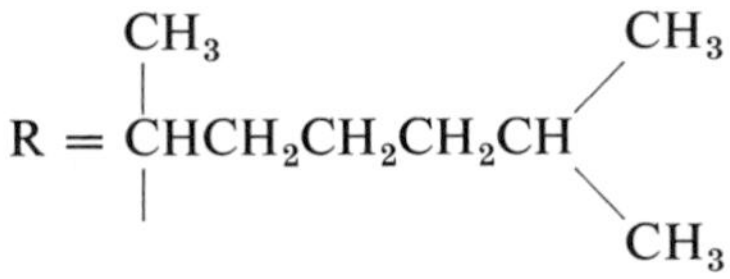

Vitamin D_4 (**2c**) $R = CH(CH_3)CH_2CH_2\overset{*}{C}H(CH_3)CH(CH_3)_2$

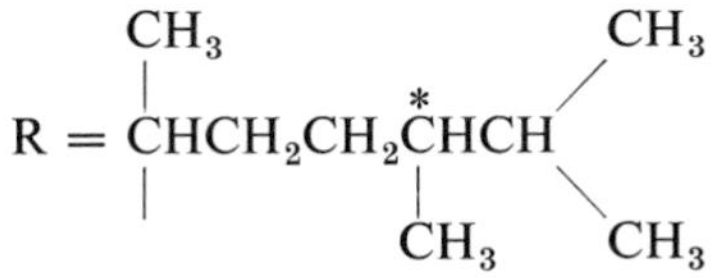

65. H. H. Inhoffen and K. Brückner, *Fortschr. Chem. Organ. Naturstoffe*, *11*, 93 (1954).

Vitamin D_5 (2d)

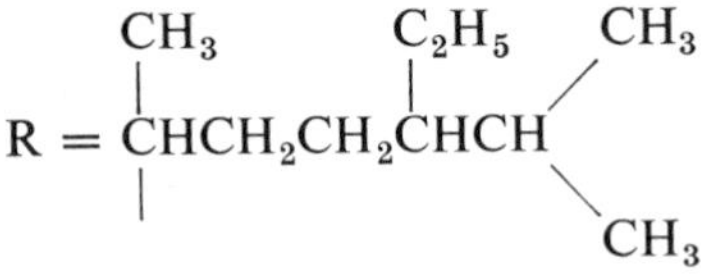

$$R = \underset{|}{\overset{CH_3}{\overset{|}{C}}}HCH_2CH_2\overset{C_2H_5}{\overset{|}{C}}HCH\begin{matrix} CH_3 \\ CH_3 \end{matrix}$$

Vitamin D_6 (2e)

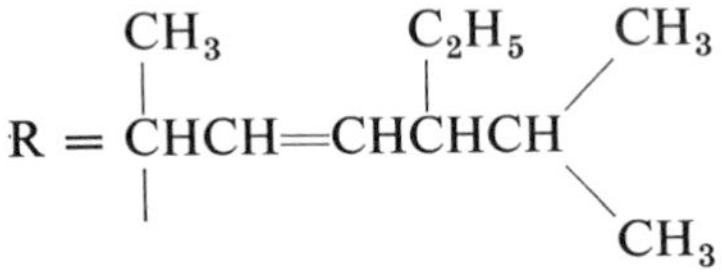

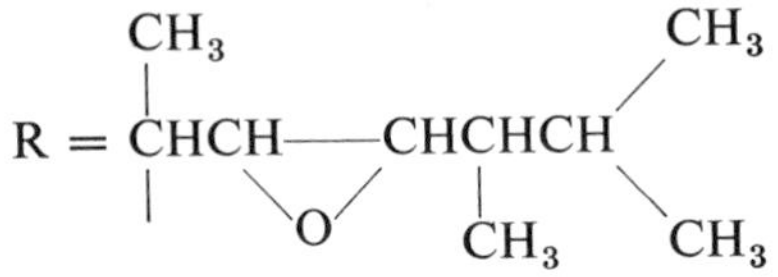

$$R = \underset{|}{\overset{CH_3}{\overset{|}{C}}}HCH{=}CH\overset{C_2H_5}{\overset{|}{C}}HCH\begin{matrix} CH_3 \\ CH_3 \end{matrix}$$

$$R = \underset{|}{\overset{CH_3}{\overset{|}{C}}}HCH\underset{O}{\text{——}}CH\underset{CH_3}{\underset{|}{C}}HCH\begin{matrix} CH_3 \\ CH_3 \end{matrix}$$

Vitamin D_7 (2f)

$$R = \underset{|}{\overset{CH_3}{\overset{|}{C}}}HCH_2CH_2\underset{*}{\overset{CH_3}{\overset{|}{C}}}HCH\begin{matrix} CH_3 \\ CH_3 \end{matrix}$$

$$R = \underset{|}{\overset{CH_3}{\overset{|}{C}}}HCH_2CH_2CH_2CH_2CH_3$$

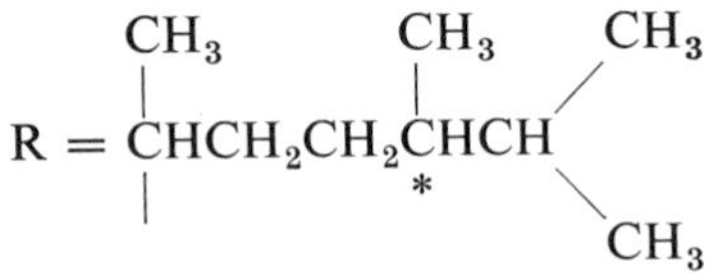

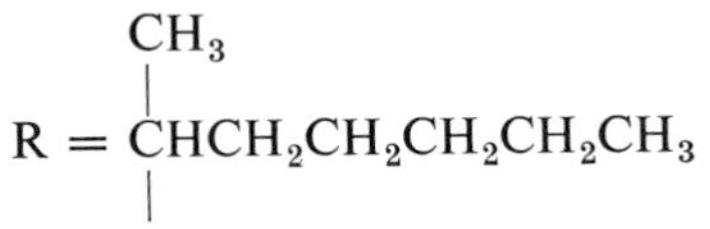

Commercial production of the D-vitamins has been restricted to ergocalciferol and cholecalciferol.[66] Prior to the availability of synthetic vitamin A, the early commercial procedures for the concentration of fish liver oils were especially important for the preparation of both the A- and D-vitamins. Since 1950, however, this method has lost its commercial advantage as a source of vitamin D.

Milk and related consumer products are fortified with the D-vitamins by irradiation. Enrichment is also accomplished by either subjecting the cow to irradiation in its stall or by feeding the animal irradiated foods such as yeast. Milk from irradiated cows is rich in cholecalciferol; milk from cows fed irradiated yeast is rich in ergocalciferol.

In general the enrichment of food with the D-vitamins is accomplished by adding natural or synthetic vitamin D concentrates to consumer products. The synthetic concentrates are prepared from either ergosterol or 7-dehydrocholesterol by irradiating ether solutions of the provitamins in the absence of air or in the presence of stabilizers. The irradiation

66. C. E. Bills, in W. H. Sebrell, Jr. and R. S. Harris, eds., *The Vitamins: Chemistry, Physiology, and Pathology*, Vol. II, Academic, N.Y., 1954, p. 210.

process is terminated when the conversion to vitamin D is fifty per cent of the theoretical yield; this arbitrary conversion point was chosen to eliminate the accumulation of tachysterols. The synthetic irradiation mixtures are purified by precipitating the unconverted provitamin from solution, and the purified product is then refined by any of a number of methods.

9. Metabolic Role

Vitamin D participates in metabolic processes associated with bone growth and development. The process of bone formation may be visualized as follows.[67] Normal growing cartilage bone is characterized by two zones, an epiphyseal or growing zone and diaphyseal or developing zone. As a first step in ossification, cartilage cells in the diaphyseal zone begin to degenerate. As the degeneration of cartilaginous cells continues, some cells disappear, and the matrix is invaded by capillaries and bone-forming cells which are designated osteoblasts. The osteoblasts, in turn, induce the mineralization of the cartilage matrix; under normal conditions the calcium and phosphorus complexes in the surrounding plasma and tissue fluids are precipitated, and the matrix is ossified by the deposition of a mineral that is structurally related to the apatite minerals. In the absence of vitamin D, an excessive amount of osteoid tissue is present since the soft organic matrix between the degenerated cartilage cells and the bone is not mineralized.

Some investigators have shown that vitamin D influences the concentration of calcium and inorganic phosphate in the plasma and have concluded that this is the primary role of the vitamin in bone metabolism. Others have considered these to be secondary metabolic effects of the vitamin and have suggested a primary role for vitamin D in the actual process of calcifying osteoid tissue. Although a precise definition of the primary role of the vitamin has not been established, the direct participation of the vitamin in the precipitation process has not been demonstrated. Among the physiological processes known to be influenced by vitamin D are: the intestinal absorption of calcium, the retention of phosphate, the conversion of organic to inorganic phosphate, and the oxidation of citrate.

The effect of vitamin D on the absorption of calcium from the digestive tract has been demonstrated in rats and chicks. In the rachitic rat, vitamin

67. B. Kramer and A. Kanof, in W. H. Sebrell, Jr. and R. S. Harris, eds., *The Vitamins: Chemistry, Physiology, and Pathology*, Vol. II, Academic, N.Y., 1954, p. 232.

D increased the absorption of orally administered radioactive calcium from the intestine.[68] It has been suggested that the absorption of calcium from the proximal region of the small intestine is rapid and independent of vitamin D, and that the effect of the vitamin in promoting the absorption of calcium from the distal portion of the small intestine and from the large intestine may be observed only when the calcium is in a slightly soluble form.[69] In the chick, vitamin D promotes the rate of absorption of calcium from the intestine and the deposition of calcium in bone when the mineral is administered orally.[70,71] However, there was no apparent difference in calcium deposition in the skeletons of normal and rachitic chicks when radioactive calcium was injected intramuscularly. These data would indicate a primary role for the vitamin in calcium transport rather than in the mineralization reaction, but the data must be evaluated critically since the concentration of radioactive calcium in the skeleton is not simply a function of "true" physiological accretion. In six- to eight-week-old rats for example, exchange between the calcium in bone and in the plasma phase is rapid; the time necessary for fifty per cent of the exchangeable calcium in the skeleton to exchange with serum calcium has been estimated to be 45–65 hours.[72]

Phosphate is another important constituent of bone; in the serum it occurs as organic and inorganic phosphate, but in bone it occurs primarily as mineral complexes of $Ca_3(PO_4)_2$. Vitamin D exerts an influence on phosphate metabolism. In the deficiency state the phosphate content of serum is reduced; administration of vitamin D decreases the excretion of phosphate.[73] The influence of the vitamin on phosphate metabolism was studied by the oral administration of radioactive phosphate to rats.[74] The net absorption of phosphate from the intestine and the transfer of phosphate from the blood to the organic fraction of bone was independent of vitamin D. The most pronounced effect of the vitamin on phosphate metabolism was evident in bone, and it was suggested that the vitamin functions in the ossification process by converting organic phosphate in the bone to inorganic phosphate. Consequently, the influence of vitamin D in promoting the retention of ingested phosphate may be regarded as a result of this conversion rather than a direct result of increased absorption.

68. D. M. Greenberg, *J. Biol. Chem.*, *157*, 99 (1945).
69. H. E. Harrison and H. C. Harrison, *J. Biol. Chem.*, *188*, 83 (1951).
70. B. B. Migicovsky and J. W. S. Jamieson, *Can. J. Biochem. Physiol.*, *33*, 202 (1955).
71. K. W. Keane, R. A. Collins, and M. B. Gillis, *Poultry Sci.*, *35*, 1216 (1956).
72. H. E. Harrison and H. C. Harrison, *J. Biol. Chem.*, *185*, 857 (1950).
73. A. F. Hess and M. G. Gutman, *J. Am. Med. Assoc.*, *78*, 29 (1922).
74. W. E. Cohn and D. M. Greenberg, *J. Biol. Chem.*, *130*, 625 (1939).

The effect of the vitamin on citrate metabolism has also been considered in conjunction with studies of the role of vitamin D in bone metabolism. Citric acid is a major constituent of normal bone, and it has been estimated that 70% of the total citric acid content of the body is in the skeleton.[75] This fact, plus the observed increases[76,77] in the citrate concentration of serum produced by the administration of vitamin D, led some investigators to suspect that the role of the vitamin in the mineralization process might be exerted through its effect on citrate metabolism. The rate of solubilization of calcium and the regulation of the calcium ion concentration by complex formation would vary with the concentration of citrate, which in turn would be regulated by vitamin D. It was shown, however, that the antirachitic activity of the vitamin is not related to its effect on citrate metabolism. In one investigation with rachitic rats,[78] a cortical hormone (cortisol) was used in conjunction with vitamin D; the hormone effectively counteracted the effect of the vitamin on citrate metabolism, but the antirachitic activity of the vitamin was not suppressed. In another study with rats, it was shown that the oxidation of citrate and isocitrate by kidney homogenates and mitochondria was severely reduced when vitamin D was added to the diet of the test animals.[79–81] Since the metabolic effect appeared to result from physical rather than enzymic inhibition,[82] and electron microscopy revealed that the structural integrity of the mitochondria was related to the vitamin D content of the animal's diet,[83] the effect of the vitamin on citrate metabolism was assumed to be indirect. A deficiency of vitamin D produces morphologically damaged mitochondria in which the oxidation of citrate is enhanced by easy access to the oxidation site; on the other hand, the maintenance of normal mitochondria by vitamin D favors decreased oxidation of citrate since access to the oxidation site is relatively restricted.

Some consideration has been given to the hypothesis that a deficiency of vitamin D, or an unknown factor, produces a primary lesion in osteoid

75. F. Dickens, *Biochem. J.*, *35*, 1011 (1941).
76. R. Nicolaysen and R. Nordbø, *Acta Physiol. Scand.*, *5*, 212 (1943).
77. H. C. Harrison and H. E. Harrison, *Yale J. Biol. Med.*, *24*, 273 (1952).
78. H. C. Harrison, H. E. Harrison, and E. A. Park, *Proc. Soc. Exptl. Biol. Med.*, *96*, 768 (1957).
79. H. F. DeLuca, F. C. Gran, and H. Steenbock, *J. Biol. Chem.*, *224*, 201 (1957).
80. H. F. DeLuca, F. C. Gran, H. Steenbock, and S. Reiser, *J. Biol. Chem.*, *228*, 469 (1957).
81. H. F. DeLuca and H. Steenbock, *Science*, *126*, 258 (1957).
82. H. F. DeLuca, S. Reiser, and H. Steenbock, *Federation Proc.*, *18*, 212 (1959).
83. H. F. DeLuca, S. Reiser, H. Steenbock, and P. Kaesberg, *Biochim. et Biophys. Acta*, *40*, 526 (1960).

tissue which prevents calcification even in the presence of adequate concentrations of calcium and phosphate, but recent data[84,85] do not support this concept. For example, *in vivo* studies have shown that the calcification of rachitic osteoid transplants occurs in rats on a normal diet, but not in rats on a rachitogenic diet.[84] Furthermore, *in vitro* studies showed that mineralization occurs with rachitic tissue in the sera of normal animals and also in the sera of rachitic animals after the addition of inorganic phosphate.[84] In another study,[85] it was shown that completely demineralized tibial bone ends from normal and rachitic rats induced mineralization with the same efficiency in an inorganic solution containing "normal" concentrations of calcium and phosphate. Since the structural integrity of the collagen in the matrix is important for inducing crystallization, it would appear that the vitamin deficiency does not produce a primary lesion at this phase of the cellular mechanism for mineralization.

10. Nutritional and Therapeutic Role

A. In Animals

The syndrome associated with a deficiency of vitamin D varies with the species; when the same metabolic areas are affected, it may be more severe in one species than in another. The avitaminosis may be induced in cattle, dogs, pigs, and poultry by feeding diets deficient in the D-vitamins. Rodents do not usually develop the classical rickets syndrome on a diet deficient in vitamin D, but the use of such diets which also contain a disproportionate amount of either calcium or phosphorus will produce rickets in the rat.

The pathology of a vitamin D deficiency in animals is most evident in bone.[86,87] Skeletal malformation and decreased growth are considered to be the primary manifestations of the deficiency syndrome. Other symptoms of the deficiency state such as decreased concentrations of calcium and phosphorus in the blood and serum, and an increase in the concentration of phosphatase appear in most species, but the intensity of the metabolic defect varies with each species.

84. M. Burger, L. S. Lavine, B. C. Deane, and A. E. Sobel, *Proc. Soc. Exptl. Biol. Med.*, *96*, 147 (1957).
85. M. Lamm and W. F. Neuman, *A.M.A. Arch. Pathol.*, *66*, 204 (1958).
86. H. R. Rosenberg, *Chemistry and Physiology of the Vitamins*, Interscience, N.Y., 1945, p. 419.
87. J. H. Jones, in W. H. Sebrell, Jr. and R. S. Harris, eds., *The Vitamins: Chemistry, Physiology, and Pathology*, Vol. II, Academic, N.Y., 1954, p. 223.

The administration of excessively large doses of vitamin D to animals produces a hypervitaminosis syndrome characterized by the resorption of bone salts and abnormal deposition of calcium in the viscera.[88,89] The resorption of calcium salts is the first effect of an overdose (e.g., 300,000–600,000 I.U.); this process renders the bones brittle and may ultimately lead to deformity and fracture. Smooth muscle is particularly susceptible to abnormal calcium deposition; the pathological sequence usually proceeds in the order: inflammation, cellular degeneration, and finally, calcification. Abnormal calcium deposits are commonly found in the vascular system, urinary tract, and the respiratory tract.

B. In the Human

A vitamin D deficiency in the human leads to rickets which is usually observed clinically during the first year of life.[90] Retarded growth and skeletal deformities characterized by enlarged junctions between bone and cartilage, and curvature of the bones are typical signs of the avitaminosis syndrome. In severe cases of rickets, the muscular tissue is weakened, and the host is particularly susceptible to infection.

A deficiency of both vitamin D and calcium in the adult diet results in the demineralization of bone and produces symptoms identical to those of the rickets of infancy. The syndrome is designated osteomalacia and is particularly evident in women during pregnancy.

A hypervitaminosis syndrome may be induced in the human by overdoses of vitamin D (e.g., 100,000 I.U. daily for the adult and 40,000 I.U. daily for the child).[90] The effects are reversible, however, if vitamin D is withdrawn in time. The syndrome is characterized by loss of appetite, nausea, excessive urinary excretion, and thirst. The calcium and phosphorus levels of serum and urine are increased, partly as a result of the demineralization of bone, and calcium may be deposited in the heart, lungs, kidneys, and other soft tissue.

An average daily dietary consumption of 400 I. U. of vitamin D (0.01 mg. of ergocalciferol or cholecalciferol) is considered adequate for the average normal infant, growing child, and adult.[91] Although calcium and phosphorus requirements are increased during pregnancy and lactation, the

88. G. M. Hass, R. E. Trueheart, C. B. Taylor, and M. Stumpe, *Am. J. Pathol.*, *34*, 395 (1958).
89. G. M. Hass, R. E. Trueheart, and A. Hemmens, *Am. J. Pathol.*, *37*, 521 (1960).
90. B. M. Kagan, in M. G. Wohl and R. S. Goodhardt, eds., *Modern Nutrition in Health and Disease*, 2nd Ed., Lea and Febiger, Philadelphia, 1960, p. 310.
91. *Recommended Dietary Allowances*, Natl. Acad. Sci., Natl. Res. Council Publication, 589, Washington, D.C., 1958, p. 16.

administration of vitamin D in excess of 400 I.U. appears to cause no further retention of these elements. Many adults are apparently able to rely on incidental sources of vitamin D such as sunshine and normal food consumption for an adequate supply of the vitamin.

The most abundant animal sources of vitamin D are the liver and viscera of certain fishes. Marginal dietary sources include the liver and milk of mammals and the liver and eggs of fowl. The provitamins are generously distributed throughout the Plant and Animal Kingdoms.

CHAPTER XVIII

The Vitamin E Group

1. Introduction

The first publications on the existence of an antisterility vitamin appeared in 1922. These studies showed that a full-term pregnancy in the rat is rare if the animal is subsisting solely on a diet containing purified protein, fat, carbohydrate, adequate minerals, and known growth factors.[1,2] The deficient diet affected the fertility of both male and female rats.[1,3] A pronounced atrophy of reproductive organs was apparent in the male rat, and although the animal was not always sterile, his progeny seldom survived long after birth. In the female rat, the dietary deficiency impaired a placental rather than an ovarian function, and the reproductive failure was characterized by resorption of the fetus rather than failure to conceive.

The addition of a small quantity of yeast[2] or fresh lettuce[1] to the purified diet restored fertility to the test animal. On the basis of this observation, it was postulated that certain natural foods contain a dietary factor, designated then as Factor X, which is essential for reproduction.[1] Further dietary studies with dried alfalfa, wheat, oats, meat, and milk fat showed that these materials were also sources of Factor X.[4] These initial observations were confirmed,[5] and it was suggested that the new factor be designated vitamin E rather than Factor X. Since the new factor was extracted from natural sources by organic solvents, the new vitamin was classified as a fat-soluble vitamin.[6]

As studies on the isolation of pure vitamin E neared completion, it became apparent that more than one naturally occurring compound prevented the gestation-resorption syndrome induced in rats by a vitamin E deficiency, and it was suggested that this group of naturally

1. H. M. Evans and K. S. Bishop, *Science*, *56*, 650 (1922).
2. H. A. Matill, *J. Biol. Chem.*, *50*, xliv (1922).
3. H. A. Matill and N. C. Stone, *J. Biol. Chem.*, *55*, 443 (1923).
4. H. M. Evans and K. S. Bishop, *J. Metabol. Research*, *1*, 319, 335 (1922); *3*, 201 (1923).
5. B. Sure, *J. Biol. Chem.*, *58*, 693 (1924).
6. B. Sure, *J. Biol. Chem.*, *62*, 397 (1924); *63*, 211 (1925).

occurring compounds be designated with a generic name.[7] The term tocopherol derived from the Greek words *tokos* (childbirth) and *phero* (to bear) was adopted, and the individual compounds of this series were designated by adding Greek alphabetical prefixes to the generic name. To date eight tocopherols have been isolated from wheat germ oil, soybean oil, and rice oil. Six have a saturated isoprenoid side chain and two have an unsaturated isoprenoid side chain. They vary significantly in biological activity.

2. Isolation

In the early procedures for the isolation of the tocopherols, a natural oil was saponified and then fractionated by precipitation of impurities, chromatography, and finally purification of the factor as a crystalline allophanate. In later studies, improved yields of certain tocopherols were obtained by omitting the saponification step and subjecting the starting material to chromatography or molecular distillation as the first step in the purification process.

Pure α-tocopherol was isolated by the following procedure.[7] Wheat germ oil was saponified by refluxing the natural material with potassium hydroxide in anhydrous methanol solution. The saponification was accomplished in an inert atmosphere, and highly purified air-free solvents were used to prevent decomposition of the active compound by oxidation. The reaction mixture was poured into air-free water, and the nonsaponifiable fraction was extracted by ether. This fraction was partially purified by precipitating the accompanying sterols from petroleum benzin solution. The filtrate was concentrated and washed with small volumes of 92% methanol to remove xanthophylls and other inert materials. The vitamin was extracted from petroleum benzin solution by methanol saturated with petroleum benzin; on cooling the lower phase, further precipitation of accompanying sterols occurred. The extractives were then dissolved in 90% ethanol and remaining sterols were removed by precipitation with digitonin.

The purified sterol-free oil was dissolved in benzene, and the solution was saturated with cyanic acid. After several days the reaction was complete, and the precipitate was filtered and washed with hot benzene to dissolve the desired allophanates. The mixture of allophanates was partially purified by crystallization from methanol, and the oily crystalline material was dissolved in acetone. The allophanate of β-amyrin precipitated from this solution and was separated by filtration. The acetone

7. H. M. Evans, O. H. Emerson, and G. A. Emerson, *J. Biol. Chem.*, *113*, 319 (1936).

filtrate was concentrated, and the residue was dissolved in hot methanol. The allophanate of α-tocopherol precipitated on cooling and was purified by several recrystallizations from methanol.

Pure α-tocopheryl allophanate was hydrolyzed in an inert atmosphere with 4% methanolic potassium hydroxide; the reaction mixture was diluted with water, and α-tocopherol was extracted with peroxide-free ether. Pure α-tocopherol was obtained as a viscous oil.

The existence of multiple forms of vitamin E was apparent before pure α-tocopherol was finally isolated from wheat germ oil. During this investigation, the methanolic mother liquor from the first purification of the allophanate mixture was allowed to stand at 0° for several weeks, and the allophanate of a second tocopherol slowly precipitated. Hydrolysis of this derivative yielded β-tocopherol.[7] Although this compound was active in preventing the gestation-resorption syndrome in the deficient rat, it appeared to be less active than α-tocopherol.[8]

The saponification and fractionation of other natural oils yielded additional new compounds having vitamin E activity. For example, γ-tocopherol was isolated from cottonseed oil;[8] this natural oil contains both α- and γ-tocopherol.

The fractionation of soybean oil yielded a fourth compound designated δ-tocopherol.[9] This member of the tocopherol group constitutes some 30% of the mixed tocopherols found in soybean oil and 5% of those found in wheat germ oil. Molecular distillation of soybean oil yielded a mixture of the α-, γ-, and δ-tocopherols, which was saponified and freed from α-tocopherol by selective adsorption. When the mixture of γ- and δ-isomers was converted to a mixture of the corresponding palmitates, γ-tocopheryl palmitate was isolated selectively by fractional crystallization. The partially purified δ-tocopheryl palmitate was then hydrolyzed, and δ-tocopherol was purified by chromatography.

Four more naturally occurring tocopherols have been detected in natural oils by paper chromatography and partition chromatography. When wheat germ oil was saponified and the nonsaponifiable fraction was partially purified by chromatography on activated fuller's earth, a fifth compound designated ε-tocopherol was detected on paper chromatographs of the eluate.[10] Wheat germ oil is a relatively poor source of ε-tocopherol, so a sufficient quantity of the new compound was not isolated for

8. O. H. Emerson, G. A. Emerson, A. Mohammad, and H. M. Evans, *J. Biol. Chem.*, *122*, 99 (1937).
9. H. M. Stern, C. D. Robeson, L. Weisler, and J. G. Baxter, *J. Am. Chem. Soc.*, *69*, 869 (1947).
10. P. W. R. Eggitt and L. D. Ward, *J. Sci. Food. Agr.*, *4*, 569 (1953).

identification. However, the oil from bran (coarse wheatfeed) is rich in this isomer; the application of reverse phase paper chromatography to the analysis of this oil confirmed the existence of ε-tocopherol and provided a method for its isolation.[11]

Two-dimensional paper chromatographic analyses of natural oils resulted in the detection of the sixth, seventh, and eighth tocopherols. When the oil from coarse wheatfeed (bran) was subjected to two-dimensional paper chromatography, first along an area of the paper impregnated with zinc carbonate and then by partition along an area of paraffin coated paper, a new isomer designated ζ-tocopherol was identified.[12] It appeared that the same isomer was also present in an extract of rice, but later studies showed that the ζ-tocopherol from wheat bran was not the same as the ζ-tocopherol from rice. The compounds are now designated ζ_1- and ζ_2-tocopherol, respectively.

A two-dimensional chromatographic analysis of the nonsaponifiable portion from an extract of ground whole rice showed the presence of three tocopherol isomers. Two were identified as α- and ζ_2-tocopherol, and the third behaved like ε-tocopherol. However, this substance, similar to ε-tocopherol on the papergram, gave a color reaction which differentiated it from ε-tocopherol. This observation constituted the discovery of the eighth tocopherol which is designated η-tocopherol.[13]

3. Structure Determination

A. α-Tocopherol

The structure of α-tocopherol was established as 2,5,7,8-tetramethyl-2-(4,8,12-trimethyltridecyl)-6-chromanol (**1**) on the basis of degradation and synthesis.

The identity of the aromatic moiety of α-tocopherol was established by

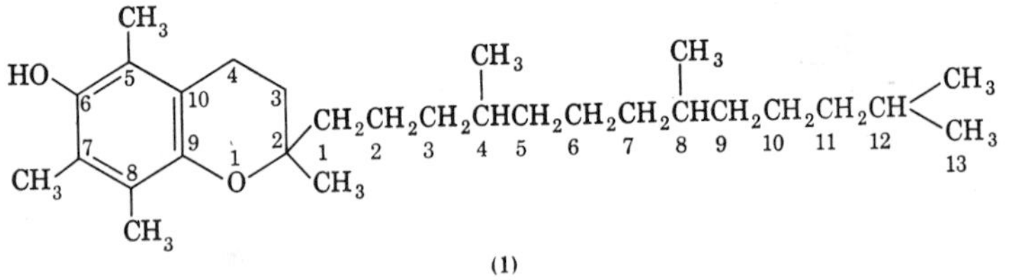

(1)

11. P. W. R. Eggitt and F. W. Norris, *J. Sci. Food Agr.*, *6*, 689 (1955).
12. J. Green, S. Marcinkiewicz, and P. R. Watt, *J. Sci. Food Agr.*, *6*, 274 (1955).
13. J. Green and S. Marcinkiewicz, *Nature*, *177*, 86 (1956).

thermal degradation. Pyrolysis of α-tocopherol at 350° yielded durohydroquinone (**2**) in yields up to 67%.[14] A hydrocarbon fraction with the approximate composition $C_{19}H_{36}$ was also obtained from the thermal cleavage reaction.

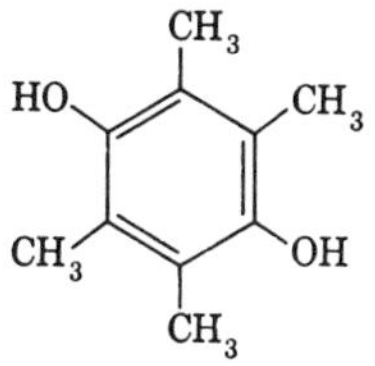

$$\text{HO}-C_6(CH_3)_4-\text{OH}$$

(2)

On the basis of these early degradation data, it was postulated that α-tocopherol might be a simple mono-ether of durohydroquinone and the C_{19}-hydrocarbon.[14] This early assumption was abandoned, however, on the basis of the following data.[15] A series of mono-ethers of durohydroquinone ranging from butyl through nonadecyl were synthesized, and their properties were compared with those of α-tocopherol. The ultraviolet absorption spectra of these model mono-ethers differed significantly from the spectrum of α-tocopherol; in the 280–300 mμ region of the spectrum, the absorption maxima of the model compounds were consistently at a shorter wavelength and of lesser intensity than the maximum of α-tocopherol. The behavior of the mono-ethers toward silver nitrate also differentiated them from α-tocopherol. The model compounds reduced a silver nitrate solution slowly and were oxidized to duroquinone; α-tocopherol reacted rapidly with this reagent, but the molecular weight of the oxidation product was of the same order as α-tocopherol. Furthermore, duroquinone was not isolated from the reaction mixture. These observations provided the first indication that the hydrocarbon moiety of the vitamin was linked to the aromatic moiety through both an ether and a carbon–carbon linkage. Support for this interpretation was obtained with the observation that mono-ethers of durohydroquinone were cleaved by the common ether cleaving reagents, whereas the same reagents failed to yield durohydroquinone from α-tocopherol.

The nature of the cyclic ether moiety and the alkyl side chain of α-tocopherol was established by chromic acid oxidation;[15] mild oxidation of α-tocopherol yielded dimethylmaleic anhydride, presumably from the durohydroquinone moiety, and a C_{21}-lactone. The lactone was converted

14. E. Fernholz, *J. Am. Chem. Soc.*, *59*, 1154 (1937).
15. E. Fernholz, *J. Am. Chem. Soc.*, *60*, 700 (1938).

to a hydroxy acid that lactonized readily on acidification. On the basis of this behavior, the lactone was assumed to be derived from either a γ- or δ-hydroxy acid.

The C_{21}-lactone was formulated as a γ-lactone on the basis of the following considerations. The lactone is derived from the aliphatic portion of the cyclic ether. Therefore, the formation of its carboxyl group may be visualized through the oxidation of the aromatic carbon atom which is linked directly to the aliphatic moiety, and its hydroxyl group may be considered as being derived from the oxygen atom of the cyclic ether function in the vitamin. On this basis, formulation of the C_{21}-lactone as a δ-lactone would imply the presence of a 7-membered ring in the vitamin. Since this formulation was considered unlikely, the lactone and corresponding hydroxy acid were formulated as γ-hydroxy derivatives.

The C_{21}-lactone was converted to the methyl ester of the corresponding γ-hydroxy acid. The hydroxyl group of this derivative could not be esterified and was stable to chromic acid oxidation. Consequently, it was assumed that the γ-hydroxyl function was tertiary.

Before further assignments could be made in the structure of the C_{21}-lactone, data were needed to determine the nature of the alkyl substituents at the γ-position. These data were obtained by more drastic oxidation of α-tocopherol with chromic acid. Oxidation of α-tocopherol with chromic acid in boiling acetic acid gave diacetyl, presumably from the benzo moiety, acetone, and a C_{16}-acid. Analyses led to the formula $C_{16}H_{32}O_2$ for the acid, and *C*-methyl determinations indicated the presence of three *C*-methyl groups. On the basis of these data, the alkyl moiety of the C_{16}-acid was visualized as three recurring saturated isoprene units, and the C_{16}-acid was formulated as 4,8,12-trimethyltridecanoic acid (**3**).

$$HOOC(CH_2CH_2\overset{\displaystyle CH_3}{\overset{|}{C}}HCH_2)_2CH_2CH_2CH(CH_3)_2$$

(**3**)

The C_{16}-acid is formally derived from the C_{21}-lactone by oxidation. Since four of the carbon atoms of the C_{21}-lactone are in the lactone ring, and sixteen carbon atoms are accounted for as a γ-alkyl substituent that would yield the C_{16}-acid (**3**) on oxidation, the placement of a methyl group on the lactone ring would complete the structural assignments for the C_{21}-γ-lactone and C_{21}-γ-hydroxy acid. Only one formulation was compatible with all the data, and the structures of the C_{21}-lactone and hydroxy acid were established as 4-methyl-4-(4,8,12-trimethyltridecyl)butyrolactone (**4**) and 4-hydroxy-4,8,12,16-tetramethylheptadecanoic acid (**5**).

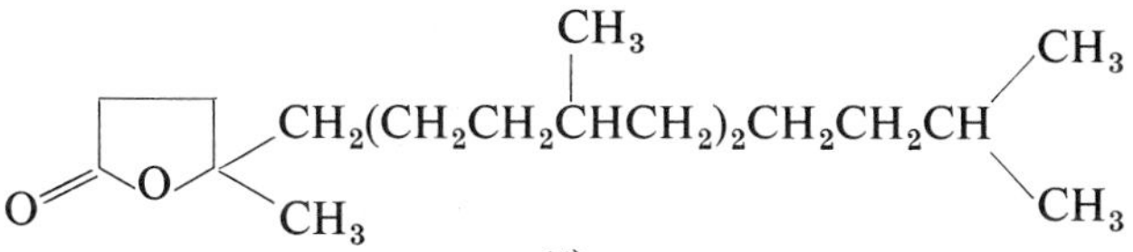

$$\text{(lactone ring, O=C–O)}\!-\!C(CH_3)\,CH_2(CH_2CH_2\overset{CH_3}{\overset{|}{C}}HCH_2)_2CH_2CH_2CH(CH_3)_2$$

(4)

$$HOOCCH_2CH_2\underset{OH}{\overset{CH_3}{C}}-CH_2(CH_2CH_2\overset{CH_3}{\overset{|}{C}}HCH_2)_2CH_2CH_2CH(CH_3)_2$$

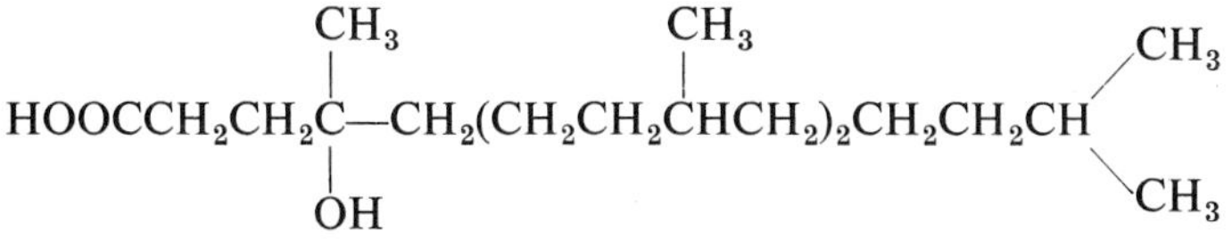

(5)

When the structures of these C_{21}-oxidation products of α-tocopherol were established, α-tocopherol was formulated as (**1**); this structure was confirmed by synthesis.

B. β-, γ-, and δ-Tocopherol

The structures of β-, γ-, and δ-tocopherol were derived from degradation reactions similar to those applied to α-tocopherol. Except for the products derived from the aromatic moiety, the degradation products were the same as those obtained from α-tocopherol. Pyrolysis of β-tocopherol yielded 2,3,6-trimethylhydroquinone (pseudocumo-hydroquinone);[16,17] γ-tocopherol was thermally cleaved to 2,3,6-trimethylhydroquinone,[18] and δ-tocopherol was pyrolyzed to 2,6-dimethylhydroquinone.[9]

After the completion of the structural studies on α-, β-, γ-, and δ-tocopherols, it was apparent that all of these compounds could be considered as methylated derivatives of the hypothetical parent compound, 2-methyl-2-(4,8,12-trimethyltridecyl)-6-chromanol (**6**), and that they differed from each other solely in the number and position of the methyl substituents on the benzo moiety of the chroman nucleus. The parent unsubstituted compound (**6**) was synthesized from hydroquinone and

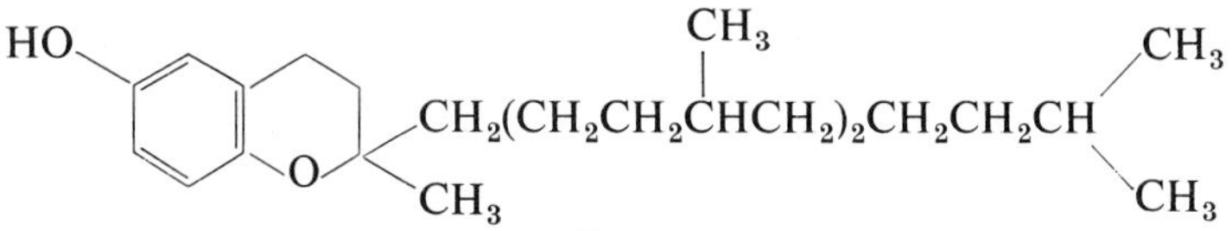

$$\text{HO–(chroman ring, O)}\!-\!C(CH_3)\,CH_2(CH_2CH_2\overset{CH_3}{\overset{|}{C}}HCH_2)_2CH_2CH_2CH(CH_3)_2$$

Tocol

(6)

16. W. John, *Z. Physiol. Chem.*, *250*, 11 (1937).
17. F. Bergel, A. R. Todd, and T. S. Work, *J. Chem. Soc.*, 253 (1938).
18. O. H. Emerson and L. I. Smith, *J. Am. Chem. Soc.*, *62*, 1869 (1942).

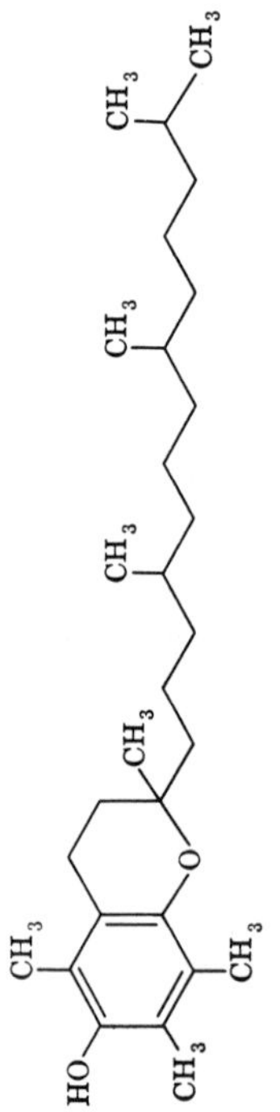

α-Tocopherol
(5,7,8-Trimethyltocol)

(1)

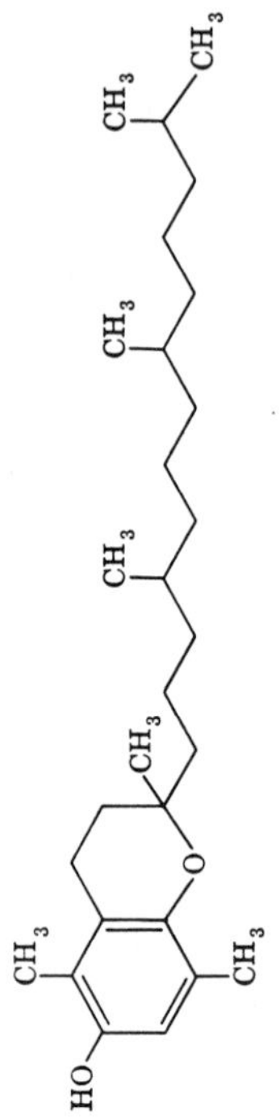

β-Tocopherol
(5,8-Dimethyltocol)

(7)

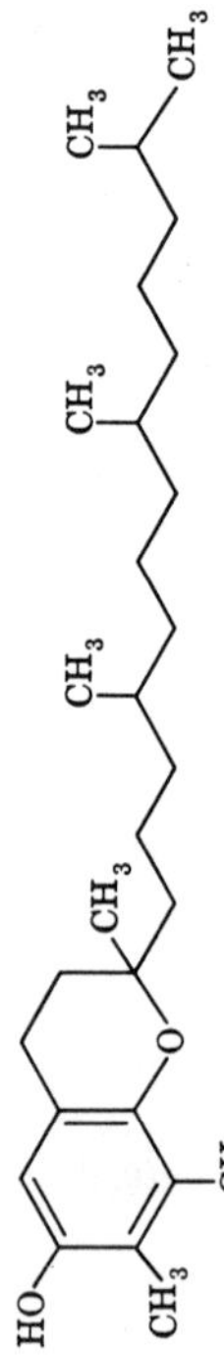

γ-Tocopherol
(7,8-Dimethyltocol)

(8)

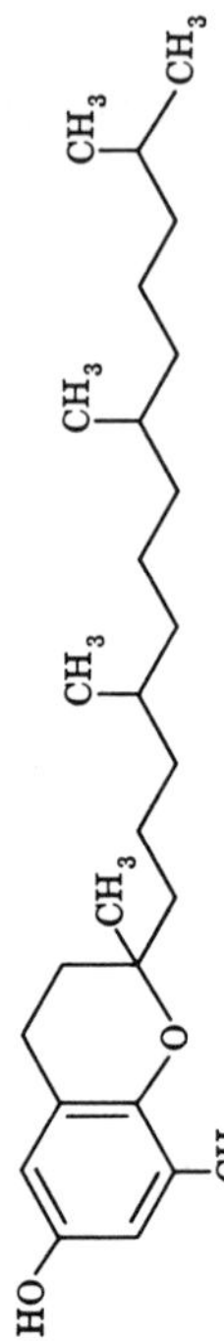

δ-Tocopherol
(8-Methyltocol)

(9)

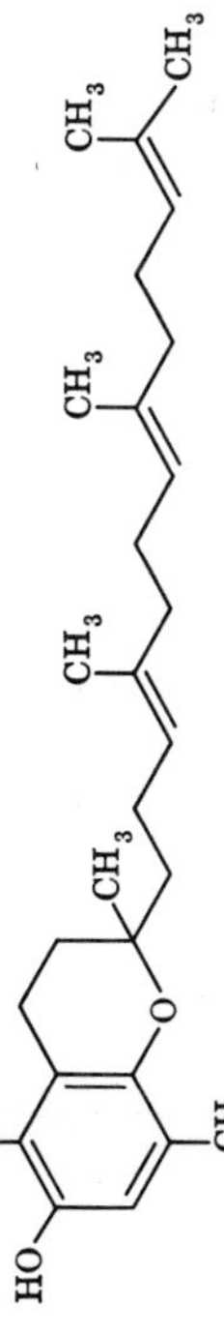

ϵ-Tocopherol

(10)

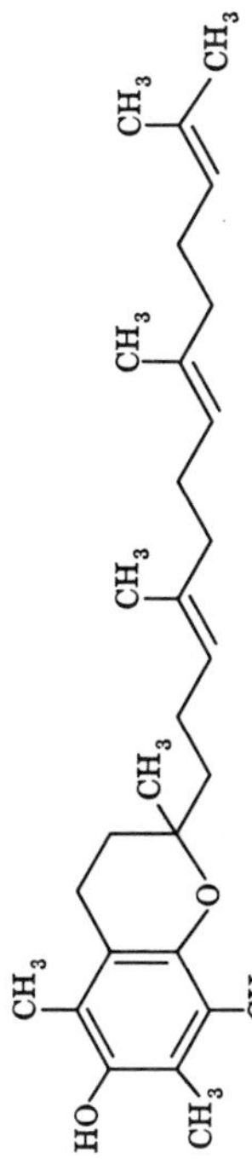

ζ_1-Tocopherol

(11)

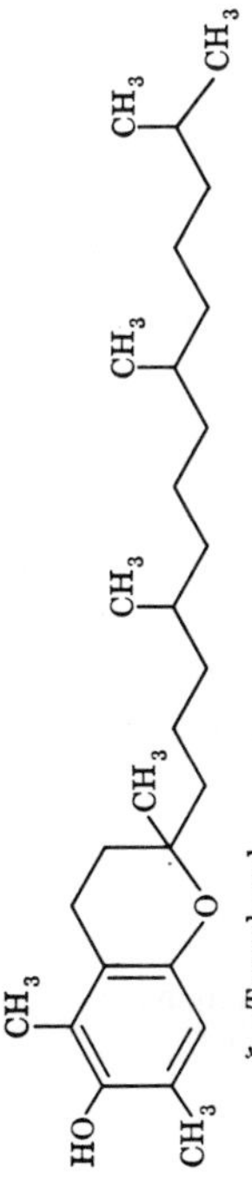

ζ_2-Tocopherol
(5,7-Dimethyltocol)

(12)

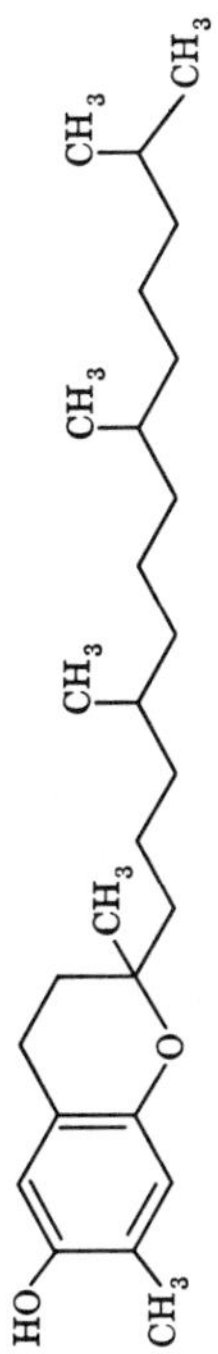

η-Tocopherol
(7-Methyltocol)

(13)

Fig. 1. The naturally occurring tocopherols.

phytol and was designated tocol.[19] Since then, six naturally occurring tocopherols (Fig. 1) have been designated as derivatives of tocol; by this nomenclature, α-tocopherol is 5,7,8-trimethyltocol (**1**); β-tocopherol is 5,8-dimethyltocol (**7**); γ-tocopherol is 7,8-dimethyltocol (**8**); and δ-tocopherol is 8-methyltocol (**9**). These compounds account for four of the seven possible mono-, di-, and trimethyl derivatives of tocol. Two of the three remaining methyltocol derivatives were eventually accounted for by ζ_2- and η-tocopherol.

C. ε-, ζ_1-, ζ_2-, and η-Tocopherol

The structures 5-methyltocol and 5,7-dimethyltocol were incorrectly assigned[10,12] to ε- and ζ_1-tocopherol on the basis of partition chromatography and two-dimensional paper chromatography which was based on adsorption along one axis and then partition along the other. The presence of a 5-methyl substituent in each compound was confirmed since neither compound reacted with *o*-anisidine. The latter reagent is especially useful since only tocopherols unsubstituted at the 5-position will couple with *o*-anisidine.

The structure originally assigned to ε-tocopherol was found to be incorrect after an authentic synthetic sample of 5-methyltocol (**14**) was obtained.[20] On the basis of chromatographic evidence and coupling

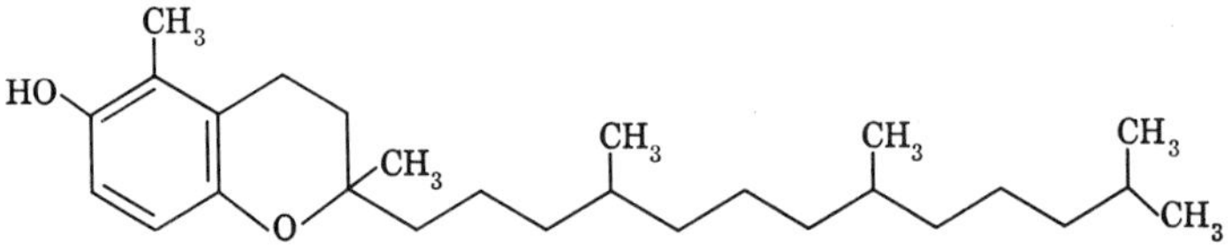

5-Methyltocol
(by synthesis only)

(14)

reactions, synthetic 5-methyltocol was different from ε-tocopherol, and it appeared that ε-tocopherol is a 5,8-disubstituted chromanol with unsaturation in the C_{16}-substituent. Further study established the structure of ε-tocopherol as 2,5,8-trimethyl-2-(4,8,12-trimethyltrideca-3,7,11-trienyl)-6-chromanol (**10**).[21] When ε-tocopherol and model compounds were chromatographed, the natural product migrated in a manner expected of a chromanol containing two methyl substituents on the benzo moiety and

19. P. Karrer and H. Fritzsche, *Helv. Chim. Acta*, *21*, 1234 (1938).
20. J. Green, D. McHale, S. Marcinkiewicz, P. Mamalis, and P. R. Watt, *J. Chem. Soc.*, 3362 (1959).
21. J. Green, P. Mamalis, S. Marcinkiewicz, and D. McHale, *Chem. & Ind.* (*London*), 73 (1960).

three aliphatic double bonds. Catalytic reduction of ε-tocopherol resulted in the facile consumption of hydrogen equivalent to three double bonds, and the reduced product was identified as β-tocopherol. According to the nuclear magnetic resonance spectra of ε-tocopherol and its 4-phenylazobenzoate, the molecule contains three olefinic hydrogen atoms, one aromatic hydrogen atom, two nonequivalent aromatic methyl substituents, a methyl group on the carbon atom adjacent to the oxygen atom of the chroman ring, and a side chain containing three isoprene units. Furthermore, ozonization and reductive cleavage of ε-tocopheryl acetate yielded acetone and levulinaldehyde. The geometrical isomerism of the side chain is unknown, but an *all-trans* configuration has been suggested on the basis of the infrared spectrum.

Two naturally occurring tocopherols had been designated ζ-tocopherol; the one isolated from palm oil and wheat bran is now designated ζ_1-tocopherol, and the other occurring in rice is designated ζ_2-tocopherol.[20] Since ζ_1-tocopherol was isolated with ε-tocopherol from wheat, it was suspected that the formula originally assigned to ζ_1-tocopherol was also in error. On the basis of the conversion of ε-tocopherol to ζ_1-tocopherol by methylation, ζ_1-tocopherol is designated as 2,5,7,8-tetramethyl-2-(4,8,12-trimethyltrideca-3,7,11-trienyl)-6-chromanol (**11**).[21] The structure 5,7-dimethyltocol (**12**), however, is valid for ζ_2-tocopherol.[21]

The structure 7-methyltocol was assigned[13] to η-tocopherol (**13**) on the basis of two-dimensional adsorption and partition chromatography on paper, a positive reaction with *o*-anisidine, and the conversion of η-tocopherol to a mixture of α- and ζ_2-tocopherol by methylation.

4. Synthesis

A. α-Tocopherol

The structure established for α-tocopherol by degradation was confirmed by synthesis.[22] Synthetic α-tocopherol was prepared by the condensation of trimethylhydroquinone (**15**) with phytyl bromide (**16**) in

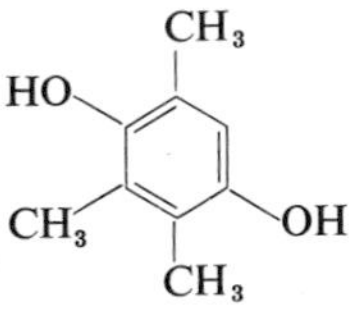

HO, OH, CH_3, CH_3, CH_3 (benzene ring)

(**15**)

$BrCH_2CH{=}C(CH_3)CH_2(CH_2CH_2CHCH_3CH_2)_2CH_2CH_2CH(CH_3)_2$

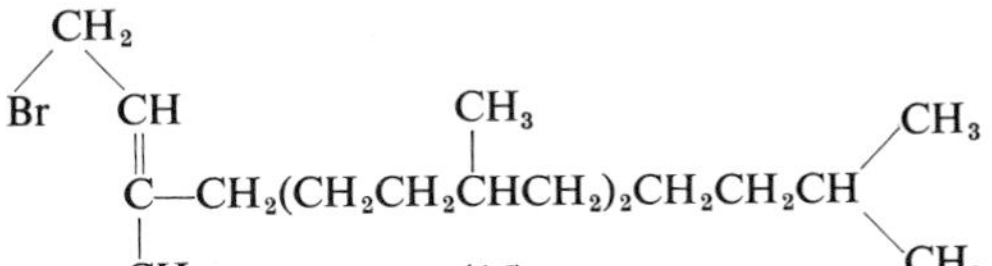

(**16**)

22. P. Karrer, H. Fritzsche, B. H. Ringier, and H. Salomon, *Helv. Chim. Acta*, *21*, 520 (1938).

the presence of anhydrous zinc chloride. The nitrophenylurethane derivative of the synthetic product appeared to be identical with that derived from the natural product, but the allophanate of the synthetic product melted at a higher temperature, and the 2,4-dinitrobenzoate of the synthetic product melted at a lower temperature than the corresponding derivatives of naturally occurring α-tocopherol. Two conclusions were considered on the basis of these observations. Firstly, the synthetic material might be a mixture of the two diastereoisomers which are epimeric at the 2-position. Secondly, during cyclization the aromatic hydroxyl group of the intermediate (**17**) might have added across the allylic system so that the final condensation product could be the substituted coumaran (**18**) instead of the desired chromanol (**1**). On further investigation, the biological activity

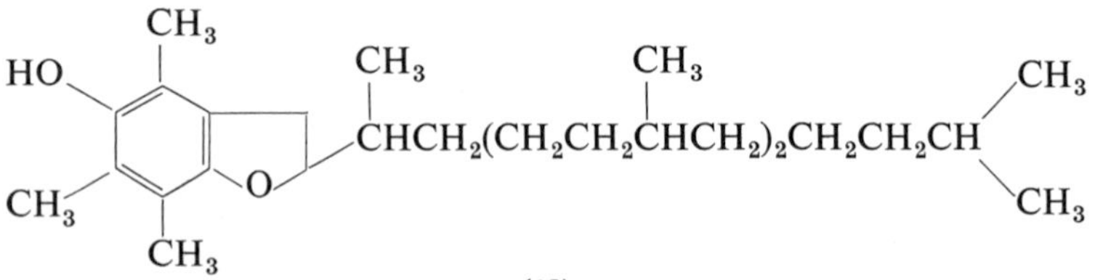

HO, CH_3, CH_3, CH_3, O, CH_3, CH_3, CH_3, CH_3

$CHCH_2(CH_2CH_2CHCH_2)_2CH_2CH_2CH$

(18)

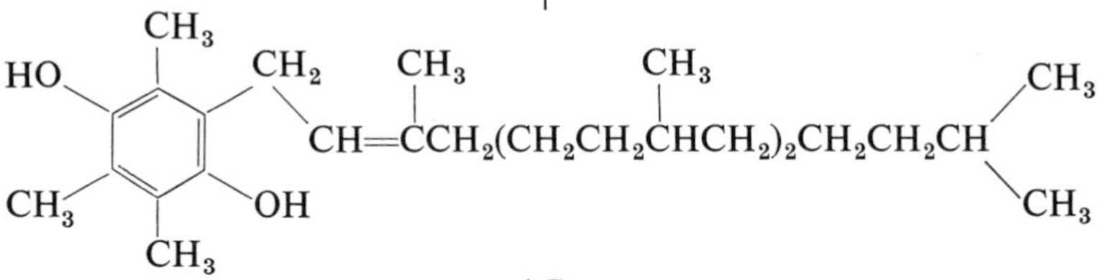

↑

HO, CH_3, CH_3, CH_3, OH, CH_2, CH_3, CH_3, CH_3, CH_3

$CH{=}CCH_2(CH_2CH_2CHCH_2)_2CH_2CH_2CH$

(17)

↓

HO, CH_3, CH_3, CH_3, O, CH_3, CH_3, CH_3, CH_3

$CH_2(CH_2CH_2CHCH_2)_2CH_2CH_2CH$

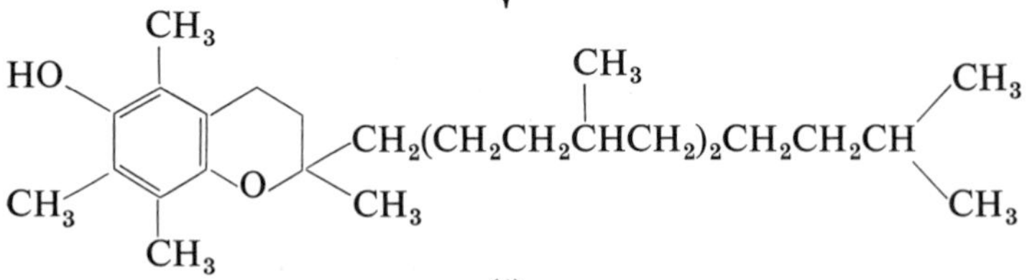

(1)

of the synthetic product appeared to be about one-half that of α-tocopherol from nature.[23] In addition, treatment of the synthetic product with

23. P. Karrer, H. Fritzsche, B. H. Ringier, and H. Salomon, *Helv. Chim. Acta*, *21*, 820 (1938).

3-bromo-(+)-camphorsulfonyl chloride yielded the dextrorotatory diastereoisomer of α-tocopheryl 3-bromo-(+)-camphorsulfonate which was identical with that derived from naturally occurring α-tocopherol. From these data, it appeared that the synthetic material was a mixture of two diastereoisomers, one of which corresponded to the naturally occurring form of α-tocopherol.

The uncertainty concerning the mode of addition of the aromatic hydroxyl group to the allylic system in the intermediate (**17**) was based on the fact that phenols condense with unsubstituted allyl halides to yield coumarans. However, it was shown that trimethylhydroquinone condenses with either γ,γ-dimethylallyl bromide or isoprene to yield a chroman.[24] By analogy, phytyl bromide is a γ,γ-disubstituted allyl bromide which reacts with trimethylhydroquinone to yield a chroman. On this basis the synthesis of α-tocopherol from trimethylhydroquinone and phytyl bromide constituted confirmation of the structure derived by degradation.

When phytol and its derivatives were not readily available in commercial quantities, the synthesis (Fig. 2) of α-tocopherol from citral (**19**) was studied;[25] the yield of α-tocopherol in this synthesis is 5%.

B. The Dimethyltocols

For the synthesis of β-, γ-, and ζ_2-tocopherol, the corresponding dimethylhydroquinone was condensed with phytol rather than with phytyl bromide.[26] If phytyl bromide was used, a side reaction occurred between two equivalents of phytyl bromide and one equivalent of the hydroquinone to yield benzodipyran derivatives, and mixtures of the tocopherols and these derivatives were obtained. Such mixtures were difficult to purify. The 5,8-, 7,8-, and 5,7-dimethyltocols (β-, γ-, and ζ_2-tocopherol) prepared from the reaction of phytol with the corresponding dimethylhydroquinone were usually purified easily by chromatography.

C. The Monomethyltocols

Although 2,3,5-trimethylhydroquinone and the three dimethylhydroquinones condense with phytol to yield in each case only one tocol, the reaction of 2-methylhydroquinone with phytol will theoretically yield 5-, 7-, and 8-methyltocol. In practice a mixture of all three isomers has been obtained.[27] To circumvent this difficulty, several alternative syntheses have been designed for the preparation of the individual monomethyltocols.

24. L. I. Smith, H. E. Unganade, and W. W. Prichard, *Science*, *88*, 37 (1938).
25. L. I. Smith and J. A. Sprung, *J. Am. Chem. Soc.*, *65*, 1276 (1943).
26. P. Karrer and H. Fritzsche, *Helv. Chim. Acta*, *21*, 1234 (1938).
27. S. Marcinkiewicz, D. McHale, P. Mamalis, and J. Green, *J. Chem. Soc.*, 3377 (1959).

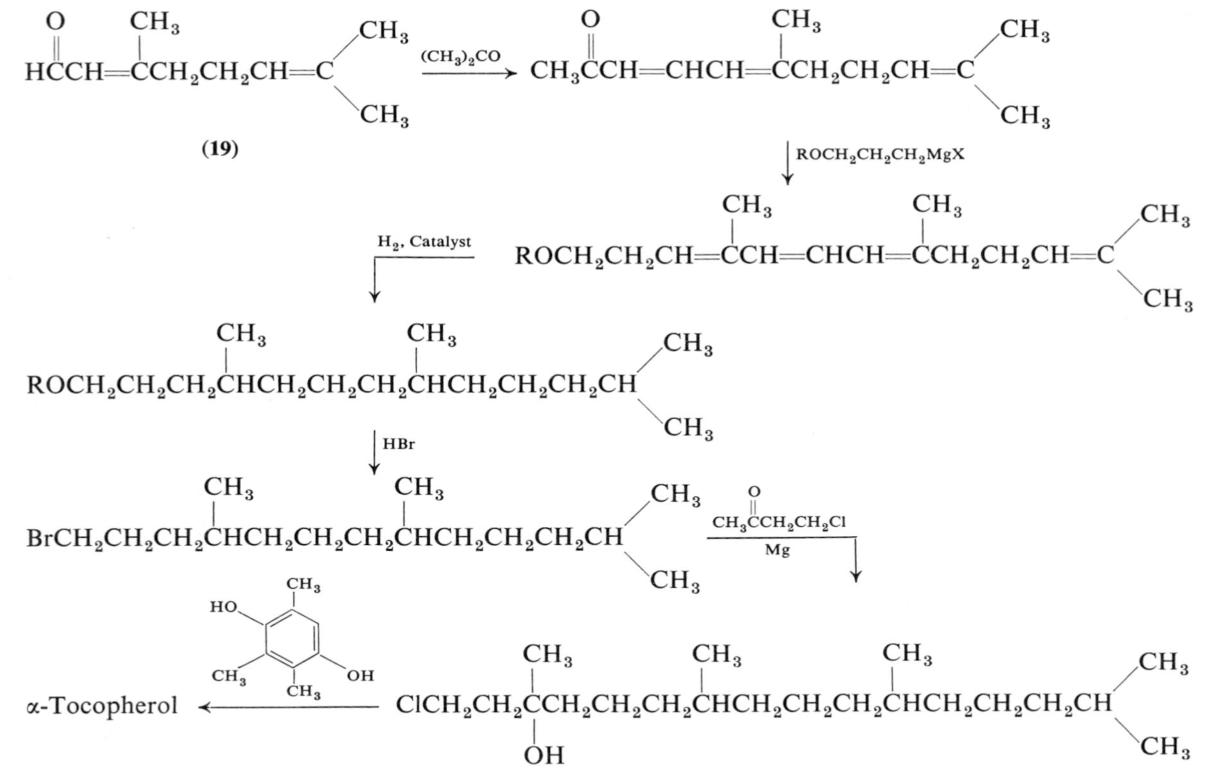

Fig. 2. Synthesis of α-tocopherol from citral.[25]

1. 8-METHYLTOCOL (δ-TOCOPHEROL). The condensation of 2-methylhydroquinone 4-benzoate (**20**) with phytol yields 8-methyltocol.[28,29] Although the synthetic product is free from the 5- and 7-isomers, the yield is poor and the purification is difficult.

C_6H_5CO (O) ... OH ... CH_3 + Phytol ⟶ 8-Methyltocol

(**20**)

In an improved synthesis of 8-methyltocol from 5-bromo-2-methylhydroquinone, the 5-position is protected by a sulfur-containing substituent, and alkylation at the 6-position is favored after esterification of the 4-hydroxyl group.[30] 5-Bromo-2-methylhydroquinone (**21**) was converted to the corresponding 5-mercapto derivative (**22**), which in turn was alkylated with chloroacetic acid to yield 5-carboxymethylthio-2-methylhydroquinone (**23**). The intermediate (**23**) was cyclized thermally to yield 6-hydroxy-7-methyl-2-oxo-1,4-benzoxathiin (**24**). Condensation of this

Br, HO, OH, CH_3 (**21**) $\xrightarrow{Na_2S}$ SH, HO, OH, CH_3 (**22**) $\xrightarrow{ClCH_2COOH}$

HOOC, CH_2, S, HO, OH, CH_3 (**23**) $\xrightarrow{180°}$ O, S, O, OH, CH_3 (**24**) $\xrightarrow{HOCH_2CH=C(CH_3)-CH_2(CH_2CH_2CH(CH_3)CH_2)_3H}$

28. A. Jacob, F. K. Sutcliffe, and A. R. Todd, *J. Chem. Soc.*, 327 (1940).
29. P. Mamalis, J. Green, S. Marcinkiewicz, and D. McHale, *J. Chem. Soc.*, 3350 (1959).
30. J. Green, D. McHale, P. Mamalis, and S. Marcinkiewicz, *J. Chem. Soc.*, 3374 (1959).

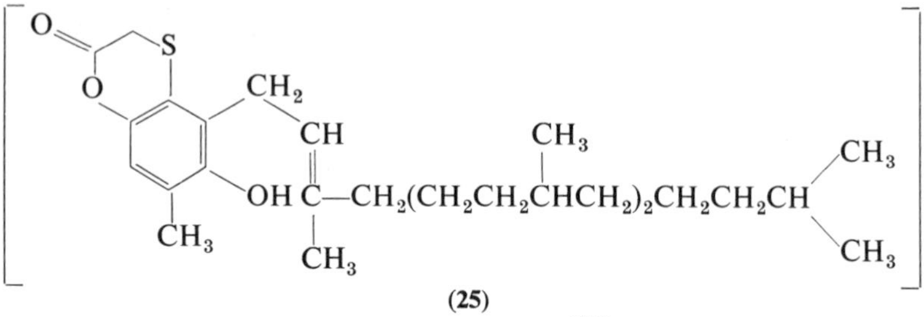

O, S, O, CH_2, CH, CH_3, CH_3, OH C—$CH_2(CH_2CH_2CHCH_2)_2CH_2CH_2CH$, CH_3, CH_3, CH_3

(**25**)

HO, CH_3, CH_3

1. Raney Ni
2. OH^-

$\longrightarrow$ $CH_2(CH_2CH_2CHCH_2)_2CH_2CH_2CH$, O, CH_3, CH_3, CH_3

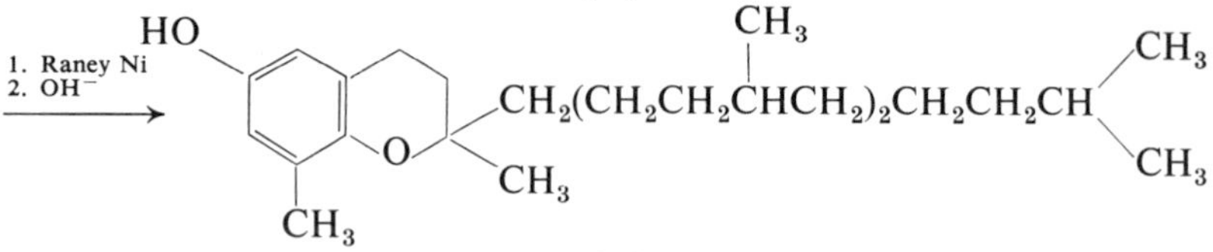

8-Methyltocol
(**9**)

product with phytol yielded the intermediate (**25**) which was not isolated. Cyclization of the condensation product, followed by desulfurization with Raney nickel and then hydrolysis yielded a mixture containing 20% 8-methyltocol (**9**); pure 8-methyltocol was isolated after chromatography and molecular distillation.

2. 5-METHYLTOCOL. Pure 5-methyltocol was synthesized from 2,3-dimethylhydroquinone (**26**) which was first converted to the corresponding dimethyl ether (**27**).[31] Bromination with *N*-bromosuccinamide yielded 3-bromomethyl-2-methylhydroquinone dimethyl ether (**28**); this intermediate was converted to the corresponding nitrile (**29**), which in turn was hydrolyzed and then esterified to yield 3-(carbomethoxymethyl)-2-methylhydroquinone dimethyl ether (**30**). Reduction of the ester moiety in the intermediate (**30**) by lithium aluminum hydride yielded 3-(β-hydroxyethyl)-2-methylhydroquinone dimethyl ether (**31**) which was brominated to 3-(β-bromoethyl)-2-methylhydroquinone dimethyl ether (**32**). The bromo intermediate (**32**) was converted to the corresponding Grignard reagent which was condensed with the ketone (**33**) derived from phytol by oxidation. The reaction product was demethylated and cyclized to yield a mixture containing 14% 5-methyltocol (**14**); pure 5-methyltocol was obtained after chromatography and molecular distillation.

3. 7-METHYLTOCOL (η-TOCOPHEROL). The synthesis of 7-methyltocol also proceeds from 5-bromo-2-methylhydroquinone (**21**).[32] This hydroquinone

31. D. McHale, P. Mamalis, S. Marcinkiewicz, and J. Green, *J. Chem. Soc.*, 3358 (1959).
32. D. McHale, P. Mamalis, J. Green, and S. Marcinkiewicz, *J. Chem. Soc.*, 1600 (1958).

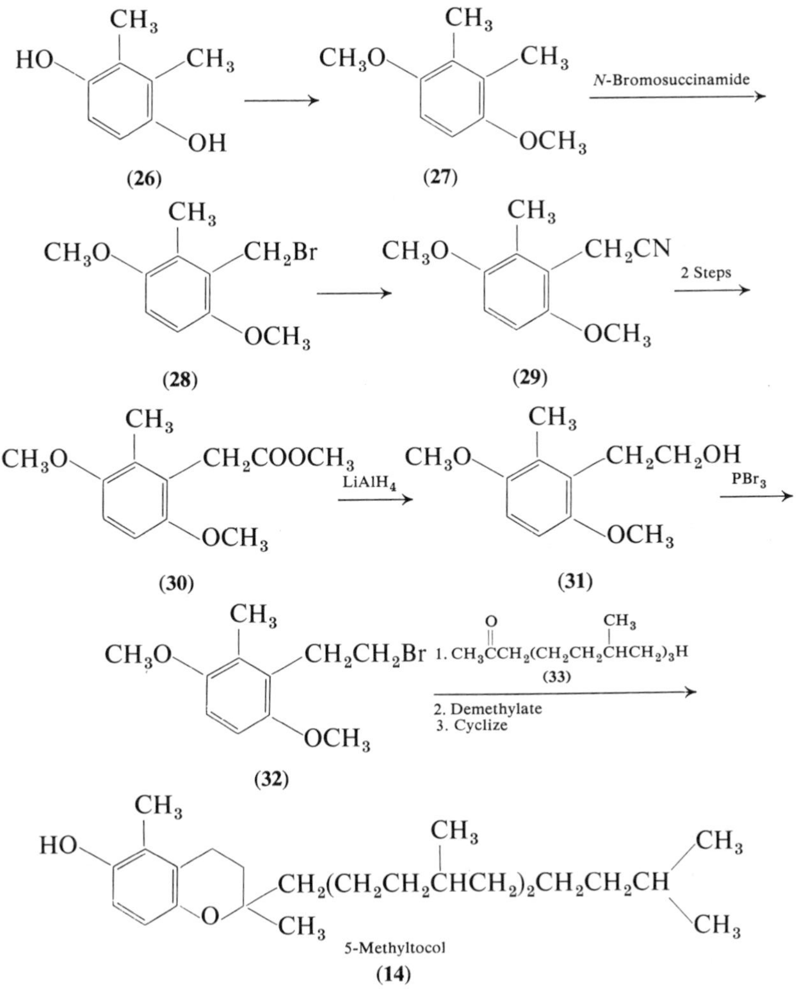

CH_3 / HO / CH_3 / OH **(26)** ⟶ CH_3 / CH_3O / CH_3 / OCH_3 **(27)** $\xrightarrow{N\text{-Bromosuccinamide}}$

CH_3 / CH_3O / CH_2Br / OCH_3 **(28)** ⟶ CH_3 / CH_3O / CH_2CN / OCH_3 **(29)** $\xrightarrow{\text{2 Steps}}$

CH_3 / CH_3O / CH_2COOCH_3 / OCH_3 **(30)** $\xrightarrow{LiAlH_4}$ CH_3 / CH_3O / CH_2CH_2OH / OCH_3 **(31)** $\xrightarrow{PBr_3}$

CH_3 / CH_3O / CH_2CH_2Br / OCH_3 **(32)**

1. $CH_3\overset{O}{\overset{\|}{C}}CH_2(CH_2CH_2\overset{CH_3}{\overset{|}{C}}HCH_2)_3H$ (33)
2. Demethylate
3. Cyclize

CH_3 / HO / O / CH_3 / $CH_2(CH_2CH_2\overset{CH_3}{\overset{|}{C}}HCH_2)_2CH_2CH_2CH(CH_3)_2$

5-Methyltocol
(14)

was converted to the corresponding dimethyl ether (**34**) and then to the Grignard reagent (**35**). The reaction of ethylene oxide with the Grignard intermediate yielded 5-(β-hydroxyethyl)-2-methylhydroquinone dimethyl ether (**36**) which was converted to 5-(β-bromoethyl)-2-methylhydroquinone dimethyl ether (**37**). The Grignard derivative of (**37**) was condensed with the ketone (**33**) which is derived from phytol by oxidation. The resulting condensation product was demethylated and then cyclized to yield a mixture containing approximately 30% 7-methyltocol (**13**). Pure 7-methyltocol was obtained after molecular distillation, chromatography,

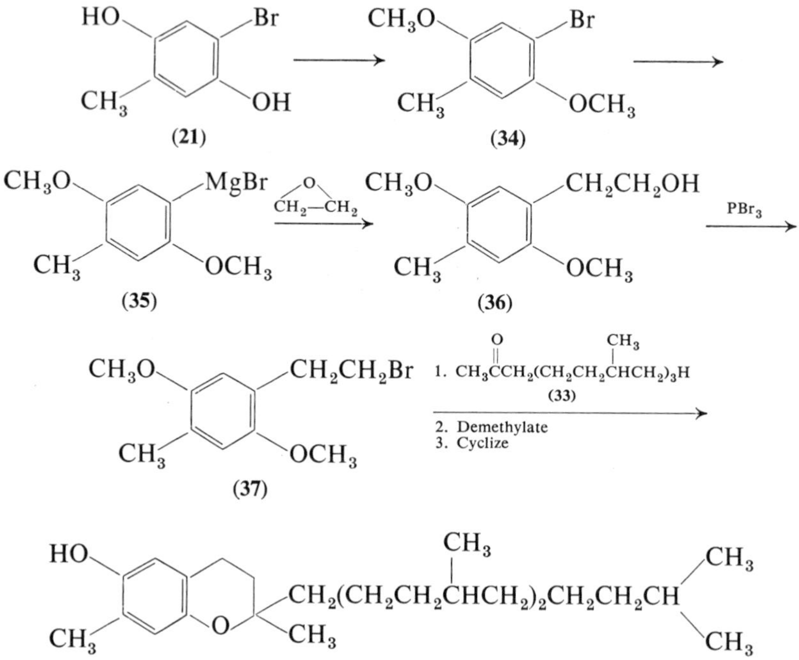

HO, Br, CH_3, OH (21) ⟶ CH_3O, Br, CH_3, OCH_3 (34) ⟶

CH_3O, MgBr, CH_3, OCH_3 (35) $\xrightarrow{\text{O}, CH_2—CH_2}$ CH_3O, CH_2CH_2OH, CH_3, OCH_3 (36) $\xrightarrow{PBr_3}$

CH_3O, CH_2CH_2Br, CH_3, OCH_3 (37)

1. $CH_3\overset{O}{\overset{\|}{C}}CH_2(CH_2CH_2\overset{CH_3}{\overset{|}{C}}HCH_2)_3H$ (33)
2. Demethylate
3. Cyclize

HO, CH_3, O, $CH_2(CH_2CH_2\overset{CH_3}{\overset{|}{C}}HCH_2)_2CH_2CH_2CH(CH_3)_2$, CH_3

7-Methyltocol

(13)

and purification as either the 3,5-dinitrophenylurethane or the 4-phenylazobenzoate.

D. Commercial Syntheses

Both synthetic and natural tocopherols are important commercially. The synthetic tocopherols of commerce are usually prepared by the condensation of a hydroquinone with phytol or phytyl chloride. The synthetic preparations are mixtures of at least two diastereoisomers depending upon the configuration of the phytol since phytol from natural sources and synthesis is used. There are also synthetic procedures that convert the naturally occurring β-, γ-, or δ-tocopherols to the more active α-tocopherol by

(a) formylation followed by hydrogenation;[33]
(b) iminoalkylation followed by hydrolysis and reduction;[34] or
(c) chloromethylation followed by reduction.[35]

33. L. Weisler, U.S. Pat. 2,592,628 (April 15, 1952).
34. L. Weisler, U.S. Pat, 2,592,629 (April 15, 1952).
35. K. C. D. Hickman and L. Weisler, U.S. Pat. 2,486,540 (Nov. 1, 1949).

The natural tocopherols are isolated from vegetable oils commercially by one or a combination of physical methods such as molecular distillation, solvent extraction, or adsorption chromatography. Although commercial extraction is still used to prepare low potency concentrates, the majority of the natural tocopherol concentrates is obtained from vegetable oils by molecular distillation. These concentrates are mixtures of tocopherols in which α-tocopherol is usually the major constituent. Since the tocopherols are susceptible to oxidation, the mixture is usually acetylated to improve stability.

5. Oxidation Reactions

Of all the features of the chemistry of the tocopherols, the behavior of the compounds on oxidation (Fig. 3) is most prominent, and from many indications it would appear that the biological activity of these compounds occurs owing to the fact that they can act as antioxidants. Mild oxidation of α-tocopherol by ferric ion in the presence of α,α′-dipyridyl yields the metastable epoxide (**38**) which is reversibly reduced to α-tocopherol by ascorbic acid.[36] On standing, the epoxide is irreversibly converted to α-tocopheryl quinone (**39**). Treatment of α-tocopherol with ferric chloride or silver nitrate gives α-tocopheryl quinone directly;[37] this quinone can be reduced to α-tocopheryl hydroquinone (**40**) that is stabilized by acylation. Treatment of α-tocopherol with more vigorous oxidizing agents such as nitric acid results in oxidation at the 5-methyl group to yield the *o*-quinone (**41**).[38]

6. Nutritional and Therapeutic Studies

A. In Animals

On casual observation, the manifestations of a vitamin E deficiency in the various animal species appear to be significantly different.[39–41] The female rat sustained on a diet deficient in vitamin E suffers a reproductive

36. P. Boyer, *J. Am. Chem. Soc.*, *73*, 733 (1951).
37. W. John, *Z. Physiol. Chem.*, *252*, 222 (1938).
38. L. I. Smith, W. B. Irwin, and H. E. Unganade, *J. Am. Chem. Soc.*, *61*, 2424 (1939).
39. K. E. Mason, in W. H. Sebrell, Jr. and R. S. Harris, eds., *The Vitamins: Chemistry, Physiology and Pathology*, Vol. III, Academic, N.Y., 1954, p. 514.
40. T. Moore, *Brit. Med. Bull.*, *12*, 44 (1956).
41. *Nutr. Revs.*, *18*, 340 (1960).

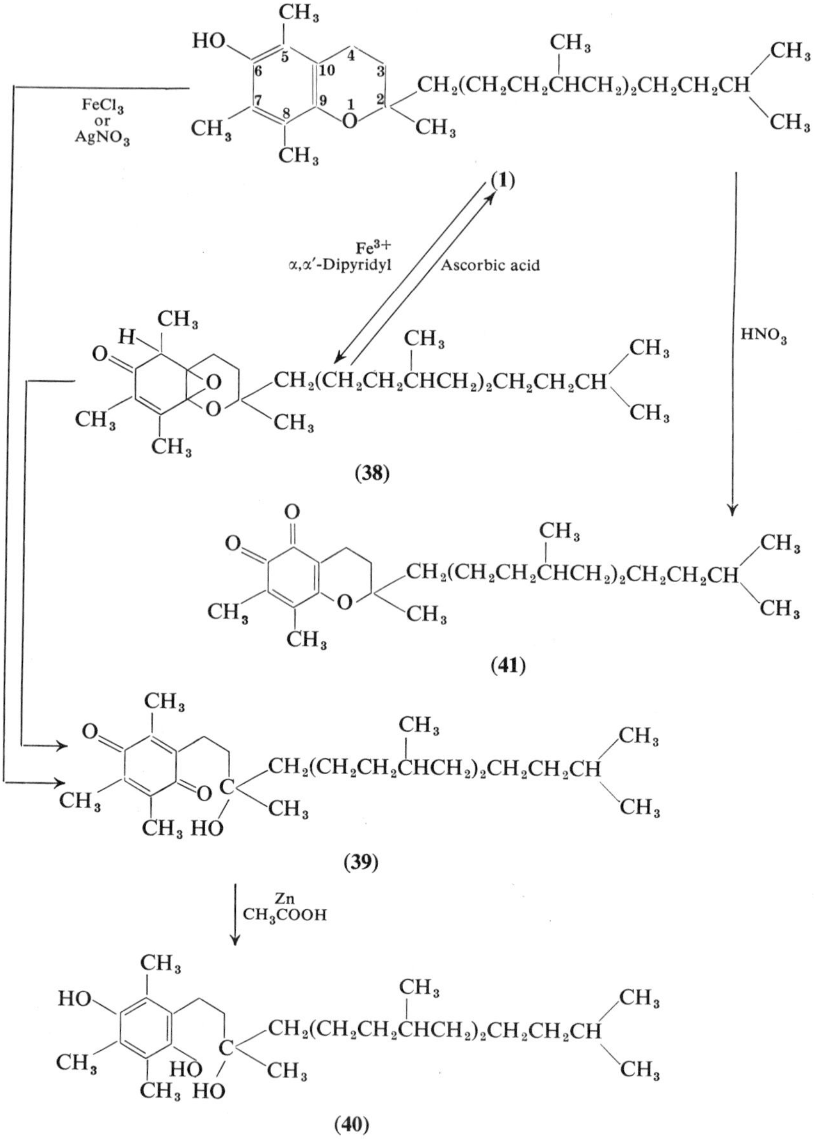

(1)

$FeCl_3$ or $AgNO_3$

Fe^{3+} α,α′-Dipyridyl

Ascorbic acid

HNO_3

(38)

(41)

(39)

Zn CH_3COOH

(40)

Fig. 3. Oxidation reactions of α-tocopherol.

failure that is characterized by resorption of the fetus. In herbivorous animals, vitamin E deficiency is characterized by myocardial degeneration, and a myocardial accident occurs occasionally during the latter half of pregnancy or shortly after calving. Dystrophy of the voluntary muscles develops in the vitamin E deficient dog and guinea pig. In the chick, the avitaminosis E syndrome is characterized by neurological degeneration, vascular degeneration, and muscular dystrophy. These different pathologic responses to a deficiency of tocopherol may be regarded as secondary manifestations of a primary muscular dystrophy. In the deficiency state, certain tissue is more susceptible to nutritionally-induced degeneration in one species than another; consequently, the metabolic defect appears in different organs, depending upon the species.

Extensive studies[42–48] have been made to discover a metabolic role for tocopherol, but there has been an increasing tendency to attribute many of its physiological effects to a nonspecific antioxidant activity rather than to a specific metabolic function.

As early as 1944 there were indications that the activity of tocopherol could be related in part to the protection of dietary components that were highly susceptible to oxidation. In the chick, it was shown that the onset of symptoms of a vitamin E deficiency could be accelerated by the addition of highly unsaturated fatty acids to the diet; on the other hand, the manifestations of the deficiency could be delayed or prevented by the addition of known antioxidants.[49] Later it was observed that ascorbic acid protected chicks from developing the characteristic lesions of a vitamin E deficiency even when the birds were fed high concentrations of polyunsaturated fats.[50] The effect of dietary bisulfite in accelerating the onset of a vitamin E deficiency in the chick receiving large quantities of polyunsaturated acids was further support for a role as an antioxidant.[51] In these studies, the deficiency was related directly to the rancidity of the oxidized unsaturated fat so it was concluded that tocopherol functions as an antioxidant.

42. A. Nason and I. R. Lehman, *Science*, *122*, 19 (1955).
43. A. Nason and I. R. Lehman, *J. Biol. Chem.*, *222*, 497, 511 (1956).
44. M. Morrison, R. Crawford, and E. Stotz, *Biochim. et Biophys. Acta*, *22*, 579 (1956).
45. K. O. Donaldson and A. Nason, *Proc. Natl. Acad. Sci.* (*U.S.*), *43*, 364 (1957).
46. K. O. Donaldson, A. Nason, K. B. Moore, and R. H. Garrett, *Biochim. et Biophys. Acta*, *26*, 665 (1957).
47. G. V. Marinetti, P. Scaramuzzino, and E. Stotz, *J. Biol. Chem.*, *224*, 819 (1957).
48. D. Deul, E. C. Slater, and L. Veldstra, *Biochim. et Biophys.*, *Acta*, *27*, 133 (1958).
49. H. Dam, *J. Nutr.*, *27*, 193 (1944).
50. L. P. Zacharias, P. Goldhaber, and V. E. Kinsey, *J. Nutr.*, *42*, 359 (1950).
51. R. F. Miller, G. Small, and L. C. Norris, *J. Nutr.*, *55*, 81 (1955).

In the rat, synthetic antioxidants such as methylene blue and *N,N′*-diphenyl-*p*-phenylenediamine were effective substitutes for tocopherol in preventing fetal resorption.[52,53] In the chick, it was found that the addition of selenium to the diet would prevent exudative diathesis which is a characteristic symptom of vitamin E deficiency in the chick.[54,55] Selenium added as either selenite, elemental selenium, or "Factor 3" was an effective replacement for tocopherol in preventing the appearance of this characteristic symptom.

The support for a specific metabolic role for tocopherol has depended on the possibility that the synthetic antioxidants preserved residual stores of tocopherol in the tissue of the deficient animal. It has been demonstrated, however, that *N,N′*-diphenyl-*p*-phenylenediamine has no effect on the depletion of tocopherol from the liver of growing rabbits and rats being fed a vitamin E deficient diet.[56] Furthermore, complete tissue depletion of tocopherol was demonstrated in both control and antioxidant-fed rabbits being sustained on a vitamin E deficient diet.[57] Traces of unsaponifiable reducing compounds remaining in the tissue were formerly believed to be residual tocopherols, but they have now been identified as chromenols derived from coenzyme Q_9 and coenzyme Q_{10} (Chapter XXI). From these data, it appears that a requirement for tocopherol is nonspecific, and the possibility of a natural role for tocopherol as a cofactor in mammalian enzymic reactions would seem to be eliminated.

In a study with the vitamin E depleted chick, it was shown that normal growth and development is maintained without dietary tocopherol or other antioxidants provided adequate dietary sources of vitamin A are available.[58] In these studies, the vitamin E depleted chick grew normally and began to lay eggs at the same time as the control chick receiving tocopherol; such results would indicate no primary role for tocopherol in intermediary metabolism except to conserve vitamin A.

In other nutritional studies, the data would suggest that tocopherol has at least two physiological functions. One function is dependent upon nonspecific antioxidant properties of tocopherol and is evident in the

52. H. H. Draper, S. Goodyear, K. D. Barbee, and B. C. Johnson, *Brit. J. Nutr.*, *12*, 89 (1958).
53. H. H. Draper and B. C. Johnson, *J. Agr. Food Chem.*, *6*, 920 (1958).
54. E. L. Patterson, R. Milstrey, and E. L. R. Stokstad, *Proc. Soc. Exptl. Biol. Med.*, *95*, 617 (1957).
55. K. Schwartz, J. G. Bieri, G. M. Briggs, and M. L. Scott, *Proc. Soc. Exptl. Biol. Med.*, *95*, 621 (1957).
56. H. H. Draper and A. S. Csallany, *Proc. Soc. Exptl. Biol. Med.*, *99*, 739 (1958).
57. A. S. Csallany and H. H. Draper, *Arch. Biochem. Biophys.*, *92*, 462 (1961).
58. J. G. Bieri, G. M. Briggs, C. J. Pollard, and M. R. Spivey Fox, *J. Nutr.*, *70*, 47 (1960).

metabolism of unsaturated lipids. The other would appear to be specific and unrelated to a nonspecific antioxidant effect. For example, early studies with synthetic antioxidants in the rat would indicate that the tocopherol had a specific metabolic function in addition to its activity as a nonspecific antioxidant.[59,60] Two observations were significant: It was shown that the synthetic antioxidants were less effective in preventing a nutritionally-induced sterility in the rat when the animal was fed a fat-free diet; furthermore, if the rat was fed a diet supplemented with untreated lard, methylene blue was effective in preventing the gestation-resorption syndrome only in the presence of small amounts of tocopherol. In the chick, it was shown that 1,2-dihydro-6-ethoxy-2,2,4-trimethylquinoline and calcium *DL*-2-hydroxy-4-methylthiobutyrate prevented some but not all symptoms of a tocopherol deficiency.[61] The quinoline derivative prevented the appearance of encephalomalacia but not muscular degeneration; the thiobutyrate derivative failed to protect the chick from encephalomalacia but prevented muscular degeneration. Tocopherol prevented both conditions. Since the quinoline derivative was more effective than tocopherol in preventing peroxide formation in chick liver homogenates and also oxidative rancidity in the diet, it was suggested that tocopherol does not function simply as an antioxidant.

Only partial remission of the symptoms of tocopherol deficiency is observed when a synthetic antioxidant is administered to the rhesus monkey. When these animals are fed a tocopherol-free diet for a period of from 6 to 13 months, an acute tocopherol deficiency develops. The syndrome is characterized by muscular dystrophy, anemia, leucocytosis, granulocytosis, increased urinary excretion of creatine, and decreased urinary excretion of creatinine;[62–64] the deficiency invariably leads to death unless the diet is supplemented.[62] The anemia, which is slightly macrocytic, is the first manifestation and is observed about 2–3 months before the physical symptoms of dystrophy are seen. The only tissues significantly affected by the deficiency are skeletal muscle and bone marrow.[63] Remission of all symptoms is complete following the administration of α-tocopheryl acetate or phosphate, but only partial when *N,N'*-diphenyl-*p*-phenylenediamine is administered. The hematological response to the administration of tocopherol is prompt. There is a

59. F. Christensen and H. Dam, *Acta Physiol. Scand.*, *36*, 82, 97 (1956).
60. F. Christensen, H. Dam, and R. A. Gortner, *Acta Physiol. Scand.*, *36*, 87 (1956).
61. L. J. Machlin, R. S. Gordon, and K. H. Meisky, *J. Nutr.*, *67*, 333 (1959).
62. J. S. Dinning and P. L. Day, *J. Exptl. Med.*, *105*, 395 (1957).
63. J. S. Dinning and P. L. Day, *J. Nutr.*, *63*, 393 (1957).
64. J. S. Dinning and P. L. Day, *J. Biol. Chem.*, *233*, 240 (1958).

pronounced reticulocyte response followed by an increase in hemoglobin. The excretion of creatine is also reduced sharply, and the dystrophic symptoms improve noticeably within a few days.

When the 6-chromanol of hexahydrocoenzyme Q_4 (Chapter XXI) was administered to the anemic and dystrophic monkey, the response was similar to that observed when α-tocopherol was given.[65] This observation raises questions as to whether

(a) both tocopherol and the 6-chromanol of hexahydrocoenzyme Q_4 function in a native biochemical sequence;

(b) only one of the two compounds is the native factor but the other can substitute for it solely on the basis of structural similarity; or

(c) one compound simply protects the other because of its antioxidant properties.

Studies of the effect of a deficiency of α-tocopherol on the tissue levels of coenzyme Q (Chapter XXI) provide additional evidence for a specific physiological effect. A deficiency of tocopherol and selenium produced a decrease in the tissue concentration of coenzyme Q in the rat and rabbit;[66,67] although selenium and tocopherol influenced the level of coenzyme Q in most tissues of the rat, only tocopherol influenced the level of coenzyme Q in the uterus. In subsequent studies, it was shown that the administration of tocopherol produced an increase in the tissue concentration of coenzyme Q before a significant increase in the concentration of tocopherol could be detected in the same tissue, and it was considered that the effect on the biosynthesis of coenzyme Q was due to a metabolite of tocopherol.[68] To test this hypothesis, the influence of a known biological degradation product of tocopherol on the coenzyme Q level of tissue was studied. Two metabolites of tocopherol had been isolated[69] earlier from rabbit urine and were identified as 2-(5-carboxy-3-hydroxy-3-methylpentyl)-3,5,6-trimethyl-1,4-benzoquinone (**42**) and its corresponding γ-lactone (**43**); it has been suggested that the compounds be designated tocopheronic acid and tocopheronolactone, respectively.[68] Tocopheronolactone was effective in restoring the tissue level of coenzyme Q in the uterus of the rat; furthermore, the maximum effect was achieved in a shorter period of time with the metabolite than with tocopherol. Next

65. J. S. Dinning, C. D. Fitch, C. H. Shunk, and K. Folkers, *J. Am. Chem. Soc.*, *84*, 2007 (1962).
66. E. E. Edwin, A. T. Diplock, J. Bunyan, and J. Green, *Biochem. J.*, *79*, 61 (1961).
67. J. Green, A. T. Diplock, J. Bunyan, and E. E. Edwin, *Biochem. J.*, *79*, 108 (1961).
68. J. Green, A. T. Diplock, J. Bunyan, E. E. Edwin, and D. McHale, *Nature*, *190*, 318 (1961).
69. E. J. Simon, A. Eisengart, A. Sundheim, and A. T. Milhorat, *J. Biol. Chem.*, *221*, 807 (1956).

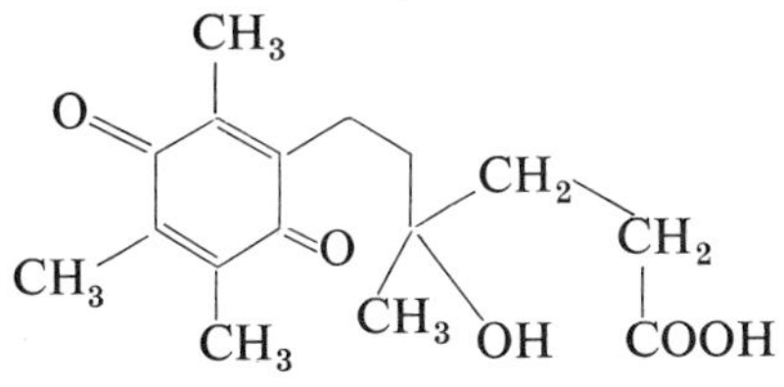

(42)

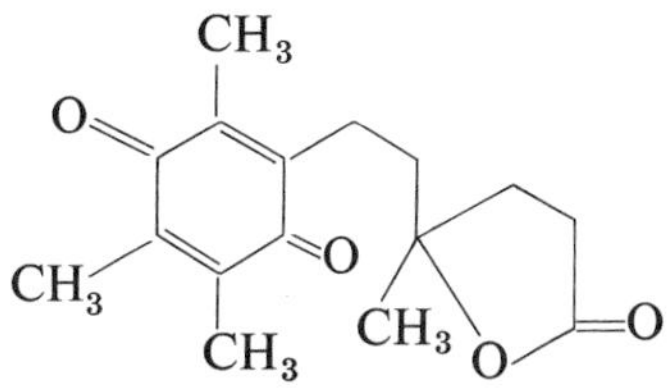

(43)

α-tocopheryl quinone (**39**) was administered and found to be active. Tocopheryl quinone was not detected in the tissue and was not converted to tocopherol. On the basis of these data, it was concluded that tocopherol produces a specific physiological effect which is not related to a nonspecific antioxidant property.[68] The effect is on the biosynthesis of coenzyme Q; the active factor is considered to be a metabolite of tocopherol and may be tocopheronolactone or a closely related compound.

In summary there are two divergent interpretations regarding the role of tocopherol in mammalian metabolism. According to one, the physiological effects of tocopherol are due solely to a nonspecific antioxidant property; according to the other, tocopherol has at least two physiological functions, one of which is not related to a nonspecific antioxidant property. There are considerable data supporting both points of view; the source of discrepancy appears to be whether the diet and the tissue of the "depleted animal" are free of tocopherol.

B. In the Human

In the past twenty-five years of research, a direct relationship between a deficiency of tocopherol and a given disease state has not been generally recognized in medicine. The vitamin has been used therapeutically in cases of habitual abortion, muscular dystrophy, cardiac and vascular disorders, and during menopause with varying degrees of success being claimed. A daily oral dose of 200–600 mg. of α-tocopherol has usually been administered in these treatments.

In 1963 a consistently positive hematologic response was reported following the administration of tocopheryl phosphate and acetate to severely malnourished infants.[70] A syndrome characterized by a macrocytic anemia and an elevated excretion of creatine has been observed in Jordanian infants suffering from severe protein-caloric malnutrition. The anemia, which has been described as a "maturation arrest," appears to be one which does not respond to cyanocobalamin, pteroylmonoglutamic acid, *L*-ascorbic acid or iron, although the anemia appears to result from a multiple deficiency. In eight infant subjects, the intramuscular administration of 100 mg. of α-tocopheryl phosphate and oral administration of 200 mg. of α-tocopheryl acetate daily for five days resulted in a positive hematologic response and a decrease in the urinary excretion of creatine. The hematologic response was characterized by a prompt increase in reticulocytes, followed shortly thereafter by a commensurate rise in hematocrit, red blood cell count, and hemoglobin.

On the basis of a detailed study with a group of thirty-eight male subjects, it was concluded that tocopherol is an important dietary constituent and that man's requirement is a function of the amount of peroxidizable lipids in the diet.[71] This observation is especially important since increased ingestion of linoleic acid has been recommended as a means to lower the levels of plasma cholesterol (Chapter XIX); although most oils with a high concentration of linoleic acid also have a high concentration of tocopherol, it has been suggested that the tocopherols are stored less efficiently in the tissue.[71] The daily dietary consumption of 5 mg. of α-tocopherol is considered adequate for a diet low in unsaturated fat; for individuals ingesting large quantities of vegetable oils over a prolonged period, the daily dietary consumption of 30 mg. of α-tocopherol is considered adequate.[71] For the present, a recommended dietary allowance for tocopherol has not been officially adopted.

The tocopherols are generously distributed in nature; among the best dietary sources are vegetable oils, cereal products, eggs, butter, liver, and legumes. American wheat germ oils are especially rich in α-tocopherol and contain, in addition, some β-tocopherol. In European wheat germ oils β-tocopherol is the preponderant type. Lettuce contains α-tocopherol. Both cottonseed oil and palm oil contain α- and γ-tocopherol but no β-tocopherol.

70. A. S. Majaj, J. S. Dinning, S. A. Azzam, and W. J. Darby, *Am. J. Clin. Nutr.*, *12*, 374 (1963).
71. M. K. Horwitt, *Am. J. Clin. Nutr.*, *8*, 451 (1960).

CHAPTER XIX

The Essential Fatty Acid Group

1. Introduction

Until the 1930's animal and vegetable fats were of nutritional interest almost solely on the basis of their being dietary sources of energy. Animal fats are generally solids and are composed of triesters of glycerol and monoesters of cholesterol; the acyl moieties are usually saturated unbranched chains consisting of an even number of carbon atoms. Vegetable fats are mostly oils composed of triesters of glycerol and monoesters of sitosterol; the acyl moieties are usually unsaturated unbranched chains composed of an even number of carbon atoms. The unsaturated acids of natural fats belong to one of three groups of acids: those derived from oleic acid (**1**); those derived from linoleic acid (**2**); and those derived from linolenic acid (**3**). The essential fatty acids belong to the linoleic acid group.

$$CH_3CH_2CH_2CH_2CH_2CH_2CH_2CH_2CH{=}CHCH_2CH_2CH_2CH_2(CH_2)_3COOH$$

Oleic acid (9-*cis*-octadecenoic acid)

(**1**)

$$CH_3CH_2CH_2CH_2CH_2CH{=}CHCH_2CH{=}CHCH_2CH_2CH_2CH_2(CH_2)_3COOH$$

Linoleic acid (9,12-di*cis*-octadecadienoic acid)

(**2**)

$$CH_3CH_2CH{=}CHCH_2CH{=}CHCH_2CH{=}CHCH_2CH_2CH_2CH_2(CH_2)_3COOH$$

Linolenic acid (9,12,15-tri*cis*-octadecatrienoic acid)

(**3**)

The role of dietary fats in providing metabolic energy, sparing protein, and promoting absorption of the fat-soluble vitamins has been known for decades, but recognition that certain fats provide nutrients that are essential for growth and good health is relatively recent knowledge. The group of polyenoic acids that promote growth and good health are designated essential fatty acids; at one time the expression vitamin F was used to designate the group, and the expression is currently used to some extent in Europe.

A syndrome related to a dietary deficiency of fat was first recognized in the weanling rat and is characterized by poor growth, skin lesions, kidney necrosis, and impaired fertility.[1,2] The administration of saturated fatty acids such as stearic acid, palmitic acid, myristic acid, or lauric acid failed to effect a cure. The symptoms disappeared, however, when linoleic acid (**2**) was added to the diet either as the pure compound or in the form of natural vegetable oils.[3] Linolenic acid (**3**) was also reported to be active,[3] but further study showed it to be far less effective than linoleic acid for the promotion of growth and alleviation of symptoms of the fat-deficiency state.[4,5]

Other polyunsaturated fatty acids were soon found to prevent the syndrome associated with fat deficiency in the rat. Arachidonic acid (**8**) proved to be more effective than linoleic acid for promoting growth in the fat-deficient rat,[6] and subsequent studies demonstrated its effectiveness

$$CH_3CH_2CH_2CH_2CH_2CH{=}CHCH_2CH{=}CHCH_2CH_2CH_2CH_2(CH_2)_3COOH$$

Linoleic acid (9,12-di*cis*-octadecadienoic acid)

(**2**)

$$CH_3CH_2CH_2CH_2CH_2CH{=}CHCH_2CH{=}CHCH_2CH{=}CHCH_2(CH_2)_3COOH$$

γ-Linolenic acid (6,9,12-tri*cis*-octadecatrienoic acid)

(**4**)

$$CH_3CH_2CH_2CH_2CH_2CH{=}CHCH_2CH{=}CHCH_2CH_2CH_2CH_2CH_2(CH_2)_3COOH$$

10,13-Di*cis*-nonadecadienoic acid

(**5**)

$$CH_3CH_2CH_2CH_2CH_2CH{=}CHCH_2CH{=}CHCH_2CH_2CH_2CH_2CH_2CH_2(CH_2)_3COOH$$

11,14-Di*cis*-eicosadienoic acid

(**6**)

$$CH_3CH_2CH_2CH_2CH_2CH{=}CHCH_2CH{=}CHCH_2CH{=}CHCH_2CH_2CH_2(CH_2)_3COOH$$

Homo-γ-linolenic acid (8,11,14-tri*cis*-eicosatrienoic acid)

(**7**)

$$CH_3CH_2CH_2CH_2CH_2CH{=}CHCH_2CH{=}CHCH_2CH{=}CHCH_2CH{=}CH(CH_2)_3COOH$$

Arachidonic acid (5,8,11,14-tetra*cis*-eicosatetraenoic acid)

(**8**)

Fig. 1. Suggested members of the essential fatty acid group.

1. G. O. Burr and M. M. Burr, *J. Biol. Chem.*, *82*, 345 (1929).
2. G. O. Burr and M. M. Burr, *J. Biol. Chem.*, *86*, 587 (1930).
3. G. O. Burr, M. M. Burr, and E. S. Miller, *J. Biol. Chem.*, *97*, 1 (1932).
4. E. M. Hume, L. C. A. Nunn, I. Smedley-MacLean, and H. H. Smith, *Biochem. J.*, *34*, 384 (1940).
5. D. M. Greenberg, C. E. Calbert, E. E. Savage, and H. J. Deuel, *J. Nutr.*, *41*, 473 (1950).
6. O. Turpeinen, *Proc. Soc. Exptl. Biol. Med.*, *37*, 37 (1937); *J. Nutr.*, *15*, 351 (1938).

in curing all symptoms of the deficiency syndrome.[7–9] By the early 1950's 6,9,12-tri*cis*-octadecatrienoic acid (**4**), which is also designated γ-linolenic acid, was found to be as active as linoleic acid for promoting growth in the fat-deficient rat.[10,11] It was also reported that 10,13-di*cis*-nonadecadienoic acid (**5**) and 11,14-di*cis*-eicosadienoic acid (**6**) were at least partially active in alleviating certain symptoms of the deficiency, and it was suggested that they might be included in the essential fatty acid group.[11,12]

The most recent addition to the essential fatty acid group is homo-γ-linolenic acid (**7**). The inclusion of this compound is based on studies of the biosynthesis of arachidonic acid which will be discussed later (Section 4) in this chapter.

When the polyenoic acids which exhibit at least partial activity in alleviating fat-deficiency in the rat are compared structurally (Fig. 1), a similarity is evident in the spacing and configuration of all the double bonds and in the skeletal positions of at least two of the double bonds. In all of these acids the ethylene moieties are conjugated one with another but not with the carboxyl group; this sequence of double bonds is sometimes referred to as either methylene interrupted or in a divinylmethane rhythm. Striking similarity is evident when the carbon chain is numbered starting from the terminal methyl group rather than by the accepted procedure of counting from the carboxyl group. When this is done, it is evident that the active polyenoic acids have double bonds at the "6"- and "9"-positions. This observation served as a basis for the "6,9(term)-hypothesis" which depicts the moiety (**9**) as the minimum structural requirement for activity

$$\overset{\text{"1"}}{C}H_3CH_2CH_2CH_2CH_2\overset{\text{"6"}}{C}H{=}CHCH_2\overset{\text{"9"}}{C}H{=}CH{-}$$

(9)

in the essential fatty acid series.[11] Since di*cis*-linoleic acid is biologically active and di*trans*- and 9-*cis*, 12-*trans*-linoleic acid are inactive,[13] the minimum structural requirement for biological activity in the essential fatty acid group may be defined more precisely in terms of a "6,9(term)"-di*cis*-decadienyl moiety.

7. G. O. Burr, J. B. Brown, J. P. Kass, and W. O. Lundberg, *Proc. Soc. Exptl. Biol. Med.*, *44*, 242 (1940).
8. E. M. Hume, L. C. A. Nunn, I. Smedley-MacLean, and H. H. Smith, *Biochem. J.*, *34*, 879 (1940).
9. I. Smedley-MacLean and L. C. A. Nunn, *Biochem. J.*, *34*, 884 (1940).
10. H. J. Thomasson, *Intern. Z. Vitaminforsch.*, *25*, 62 (1953).
11. H. J. Thomasson, *Nature*, *173*, 452 (1954).
12. H. DeIongh and H. J. Thomasson, *Nature*, *178*, 1051 (1956).
13. O. S. Privett, F. J. Pusch, and R. T. Holman, *Arch. Biochem. Biophys.*, *57*, 156 (1955).

2. Isolation

For the isolation of essential fatty acids from natural sources, the fat is usually subjected to either hydrolysis or alcoholysis in the absence of oxygen.[14–18] The fatty acids are isolated from the reaction mixture by extraction with ether, and the crude fraction is purified by one of two methods. The saturated fatty acids may be precipitated from a petroleum ether solution of the crude mixture, or the unsaturated fatty acids may be fractionally crystallized at low temperature from an acetone solution of the fatty acid mixture. The polyunsaturated fatty acids are then separated from the monounsaturated fatty acids by brominating the partially purified mixture and fractionally crystallizing the bromine addition products. The polyunsaturated fatty acid is regenerated from the purified bromine adduct by debromination with zinc, or zinc and acid. High-purity samples are usually prepared from the regenerated polyunsaturated acid by chromatography on silicic acid or by distillation, and the compounds are stored in an oxygen-free atmosphere.

Linoleic and γ-linolenic acid were isolated from vegetable oils. Linseed, cottonseed, and poppyseed oils are sources of linoleic acid. The seed oils of the evening primrose *Oenothera biennis* and closely related *Oenothera Lamarckiana* serve as sources for γ-linolenic acid.[19,20] Animal fats were used as sources of arachidonic acid; the best source is a lipid phosphatide fraction from the beef suprarenal gland.[14]

3. Structure Determination and Synthesis

A. Linoleic Acid

Linoleic acid was identified as an unbranched C_{18}-carboxylic acid with double bonds at the 9- and 12-positions by oxidative degradation. Treatment of a cold acetone solution of linoleic acid (**2**) with potassium

14. W. C. Ault and J. B. Brown, *J. Biol. Chem.*, *107*, 607 (1934).
15. W. C. Ault and J. B. Brown, *J. Biol. Chem.*, *107*, 615 (1934).
16. J. B. Brown and J. Frankel, *J. Am. Chem. Soc.*, *60*, 54 (1938).
17. G. Y. Shinowara and J. B. Brown, *J. Am. Chem. Soc.*, *60*, 2734 (1938).
18. J. W. McCutcheon, in E. C. Horning, ed., *Organic Syntheses*, Vol. III, Wiley, N.Y., 1955, pp. 526, 531.
19. A. Heiduschka and K. Lüft, *Arch. Pharm.*, *257*, 33 (1919).
20. J. F. Mead and D. R. Howton, in H. M. Sinclair, ed., *Essential Fatty Acids, Proc. Intern. Conf. Biochem. Probl. Lipids, 4th*, Academic, N.Y., 1958, p. 65.

$$CH_3(CH_2)_3CH_2CH{=}CHCH_2CH{=}CHCH_2(CH_2)_5CH_2COOH$$

(2)

$$\downarrow KMnO_4$$

$$CH_3(CH_2)_3CH_2COOH + [HOOCCH_2COOH] + HOOCCH_2(CH_2)_5CH_2COOH$$

(10)

$$\downarrow KMnO_4$$

$$\begin{array}{c} COOH \\ | \\ COOH \end{array}$$

permanganate yielded hexanoic acid, oxalic acid, and azelaic acid (**10**).[21] Ozonolysis of ethyl linoleate (**11**) gave hexanoic acid, acetaldehyde, carbon dioxide, and the monoethyl ester (**12**) of azelaic acid.[22]

$$CH_3(CH_2)_3CH_2CH{=}CHCH_2CH{=}CHCH_2(CH_2)_5CH_2COOC_2H_5$$

(11)

$$\downarrow O_3$$

$$CH_3(CH_2)_3CH_2COOH + [HOOCCH_2CHO] + HOOCCH_2(CH_2)_5CH_2COOC_2H_5$$

(12)

$$\downarrow$$

$$CO_2 + CH_3CHO$$

According to the Raman and infrared spectra of methyl linoleate, the double bond at the 9-position is in the *cis* configuration, and it was concluded that both double bonds are *cis* oriented.[23] The same conclusion was reached on the basis of the following chemical evidence.[24] Addition of one equivalent of bromine to linoleic acid (**2**) yielded 12,13-dibromo-9-*cis*-octadecenoic acid (**13**). *Trans*-hydroxylation of the dibromo intermediate with potassium permanganate, followed by debromination and hydrogenation yielded the *trans* isomer of 9,10-dihydroxystearic acid (**14**), which was identical with that obtained from the *trans*-hydroxylation of 9-*cis*-octadecenoic acid. When the intermediate dibromo derivative (**13**)

21. R. D. Haworth, *J. Chem. Soc.*, 1456 (1929).
22. C. L. Arcus and I. Smedley-MacLean, *Biochem. J.*, *37*, 1 (1943).
23. J. W. McCutcheon, M. F. Crawford, and H. L. Welch, *Oil Soap* (*Egypt*), *18*, 9 (1941).
24. A. F. McKay and A. R. Bader, *J. Org. Chem.*, *13*, 75 (1948).

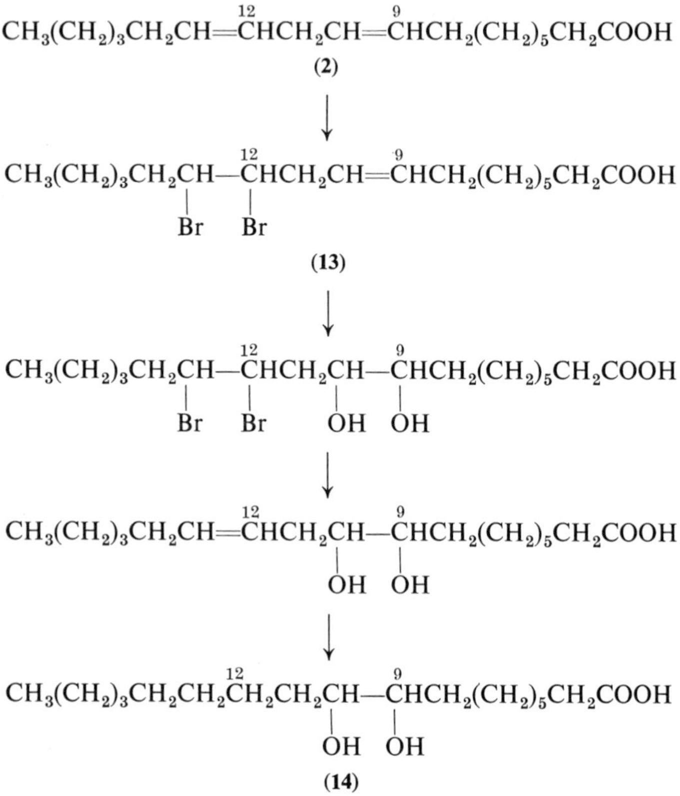

$$\mathrm{CH_3(CH_2)_3CH_2CH{=}\overset{12}{C}HCH_2CH{=}\overset{9}{C}HCH_2(CH_2)_5CH_2COOH}$$

(2)

$$\downarrow$$

$$\mathrm{CH_3(CH_2)_3CH_2\underset{|\atop Br}{CH}{-}\overset{12}{\underset{|\atop Br}{C}}HCH_2CH{=}\overset{9}{C}HCH_2(CH_2)_5CH_2COOH}$$

(13)

$$\downarrow$$

$$\mathrm{CH_3(CH_2)_3CH_2\underset{|\atop Br}{CH}{-}\overset{12}{\underset{|\atop Br}{C}}HCH_2\underset{|\atop OH}{CH}{-}\overset{9}{\underset{|\atop OH}{C}}HCH_2(CH_2)_5CH_2COOH}$$

$$\downarrow$$

$$\mathrm{CH_3(CH_2)_3CH_2CH{=}\overset{12}{C}HCH_2\underset{|\atop OH}{CH}{-}\overset{9}{\underset{|\atop OH}{C}}HCH_2(CH_2)_5CH_2COOH}$$

$$\downarrow$$

$$\mathrm{CH_3(CH_2)_3CH_2CH_2\overset{12}{C}H_2CH_2\underset{|\atop OH}{CH}{-}\overset{9}{\underset{|\atop OH}{C}}HCH_2(CH_2)_5CH_2COOH}$$

(14)

was *cis*-hydroxylated with peracetic acid in the same reaction sequence (**2** → **14**), the *cis*-isomer of 9,10-dihydroxystearic acid (**14**) was obtained. The latter isomer was identical with that obtained by the *cis*-hydroxylation of 9-*cis*-octadecenoic acid. These data in conjunction with the results of oxidative degradation established the structure of naturally occurring linoleic acid as 9,12-di*cis*-octadecadienoic acid.

The structure of linoleic acid was confirmed by synthesis (Fig. 2).[25] Sodium acetylide was condensed with 1,6-dibromohexane to yield 1,9-decadiyne (**15**), which was treated with thioacetic acid to yield 1-decen-9-ynyl thioacetate (**16**). The latter compound was converted to 1-oximino-9-decyne (**17**) by treatment with hydroxylamine, and the oxime was converted to the corresponding ethylene acetal (**18**). This acetal was converted to 1-ethylenedioxy-9-decyn-10-yl magnesium bromide (**19**), which

25. H. M. Walborsky, R. H. Davis, and D. R. Howton, *J. Am. Chem. Soc.*, *73*, 2590 (1951).

$$BrCH_2(CH_2)_4CH_2Br \xrightarrow{2\ NaC\equiv CH} \underset{(15)}{HC\equiv CCH_2(CH_2)_4CH_2C\equiv CH} \xrightarrow{CH_3\overset{O}{\overset{\|}{C}}SH}$$

$$\underset{(16)}{HC\equiv CCH_2(CH_2)_4CH_2CH=CH-S\overset{O}{\overset{\|}{C}}CH_3} \xrightarrow{NH_2OH} \underset{(17)}{HC\equiv CCH_2(CH_2)_4CH_2CH_2\overset{H}{C}=NOH}$$

$$\xrightarrow[HOCH_2CH_2OH]{H^+} \underset{(18)}{HC\equiv CCH_2(CH_2)_5CH_2CH\begin{matrix}O-CH_2\\ |\\ O-CH_2\end{matrix}} \xrightarrow{C_2H_5MgBr} \underset{(19)}{BrMgC\equiv CCH_2(CH_2)_5CH_2CH\begin{matrix}O-CH_2\\ |\\ O-CH_2\end{matrix}}$$

$$\xrightarrow{\underset{(20)}{CH_3(CH_2)_3CH_2C\equiv CCH_2MgBr}} \underset{(21)}{CH_3(CH_2)_3CH_2C\equiv CCH_2C\equiv CCH_2(CH_2)_5CH_2CH\begin{matrix}O-CH_2\\ |\\ O-CH_2\end{matrix}} \xrightarrow[2.\ Ag_2O]{1.\ H^+}$$

$$\underset{(22)}{CH_3(CH_2)_3CH_2C\equiv CCH_2C\equiv CCH_2(CH_2)_5CH_2COOH} \xrightarrow[\text{hydrogenation}]{\text{Partial}}$$

$$\underset{(2)\ (dicis)}{CH_3(CH_2)_3CH_2CH=CHCH_2CH=CHCH_2(CH_2)_5CH_2COOH} \xrightarrow{Br_2}$$

$$\underset{(23)}{CH_3(CH_2)_3CH_2\underset{Br}{C}H\underset{Br}{C}HCH_2\underset{Br}{C}H\underset{Br}{C}HCH_2(CH_2)_5CH_2COOH}$$

Fig. 2. Synthesis of di*cis*-linoleic acid.[25]

was condensed with 2-octynyl magnesium bromide (**20**) to yield 1-ethylenedioxy-9,12-octadecadiyne (**21**). Cleavage of the ethylenedioxy group in the diyne (**21**), followed by oxidation of the aldehyde function with silver oxide yielded 9,12-octadecadiynoic acid (**22**). Partial reduction of the diynoic acid (**22**) yielded 9,12-di*cis*-octadecadienoic acid (**2**); this acid was converted to the tetrabromide (**23**) which was identical to that derived from naturally occurring linoleic acid.

B. γ-Linolenic Acid

γ-Linolenic acid (**4**) was isolated from fatty acid mixtures as the corresponding hexabromide, which also served as starting material for structural studies. Debromination followed by esterification yielded methyl γ-linolenate; on the basis of the saponification equivalent, iodine titration, and alkaline isomerization at high temperature, the compound was assumed to be an isomer of linolenic acid (**3**).[26] Earlier studies had shown that ozonolysis of pure γ-linolenic acid yielded hexanal, carbon dioxide,

$$CH_3(CH_2)_3CH_2CH{=}CHCH_2CH{=}CHCH_2CH{=}CHCH_2(CH_2)_2CH_2COOH$$

(4)

$$\downarrow O_3$$

$$CH_3(CH_2)_3CH_2CHO + 2[HOOCCH_2COOH] + HOOCCH_2(CH_2)_2CH_2COOH$$

(24)

$$\downarrow$$

$$2CO_2 + 2CH_3COOH$$

acetic acid, and adipic acid (**24**).[27] These data established the structure of γ-linolenic acid as 6,9,12-octadecatrienoic acid.

The structure of γ-linolenic acid and the *cis* configuration of the double bonds was confirmed by synthesis (Fig. 3).[28,29] The Grignard complex (**26**) of 1-heptyne, prepared from 1-heptyne (**25**) and ethyl magnesium bromide, was condensed with formaldehyde to yield 2-octynol (**27**). The latter compound was converted to the corresponding bromide (**28**) by

$$\underset{(25)}{CH_3(CH_2)_4C{\equiv}CH} \xrightarrow{C_2H_5MgBr} \underset{(26)}{CH_3(CH_2)_4C{\equiv}CMgBr} \xrightarrow{HCHO}$$

$$\underset{(27)}{CH_3(CH_2)_4C{\equiv}CCH_2OH} \xrightarrow{PBr_3}$$

$$\underset{(28)}{CH_3(CH_2)_4C{\equiv}CCH_2Br} \xrightarrow[\text{(29)}]{BrMgC{\equiv}CCH_2OMgBr}$$

$$\underset{(30)}{CH_3(CH_2)_4C{\equiv}CCH_2C{\equiv}CCH_2OH} \xrightarrow[\text{(31)}]{\text{1. } PBr_3 \;\; \text{2. } BrMgC{\equiv}CCH_2(CH_2)_3COOMgBr}$$

$$\underset{(32)}{CH_3(CH_2)_4C{\equiv}CCH_2C{\equiv}CCH_2C{\equiv}CCH_2(CH_2)_3COOH} \xrightarrow{H_2}$$

$$\underset{(4)\ (\text{tri}cis)}{CH_3(CH_2)_4CH{=}CHCH_2CH{=}CHCH_2CH{=}CHCH_2(CH_2)_3COOH}$$

Fig. 3. Synthesis of tri*cis*-γ-linolenic acid.[28,29]

26. J. P. Riley, *J. Chem. Soc.*, 2728 (1949).
27. A. Eibner, L. Widenmayer, and E. Schild, *Chem. Umschau, Fette, Oele, Wachse Harze*, *34*, 312 (1927).
28. J. M. Osbond, P. G. Philpott, and J. C. Wickens, *J. Chem. Soc.*, 2779 (1961).
29. J. M. Osbond, *J. Chem. Soc.*, 5270 (1961).

treatment with phosphorus tribromide. Condensation of 2-octynyl bromide (**28**) with the di-Grignard complex (**29**) of propargyl alcohol yielded 2,5-undecadiynol (**30**), which was converted to the corresponding bromo derivative and then condensed with the di-Grignard complex (**31**) of 6-heptynoic acid to yield 6,9,12-octadecatriynoic acid (**32**). Partial reduction of the triynoic acid (**32**) in the presence of Lindlar's catalyst yielded 6,9,12-tri*cis*-octadecatrienoic acid (**4**). The identity of the synthetic product with the naturally occurring compound was established by comparing the corresponding hexabromo derivatives.

C. *Arachidonic Acid*

In an early study of the oxidative degradation of arachidonic acid (**8**) with alkaline potassium permanganate, oxalic, succinic, and glutaric acids were isolated in low yield; in addition a fraction of volatile monocarboxylic acids was obtained, which appeared to be a mixture of valeric and caproic acids.[30] The structure 5,8,11,14-eicosatetraenoic acid suggested for the natural product on the basis of these limited data was confirmed by detailed quantitative studies of the ozonolysis and potassium permanganate oxidation of methyl arachidonate.[22,31] Oxidation of the ester (**33**) with potassium permanganate in acetone solution yielded caproic acid (**34**), oxalic acid, succinic acid (**35**), and glutaric acid (**36**); ozonolysis yielded caproic acid (**34**), malonic acid, acetaldehyde, carbon dioxide, acetic acid, succinic acid (**35**), and glutaric acid (**36**). The nature of the degradation products and the yield of each were in full accord with the proposed structure.

The synthesis of tetra*cis*-arachidonic acid (Fig. 4) was accomplished in three stages.[32] The lithium derivative (**37**) of 2-propargyloxytetrahydropyran was condensed with 1-bromo-3-chloropropane to yield 6-chloro-1-(tetrahydro-2-pyranoxy)-2-hexyne (**38**). The tetrahydropyran moiety was removed by acid hydrolysis, and the product was treated with phosphorus tribromide to yield 1-bromo-6-chloro-2-hexyne (**39**). This bromo intermediate was condensed with the Grignard derivative of 2-propargyloxytetrahydropyran to yield 9-chloro-1-(tetrahydro-2-pyranoxy)-2,5-nonadiyne (**40**). Acid cleavage of the tetrahydropyran moiety of the diyne (**40**), followed by bromination of the product with phosphorus tribromide yielded 1-bromo-9-chloro-2,5-nonadiyne (**41**).

1,4-Decadiyne (**44**) was synthesized for condensation with the 2,5-nonadiyne derivative (**41**). Bromopentane was treated with sodium acetylide

30. D. E. Dolby, L. C. A. Nunn, and I. Smedley-MacLean, *Biochem. J.*, *34*, 1422 (1940).
31. D. T. Mowry, W. R. Brode, and J. B. Brown, *J. Biol. Chem.*, *142*, 679 (1942).
32. A. I. Rachlin, N. Wasyliw, and M. W. Goldberg, *J. Org. Chem.*, *26*, 2688 (1961).

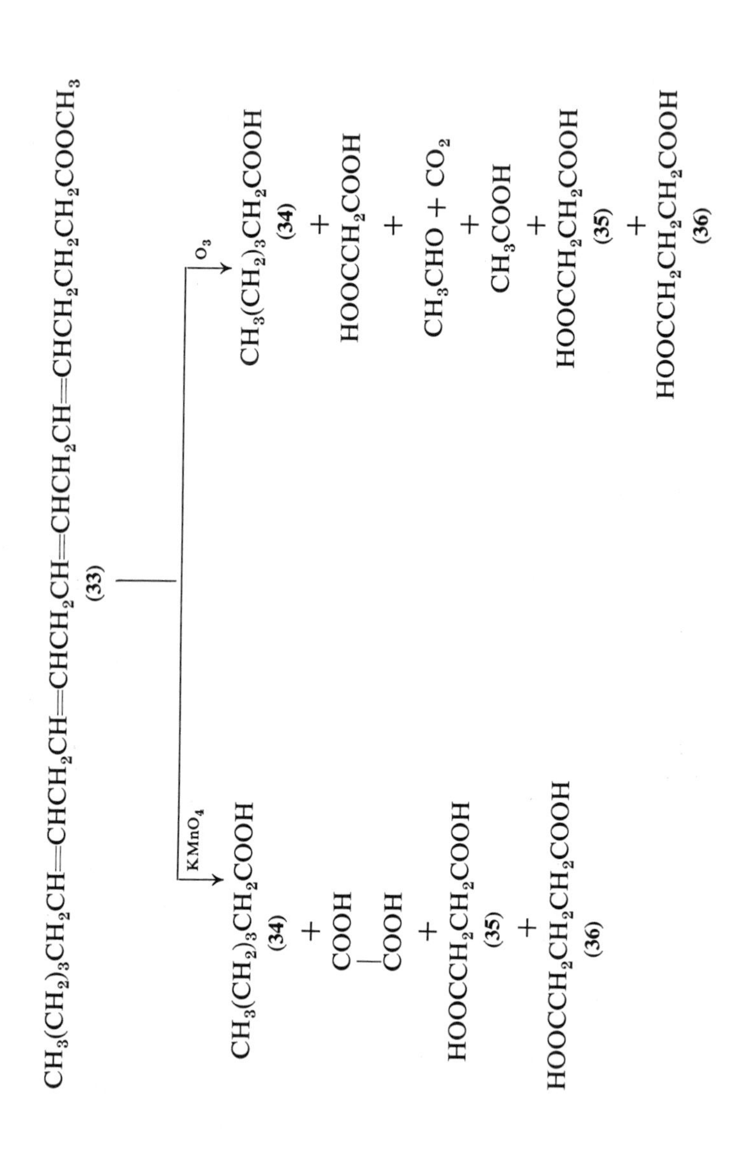
$CH_3(CH_2)_3CH_2CH{=}CHCH_2CH{=}CHCH_2CH{=}CHCH_2CH{=}CHCH_2CH_2CH_2COOCH_3$
(33)
$KMnO_4$
$CH_3(CH_2)_3CH_2COOH$
(34)
+
COOH
|
COOH
+
$HOOCCH_2CH_2COOH$
(35)
+
$HOOCCH_2CH_2CH_2COOH$
(36)
O_3
$CH_3(CH_2)_3CH_2COOH$
(34)
+
$HOOCCH_2COOH$
+
$CH_3CHO + CO_2$
+
CH_3COOH
+
$HOOCCH_2CH_2COOH$
(35)
+
$HOOCCH_2CH_2CH_2COOH$
(36)

$OCH_2C{\equiv}CLi$
(37)

↓ $BrCH_2CH_2CH_2Cl$

$OCH_2C{\equiv}CCH_2CH_2CH_2Cl$
(38)

↓ 1. H_3O^+ 2. PBr_3

$BrCH_2C{\equiv}CCH_2CH_2CH_2Cl$
(39)

↓ $OCH_2C{\equiv}CMgBr$

$OCH_2C{\equiv}CCH_2C{\equiv}CCH_2CH_2CH_2Cl$
(40)

↓ 1. H_3O^+ 2. PBr_3

$BrCH_2C{\equiv}CCH_2C{\equiv}CCH_2CH_2CH_2Cl$
(41)

$CH_3(CH_2)_3CH_2Br$

↓ $NaC{\equiv}CH$

$CH_3(CH_2)_3CH_2C{\equiv}CH$
(42)

↓

$CH_3(CH_2)_3CH_2C{\equiv}CMgBr$
(43)

↓ $BrCH_2C{\equiv}CH$

$CH_3(CH_2)_3CH_2C{\equiv}CCH_2C{\equiv}CH$
(44)

↓

$CH_3(CH_2)_3CH_2C{\equiv}CCH_2C{\equiv}CMgBr$
(45)

(45) + (41) ↓

$CH_3(CH_2)_3CH_2C{\equiv}CCH_2C{\equiv}CCH_2C{\equiv}CCH_2C{\equiv}CCH_2CH_2CH_2Cl$
(46)

↓ H_2

$CH_3(CH_2)_3CH_2CH{=}CHCH_2CH{=}CHCH_2CH{=}CHCH_2CH{=}CHCH_2CH_2CH_2Cl$
(47)

↓ 1. Mg 2. CO_2

$CH_3(CH_2)_3CH_2CH{=}CHCH_2CH{=}CHCH_2CH{=}CHCH_2CH{=}CHCH_2CH_2CH_2COOH$
(8)

Fig. 4. Synthesis of tetra*cis*-arachidonic acid.[32]

to yield 1-heptyne (**42**), which was converted to the corresponding Grignard derivative (**43**) and condensed with propargyl bromide to form 1,4-decadiyne (**44**).

For the final stage of the synthesis, 1,4-decadiyne was converted to the Grignard derivative (**45**) which was condensed with 1-bromo-9-chloro-2,5-nonadiyne (**41**) to yield 1-chloro-4,7,10,13-nonadecatetrayne (**46**). The tetrayne (**46**) was partially reduced over Lindlar's catalyst to yield 1-chloro-4,7,10,13-tetra*cis*-nonadecatetraene (**47**). Conversion of the latter intermediate to the corresponding Grignard derivative followed by treatment with carbon dioxide yielded tetra*cis*-arachidonic acid (**8**), which was isolated and characterized as the methyl ester. On the basis of infrared absorption, the synthetic ester was essentially identical with the methyl ester derived from naturally occurring arachidonic acid.

4. Metabolic Studies

The polyunsaturated acids which are found in animals have been divided into three categories; some are considered as being derived from oleic acid (9-*cis*-octadecenoic acid) and some from either linoleic acid (9,12-di*cis*-octadecadienoic acid) or linolenic acid (9,12,15-tri*cis*-octadecatrienoic acid). Of the three parent acids, oleic acid is the only one capable of being biosynthesized in significant amounts by the animal; the others are obtained principally from dietary sources. The metabolic conversions which take place *in vivo* within each of the three groups have been elucidated, and enzymic mechanisms have been suggested to account for the normal and abnormal metabolism of unsaturated fatty acids.

A. Biosynthesis of Arachidonic Acid

Early evidence suggested that linoleic acid functioned as a biosynthetic precursor for arachidonic acid. For example, the concentration of tetraenoic acids in the fatty acids of the body increased when linoleic acid was fed to rats being sustained on fat-free diets.[33,34] When linolenic acid was fed under similar conditions, there was an increase in the concentration of pentaenoic and hexaenoic acids in the body fat.[34,35]

It was gradually recognized that certain members of the linoleic acid family (Fig. 1) comprise the essential fatty acid group, and it was generally assumed that linoleic acid is the primary biosynthetic precursor of the

33. I. G. Rieckehoff, R. T. Holman, and G. O. Burr, *Arch. Biochem.*, *20*, 331 (1947).
34. C. Widmer, Jr. and R. T. Holman, *Arch. Biochem.*, *25*, 1 (1950).
35. R. Reiser, *J. Nutr.*, *44*, 159 (1951).

group and must be provided from an exogenous source. However, two monoenoic acids have recently been studied as possible precursors of linoleic acid in animals. In one study 1-C^{14}-2-*cis*-octenoic acid was fed to a laying hen, and the linoleic acid fraction was isolated from subsequent eggs.[36] On the basis of the labeling pattern in the biosynthetic linoleic acid, it was concluded that 2-*cis*-octenoic acid was converted to linoleic acid *in vivo*. In the other study 12-*cis*-octadecenoic acid was reconsidered as a potential biosynthetic precursor for linoleic acid.[37] Earlier studies had shown that ethyl 12-octadecenoate or an equimolar mixture of 11- and 12-octadecenoic acids failed to alleviate symptoms of fat-deficiency in the rat.[10,38] These data precluded a precursor role for 12-octadecenoic acid, but the results were challenged on the basis of the preparation of the test compounds.[37] The original conclusion was verified, however, when 1-C^{14}-12-*cis*-octadecenoic acid was fed to rats and little or no labeled linoleic acid was found in the body fat.[37]

A primary precursor role for linoleic acid in the biosynthesis of essential fatty acids was suggested by two experiments. Firstly, it was shown that 1-C^{14}-acetate was incorporated into arachidonic acid but not into linoleic acid in the organ and depot fat of the young rat.[39] Degradation of the labeled arachidonic acid proved that the C^{14} was predominantly in the 1-position, and it was concluded that arachidonic acid was biosynthesized from acetate and a C_{18}-precursor. Secondly, the C_{18}-precursor was identified as linoleic acid.[40] In this study methyl 1-C^{14}-linoleate was fed to mature rats, and the arachidonic acid was isolated from the organ and depot fat shortly after the labeled compound was fed. The labeled arachidonic acid was reduced to the octahydro derivative arachidic acid, which was degraded from the carboxyl position one carbon atom at a time until the first three carbon atoms had been isolated as carboxyl groups of benzoic acid. Since the distribution of radioactivity in the terminal eighteen carbon atoms of the labeled arachidonic acid was the same as in the methyl 1-C^{14}-linoleate that was fed, it was concluded that linoleic acid was the C_{18}-precursor for the biosynthesis of arachidonic acid.

The intermediate steps of the biosynthetic pathway between linoleic acid and arachidonic acid were elucidated by feeding potential intermediates to the rat. Homolinoleic acid (11,14-eicosadienoic acid), which has two

36. R. Reiser and N. L. Murty, *Biochem. Biophys. Res. Commun.*, *5*, 265 (1961).
37. A. J. Fulco and J. F. Mead, *J. Biol. Chem.*, *235*, 3379 (1960).
38. O. Turpeinen, *J. Nutr.*, *15*, 351 (1938).
39. J. F. Mead, G. Steinberg, and D. R. Howton, *J. Biol. Chem.*, *205*, 683 (1953).
40. G. Steinberg, W. H. Slaton, Jr., D. R. Howton, and J. F. Mead, *J. Biol. Chem.*, *220*, 257 (1956).

more methylene units between the carboxyl group and the first unsaturated position than linoleic acid, was tested in two laboratories. The results of one study indicated that homolinoleic acid was inactive in the rat;[41] a second investigator showed that the homolog was active, but only about forty per cent as effective as linoleic acid for the prevention of symptoms of essential fatty acid deficiency in the rat.[10] On the basis of these data, homolinoleic acid was eliminated from further consideration as a biosynthetic intermediate between linoleic acid and arachidonic acid.

When 1-C^{14}-γ-linolenic acid (6,9,12-tri*cis*-octadecatrienoic acid) was fed to the rat, the arachidonic acid in the lipid fraction contained most of the radioactivity.[42] Since the C^{14} of the labeled arachidonic acid was found almost exclusively at the 3-position, a rapid and complete biological conversion of γ-linolenic acid to arachidonic acid was indicated, and γ-linolenic acid was established as the first intermediate on the biosynthetic pathway between linoleic acid and arachidonic acid.

The final compound on the biosynthetic pathway between linoleic acid and arachidonic acid was identified as homo-γ-linolenic acid (8,11,14-tri*cis*-eicosatrienoic acid).[43] Methyl 2,3-C^{14}-8,11,14-tri*cis*-eicosatrienoate was fed to rats, and the arachidonic acid in the lipid fraction was isolated and reduced to arachidic acid. Selective degradation of the first three carbon atoms of arachidic acid, one at a time starting at the 1-position, showed that the distribution of radioactivity in the biosynthetic product was almost identical with that of the 8,11,14-eicosatrienoic acid that was fed.

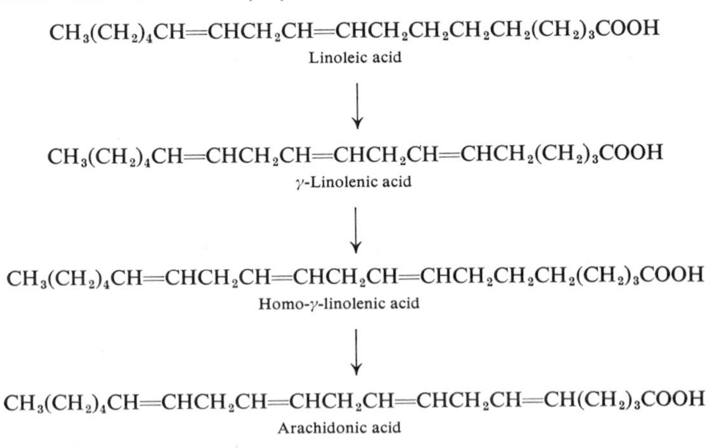

Fig. 5. Biosynthetic pathway from linoleic acid to arachidonic acid.[44]

41. P. Karrer and H. Koenig, *Helv. Chim. Acta*, *26*, 619 (1943).
42. J. F. Mead and D. R. Howton, *J. Biol. Chem.*, *219*, 705 (1956).
43. D. R. Howton and J. F. Mead, *J. Biol. Chem.*, *235*, 3385 (1960).

On the basis of all these data, the biosynthesis of arachidonic acid from linoleic acid (Fig. 5) proceeds with the introduction of a double bond at the 6-position to yield γ-linolenic acid. A two-carbon unit is then introduced at the carboxyl end of the chain to form homo-γ-linolenic acid. Dehydrogenation of this intermediate at the 5-position yields arachidonic acid.

B. Mechanism of the Metabolic Conversion of Linoleic Acid to Arachidonic Acid.

A general mechanism for the biosynthesis of polyunsaturated fatty acids visualizes a series of successive dehydrogenation and chain-lengthening steps starting from either dietary unsaturated acids or unsaturated acids which are biosynthesized from acetate by way of saturated acids.[44] The substrate forms of the unsaturated acid for both the enzymic dehydrogenation and the condensation reaction are presumably coenzyme A derivatives. According to results from animal feeding studies[44] and *in vitro* studies with a mammalian microsomal system,[45] the double bonds are introduced only in the direction of the carboxyl group and in a 1,4-relationship to the nearest double bond so that the divinylmethane sequence of the carbon chain is preserved. The chain-lengthening step is accomplished by an acyl transferase which facilitates condensation of the unsaturated acid, most likely in the form of a coenzyme A derivative, through its carbonyl group to the methyl group of acetyl coenzyme A (see Coenzyme A, Chapter VI).

5. Nutritional and Therapeutic Role

A. In Animals

The role of essential fatty acids in animal nutrition has been studied to a large degree in the smaller animal species such as the rat, mouse, guinea pig, dog, and chick. In general, a deficiency of essential fatty acids in these animals is reflected by a low survival rate among the newborn, subnormal growth, skin lesions, and impaired ability to reproduce.

The deficiency syndrome has been studied most extensively in the rat, and the macrocytic symptoms were described completely in the early studies which led to recognition of the fat-deficiency syndrome.[1,2] Growth ceases within three months after the young rat is placed on a fat-free diet and is resumed only after an essential fatty acid is added to the experimental diet. The skin lesions which develop in the deficiency state are most evident in the tail, but also occur on other parts of the body. Hemorrhagic spots appear along the entire length of the tail, and the tip of

44. J. F. Mead, *Am. J. Clin. Nutr.*, *8*, 55 (1960).
45. W. Stoffel, *Biochem. Biophys. Res. Commun.*, *6*, 270 (1961).

the tail becomes scaly and rigid. Ovulation becomes irregular or ceases in the deficient female and if litters are produced, the newborn fail to survive. The deficient male becomes sterile. The addition of essential fatty acids to the diet cures or prevents reproductive abnormalities in both sexes. Kidney necrosis is another macroscopic manifestation of an essential fatty acid deficiency in the rat and is apparently a common cause of death in deficient animals.

The microscopic manifestations of an essential fatty acid deficiency are generally confined to the skin, kidneys, and sex organs. Histological studies of the skin of deficient animals revealed hyperkeratosis and a marked increase in the thickness of the surface epithelium, especially at the openings of hair follicles.[46–49] In a severe deficiency the sebaceous glands become atrophic and degenerate.

Metabolic manifestations of essential fatty acid deficiency include an abnormal distribution of polyenoic acids,[33,34,50] an increased basal metabolic rate, a marked increase in water intake, and a pronounced decrease in urine output.[2,48,51] Of these, the abnormal distribution of polyenoic acid has been studied most extensively in the rat. The metabolic defect is characterized by a pronounced increase in the concentration of palmitoleic acid in the organ and depot fat[52] and an increase in both the palmitoleic acid and oleic acid in the plasma of the rat.[53] The concentration of trienoic acids in the organs and carcass is also increased, and there is a concomitant decrease in the concentration of pentaenoic and hexaenoic acids. The effect of the deficiency on the absolute concentration of various polyenoic acids varies widely in different organs, and it has been suggested that the ratio between the concentration of trienoic and tetraenoic acids be used to evaluate the degree of essential fatty acid deficiency.[54]

In the monkey a deficiency of essential fatty acids results in a marked increase in the concentration of palmitoleic and oleic acids and a decrease in the concentration of linoleic and arachidonic acid in the plasma and erythrocytes.[55] There is a significant increase in the concentration of

46. E. Aaes-Jørgensen, J. P. Funch, P. F. Engel, and H. Dam, *Brit. J. Nutr.*, *10*, 292 (1956).
47. T. C. Panos and J. C. Finerty, *J. Nutr.*, *49*, 397 (1953); *54*, 315 (1954).
48. V. Ramalingaswami and H. M. Sinclair, *Brit. J. Nutr.*, *5*, x (1951).
49. R. Williamson, *Biochem. J.*, *35*, 1003 (1941).
50. L. C. A. Nunn and I. Smedley-MacLean, *Biochem. J.*, *32*, 2178 (1938).
51. E. L. Hove and P. L. Harris, *J. Nutr.*, *31*, 699 (1946).
52. J. F. Mead, *J. Biol. Chem.*, *227*, 1025 (1957).
53. D. R. Howton and S. Hashimoto, *Am. J. Clin. Nutr.*, *8*, 50 (1960).
54. R. T. Holman, *J. Nutr.*, *70*, 405 (1960).
55. L. D. Greenberg and H. D. Moon, *Arch. Biochem. Biophys.*, *94*, 405 (1961).

eicosatrienoate in the plasma of the deficient animal, but a corresponding increase of eicosatrienoate in the erythrocytes was considerably delayed. The latter observation was attributed to the relatively high turnover of erythrocytes.

B. In the Human

Relatively few studies have been made on the effect of an essential fatty acid deficiency in the human. On the basis of observations with three infants and one adult on low-fat diets, the basal metabolic rate increases, and there is an increased susceptibility to infection and a tendency to develop a mild dermatitis in the deficient human.[56] The rate of growth and development appeared to be satisfactory. In another study dermatitis and an abnormal distribution of polyenoic acids in the plasma were found in infants being sustained on a diet low in fat and essential fatty acids; when as little as 1.3% of the caloric intake was provided in the form of linoleic acid, these symptoms disappeared within 2–4 weeks.[57]

Essential fatty acids are being studied clinically for the treatment or prevention of atherosclerosis in the human. These studies were initiated on the basis of a theory that atherogenesis is related to abnormal cholesterol-lipid-lipoprotein metabolism which results primarily from nutritional habits. According to this concept, atherogenesis may result from the ingestion of high-cholesterol fat or a deficiency of certain vitamins.

Data supporting the cholesterol-intoxication theory of atherogenesis have been summarized as follows.[58]

(a) Premature atherosclerosis is frequently encountered in diseases characterized by prolonged hypercholesterolemia.

(b) The pathology of cells constituting the atherosclerotic plaques and intima of atherosclerotic arteries reveals an abnormally high cholesterol and cholesterol-lipid content.

(c) The incidence of atherosclerosis on a national basis may be related directly to the characteristic fat diet of that country. Nations such as Japan, Rhodesia, and India with low cholesterol-fat consumption have a low incidence of atherosclerosis; nations such as the United States, England, Italy, and the Netherlands with high cholesterol-fat consumption have a high incidence of atherosclerosis.

(d) Atherosclerosis has been induced or reversed, respectively, in

56. A. E. Hansen and H. F. Wiese, in W. H. Sebrell, Jr., and R. S. Harris, eds., *The Vitamins, Chemistry, Physiology, Pathology*, Vol. II, Academic, N.Y., 1954, p. 300.
57. A. E. Hansen, M. E. Haggard, A. N. Boelsche, D. J. D. Adam, and H. F. Wiese, *J. Nutr.*, *66*, 565 (1958).
58. L. N. Katz, J. Stamler, and R. Pick, *Federation Proc.*, *15*, 885 (1956).

animals by feeding or withdrawing cholesterol or high cholesterol-fat diets.

The deficiency theory of atherogenesis is supported by evidence showing deposition of abnormal lipids in animals deprived of choline, methionine, inositol, essential fatty acids, pantothenic acid, pyridoxol, cyanocobalamin, nicotinic acid, or magnesium.(59)

In one clinical approach to prevent or reverse atherogenesis in the human, vegetable oils are substituted for the high-cholesterol fats in the diet. These oils are excellent sources of essential fatty acids and usually contain a sitosterol component rather than a cholesterol component. The substitution of polyunsaturated fats for saturated fats in the diet resulted in decreased levels of cholesterol in the serum and of the vegetable oils tested, corn oil was reported to produce the greatest decrease.(60) The effect of corn oil was accounted for in part by its content of linoleic acid and in part by the presence of β-sitosterol.(61)

A recommended dietary allowance for essential fatty acids has not been formulated, but it has been concluded that reasonable variations in the diet will provide sufficient essential fatty acids for good health. Vegetable oils constitute the most abundant natural sources of the essential fatty acids.

59. E. Van Handel, *Am. J. Digest. Diseases*, *22*, 206 (1955).
60. J. T. Anderson, A. Keys, and F. Grande, *J. Nutr.*, *62*, 421 (1957).
61. J. M. R. Beveridge, W. F. Connell, and G. A. Mayer, *Can. J. Biochem. Physiol.*, *35*, 257 (1957).

CHAPTER XX

The Vitamin K Group

1. Introduction

The first indications for the existence of an antihemorrhagic vitamin were obtained from studies on the effect of diet on cholesterol metabolism in the chick and from studies designed to evaluate materials such as fish meal and meat meal as sources of vitamin A and D in chick nutrition.

In 1929 during a study of cholesterol metabolism in chicks, it was observed that chicks developed a characteristic syndrome of the blood when they were fed exclusively on artificial diets that were deficient in lipids.[1,2] The nutritional deficiency was characterized by subcutaneous and intramuscular hemorrhage, anemia, and a prolonged blood clotting time. As a result of further study, it was shown that the syndrome did not result from either a cholesterol deficiency or a deficiency of vitamins A, C, D, or E.[3,4]

In 1931 evidence for a nutritionally-induced blood disease was published by a second group of investigators. It was observed that chicks grew normally when they were fed diets containing fish meal as the sole source of fat-soluble vitamins.[5,6] A particularly high mortality rate was observed, however, if the fish meal had been extracted with ether. Mortality in the group being fed a lipid-deficient diet resulted from hemorrhage that followed the insertion of identifying bands in the wings.

By 1935 it was shown that a fat-soluble factor in green leaves and certain vegetables protected the chick from hemorrhage.[7,8] Since the addition of large amounts of vitamins A, D, and E to the purified diet failed to protect the chick, the existence of a new fat-soluble vitamin designated vitamin K

1. H. Dam, *Biochem. Z.*, *215*, 475 (1929).
2. H. Dam, *Biochem. Z.*, *220*, 158 (1930).
3. H. Dam, *Nature*, *133*, 909 (1934).
4. H. Dam and F. Schønheyder, *Biochem. J.*, *28*, 1355 (1934).
5. W. D. McFarlane, W. R. Graham, Jr., and G. E. Hall, *J. Nutr.*, *4*, 331 (1931).
6. W. D. McFarlane, W. R. Graham, Jr., and F. Richardson, *Biochem. J.*, *25*, 358 (1931).
7. H. Dam, *Nature*, *135*, 652 (1935).
8. H. Dam, *Biochem. J.*, *29*, 1273 (1935).

(*Koagulations-vitamin*) was postulated.[7,8] Independent corroborative evidence for a new fat-soluble vitamin was obtained when chicks developed the characteristic hemorrhagic syndrome while being fed a diet consisting of ether-extracted fish meal, ether-extracted brewer's yeast, polished rice, cod liver oil, and essential minerals.[9]

It was shown that the blood condition did not result from a deficiency of thrombokinase in tissue, a deficiency of fibrinogen, or an accumulation of anticoagulants in the plasma.[10,11] Since an abnormally low concentration of thrombin was formed in the plasma of the deficient chick after the addition of thrombokinase, it was suggested that the activity of vitamin K was associated with the maintenance of sufficient concentrations of the blood clotting accelerator prothrombin.

As studies for the isolation of the new vitamin from natural materials progressed, it appeared that more than one compound could elicit this activity. At first there appeared to be two vitamins. One, designated vitamin K_1, was isolated from the chloroplasts of green plants; the other, designated vitamin K_2, was of microbial origin and was isolated from putrefying plant and animal materials. Both compounds were related structurally, but differed in both the length and the degree of unsaturation of an isoprenoid side chain. As a result of more recent studies, a number of analogs of both vitamin K_1 and vitamin K_2 were isolated and/or synthesized. To distinguish between the various members of each homologous series, the designations vitamin K_1 and K_2 have been used with a parenthetical numerical subscript corresponding to the total number of carbon atoms in the side chain. Other derivatives that are not homologous with vitamin K_1 and K_2 are designated as vitamins K by using the subscripts $_3$, $_4$, $_5$, etc.

2. Isolation

In the early procedures for isolation the vitamin was extracted from the source material with solvents such as ether, petroleum ether, or hexane.[12–15] Preliminary purification was achieved by adsorption chromatography, and the purified concentrate was distilled. Further purification was

9. H. J. Almquist and E. L. R. Stokstad, *J. Nutr.*, *12*, 329 (1936).
10. F. Schønheyder, *Nature*, *135*, 653 (1935).
11. F. Schønheyder, *Biochem. J.*, *30*, 890 (1936).
12. H. J. Almquist, *J. Biol. Chem.*, *114*, 241 (1936); *115*, 589 (1936).
13. H. Dam and F. Schønheyder, *Biochem. J.*, *30*, 897 (1936).
14. S. A. Thayer, D. W. MacCorquodale, S. B. Binkley, and E. A. Doisy, *Science*, *88*, 243 (1938).
15. R. W. McKee, S. B. Binkley, D. W. MacCorquodale, S. A. Thayer, and E. A. Doisy, *J. Am. Chem. Soc.*, *61*, 1295 (1939).

accomplished by precipitation of impurities, and the concentrate was chromatographed on adsorbents such as carbon, sucrose, magnesium oxide, or synthetic zeolites such as Decalso and Permutit. Following four or five such chromatographs, the vitamin was finally purified by molecular distillation.

After it had been established that the vitamins were derivatives of naphthoquinone, the isolation procedure was simplified. In the simplified process the concentrate was treated with sodium hydrosulfite, and the vitamin was reduced to the hydroquinone form.[16] The dihydrovitamin was extracted into petroleum ether and from this solution into Claisen's alkali. The pure vitamin was isolated after diluting the alkaline extract with water, extracting the dihydrovitamin into ether, and oxidizing the dihydrovitamin to the quinone form.

A. Vitamin $K_{1(20)}$ (Phylloquinone)

The isolation of pure vitamin $K_{1(20)}$ from dried alfalfa meal was announced at about the same time by two groups of investigators.[17–19] Highlights of both processes for the isolation of vitamin $K_{1(20)}$ are as follows.

In one study dried alfalfa was extracted with boiling petroleum ether, and the extract was stirred with powdered zinc carbonate to remove chlorophyll.[19] The extract was then concentrated, cooled, and filtered. Next the extract was concentrated, and the residue was distilled *in vacuo* at 150°. The distillate was dissolved in acetone, and the solution was cooled, filtered, and concentrated. The residue was dissolved in petroleum ether, and the solution was passed through a column of anhydrous magnesium sulfate. The column was developed with petroleum ether and then petroleum ether containing 10% benzene. The eluate was concentrated, the residue was dissolved in petroleum ether, and the solution was passed through a column of zinc carbonate. The column was developed with petroleum ether and then petroleum ether containing 10% benzene. The adsorption bands were separated mechanically, and the vitamin-rich bands were selected on the basis of color and extinction coefficient of the eluates at 248 mμ. The combined eluates were again chromatographed on zinc

16. L. F. Fieser, *J. Am. Chem. Soc.*, *61*, 2561 (1939).
17. H. Dam, A. Geiger, J. Glavind, P. Karrer, W. Karrer, E. E. Rothschild, and H. Salomon, *Helv. Chim. Acta*, *22*, 310 (1939).
18. S. B. Binkley, D. W. MacCorquodale, S. A. Thayer, and E. A. Doisy, *J. Biol. Chem.*, *130*, 219 (1939).
19. P. Karrer, A. Geiger, R. Legler, A. Ruegger, and H. Salomon, *Helv. Chim. Acta*, *22*, 1464 (1939).

carbonate. After seven or eight such chromatographic separations, pure vitamin $K_{1(20)}$ was obtained as a yellow oil.

In the other study for the isolation of vitamin $K_{1(20)}$ from dried alfalfa meal, purification was achieved primarily by adsorption chromatography.[18] Dried alfalfa meal was extracted with boiling petroleum ether, and the solution was concentrated. The extract was then passed through a column of Decalso, and fractions were eluted with petroleum ether. Eluates that were essentially free of chlorophyll were combined for a second purification over Decalso. In this manner 20–40-fold concentration of activity was achieved. Selected fractions from the second purification on Decalso were then dissolved in petroleum ether and passed through a column of Permutit. After the column was developed with petroleum ether, fractions were eluted with petroleum ether containing 10% benzene. Selected fractions were combined and concentrated, and the concentrate was subjected to a further purification on Permutit. Selected eluates from the second purification on Permutit were combined and concentrated; a 10–50-fold concentration of the vitamin was achieved by this step. The most active fractions were then dissolved in absolute ethanol, and the mixture was filtered. The filtrate was passed through a column of Darco and after the column was developed stepwise with ethanol, petroleum ether, and 50% ethanol-benzene, a band was eluted with benzene. An additional 3-fold concentration of activity was achieved, and the resulting oil was essentially pure vitamin $K_{1(20)}$. About 90% of the material distilled between 114° and 140°, and the activity of the distillate was essentially the same as the activity of the material prior to distillation. The product was crystallized from ethanol-acetone solution at low temperature and melted at −20°. Finally the vitamin was characterized by conversion to the stable crystalline diacetate of the hydroquinone form.

B. Vitamin $K_{2(35)}$

Vitamin $K_{2(35)}$ was isolated from fish meal that had putrefied; the vitamin had been derived from microbial synthesis.[20] Commercial sardine meal was extracted with hot isopropyl ether to remove lipids prior to the putrefaction process. The extracted meal was freed of solvent, moistened with water, and incubated at 32–40°. After an incubation period of five to six days, the meal was dried and extracted with petroleum ether. The petroleum ether extract was concentrated, and the solution was passed through a column of Decalso. After the column was developed with petroleum ether, fractions were eluted with petroleum ether containing

20. R. W. McKee, S. B. Binkley, S. A. Thayer, D. W. MacCorquodale, and E. A. Doisy, *J. Biol. Chem.*, *131*, 327 (1939).

20% benzene. Selected fractions were concentrated, the residues were dissolved in petroleum ether, and the solution was percolated through a column of Permutit. After the column was developed with petroleum ether and petroleum ether containing 10% benzene, the major band containing the vitamin was eluted with petroleum ether containing 15% or 20% benzene. Selected fractions were combined and concentrated, and the residue was crystallized six times from ethanol-acetone, twice from acetone, and twice from petroleum ether to yield pure vitamin $K_{2(35)}$ melting at 52–53.5°.

C. *Vitamin $K_{2(30)}$*

Vitamin $K_{2(30)}$ was also isolated from putrefied sardine meal but about twenty years after the isolation of vitamin $K_{2(35)}$.[21] The meal was extracted with methylene chloride to remove lipids, and the residue was then moistened and incubated at 40° for about three weeks. The putrefied material was extracted with acetone; the acetone extract was concentrated, and the residue was extracted with petroleum ether. Concentration of the petroleum ether extract yielded a dark brown solution which was washed six to eight times with small portions of 95% methanol to remove the major portion of colored impurities and acids. The purified petroleum ether solution was then concentrated, and the residue was dried over phosphorus pentoxide. The resulting mixture was dissolved in petroleum ether and chromatographed on Decalso. The column was developed with petroleum ether, and two broad bands were formed; the upper dark brown band was removed from the top of the column prior to further development; the lower light yellow band was then eluted with a mixture of petroleum ether-benzene (5:1) to yield a product melting at 30–40°. After three recrystallizations of this material from ethanol, acetone, and petroleum ether, pure vitamin $K_{2(35)}$ was obtained.

The mother liquors from the crystallization of vitamin $K_{2(35)}$ were combined, concentrated, and chromatographed on Decalso. Only the first 70% of the eluate which contained vitamin K activity was used for further purification; concentration of this portion of the eluate yielded material melting at 28–42°. Recrystallization of this material from acetone or petroleum ether at −20° removed a higher melting fraction. After several such purifications, the filtrate yielded material melting at about 25°. About 30% of this fraction was vitamin $K_{2(30)}$; the remaining 70% was vitamin $K_{2(35)}$. This material was further purified by partition on silicone-treated cellulose powder using isopropanol-acetic acid-water (60:2.5:37.5).

21. O. Isler, R. Rüegg, L. H. Chopard-dit-Jean, A. Winterstein, and O. Wiss, *Helv. Chim. Acta*, *41*, 786 (1958).

The first eluates from the column yielded vitamin $K_{2(30)}$ which was recrystallized several times from ethanol to yield pure vitamin $K_{2(30)}$ melting at 49–50°.

3. Structure Determination

A. Vitamin $K_{1(20)}$ (Phylloquinone)

The structure of vitamin $K_{1(20)}$ (phylloquinone) was established as (−)-2-methyl-3-phytyl-1,4-naphthoquinone (**1**) by degradation and synthesis. Analytical data corresponded to the empirical formula $C_{31}H_{46}O_2$, and the molecular weight was established as 450 by potentiometric titration with sodium hydrosulfite.[22]

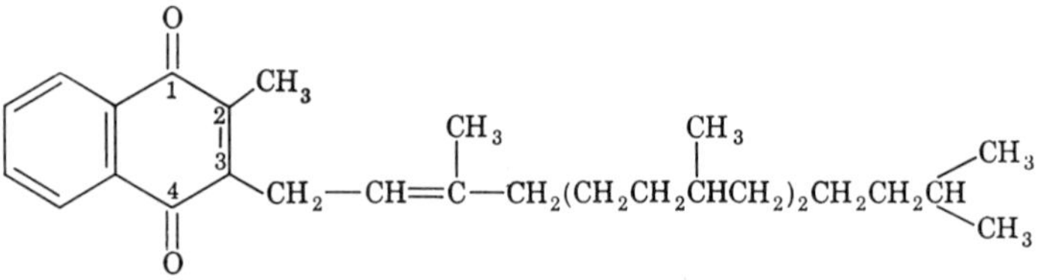

O, CH3, 1, 2, 3, 4, O

$CH_2{-}CH{=}C(CH_3){-}CH_2(CH_2CH_2CH(CH_3)CH_2)_2CH_2CH_2CH(CH_3)_2$

(1)

A quinoid moiety in the vitamin was first suggested on the basis of oxidation-reduction reactions.[15] Catalytic reduction of vitamin $K_{1(20)}$ yielded the colorless octahydro compound (**2**), which was oxidized to the

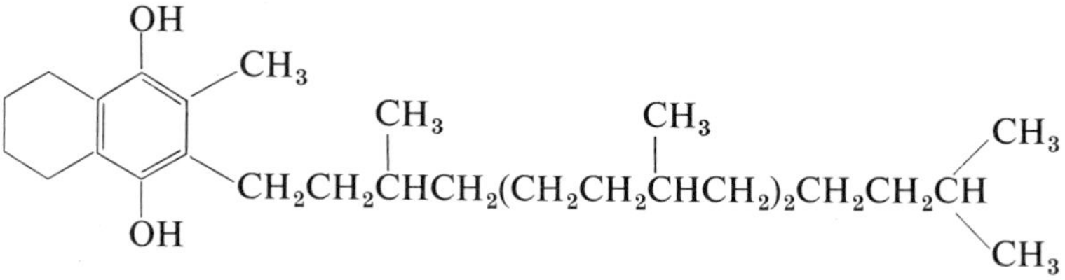

OH, CH3, OH

$CH_2CH_2CH(CH_3)CH_2(CH_2CH_2CH(CH_3)CH_2)_2CH_2CH_2CH(CH_3)_2$

(2)

O, CH3, O

$CH_2CH_2CH(CH_3)CH_2(CH_2CH_2CH(CH_3)CH_2)_2CH_2CH_2CH(CH_3)_2$

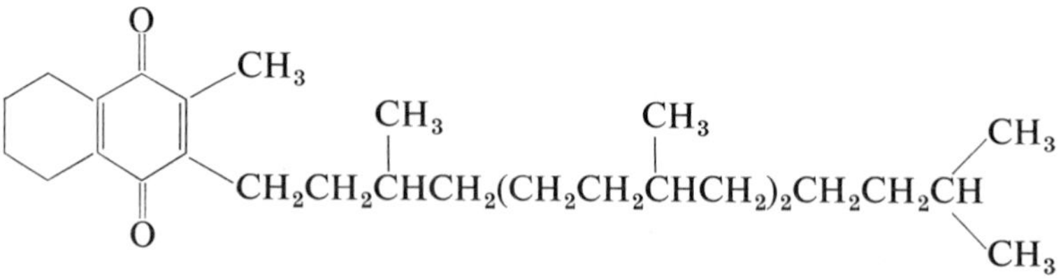

(3)

22. P. Karrer and A. Geiger, *Helv. Chim. Acta*, *22*, 945 (1939).

yellow hexahydroquinone (**3**) on exposure to air. Catalytic hydrogenation of the yellow hexahydroquinone gave the colorless octahydro compound.

On the basis of the yellow color of vitamin $K_{1(20)}$ it was suggested that the quinone moiety was a 1,4- rather than a 1,2-quinone (red); furthermore, the oxidation-reduction potential of the vitamin was found to be similar to that of many known 1,4-quinones.[23] The ultraviolet absorption spectra of the vitamin and several of its derivatives were found to be closely related to those of a series of 2,3-disubstituted 1,4-naphthoquinones and their corresponding derivatives,[15,24] so it was assumed that vitamin $K_{1(20)}$ contains the 2,3-disubstituted 1,4-naphthoquinone moiety (**4**).

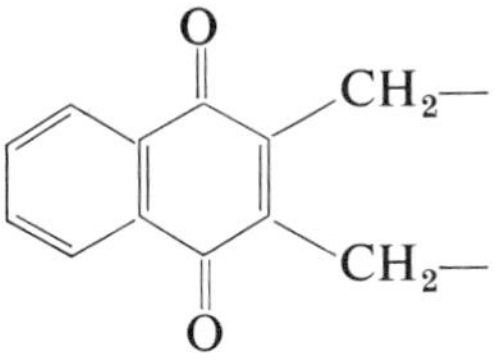

(**4**)

Chromic acid oxidation of vitamin $K_{1(20)}$ yielded products which confirmed the presence of a 2,3-disubstituted 1,4-naphthoquinone moiety.[25] Two acidic products were isolated from the oxidation reaction. The major constituent was phthalic acid (**5**) and the second acidic product, obtained in very low yield, was identified as 2-methyl-1,4-naphthoquinone-3-acetic acid (**6**). The identity of this latter product was established by comparing its methyl ester with an authentic specimen synthesized from 1,4-diacetoxy-2-methylnaphthalene-3-acetic acid (**7**).[26]

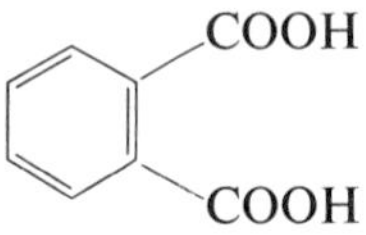

(**5**) 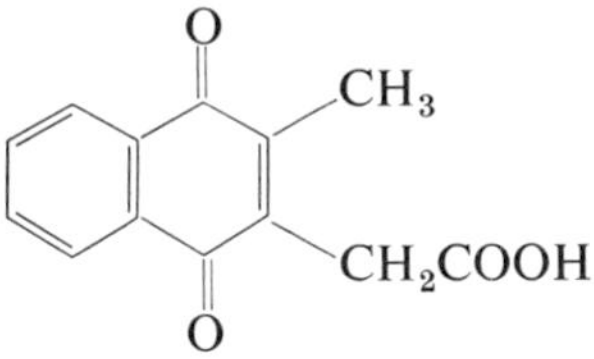 (**6**)

23. S. B. Binkley, D. W. MacCorquodale, L. C. Cheney, S. A. Thayer, R. W. McKee, and E. A. Doisy, *J. Am. Chem. Soc.*, *61*, 1612 (1939).
24. D. T. Ewing, J. M. Vandenbelt, and O. Kamm, *J. Biol. Chem.*, *131*, 345 (1939).
25. D. W. MacCorquodale, S. B. Binkley, S. A. Thayer, and E. A. Doisy, *J. Am. Chem. Soc.*, *61*, 1928 (1939).
26. D. W. MacCorquodale, L. C. Cheney, S. B. Binkley, W. F. Holcomb, R. W. McKee, S. A. Thayer, and E. A. Doisy, *J. Biol. Chem.*, *131*, 357 (1939).

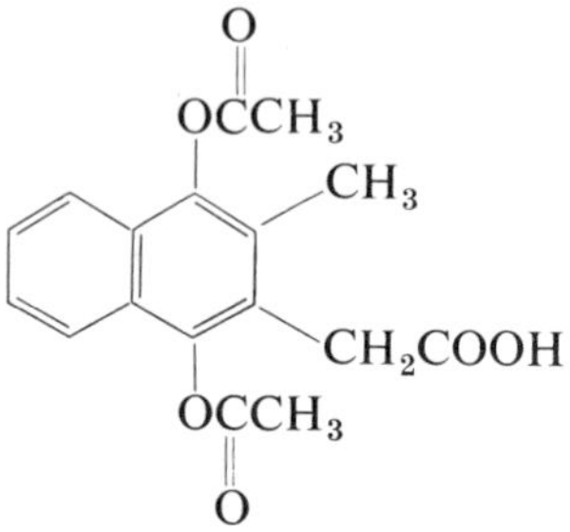

$$\text{1,4-(CH}_3\text{COO)}_2\text{-2-CH}_3\text{-3-(CH}_2\text{COOH)C}_{10}\text{H}_4$$

(7)

The nature of the side chain of vitamin $K_{1(20)}$ was established by oxidation.[23,26] It was assumed that the side chain contains one carbon-carbon double bond since catalytic hydrogenation of the vitamin to the corresponding octahydro derivative (**2**) consumed one mole of hydrogen in excess of that required for the reduction of the naphthoquinone moiety. The vitamin was reductively acetylated to crystalline diacetyldihydrovitamin $K_{1(20)}$ (**8**), which retained the unsaturation in the side chain. Mild chromic acid oxidation of this derivative yielded 1,4-diacetoxy-2-methylnaphthalene-3-acetic acid (**7**) and the ketone 6,10,14-trimethyl-2-pentadecanone (**9**). Better yields of the ketone (**9**) were obtained from the diacetyldihydrovitamin (**8**) by ozonolysis. The structure of the ketone

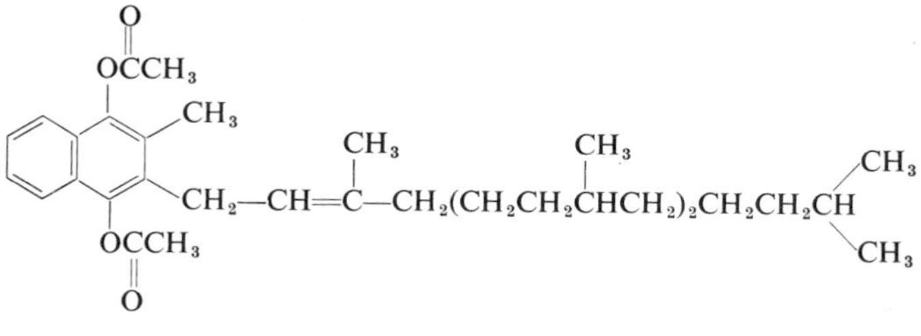

$$\text{1,4-(CH}_3\text{COO)}_2\text{-2-CH}_3\text{-3-C}_{10}\text{H}_4\text{—CH}_2\text{—CH=C(CH}_3\text{)—CH}_2\text{(CH}_2\text{CH}_2\text{CH(CH}_3\text{)CH}_2\text{)}_2\text{CH}_2\text{CH}_2\text{CH(CH}_3\text{)}_2$$

(**8**)

$$\text{1,4-(CH}_3\text{COO)}_2\text{-2-CH}_3\text{-3-(CH}_2\text{COOH)C}_{10}\text{H}_4 \qquad \text{O=C(CH}_3\text{)—CH}_2\text{(CH}_2\text{CH}_2\text{CH(CH}_3\text{)CH}_2\text{)}_2\text{CH}_2\text{CH}_2\text{CH(CH}_3\text{)}_2$$

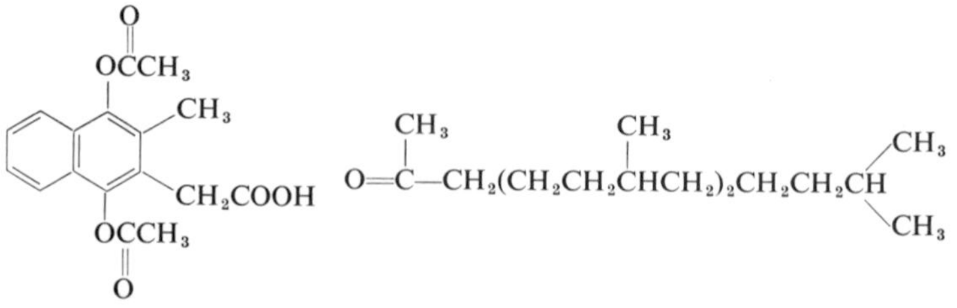

(7) (9)

(**9**) was established by comparing its semicarbazone with that of a ketone previously derived from phytol by oxidation.[27]

On the basis of the structure of the oxidation products (**7**) and (**9**), vitamin $K_{1(20)}$ was formulated as 2-methyl-3-phytyl-1,4-naphthoquinone. The structural conclusion was confirmed quickly by synthesis.

B. Vitamin $K_{2(35)}$

The structure 2-methyl-3-farnesylfarnesyl-1,4-naphthoquinone was originally assigned to vitamin K_2 on the basis of degradation studies,[28,29] but a recent synthetic study has established its structure as 2-methyl-3-*all-trans*-farnesylgeranylgeranyl-1,4-naphthoquinone (**10**) or vitamin $K_{2(35)}$.[21]

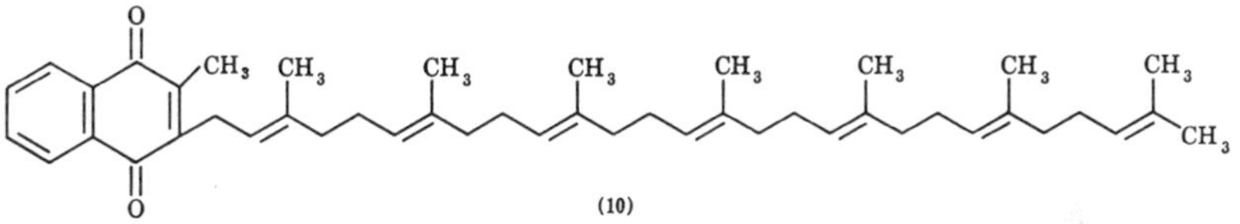

(10)

The nature of the quinone moiety of vitamin K_2 was established exactly as described for the determination of the structure of vitamin $K_{1(20)}$. The vitamin was reduced to a colorless hydroquinone which was readily reoxidized to the quinone. The yellow color of the vitamin suggested a 1,4- rather than a 1,2-quinone moiety, and comparison of its ultraviolet absorption spectrum with the spectra of vitamin $K_{1(20)}$, 1,4-naphthoquinone, and substituted 1,4-naphthoquinones suggested the presence of a 2,3-disubstituted 1,4-naphthoquinone moiety.[24]

The side chain was erroneously assumed to contain six double bonds since hydrogenation of vitamin K_2 appeared to require six moles of hydrogen in addition to that consumed by the naphthoquinoid ring system.[15] The absence of a conjugated double bond system in the side chain was indicated from the ultraviolet absorption spectrum and the failure to form addition products with maleic anhydride.

Diacetyldihydrovitamin K_2 (**11**) appeared to consume six moles of hydrogen on catalytic hydrogenation and six moles of bromine on bromination. Treatment of diacetyldihydrovitamin K_2 with ozone and decomposition of the corresponding ozonide with zinc and acetic acid yielded acetone, 1,4-diacetoxy-2-methylnaphthalene-3-acetaldehyde (**12**), and approximately five moles of levulinic acid (**13**). On the basis of these data it was

27. G. F. Fisher and K. Löwenberg, *Ann.*, *464*, 69 (1928).
28. P. Karrer and A. Epprecht, *Helv. Chim. Acta*, *23*, 272 (1940).
29. S. B. Binkley, R. W. McKee, S. A. Thayer, and E. A. Doisy, *J. Biol. Chem.*, *133*, 721 (1940).

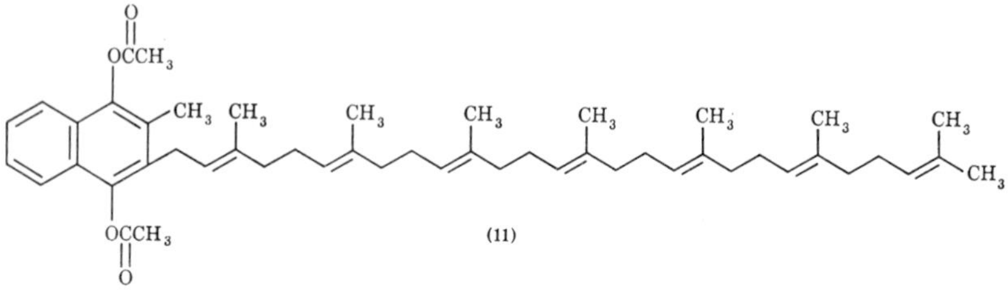

(11)

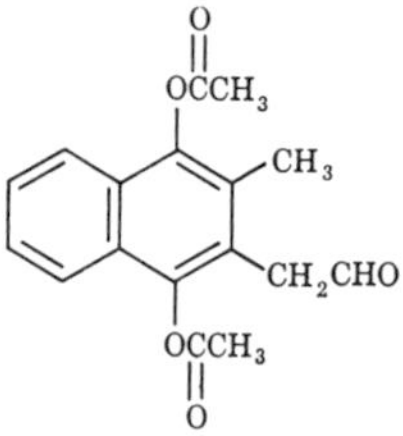

(12)

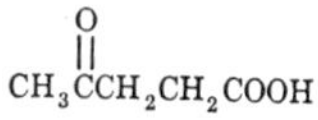

$CH_3COCH_2CH_2COOH$

(13)

assumed that the vitamin contained a difarnesyl side chain at the 3-position.

In the absence of a confirmatory synthesis these structural interpretations were accepted until about 1958, when the synthesis of ten members of the vitamin K_2 series was reported.[21] Comparison of the major vitamin K of microbial origin with synthetic 2-methyl-3-*all-trans*-farnesylgeranylgeranyl-1,4-naphthoquinone established the 3-substituent of the major product as an isoprenoid side chain containing thirty-five carbon atoms rather than thirty as originally deduced by degradation. On the basis of these data, the vitamin K_2 originally isolated from putrefied fish meal is now designated vitamin $K_{2(35)}$ **(10)**.

C. *Vitamin* $K_{2(30)}$ (*Farnoquinone*)

The structure 2-methyl-3-farnesylfarnesyl-1,4-naphthoquinone **(14)**, which was originally assigned to the vitamin K_2 melting at 54°, is now

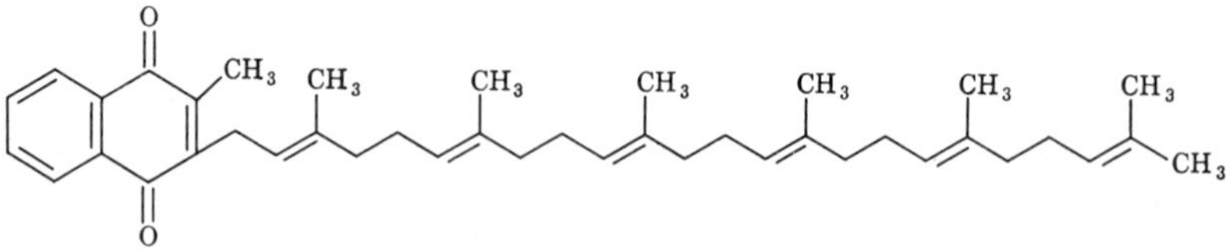

(14)

identified with a vitamin K_2 of microbial origin which melts at 50°. The structural conclusion is based on the identity of the natural product with synthetic 2-methyl-3-*all-trans*-farnesylfarnesyl-1,4-naphthoquinone.[21]

4. Synthesis

A. Vitamin $K_{1(20)}$

Syntheses confirming the structure of vitamin $K_{1(20)}$ were published at nearly the same time. In one synthesis 2-methyl-1,4-naphthoquinone **(16)** was condensed with phytyl bromide (**15**); the product was obtained by molecular distillation and was characterized by elemental analysis, color tests, and blood clotting efficiency.[30]

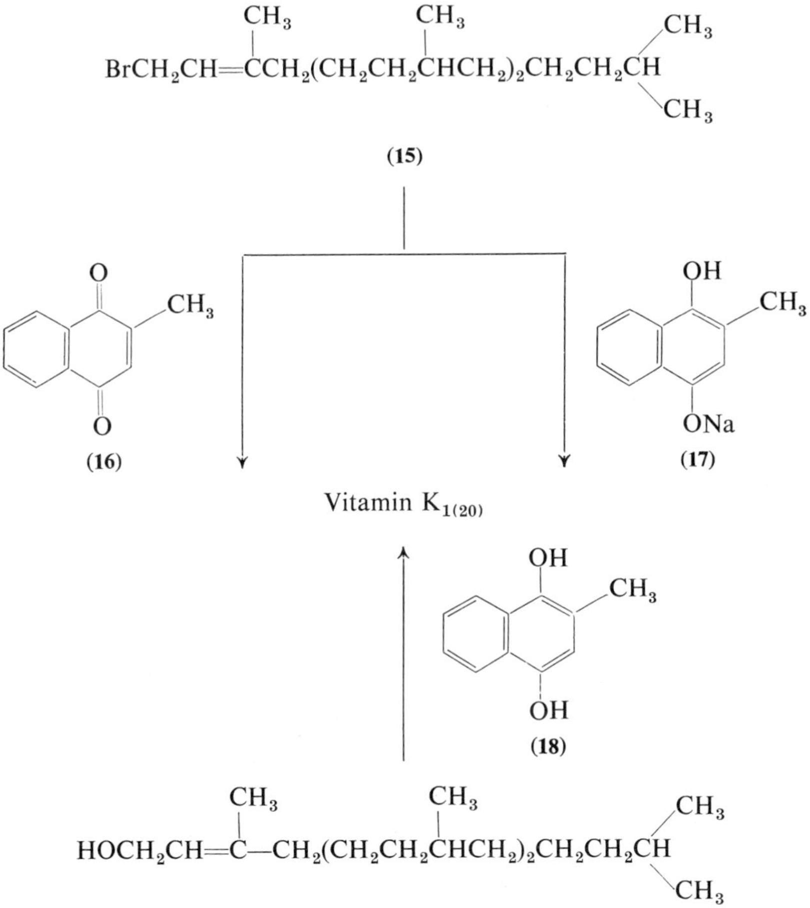

$$BrCH_2CH{=}C(CH_3)CH_2(CH_2CH_2CH(CH_3)CH_2)_2CH_2CH_2CH(CH_3)_2$$

(15)

(16) 2-methyl-1,4-naphthoquinone, O, O, CH_3 → Vitamin $K_{1(20)}$ ← (17) OH, CH_3, ONa

Vitamin $K_{1(20)}$

(18) OH, CH_3, OH

$$HOCH_2CH{=}C(CH_3){-}CH_2(CH_2CH_2CH(CH_3)CH_2)_2CH_2CH_2CH(CH_3)_2$$

(19)

30. H. J. Almquist and A. A. Klose, *J. Am. Chem. Soc.*, *61*, 2557 (1939); *J. Biol. Chem.*, *132*, 469 (1940).

Synthesis was also achieved by condensing the monosodium salt **(17)** of 2-methyl-1,4-naphthohydroquinone with phytyl bromide.[31] The product, after oxidation and purification by molecular distillation, was characterized by reductive acetylation to the known crystalline 1,4-diacetyldihydrovitamin $K_{1(20)}$.

The condensation of 2-methyl-1,4-naphthohydroquinone **(18)** with phytol **(19)** in the presence of catalysts such as oxalic acid or chloroacetic acid was also used for the synthesis of vitamin $K_{1(20)}$.[32] The condensation product was purified as the hydroquinone and then oxidized with silver oxide. The resulting quinone, which was active in the blood clotting test, was converted to crystalline diacetyldihydrovitamin $K_{1(20)}$ for further chemical identification.

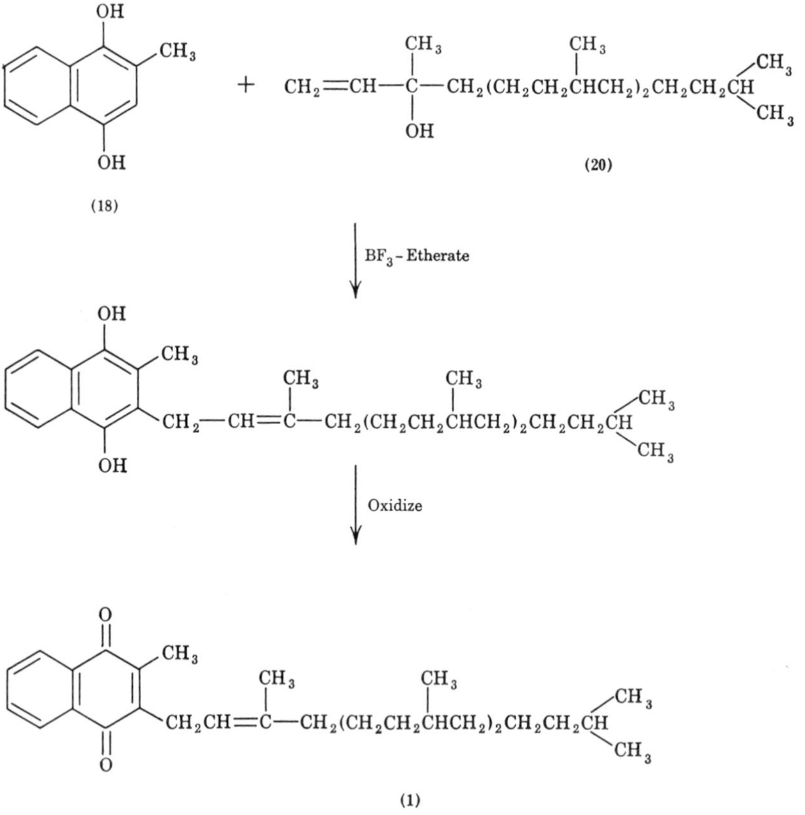

OH, CH_3, OH (18) + $CH_2{=}CH{-}C(CH_3)(OH){-}CH_2(CH_2CH_2CH(CH_3)CH_2)_2CH_2CH_2CH(CH_3)_2$ (20)

↓ BF_3-Etherate

OH, CH_3, $CH_2{-}CH{=}C(CH_3){-}CH_2(CH_2CH_2CH(CH_3)CH_2)_2CH_2CH_2CH(CH_3)_2$, OH

↓ Oxidize

O, CH_3, $CH_2CH{=}C(CH_3){-}CH_2(CH_2CH_2CH(CH_3)CH_2)_2CH_2CH_2CH(CH_3)_2$, O

(1)

31. S. B. Binkley, L. C. Cheney, W. F. Holcomb, R. W. McKee, S. A. Thayer, D. W. MacCorquodale, and E. A. Doisy, *J. Am. Chem. Soc.*, *61*, 2558 (1939).
32. L. Fieser, *J. Am. Chem. Soc.*, *61*, 2559, 3467 (1939).

Vitamin $K_{1(20)}$ has also been synthesized by the condensation of 2-methyl-1,4-naphthohydroquinone (**18**) with isophytol (3,7,11,15-tetramethyl-1-hexadecen-3-ol) (**20**) in the presence of boron trifluoride etherate.[33,34] With synthetic isophytol, racemic vitamin $K_{1(20)}$ was obtained; when optically active isophytol was prepared from phytol and then condensed with 2-methyl-1,4-naphthohydroquinone, the product was identical with natural vitamin $K_{1(20)}$ and with vitamin $K_{1(20)}$ which had been synthesized from phytol.

The synthesis of vitamin $K_{1(20)}$ by the condensation of 2-methyl-1,4-naphthohydroquinone and phytol was used commercially with little or no modification until 1954.[32] The over-all yield of the process was about 25%, with phytadiene and 2-methyl-2-phytyl-2,3-dihydro-1,4-naphthoquinone (**21**) constituting the major portion of the by-products.[35]

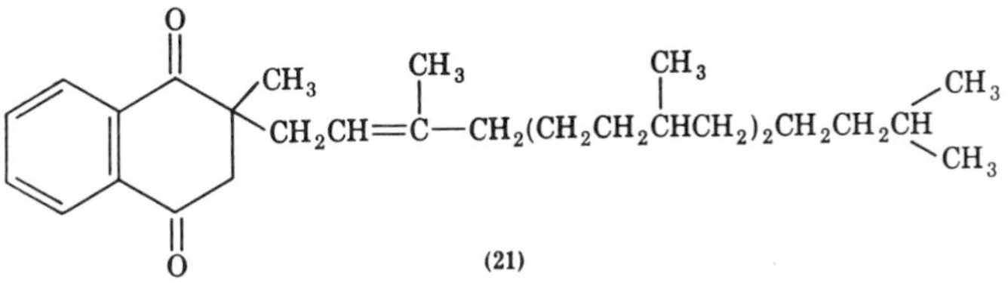

$$\text{(2,3-dihydro-1,4-naphthoquinone, C-2: } CH_3,\ CH_2CH{=}\overset{\overset{CH_3}{|}}{C}{-}CH_2(CH_2CH_2\overset{\overset{CH_3}{|}}{C}HCH_2)_2CH_2CH_2CH(CH_3)_2\text{)}$$

(21)

Several modifications of this basic condensation reaction were reported,[36] and the over-all yield of vitamin $K_{1(20)}$ was increased to 66%. It was found that the oxalic acid catalyst effectively removed phytol from the condensation reaction by reacting with it to form the oxalic acid ester of phytol; the phytadiene by-product was derived from this ester during the distillation of the condensation product. Potassium acid sulfate and boron trifluoride etherate were found to be effective catalysts for the condensation, and there was less esterification of phytol.

The formation of the 2-phytyl-2,3-dihydro derivative (**21**) in the condensation reaction was eliminated by substituting 1-*O*-acetyl-2-methyl-1,4-naphthohydroquinone (**22**) for 2-methyl-1,4-naphthohydroquinone in the synthesis. The intermediate 1-monoacetyldihydrovitamin $K_{1(20)}$ (**23**) is superior to dihydrovitamin $K_{1(20)}$ as an intermediate. It is more resistant to oxidation, and the necessity for reduction prior to purification is eliminated. The monoacetyldihydro derivative (**23**) was separated from neutral by-products by extraction with Claisen's alkali. In the alkaline

33. O. Isler and K. Doebel, *Angew. Chem.*, *65*, 264 (1953).
34. O. Isler and K. Doebel, *Helv. Chim. Acta*, *37*, 225 (1954).
35. M. Tishler, L. F. Fieser, and N. L. Wendler, *J. Am. Chem. Soc.*, *62*, 1982 (1940).
36. R. Hirschmann, R. Miller, and N. L. Wendler, *J. Am. Chem. Soc.*, *76*, 4592 (1954).

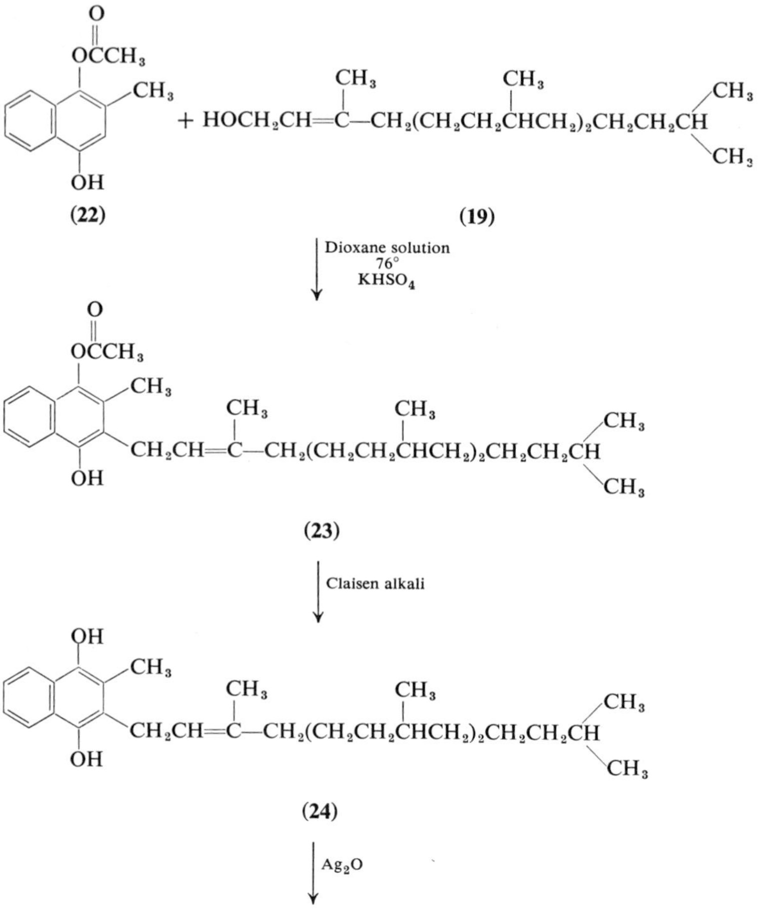

$$\text{(22)}\ \text{1-}OCOCH_3\text{-2-}CH_3\text{-4-}OH\text{-naphthalene} + HOCH_2CH{=}\overset{CH_3}{\overset{|}{C}}{-}CH_2(CH_2CH_2\overset{CH_3}{\overset{|}{C}}HCH_2)_2CH_2CH_2CH(CH_3)_2\ \text{(19)}$$

Dioxane solution
76°
$KHSO_4$

$$\text{(23)}\ \text{1-}OCOCH_3\text{-2-}CH_3\text{-3-}[CH_2CH{=}\overset{CH_3}{\overset{|}{C}}{-}CH_2(CH_2CH_2\overset{CH_3}{\overset{|}{C}}HCH_2)_2CH_2CH_2CH(CH_3)_2]\text{-4-}OH\text{-naphthalene}$$

Claisen alkali

$$\text{(24)}\ \text{1,4-}(OH)_2\text{-2-}CH_3\text{-3-}[CH_2CH{=}\overset{CH_3}{\overset{|}{C}}{-}CH_2(CH_2CH_2\overset{CH_3}{\overset{|}{C}}HCH_2)_2CH_2CH_2CH(CH_3)_2]\text{-naphthalene}$$

Ag_2O

Vitamin $K_{1(20)}$

separation step, the 1-acetyl group was hydrolyzed and the product, dihydrovitamin $K_{1(20)}$ (**24**), was sufficiently pure for direct oxidation to vitamin $K_{1(20)}$.

B. Vitamin $K_{2(35)}$

The synthesis of *all-trans* vitamin $K_{2(35)}$ proceeds (Fig. 1) by the condensation of acetone with sodium acetylide in liquid ammonia.[21] The condensation product (**25**) was partially reduced to the allylic carbinol (**26**), which underwent allylic rearrangement on treatment with phosphorus tribromide to yield 3-methyl-2-butenyl bromide (**27**). Condensation of this bromide with acetoacetic ester yielded 2-methyl-2-hepten-6-one (**28**). The

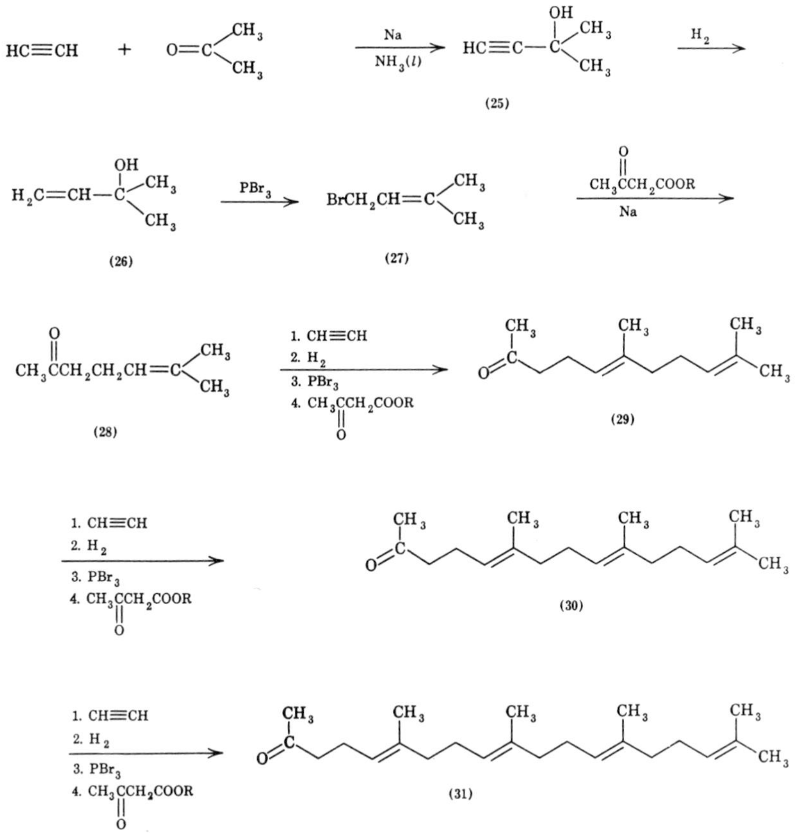

(con't)

Fig. 1. The synthesis of *all-trans* vitamin $K_{2(35)}$.[21]

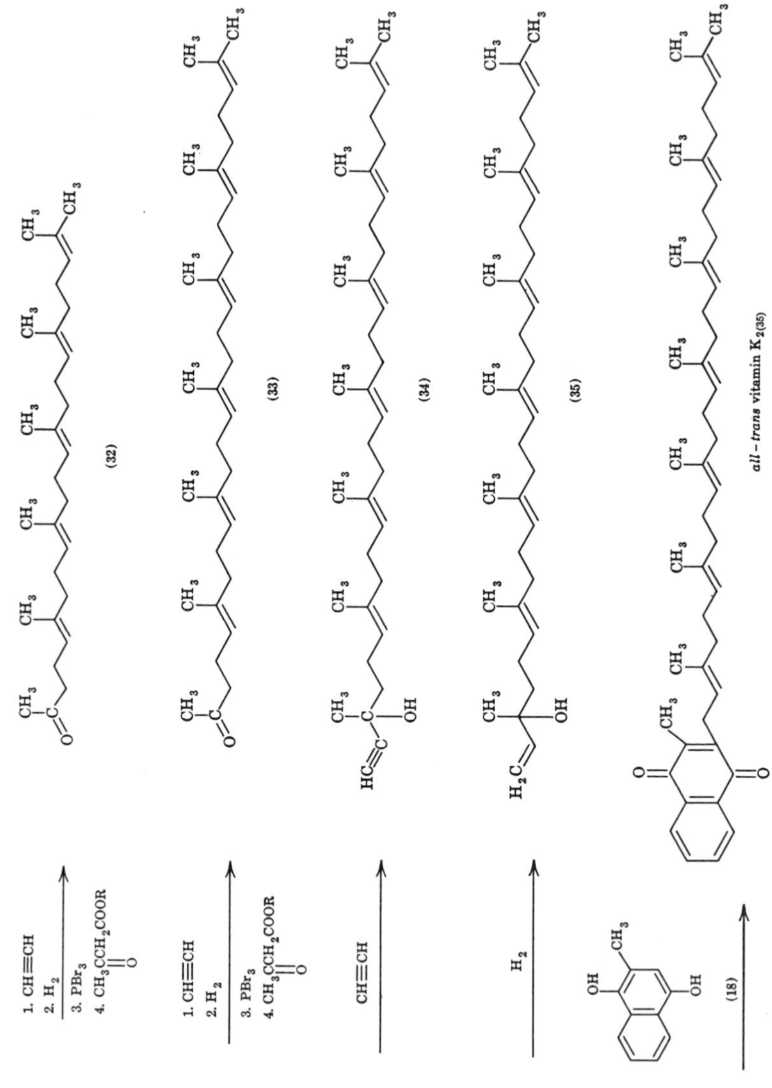

1. $CH{\equiv}CH$
2. H_2
3. PBr_3
4. $CH_3\overset{\displaystyle O}{\overset{\|}{C}}CH_2COOR$

(32)

1. $CH{\equiv}CH$
2. H_2
3. PBr_3
4. $CH_3\overset{\displaystyle O}{\overset{\|}{C}}CH_2COOR$

(33)

$CH{\equiv}CH$

(34)

H_2

(35)

(18)

all-trans vitamin $K_{2(35)}$

carbon chain of the intermediate (**28**) was then extended by one isoprene unit using the same sequence of reactions to yield geranylacetone (**29**). The pure *trans* form of geranylacetone was isolated by fractional distillation. The acetylide reaction, partial reduction, bromination, and acetoacetate condensation reactions were used sequentially for the introduction of each of the next four isoprenoid units. After the introduction of each isoprenoid unit, the *cis* and *trans* isomers were separated by fractional crystallization of the isoprenoid ketones farnesylacetone (**30**), geranylgeranylacetone (**31**), farnesylgeranylacetone (**32**), and farnesylfarnesylacetone (**33**).

The two remaining carbon atoms of the side chain were introduced by condensing farnesylfarnesylacetone (**33**) with sodium acetylide in liquid ammonia. Partial hydrogenation of the acetylenic bond in the intermediate (**34**) yielded the allylic carbinol (**35**) which was condensed with 2-methyl-1,4-naphthohydroquinone (**18**) in the presence of boron trifluoride etherate to yield *all-trans* vitamin $K_{2(35)}$.

C. *Vitamin $K_{2(30)}$*

Vitamin $K_{2(30)}$ was synthesized by the condensation of 2-methyl-1,4-naphthohydroquinone and farnesylnerolidol (**36**) in the presence of boron trifluoride etherate.[21] The allylic carbinol (**36**) was synthesized by the condensation of farnesylgeranylacetone (**32**) with sodium acetylide followed by partial reduction.

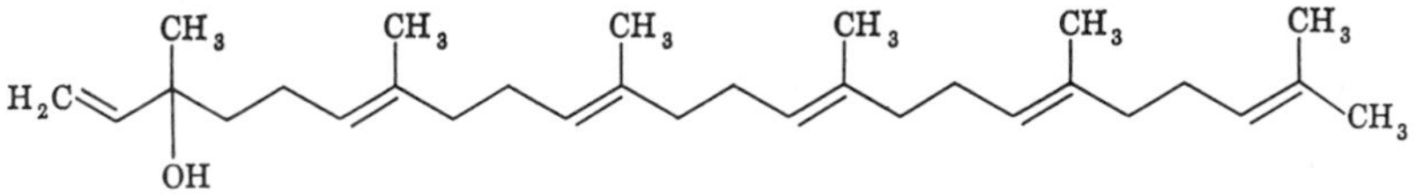

(36)

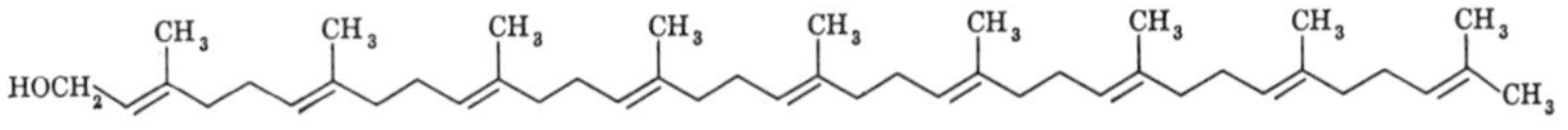

(37)

D. *Vitamin $K_{2(45)}$*

A higher homolog of vitamin $K_{2(35)}$ was synthesized by condensing 2-methyl-1,4-naphthohydroquinone with solanesol (**37**) in the presence of boron trifluoride etherate.[37] After it was shown that solanesol, a polyisoprenol isolated from tobacco, was composed of nine isoprenoid units, the condensation product 2-methyl-3-solanesyl-1,4-naphthoquinone was

37. C. H. Shunk, R. E. Erickson, E. L. Wong, and K. Folkers, *J. Am. Chem. Soc.*, *81*, 5000 (1959).

designated vitamin $K_{2(45)}$.[38] A comparison[39] of synthetic vitamin $K_{2(45)}$ with the K-vitamin obtained from *Mycobacterium tuberculosis*[40,41] established the identity of the natural higher homolog of vitamin K_2.

E. Vitamin K_3 (Menadione)

The compound 2-methyl-1,4-naphthoquinone (**16**) is designated vitamin K_3 or menadione. It was synthesized as early as 1925 by the chromic acid oxidation of 2-methylnaphthalene,[42] and it was shown to have a high order of antihemorrhagic activity in the chick assay.[43] Although menadione has not been isolated from nature, it has been considered to have an important role in metabolism.

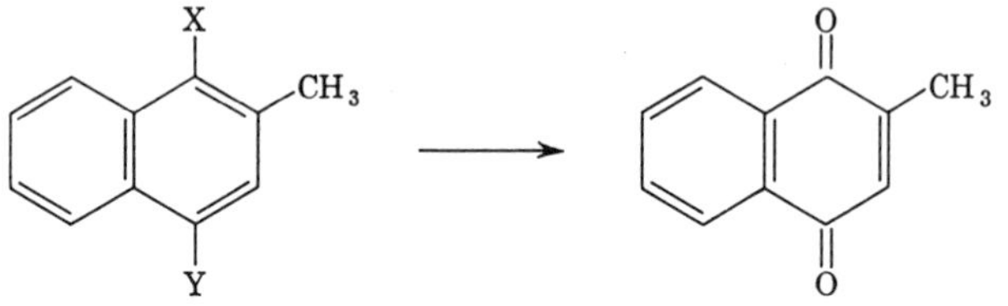

X and Y=H, NH_2, OH, OCH_3

(38)

(16)

Menadione (**16**) has been synthesized by two general methods. One method employs the oxidation of either 2-methylnaphthalene or the corresponding 1- or 1,4-substituted amino, hydroxy, or methoxy derivatives (**38**). Oxidizing agents such as ferric chloride, hydrogen peroxide, chromic acid, or nitric acid have been used.

A second approach to the synthesis of menadione requires a Diels-Alder condensation between an alicyclic or cyclic diene and a substituted *p*-quinone. For example, butadiene (**39**) condensed with 2-methyl-1,4-benzoquinone (**40**) to yield 5,8,9,10-tetrahydro-2-methyl-1,4-naphthoquinone (**41**).[44] The tetrahydroquinone (**41**) was isomerized to 5,8-dihydro-2-methyl-1,4-naphthohydroquinone (**42**), which was oxidized to

38. R. E. Erickson, C. H. Shunk, N. R. Trenner, B. H. Arison, and K. Folkers, *J. Am. Chem. Soc.*, *81*, 4999 (1959).
39. H. Noll, R. Rüegg, U. Gloor, G. Ryser, and O. Isler, *Helv. Chim. Acta*, *43*, 433 (1960).
40. J. Francis, J. Madinaveitia, H. M. MacTurc, and G. A. Snow, *Nature*, *163*, 365 (1949).
41. H. Noll, *J. Biol. Chem.*, *232*, 919 (1958).
42. V. Vesley and J. Kapp, *Rec. Trav. Chim.*, *44*, 360 (1925).
43. S. Ansbacher and E. Fernholz, *J. Am. Chem. Soc.*, *61*, 1924 (1939).
44. C-K. Chuang and C-T. Han, *Ber.*, *68*, 876 (1935).

menadione in about 50% yield by chromic acid.[45] When silver oxide was used to oxidize 5,8-dihydro-2-methyl-1,4-naphthohydroquinone (**42**), the intermediate 5,8-dihydro-2-methyl-1,4-naphthoquinone (**43**) was formed.

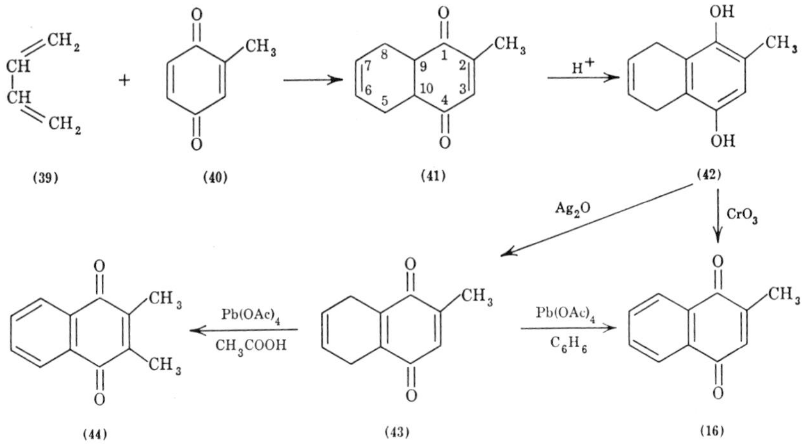

(39) (40) (41) (42)

H^+ Ag_2O CrO_3

$Pb(OAc)_4$ / CH_3COOH $Pb(OAc)_4$ / C_6H_6

(44) (43) (16)

Oxidation of the dihydroquinone (**43**) with lead tetraacetate in benzene solution yielded menadione; treatment of the same intermediate with an excess of lead tetraacetate in acetic acid solution yielded 2,3-dimethyl-1,4-naphthoquinone (**44**).

A Diels-Alder condensation between 1,3-cyclohexadiene (**45**) and 2-methyl-1,4-benzoquinone (**40**) has also been applied to the synthesis of

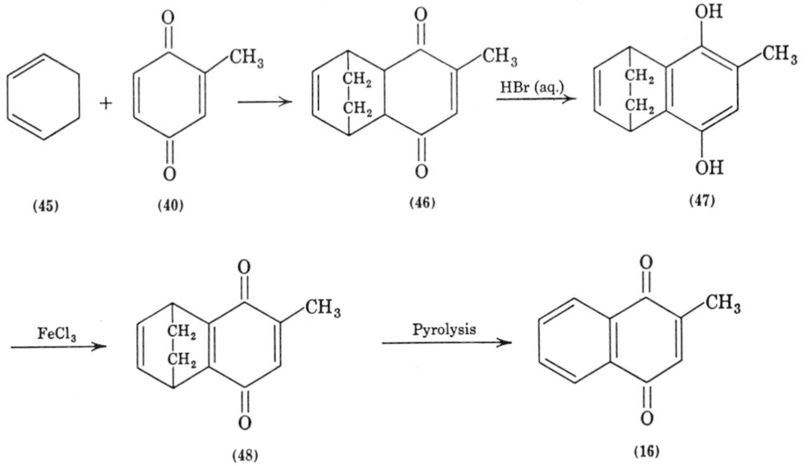

(45) (40) (46) HBr (aq.) (47)

$FeCl_3$ (48) Pyrolysis (16)

45. L. F. Fieser and F. C. Chang, *J. Am. Chem. Soc.*, *64*, 2043 (1942).

menadione.[46] The product of this condensation, 5,8-ethylene-5,8,9,10-tetrahydro-2-methyl-1,4-naphthoquinone (**46**), was isomerized catalytically to 5,8-ethylene-5,8-dihydro-2-methyl-1,4-naphthohydroquinone (**47**) with aqueous hydrobromic acid. The intermediate hydroquinone (**47**) was oxidized to 5,8-ethylene-5,8-dihydro-2-methyl-1,4-naphthoquinone (**48**) with ferric chloride and after deethanation of this intermediate by pyrolysis, menadione was obtained in a 75% over-all yield.

F. *Vitamin K_4*

The designation vitamin K_4 is used for 2-methyl-1,4-naphthohydroquinone. It is obtained in the form of the diacetate by reducing 2-methyl-1,4-naphthoquinone with zinc and acetic acid in the presence of acetic anhydride.

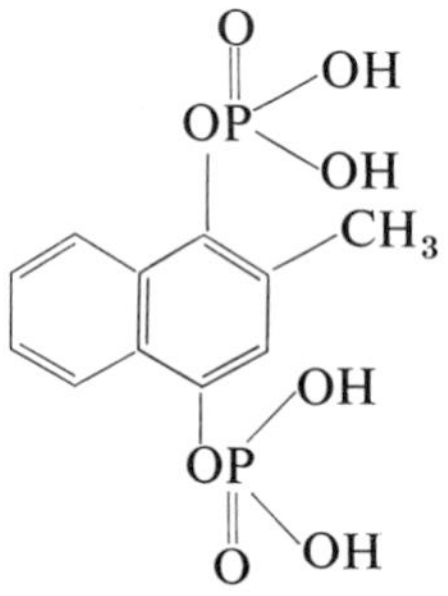

(49)

The tetrasodium salt of the diphosphate (**49**) was obtained by phosphorylating 2-methyl-1,4-naphthohydroquinone with phosphorus oxychloride in pyridine solution and hydrolyzing the product with sodium carbonate.[47]

G. *Vitamins K_5 and K_6*

Two water-soluble compounds showing antihemorrhagic activity are 4-amino-2-methyl-1-naphthol hydrochloride (vitamin K_5) (**51**) and 1,4-diamino-2-methylnaphthalene dihydrochloride (vitamin K_6) (**52**). Both compounds have been synthesized (Fig. 2) from 2-methylnaphthalene (**50**).[48]

46. M. R. Grdinic and V. K. Jugovic, *Archiv. Khem.*, *23*, 73 (1951); *Chem. Abstr.*, *46*, 11165*g* (1952).
47. L. F. Fieser and E. M. Fry, *J. Am. Chem. Soc.*, *62*, 228 (1940).
48. H. Veldstra and P. W. Wiardi, *Rec. Trav. Chim.*, *62*, 75 (1943).

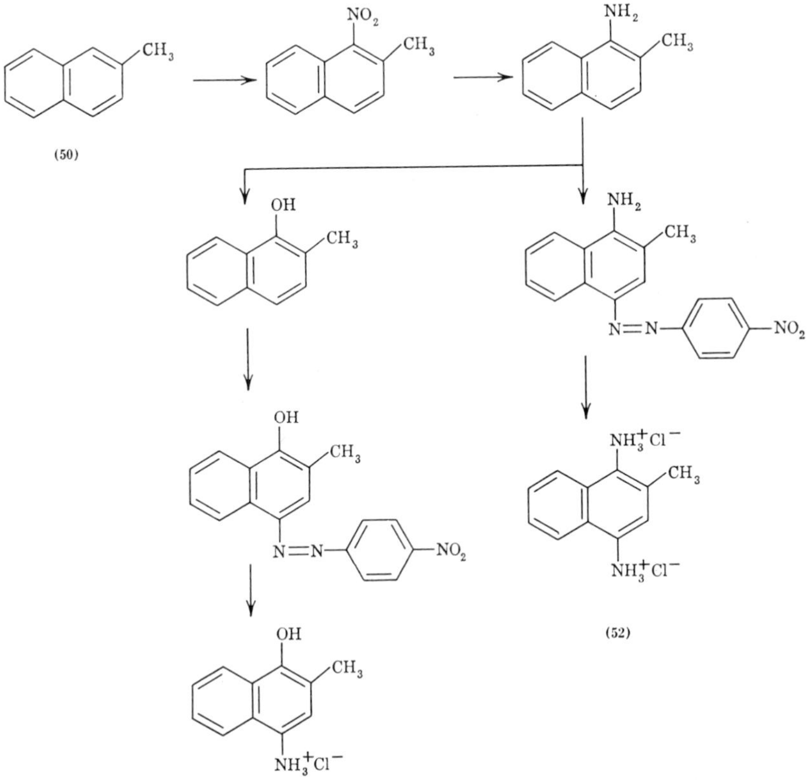

(50)

(51)

(52)

Fig. 2. Synthesis of vitamin K_5 and vitamin K_6.[48]

H. Vitamin K_7

Vitamin K_7 is 4-amino-3-methyl-1-naphthol hydrochloride (**53**). This water-soluble compound is an isomer of vitamin K_5 and has been synthesized in a manner analogous to that shown in Figure 2.[49]

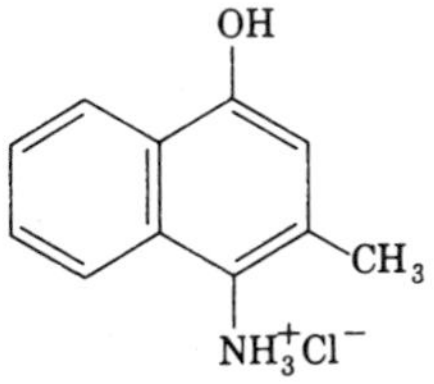

(53)

49. P. P. T. Sah, *Z. Vitamin-, Hormon- Fermentforsch.*, *3*, 324 (1950).

5. Biosynthesis

It appears that vitamin $K_{2(20)}$ (**54**) is the significant form of vitamin K activity in mammalian metabolism, and it has been suggested that the other K-vitamins of dietary origin are metabolized by conversion to menadione, which is then alkylated with geranylgeranyl pyrophosphate to yield vitamin $K_{2(20)}$.

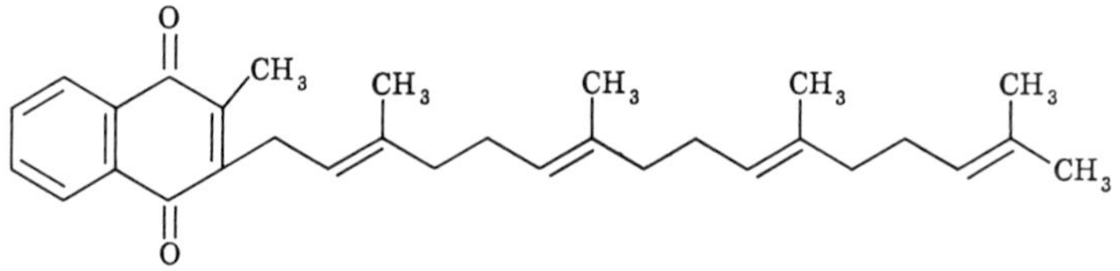

(54)

The conversion of dietary vitamin $K_{1(20)}$ to vitamin $K_{2(20)}$ *in vivo* was demonstrated by using vitamin $K_{1(20)}$ that was labeled with tritium in the aromatic nucleus and C^{14} in the 3-substituent.[50] The vitamin K was isolated from the liver, kidney, skeletal muscle, and heart of the chick and was analyzed by countercurrent distribution. Vitamin $K_{1(20)}$ was found exclusively in the liver. Vitamin $K_{2(20)}$ was isolated from the kidney, skeletal muscle, heart, and also from the liver; tritium was the only isotopic label in the biosynthetic product. The conversion of vitamin $K_{2(30)}$ to vitamin $K_{2(20)}$ *in vivo* was also established when tritium labeled vitamin $K_{2(30)}$ was administered to the chick, pigeon, or rat in a comparable series of studies.[51] The vitamin was efficiently converted to vitamin $K_{2(20)}$, and the distribution of the administered vitamin and its metabolic product in the various organs was comparable to that observed with vitamin $K_{1(20)}$. On the basis of the quantitative distribution of vitamin $K_{2(20)}$ in the various organs, it was concluded that the K-vitamins of dietary origin are stored in the liver. The 3-substituent of the dietary K-vitamin is then metabolized in this organ to yield menadione; part of the menadione is converted to vitamin $K_{2(20)}$ in the liver and part is transported to other tissue before conversion to vitamin $K_{2(20)}$.

The conversion of menadione to vitamin $K_{2(20)}$ *in vivo* was demonstrated by the administration of 2-C^{14}-methyl-1,4-naphthoquinone to chicks and rats.[52,53] The vitamin K was isolated from the liver and heart of the

50. M. Billeter and C. Martius, *Biochem. Z.*, *333*, 430 (1960).
51. M. Billeter and C. Martius, *Biochem. Z.*, *334*, 304 (1961).
52. C. Martius, *Biochem. Z.*, *327*, 407 (1956).
53. C. Martius and H. O. Esser, *Biochem. Z.*, *331*, 1 (1958).

experimental animal, and the active substance was identified by countercurrent distribution. On the basis of comparison with a series of vitamin K_2 homologs, the active substance was identified as 2-methyl-3-geranylgeranyl-1,4-naphthoquinone (**54**) or vitamin $K_{2(20)}$.

Next it was demonstrated that vitamin $K_{2(20)}$ is synthesized *in vitro* from menadione by particulate fractions derived from rat or chicken liver homogenates.[54] The enzyme system, which is localized in the mitochondrial fraction, catalyzes the condensation of 2-methyl-1,4-naphthoquinone with geranylgeranyl pyrophosphate to yield vitamin $K_{2(20)}$. The enzymic activity of the particulate fraction is not specific since geranyl- and farnesyl pyrophosphate also reacted to yield the corresponding vitamins $K_{2(10)}$ and $K_{2(15)}$. Phytyl pyrophosphate, however, did not react. Vitamin $K_{2(45)}$ and vitamin $K_{2(50)}$ were also isolated during these *in vitro* studies. Vitamin $K_{2(45)}$ was biosynthesized in the enzyme system from rat liver, and vitamin $K_{2(50)}$ was isolated from the enzyme system derived from chick liver.

To reconcile the conversion of a K-vitamin to vitamin $K_{2(20)}$ exclusively *in vivo* with the enzymic conversion of menadione to vitamin $K_{2(20)}$ and vitamin $K_{2(45)}$ or vitamin $K_{2(50)}$ *in vitro*, it has been suggested that the several "alkylating enzymes" for the incorporation of specific isoprenoid side chains are in every cell, but each is localized at a different region.[55] In this manner, the C_{20}-side chain is incorporated exclusively in the biosynthesis *in vivo* of vitamin $K_{2(20)}$. In the *in vitro* systems, however, all of the soluble enzymes from the disrupted cell are available for the biosynthesis of various members of the vitamin K_2 group.

The biosynthesis of vitamin $K_{2(20)}$ from menadione was also demonstrated in tissue culture.[56] In cell cultures derived from either the liver or heart of the chick and rat, it was shown that menadione was converted *in vitro* to vitamin $K_{2(10)}$, vitamin $K_{2(15)}$, vitamin $K_{2(20)}$, and vitamin $K_{2(45)}$ or vitamin $K_{2(50)}$, depending upon the source of liver. The synthesis of K-vitamins other than vitamin $K_{2(20)}$ is explained on the basis of the unusually high concentration of menadione in the culture medium which allows menadione to trap intermediates for the biosynthesis of cholesterol and coenzyme Q as well as those for the biosynthesis of vitamin $K_{2(20)}$. Such unusually high concentrations of menadione should not occur *in vivo*; consequently only vitamin $K_{2(20)}$ is biosynthesized in the intact animal.

54. W. Stoffel and C. Martius, *Angew. Chem.*, *72*, 627 (1960); *Biochem. Z.*, *333*, 440 (1960).

55. C. Martius, in G. E. W. Wolstenholme and C. M. O'Connor, eds., *Ciba Foundation Symposium on Quinones in Electron Transport*, Churchill, London, or Little, Brown, Boston, 1961, p. 312.

56. H.-G. Schiefer and C. Martius, *Biochem. Z.*, *333*, 454 (1960).

6. Metabolic Role

It has been suggested that certain K-vitamins function in the respiratory enzyme system by participating in coupled electron transport and phosphorylation. A role for the vitamin in this metabolic area was indicated by studies showing that dicumarol, a competitive inhibitor of vitamin K, is an effective uncoupling agent in mammalian mitochondria.[57] The low phosphorus to oxygen ratios observed during the respiration of mitochondria from the vitamin K-deficient chick constituted further evidence for the participation of K-vitamins in the coupled process.[58] In addition, vitamin $K_{1(20)}$ and related naphthoquinones appeared to be required for electron transport and coupled phosphorylation in a cell-free system derived from *Mycobacterium phlei*.[59]

The effect of vitamin K on coupled electron transport and phosphorylation in bacterial systems was studied by deactivating a cell-free extract from *M. phlei* with light at 360 mμ, and observing the structural requirements for homologs of the vitamin K series to reactivate this system.[60–65] Although many analogs of vitamin K reactivated electron transport in the cell-free system, only those containing a 2-methyl substituent and a 3-substituent containing at least five carbon atoms and an unsaturated center at the 2′-position appeared to reactivate electron transport and coupled phosphorylation.[60–62] Further information was derived by adding vitamin $K_{1(20)}$ in substrate amounts to the cell-free extract from *M. phlei* and trapping intermediate enzymic forms by acetylation.[64,65] Two crude compounds were isolated. One was identified as diacetyldihydrovitamin $K_{1(20)}$ by its ultraviolet absorption and by its conversion to vitamin $K_{1(20)}$ on hydrolysis. The other compound appeared to be the 6-chromanyl acetate derivative (**55**) of vitamin $K_{1(20)}$ on the basis of spectral and chromatographic properties. The 6-chromanyl acetate was isolated from

57. C. Martius and D. Nitz-Litzow, *Biochim. et Biophys. Acta*, *12*, 134 (1953).
58. C. Martius and D. Nitz-Litzow, *Biochim. et Biophys. Acta*, *13*, 152 (1954).
59. A. F. Brodie, *Abstracts 132nd. Meeting Am. Chem. Soc.*, 52C (1957).
60. A. F. Brodie, M. W. Weber, and C. T. Gray, *Biochim. et Biophys. Acta*, *25*, 448 (1957).
61. A. F. Brodie and J. Ballantine, *J. Biol. Chem.*, *235*, 226 (1960).
62. A. F. Brodie and J. Ballantine, *J. Biol. Chem.*, *235*, 232 (1960).
63. A. F. Brodie and B. R. Davis, *Federation Proc.*, *18*, 198 (1959).
64. P. J. Russell, Jr., and A. F. Brodie, *Federation Proc.*, *19*, 38 (1960); *Biochim. et Biophys. Acta*, *50*, 76 (1961).
65. A. F. Brodie, P. J. Russell, Jr., and E. Kashet, *Abstracts 137th. Meeting Am. Chem. Soc.*, *25*C (1960).

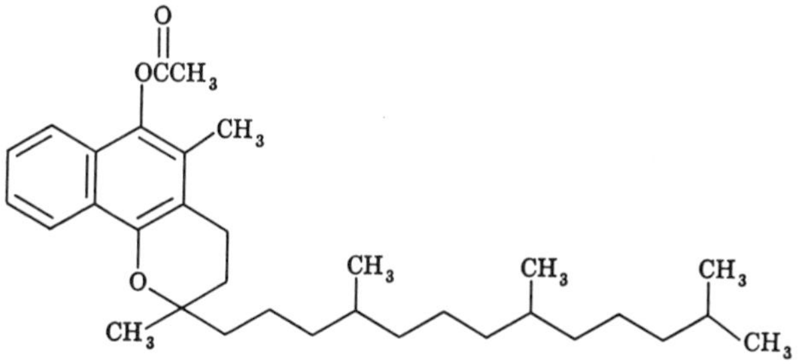

(55)

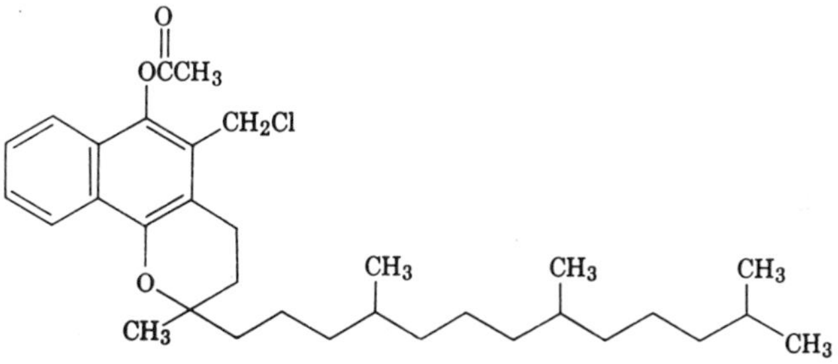

(55a)

the enzymic and acetylated reaction mixture and was identified, but detailed studies of the acetylation reaction showed that the 6-chromanyl acetate (**55**) in the enzymic and acetylated reaction mixture could result from an enzymic or a nonenzymic reaction, or both.[66] Further fractionation of the enzymic and acetylated reaction mixture yielded a second chromanol derivative of vitamin $K_{1(20)}$. This compound was established as the 5-chloromethyl-6-chromanyl acetate derivative (**55a**) of vitamin $K_{1(20)}$, and its nonenzymic origin was established shortly thereafter.[66a] As a result of these studies, new data are required to confirm the enzymic formation of a 6-chromanol derivative of vitamin $K_{1(20)}$ in a cell-free extract of *M. phlei* and the conclusions drawn from the early data.

On the basis of early observations, it was considered that K-vitamins which catalyze electron transport and coupled phosphorylation must contain a 2-methyl substituent and a 3-substituent capable of participating

66. A. F. Wagner, P. E. Wittreich, C. H. Hoffman, K. Folkers, and A. F. Brodie, *Biochem. Biophys. Res. Commun.*, *8*, 38 (1962).
66a. A. F. Wagner, P. E. Wittreich, A. Lusi, R. E. Erickson, B. Arison, N. R. Trenner, K. Folkers, and A. F. Brodie, *Arch. Biochem. Biophys.*, *102*, 11 (1963).

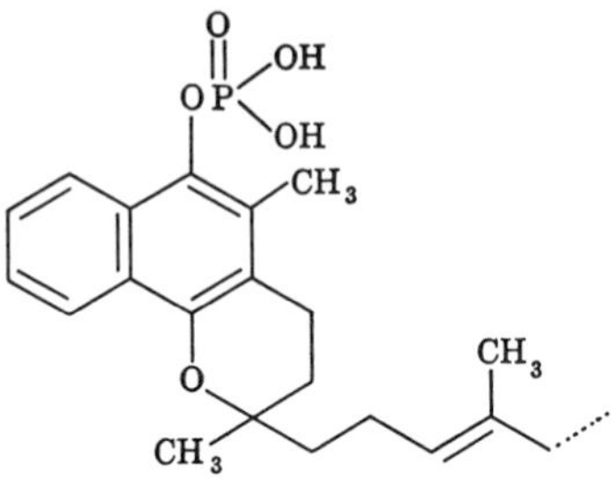

(56)

in the formation of a chroman moiety. In the bacterial system a phosphorylated chroman intermediate such as (**56**) has been regarded as a form participating in the transfer of an electron to the cytochrome system. Electron transfer would result in the activation of the phosphate group, which would then be transferred to adenosine diphosphate to yield adenosine triphosphate and the original K-vitamin. To support or eliminate further interest in this structure, which is only one of those under current consideration in oxidative phosphorylation, the 6-chromanyl phosphate

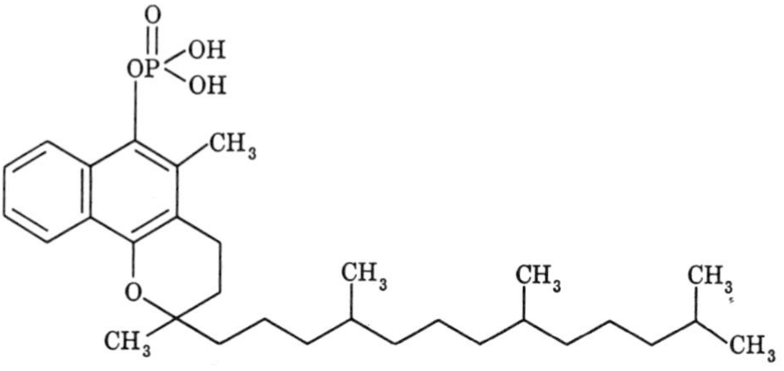

(57)

(**57**) of vitamin $K_{1(20)}$ was synthesized,[67,68] and the pure crystalline compound was tested in the cell-free system from *M. phlei.*[68] In the anaerobic system, the reduction of cytochrome *c* was dependent upon the addition of an electron donor such as DPNH or the 6-chromanyl phosphate (**57**), and the formation of adenosine triphosphate was dependent upon the addition of the 6-chromanyl phosphate. However, it was not established that the 6-chromanyl phosphate (**57**) was transferring phosphate directly to adenosine diphosphate.

67. A. F. Wagner, P. E. Wittreich, B. Arison, N. R. Trenner, and K. Folkers, *J. Am. Chem. Soc.*, *85*, 1178 (1963).
68. A. Asano, A. F. Brodie, A. F. Wagner, P. E. Wittreich, and K. Folkers, *J. Biol. Chem.*, *237*, 2411 (1962).

7. Therapeutic Role

A. Role in the Blood Clotting Process

Vitamin K has a role in the blood coagulation mechanism and is effective in preventing hemorrhage in humans who have hypoprothrombinemia. This term is descriptive of a state in which the blood clotting time is prolonged either by a deficiency of prothrombin, the precursor of the blood clotting enzyme, or by a deficiency of certain plasma factors that are necessary for the activation and conversion of prothrombin to thrombin.

The process of blood coagulation is a complex but orderly sequence of events triggered by the action of certain factors.[69] The exact mechanism for the participation of vitamin K in this process is unknown, but it has been shown that a deficiency of vitamin K influences the concentration of prothrombin, proconvertin, and thromboplastin in the plasma.[70,71]

B. The Relationship between Structure and Activity

The effect of nuclear and side chain substituents on the vitamin K activity of naphthalene derivatives in the depleted chick has been summarized.[72] Antihemorrhagic activity was found only in the 1,4-naphthoquinone series or in compounds readily converted to 1,4-naphthoquinones. The highest activities were obtained when the compound had a 2-methyl substituent; an increase in the number of carbon atoms in the 2-substituent lowered activity significantly. A 3-substituent was not necessary for activity. Among the active compounds having a 3-substituent, however, those having an isoprenoid side chain were more active than those having an unbranched chain at this position; the activity of these compounds increased as a function of the length of the side chain in the 3-position, up to a maximum of 20–30 carbon atoms. The double bond at the 2′-position of the 3-substituent was the only center of unsaturation which increased activity; carbon-carbon double bonds at remote points of the 3-substituent were without effect. The presence of a hydroxyl group in either the 1,4-naphthoquinone nucleus or in the side chain resulted in the loss of activity.

The structure-activity requirements for the effective reversal of vitamin K antagonists are different from those required to prevent the characteristic hemorrhagic syndrome in the dietary-induced deficiency. It was

69. A. J. Quick, *Hemorrhagic Diseases*, Lea and Febiger, Philadelphia, Pa., 1957.
70. H. S. Sise, D. M. Kimball, and D. Adamis, *Proc. Soc. Exptl. Biol. Med.*, *89*, 81 (1955).
71. R. L. Maeye, *Proc. Soc. Exptl. Biol. Med.*, *91*, 101 (1956).
72. L. F. Fieser, M. Tishler, and W. L. Sampson, *J. Biol. Chem.*, *137*, 659 (1941).

found that only those derivatives with a comparatively large substituent at the 3-position were effective in reversing the antagonism of dicumerol in the rat and dog.[73] Derivatives with less than eight carbon atoms in the side chain were essentially inactive. Methyl branching or unsaturation in the side chain were not essential for activity, but such functional groups enhanced activity.

C. Therapeutic Applications

The K-vitamins are administered therapeutically for the prevention of hypoprothrombinemic hemorrhage in infants during the first few days of life. The vitamin is administered either as vitamin $K_{1(20)}$ or as one of the water-soluble analogs, during the last two weeks of pregnancy or just before or immediately after birth. Vitamin $K_{1(20)}$ appears to be effective for a longer period of time than the water-soluble analogs.[69]

The K-vitamins are also effective in preventing hemorrhage in cases where hypoprothrombinemia develops owing to inadequate supplies of bile. They are especially useful in the prevention of postoperative hemorrhage in patients with obstructive jaundice. Since hypoprothrombinemia develops in these patients because of poor intestinal absorption of vitamin $K_{1(20)}$, a water-soluble analog is usually administered since it is absorbed from the intestine in the absence of bile.

In anticoagulant therapy a vitamin K antagonist such as dicumerol is administered, but at times the antagonist decreases the prothrombin level sufficiently to allow hemorrhage. The water-soluble analogs of menadione are ineffective when used as an antidote for dicumerol therapy, but vitamin K_1 or its oxide are effective.[74] Vitamin K_1 is usually administered intravenously in a solubilized form or in the form of aqueous colloidal suspensions.

The routine administration of a vitamin K either maternally or neonatally for the prevention of hemorrhage in the infant has been questioned.[75] It has been suggested that synthetic water-soluble analogs of menadione be administered in doses of 2–5 mg. for the mother or 1–2 mg. for the infant only in situations such as premature delivery, anoxia, or erythroblastosis which are normally conducive to neonatal hemorrhage. There appears to be no reason to supplement maternal diets with a K-vitamin in the absence of liver disease.

73. O. Isler, R. Rüegg, A. Studer, and R. Jurgens, *Z. Physiol. Chem.*, *295*, 290 (1953).
74. H. Dam, in R. T. Holman, W. O. Lundberg, and T. Malkin, eds., *Progress in the Chemistry of Fats and Other Lipids*, Vol. III, Pergamon, N.Y., 1955, p. 198.
75. *Recommended Dietary Allowances*, *Natl. Acad. Sci., Natl. Res. Council Publ.*, *589*, Washington D.C., 1958, p. 25.

CHAPTER XXI

The Coenzyme Q or Ubiquinone Group

1. Introduction

The discovery of coenzyme Q_{10} or ubiquinone(50) stemmed from two independent investigations. One study was concerned with the metabolic role of vitamin A and eventually resulted in the isolation of a substance which was designated ubiquinone(50). The other investigation was devoted to a study of the components and mechanism of electron transport in mitochondria and culminated in the first report of the isolation of the crystalline and coenzymically active compound which became known as coenzyme Q_{10}. Shortly thereafter, similarities in certain properties of the two products were recognized, and it was suggested that ubiquinone(50) and coenzyme Q_{10} were closely related or possibly identical.

Investigations to elucidate the mode of systemic action of vitamin A were initiated by fractionating the unsaponifiable portion of liver from rats that were deficient in vitamin A.[1–3] The composition of this fraction was compared with that of a corresponding fraction derived from the liver of control rats. On further purification, one fraction was of particular interest since it contained a substance which appeared to be in greater concentration in the tissues of rats deficient in vitamin A than in the tissue of normal rats. The major component of this fraction, designated SA, was characterized by an absorption maximum at 272 mμ in the ultraviolet absorption spectrum.[2] A similar material was isolated from the unsaponifiable fraction from yeast.[4] The latter was observed in a study testing a claim that yeast contained vitamin A; instead of vitamin A, a yellow oily fraction was obtained which was considered identical or closely related to SA on the basis of its ultraviolet absorption spectrum.

Similarities in the ultraviolet absorption spectra of SA and certain enedione derivatives of the steroids led to the provisional characterization of

1. J. S. Lowe, R. A. Morton, and R. G. Harrison, *Nature*, *172*, 716 (1953).
2. G. N. Festenstein, F. W. Heaton, J. S. Lowe, and R. A. Morton, *Biochem. J.*, *59*, 558 (1955).
3. F. W. Heaton, J. S. Lowe, and R. A. Morton, *Biochem. J.*, *60*, xviii (1955); *67*, 208 (1957).
4. F. W. Heaton, J. S. Lowe, and R. A. Morton, *J. Chem. Soc.*, 4094 (1956).

this substance as a steroid. Further investigation, however, revealed that SA is in fact not a steroid but a quinone derivative, and the substance was eventually designated ubiquinone(50).

The isolation of coenzyme Q_{10} in studies of mitochondrial electron transport stemmed from the hypothesis that lipid was intimately associated with the electron transport process in these particles. At the time there was no reason to suspect that the lipid fraction participated as an oxidation-reduction carrier. On the other hand, the observed effects of α-tocopherol on electron transport systems[5] and the observation that carotenoid-like substances appeared to be present in lipid fractions from beef heart and cauliflower mitochondria[6] provided a basis to suggest that oxidation-reduction carriers might be found in lipid components, especially those characterized by absorption bands in the visible or ultraviolet region of the spectrum.

Mitochondrial lipid extracts were examined systematically by chromatography, and a yellow component was isolated. This product was characterized by strong ultraviolet absorption at 275 mμ which disappeared on reduction. The reduction product was characterized by an absorption maximum at 290 mμ and was rapidly reoxidized by ferric chloride or more slowly by oxygen. Next the 275-mμ absorbing substance was isolated as a crystalline yellow compound from beef heart mitochondria. On the basis of its recognized quinone functionality, the compound was tentatively designated Q-275.[7,8] When later studies showed that Q-275 undergoes oxidation-reduction in mitochondria, and that acetone-extracted mitochondria regain their capacity to oxidize succinate after the addition of catalytic amounts of Q-275, the designation coenzyme Q was deemed appropriate for this new compound. The compound was eventually designated coenzyme Q_{10}.

Similarities in the spectra and properties of coenzyme Q_{10} and the samples originally designated SA led to the early suggestion that the products were closely related or identical. Later studies[9,10] showed that the compound is particularly susceptible to an alkali-catalyzed alkoxyl

5. A. Nason and I. R. Lehman, *Science*, *122*, 19 (1955).
6. F. L. Crane, *Plant Physiol.*, *32*, 619 (1957).
7. F. L. Crane, Y. Hatefi, R. L. Lester, and C. Widmer, *Biochim. et Biophys. Acta*, *25*, 220 (1957).
8. F. L. Crane, R. L. Lester, C. Widmer, and Y. Hatefi, *Biochim. et Biophys. Acta*, *32*, 73 (1959).
9. B. O. Linn, N. R. Trenner, C. H. Shunk, and K. Folkers, *J. Am. Chem. Soc.*, *81*, 1263 (1959).
10. B. O. Linn, N. R. Trenner, B. H. Arison, R. G. Weston, C. H. Shunk, and K. Folkers, *J. Am. Chem. Soc.*, *82*, 1647 (1960).

exchange reaction, and in view of the method used to isolate the early SA preparations and the chemical and physical properties of SA, it was apparent that the early ubiquinone samples were ethoxy homologs of the natural methoxy product.

An examination of other source materials, particularly yeast and other microorganisms, was undertaken to extend the data on the distribution of the new quinone.[11,12] Four new quinones that were closely related in structure to the coenzyme Q_{10} of beef heart mitochondria were isolated; later studies showed that they differed solely in the length of an isoprenoid side chain.

The time lapse between the isolation and the recognition of the identity of coenzyme Q_{10} and ubiquinone(50) was sufficient to allow a dual system of nomenclature to develop for this series of naturally occurring quinones. According to one system each compound is designated as a coenzyme Q with a subscript to indicate the number of isoprenoid units in the side chain. According to the other system each compound is designated as a ubiquinone with a parenthetical expression to indicate the number of carbon atoms in the isoprenoid side chain. Thus, the benzoquinone derivative with a side chain of ten isoprenoid units has been designated as coenzyme Q_{10} as well as ubiquinone(50). Neither system has been adopted officially, and a subcommittee has been appointed by the Commission for the Nomenclature of Biological Chemistry of the International Union of Pure and Applied Chemistry to recommend a system of nomenclature for quinones with isoprenoid side chains.

2. Isolation

A. Coenzyme Q_{10}

Coenzyme Q_{10} is a neutral lipid that is insoluble in water, slightly soluble in polar organic solvents, and highly soluble in nonpolar solvents, particularly hydrocarbons. Extraction of the coenzyme from source material is accomplished by saponification of the starting material followed by extraction with heptane or isooctane. Alternatively, the compound may be isolated by direct extraction of the source material with ethanol-ether. The extract is partially purified by concentration and dilution with petroleum ether prior to chromatography. Two precautions are desirable if the starting material is saponified prior to extraction. First, considerable pyrogallol is added to the saponification mixture to prevent the destructive oxidation of the desired product in alkaline solution;

11. R. L. Lester, F. L. Crane, and Y. Hatefi, *J. Am. Chem. Soc.*, *80*, 4751 (1958).
12. U. Gloor, O. Isler, R. A. Morton, R. Rüegg, and O. Wiss, *Helv. Chim. Acta*, *41*, 2357 (1958).

second, methanolic alkali is used as a saponification medium to prevent the formation of ethoxy artifacts by the exchange reaction.

The initial extracts of coenzyme Q_{10} are further purified by chromatography. Adsorbents such as alumina, Decalso, Florisil, and silica gel are used. Decalso is the most efficient adsorbent for the purification of extracts from saponified material; silica gel is preferred for the purification of ethanol-ether extracts of unsaponified source material. The compound is usually adsorbed from heptane or isooctane solution and is eluted with slightly more polar solvent mixtures such as ether-isooctane or ethanol-isooctane. Coenzyme Q_{10} may be crystallized from methanol, ethanol, acetone, acetic acid, or ethyl acetate.

The following modified procedure[10] for the isolation of coenzyme Q_{10} by the saponification method demonstrates an early technique.[8] The fat and connective tissue were removed from fresh beef hearts and the myocardial tissue was ground. A solution of 136 kg. of potassium hydroxide in 180 l. of methanol was prepared, and 9 kg. of pyrogallol and 136 kg. of ground beef myocardial tissue were added. The system was flushed with nitrogen, and the mixture was stirred and heated at reflux for 90 minutes. The mixture was cooled rapidly and extracted successively with a 130-l. and two 60-l. portions of *n*-hexane. Each hexane extract was washed separately with warm water until all the dark brown color and alkali were removed, and the organic extracts were combined, washed with water, and dried over anhydrous sodium sulfate. The solution was concentrated under reduced pressure to about a 20-l. volume.

The concentrates from three such batches were combined, and the products were adsorbed on a column consisting of 4 kg. of Florisil packed in *n*-hexane. After the column was washed with about 30 l. of *n*-hexane, the products were eluted with a mixture of *n*-hexane-ether (10:1). A mixture presumably containing carotenes was obtained from the first 40 l. of the eluate and was discarded. Coenzyme Q_{10} and cholesterol were eluted by the next 12-l. batch of solvent. This fraction was concentrated to a 1-l. volume under reduced pressure and cooled to 5°. The cholesterol that precipitated was isolated by filtration and washed with small portions of *n*-hexane. The combined filtrate and washings were concentrated under reduced pressure to a volume of about 500 ml. and filtered. The second crop of cholesterol was washed with *n*-hexane, and the combined filtrate and washings were concentrated under reduced pressure. Final traces of *n*-hexane were removed by dissolving the product in 100 ml. of absolute ethanol and concentrating the solution under reduced pressure. The residue was dissolved in 1 l. of absolute ethanol at 60°, and the hot solution was decanted from a dark insoluble oil. The residual oil was leached with

100 ml. of hot absolute ethanol, and the combined ethanol extracts were allowed to cool slowly to room temperature in the dark. The orange crystalline product was isolated by filtration and recrystallized from 500 ml. of absolute ethanol. The product was isolated by filtration, washed with absolute ethanol, and dried *in vacuo*.

By this procedure 66 mg. of coenzyme Q_{10} was isolated from each kilogram of moist myocardial tissue processed. Typical preparations of the crystalline product melted over a one-degree range starting at 48–50.5° and were established as 95–100% pure by spectrophotometric analysis. The absence of ethoxy homologs in these crystalline products and their mother liquors was demonstrated by chromatographic analysis on paper.

B. Coenzymes Q_6–Q_9

On further investigation of source materials for coenzyme Q_{10}, it was found that the compound is widely distributed in nature and that cells with high aerobic respiratory activity are especially rich sources of the coenzyme. When a number of microorganisms were investigated, it was recognized that there exists in nature a family of quinones related to the coenzyme Q_{10} first isolated from beef heart mitochondria. From these studies,[13–15] four new coenzymes Q were isolated from microbial sources. One was isolated from *Azotobacter vinelandii*, two from *Torulopsis utilis*, and one from *Saccharomyces cerevisiae*. These new compounds and the coenzyme Q_{10} isolated from beef heart mitochondria have a common quinoid function; the differences in their properties are due solely to a difference in the length of the isoprenoid side chain. On the basis of early structural observations, these four new compounds were designated as coenzymes Q_9, Q_8, Q_7, and Q_6.

As a result of all of these isolation studies, the five quinones that constitute the presently known coenzyme Q group may be summarized as follows (Table I):

TABLE I

The Coenzyme Q Group of Quinones

Coenzyme	Source	Melting Point
Q_6	*Saccharomyces cerevisiae*	19–20°
Q_7	*Torulopsis utilis* A	30.5°
Q_8	*Azotobacter vinelandii*	37.0°
Q_9	*Torulopsis utilis* B	45.2°
Q_{10}	Beef heart, alfalfa	48.0–49.0°

13. R. L. Lester, F. L. Crane, and Y. Hatefi, *J. Am. Chem. Soc.*, *80*, 4751 (1958).
14. R. L. Lester and F. L. Crane, *Biochim. et Biophys. Acta*, *32*, 492 (1959).
15. R. L. Lester, Y. Hatefi, C. Widmer, and F. L. Crane, *Biochim. et Biophys. Acta*, *33*, 169 (1959).

3. Structure Determination

A. Coenzyme Q_{10}

On the basis of degradative and spectral evidence, the structure of coenzyme Q_{10} was established as 2,3-dimethoxy-5-methyl-6-[3-methyl-2-butenyl-*enakis*-(3-methyl-2-butenylene)]-1,4-benzoquinone (**1**) in independent studies.[16–20]

In one study elemental and functional group analysis showed coenzyme Q_{10} to have the molecular formula $C_{59}H_{90}O_4$ and established the presence of two methoxyl groups.[16,17] The compound was reduced under mild conditions; one equivalent of hydrogen was absorbed, and the ultraviolet absorption maximum shifted from 275 mμ to 290 mμ. This observation indicated the presence of a *p*-quinoid function in the molecule. On the basis of these data, all four oxygen atoms of the molecule were accounted for in the form of two methoxyl groups and a *p*-quinoid moiety.

Ultraviolet absorption spectroscopy indicated that coenzyme Q_{10} is a tetrasubstituted benzoquinone derivative.[16,18] The spectra of aurantiogliocladin (2,3-dimethoxy-5,6-dimethyl-1,4-benzoquinone) and its corresponding hydroquinone were very similar to those of coenzyme Q_{10} and dihydrocoenzyme Q_{10}, respectively. This similarity did not constitute proof that coenzyme Q_{10} is a 2,3-dimethoxy-1,4-benzoquinone derivative, however, since the ultraviolet absorption spectra of the isomeric 2,6-dimethoxy-3,5-dimethyl- and 2,5-dimethoxy-3,6-dimethyl-1,4-benzoquinones are quite similar to that of aurantiogliocladin.

On the basis of chemical evidence at least one substituent of the *p*-quinoid moiety in coenzyme Q_{10} appeared to be polyisoprenoid in nature.[16,17] Catalytic hydrogenation of coenzyme Q_{10} resulted in the absorption of about eleven equivalents of hydrogen to yield the eicosahydro-hydroquinone (**3**), which was oxidized to eicosahydro-coenzyme Q_{10} (**4**). Oxidation of coenzyme Q_{10} with alkaline potassium permanganate yielded levulinic acid, acetic acid, and succinic acid to constitute further evidence for the presence of a polyisoprenoid substituent.

16. D. E. Wolf, C. H. Hoffman, N. R. Trenner, B. H. Arison, C. H. Shunk, B. O. Linn, J. F. McPherson, and K. Folkers, *J. Am. Chem. Soc.*, *80*, 4752 (1958).
17. R. L. Lester, F. L. Crane, and Y. Hatefi, *J. Am. Chem. Soc.*, *80*, 4751 (1958).
18. C. H. Shunk, B. O. Linn, E. L. Wong, P. E. Wittreich, F. M. Robinson, and K. Folkers, *J. Am. Chem. Soc.*, *80*, 4753 (1958).
19. R. A. Morton, *Nature*, *182*, 1764 (1958).
20. R. A. Morton, U. Gloor, O. Schindler, G. M. Wilson, L. H. Chopard-dit-Jean, L. H. Hemming, O. Isler, W. M. F. Leat, J. F. Pennock, R. Rüegg, U. Schwieter, and O. Wiss, *Helv. Chim. Acta*, *41*, 2343 (1958).

Nuclear magnetic resonance spectroscopy studies with coenzyme Q_{10} and several synthetic model quinones provided significant data for structural elucidation.[16] The presence of a tetrasubstituted *p*-benzoquinone moiety was confirmed since the nuclear magnetic resonance data excluded the presence of an aromatic proton. In conjunction with the earlier structural indications, the nuclear magnetic resonance spectrum established that coenzyme Q_{10} contained two methoxyl groups, a methyl group, and a ten-unit isoprenoid chain attached to the *p*-benzoquinone nucleus.

The combination of evidence from ultraviolet and nuclear magnetic

OH
CH_3O
CH_3
CH_3
CH_3O
$(CH_2CH_2CHCH_2)_{10}H$
OH
(3)

O
CH_3O
CH_3
CH_3
CH_3O
$(CH_2CH_2CHCH_2)_{10}H$
O
(4)

O
CH_3O
CH_3
CH_3
CH_3O
$(CH_2CH{=}C{-}CH_2)_{10}H$
O
(1)

Zn+HOAc
$FeCl_3$ or Ag_2O

OH
CH_3O
CH_3
CH_3
CH_3O
$(CH_2CH{=}C{-}CH_2)_{10}H$
OH
(2)

$(CH_3O)_2SO_2$

OCH_3
CH_3O
CH_3
CH_3
CH_3O
$(CH_2CH{=}C{-}CH_2)_{10}H$
OCH_3
(5)

Excess $KMnO_4$
100°

OCH_3
O
CH_3O
C
O
CH_3O
C
OCH_3
O
(6)

10 Equiv. $KMnO_4$

OCH_3
CH_3O
CH_3
CH_3O
CH_2COOH
OCH_3
(7)

+ $CH_3\overset{O}{\overset{\|}{C}}CH_2CH_2COOH$ + $HOOCCH_2CH_2COOH$
(8) (9)

Fig. 1. Structure determination of coenzyme Q_{10}.[16]

resonance spectroscopy strongly suggested that coenzyme Q_{10} was a 2,3-dimethoxy-1,4-benzoquinone derivative, but additional data were necessary (Fig. 1) to establish the positions of the substituents on the tetrasubstituted benzoquinone moiety. Conclusive evidence demonstrating the position of substituents on the quinoid moiety was obtained by oxidative degradation.[16] Coenzyme Q_{10} (**1**) was reduced to dihydrocoenzyme Q_{10} (**2**), which in turn was methylated to yield crystalline dimethoxydihydrocoenzyme Q_{10} (**5**). Oxidation of this tetramethoxy intermediate with an excess of hot aqueous potassium permanganate, followed by sublimation of an acidic oxidation product yielded tetramethoxyphthalic anhydride (**6**). When dimethoxydihydrocoenzyme Q_{10} (**5**) was oxidized with ten equivalents of potassium permanganate in acetone solution, 2-methyl-3,4,5,6-tetramethoxyphenylacetic acid (**7**), levulinic acid (**8**), and succinic acid (**9**) were identified. These oxidative degradation data in conjunction with the spectral data established the structure of coenzyme Q_{10} as (**1**).

Other independent investigations resulted in the same structural formulation for ubiquinone(50) (coenzyme Q_{10}).[19,20] The combination of data from a series of quantitative catalytic reductions, an ebullioscopic determination of molecular weight, and elemental analysis established the molecular formula $C_{59}H_{90}O_4$. Absorption bands characteristic of a quinoid, ether, and an *all-trans*-polyisoprenoid function were observed in the infrared spectrum, and the presence of two methoxyl groups was established by cleavage of the ether functions with hydriodic acid. Comparison of the ultraviolet absorption spectra of ubiquinone(50) and eicosahydroubiquinone(50) with those of several 2,3-dimethoxy-5-methyl-1,4-benzoquinone derivatives provided further insight to the nature of the tetrasubstituted 1,4-benzoquinone nucleus.

For the oxidative degradation studies, ubiquinone(50) was converted to the corresponding diacetylhydroquinone.[20] Ozonization of the latter intermediate, followed by reductive cleavage of the ozonide yielded acetone and levulinaldehyde. Oxidation of the ether-soluble fraction from the ozonolysis reaction with potassium permanganate yielded 3,6-diacetoxy-4,5-dimethoxy-2-methylphenylacetic acid. These data in conjunction with the spectral data constituted an independent proof of structure for ubiquinone(50) (coenzyme Q_{10}).

B. *Coenzymes* Q_6–Q_9

The structural elucidation of coenzyme Q_{10} established the generic structure (**10**) for the coenzyme Q group. The presence of a common *p*-quinoid chromaphore in all the members of the group was determined from ultraviolet and visible absorption spectra; decreasing extinction

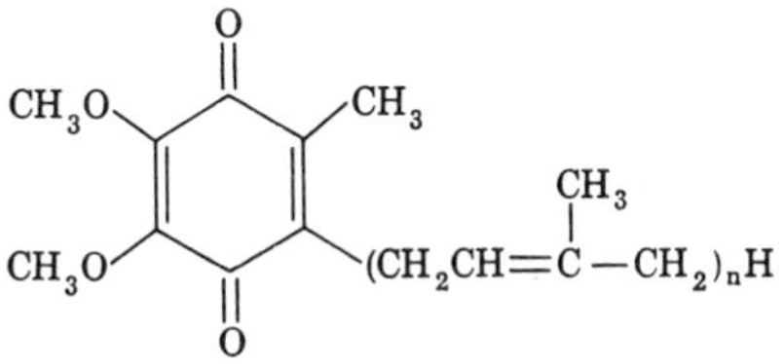

O
CH_3O CH_3
CH_3
CH_3O $(CH_2CH{=}C{-}CH_2)_nH$
O

(10) (n = 6, 7, 8, 9, 10)

coefficients were associated with increasing length of the isoprenoid side chain. Equivalent weight determinations by oxidation-reduction titration and molecular weight determinations by the X-ray method confirmed that each quinone differed from the next homolog in the series by one isoprenoid unit. The number of isoprenoid units in each compound was also determined by hydrogenation. On the basis of these data, the quinones isolated from microbial sources were established as coenzyme Q_6 (*Saccharomyces cerevisiae*), coenzyme Q_7 (*Torulopsis utilis* A), coenzyme Q_8 (*Azotobacter vinelandii*), and coenzyme Q_9 (*Torulopsis utilis* B).[17]

4. Synthesis

A. "Coenzyme Q_0"

2,3-Dimethoxy-5-methyl-1,4-benzoquinone (**15**) is a key intermediate for the synthesis of members of the coenzyme Q group. This quinone has been referred to as "coenzyme Q_0," and its position in the coenzyme Q series is structurally comparable to that of menadione in the vitamin K group. A corresponding biological analogy between "coenzyme Q_0" and menadione (Chapter XX) has not been established. However, "coenzyme Q_0" has functioned as a biosynthetic precursor for coenzymes Q_4, Q_9, and Q_{10} in mitochondrial and cell culture systems.

"Coenzyme Q_0" was synthesized (Fig. 2) prior to the discovery of the coenzyme Q group.[21] Nitration of 4-hydroxy-3-methoxytoluene (creosol) (**11**) with fuming nitric acid in ether solution yielded the corresponding 5-nitro intermediate (**12**). The free hydroxyl group in (**12**) was converted to a methoxyl group and the intermediate 3,4-dimethoxy-5-nitrotoluene (**13**) was reduced to the corresponding amino derivative, 5-amino-3,4-dimethoxytoluene (**14**). Oxidation of the amino intermediate (**14**) yielded 2,3-dimethoxy-5-methyl-1,4-benzoquinone ("coenzyme Q_0") (**15**).

An alternative synthesis (Fig. 2) of "coenzyme Q_0" from methyl trimethylgallate (**16**) was reported following the discovery and structural

21. W. K. Anslow, J. N. Ashley, and H. Raistrick, *J. Chem. Soc.*, 439 (1938).

CH_3O CH_3 HO (11)

HNO_3 →

CH_3O CH_3 HO NO_2 (12)

$(CH_3O)_2SO_2$ →

CH_3O CH_3 CH_3O NO_2 (13)

H_2/Pd ↓

CH_3O CH_3 CH_3O NH_2 (14)

$Na_2Cr_2O_7$ ←

O CH_3O CH_3 CH_3O O (15) "Coenzyme Q_0"

→

NH_2 CH_3O CH_3 CH_3O OCH_3 (19)

↑ Reduce

$N{=}N{-}C_6H_4(NO_2)p$ CH_3O CH_3 CH_3O OCH_3 (18)

$p(NO_2)C_6H_4N{=}N^+$ ←

CH_3O CH_3 CH_3O OCH_3 (17)

↑ H_2 Copper Chromite

CH_3O $COOCH_3$ CH_3O OCH_3 (16)

Fig. 2. Syntheses of "coenzyme Q_0."[21,22]

elucidation of the coenzyme Q group.[22] In this synthesis, the methyl ester (**16**) of trimethylgallic acid was converted to 3,4,5-trimethoxytoluene (**17**) by catalytic hydrogenation over copper chromite. Coupling of a *p*-nitrophenyldiazonium salt with 3,4,5-trimethoxytoluene yielded the corresponding 2-diazo intermediate (**18**), which in turn was reduced to 2-amino-3,4,5-trimethoxytoluene (**19**). Oxidation of the 2-amino intermediate (**19**) yielded 2,3-dimethoxy-5-methyl-1,4-benzoquinone (**15**).

B. Coenzymes Q_1–Q_{10}

Coenzymes Q_1–Q_{10} were synthesized (Fig. 3) by the acid catalyzed condensation of 2,3-dimethoxy-5-methylhydroquinone (**20**) with the

22. O. Isler, R. Rüegg, A. Langemann, P. Schundel, G. Ryser, and J. Würsch, in G. E. W. Wolstenholme and C. M. O'Connor, eds., *Ciba Foundation Symposium on Quinones in Electron Transport*, Churchill, London, 1961, p. 82.

(15) $\xrightarrow{SO_2}$ (20)

(20) $\xrightarrow{ZnCl_2 \text{ or } BF_3}$

1. $HO(CH_2CH{=}C(CH_3){-}CH_2)_nH$ (21)
2. Ag_2O or $FeCl_3$

→ 2,3-dimethoxy-5-methyl-6-$(CH_2CH{=}C(CH_3){-}CH_2)_nH$-1,4-benzoquinone

1. $CH_2{=}CH{-}C(CH_3)(OH){-}CH_2(CH_2CH{=}C(CH_3){-}CH_2)_nH$ (22)
2. Ag_2O or $FeCl_3$

→ 2,3-dimethoxy-5-methyl-6-$CH_2CH{=}C(CH_3){-}CH_2(CH_2CH{=}C(CH_3){-}CH_2)_nH$-1,4-benzoquinone

Synthetic Quinone	m.p.	λ max 270 mμ in Petroleum Ether: $E^{1\%}_{1\ cm.}$	λ max 270 mμ in Petroleum Ether: ε
Coenzyme Q_1	oil	590	148×10^3
Coenzyme Q_2	oil	455	145×10^3
Coenzyme Q_3	oil	390	151×10^3
Coenzyme Q_4	oil	326	148×10^3
Coenzyme Q_5	oil	292	152×10^3
Coenzyme Q_6	19–20°	260	153×10^3
Coenzyme Q_7	31–32°	229	151×10^3
Coenzyme Q_8	37–38°	206	150×10^3
Coenzyme Q_9	44–45°	187	149×10^3
Coenzyme Q_{10}	49°	176	152×10^3

Fig. 3. Syntheses of coenzymes Q_1–Q_{10}.[23–27]

appropriate *all-trans*-allylic alcohol (**21**) or alternatively with the appropriate *all-trans*-tertiary carbinol (**22**).[23-27] Zinc chloride, boron trifluoride etherate, or both are preferred catalysts for the condensation. The product of the condensation reaction is a hydroquinone derivative which is oxidized to the corresponding quinone, preferably with silver oxide.

Coenzyme Q_1 was synthesized from 3,3-dimethylallyl alcohol (**21**, $n = 1$); coenzymes Q_2, Q_3, and Q_9, respectively, were synthesized from the naturally occurring *all-trans*-allylic alcohols—geraniol, farnesol, and solanesol (**21**, $n = 2, 3, 9$, respectively). Coenzyme Q_3 was also synthesized from the appropriate *all-trans*-tertiary carbinol, nerolidol (**22**, $n = 2$). Coenzymes Q_4–Q_8 and Q_{10} were synthesized from either the corresponding *all-trans*-allylic carbinol (**21**) or the appropriate *all-trans*-tertiary alcohol (**22**). Both methods yielded the desired product, but the yields were not always comparable. The intermediate carbinols (**21**) and (**22**) for the synthesis of the higher coenzyme Q homologs were prepared from the lower naturally occurring isoprenols by the sequence of condensation reactions that was used for synthesis of members of the vitamin K_2 group (see Fig. 1, Chapter XX).

5. Biosynthesis

A. The Isoprenoid Side Chain

The role of mevalonic acid (**23**) in the mammalian biosynthesis of coenzymes Q_9 and Q_{10} was demonstrated by the administration of 2-C^{14}-mevalonic acid to rats; isotope incorporation was higher when the precursor was administered by the oral rather than the parenteral route.[28] It was especially significant that the specific activity of the coenzyme Q fraction from the liver was of the same order as that of the cholesterol fraction since the latter was previously known to be biosynthetically derived from mevalonate. Purification of the coenzyme Q fraction from

23. C. H. Shunk, B. O. Linn, E. L. Wong, P. E. Wittreich, F. M. Robinson, and K. Folkers, *J. Am. Chem. Soc.*, *80*, 4753 (1958).
24. U. Gloor, O. Isler, R. A. Morton, R. Rüegg, and O. Wiss, *Helv. Chim. Acta*, *41*, 2357 (1958).
25. C. H. Shunk, R. E. Erickson, E. L. Wong, and K. Folkers, *J. Am. Chem. Soc.*, *81*, 5000 (1959).
26. R. Rüegg, U. Gloor, R. N. Goel, G. Ryser, O. Wiss, and O. Isler, *Helv. Chim. Acta*, *42*, 2616 (1959).
27. R. Rüegg, U. Gloor, A. Langemann, M. Kofler, C. von Planta, G. Ryser, and O. Isler, *Helv. Chim. Acta*, *43*, 1745 (1960).
28. U. Gloor and O. Wiss, *Experientia*, *14*, 410 (1958).

liver by chromatography showed that the isotope from 2-C^{14}-mevalonic acid was incorporated to the same extent in coenzymes Q_9 and Q_{10} in the intact rat.[29] Similar studies with labeled acetate in the rat confirmed these observations on isotope incorporation.[30–32] When these data were considered in the light of the role previously demonstrated for mevalonic acid in intermediary metabolism, it was suggested that mevalonic acid participated in the biosynthesis of the isoprenoid side chains, but not in the biosynthesis of the aromatic nucleus of the coenzyme Q group.

Restriction of the role of mevalonic acid to the biosynthesis of the isoprenoid side chain was established by the oxidative degradation of labeled biosynthetic coenzyme Q_9.[33] A sample of C^{14}-coenzyme Q_9 biosynthesized

$HOCH_2CH_2C(CH_3)(OH)-\overset{*}{C}H_2COOH$ (23) —Biosynthesis→ 2,3-dimethoxy-5-methyl-1,4-benzoquinone with $-CH_2CH=\overset{*}{C}(CH_3)-CH_2(CH_2CH=\overset{*}{C}(CH_3)-CH_2)_8H$

—Reductive Acetylation→ 1,4-diacetoxy-2,3-dimethoxy-5-methyl-6-[$CH_2CH=\overset{*}{C}(CH_3)-CH_2(CH_2CH=\overset{*}{C}(CH_3)-CH_2)_8H$]benzene (24)

—Ozonolysis→ 1,4-diacetoxy-2,3-dimethoxy-5-methyl-6-(CH_2COOH)benzene (25) + $O=\overset{*}{C}(CH_3)-CH_2CH_2CHO$ (26) + $O=C(CH_3)-\overset{*}{C}H_3$

29. U. Gloor and O. Wiss, *Arch. Biochem. Biophys.*, *83*, 216 (1959).
30. G. H. Dialameh and R. E. Olson, *Federation Proc.*, *18*, 214 (1959).
31. R. E. Olson and G. H. Dialameh, *Biochem. Biophys. Res. Commun.*, *2*, 198 (1960).
32. R. E. Olson, G. H. Dialameh, and R. Bentley, *Federation Proc.*, *19*, 220 (1960).
33. U. Gloor, O. Schindler, and O. Wiss, *Helv. Chim. Acta*, *43*, 2089 (1960).

from 2-C^{14}-mevalonic acid was reductively acetylated to diacetyl-C^{14}-dihydrocoenzyme Q_9 (**24**), which in turn was selectively degraded by ozonolysis. Radioactive levulinaldehyde (**26**) and acetone were isolated from the reaction mixture as the corresponding dinitrophenylhydrazones. 3,6-Diacetoxy-4,5-dimethoxy-2-methylphenylacetic acid (**25**), a degradation product derived from the aromatic moiety of the coenzyme, was isolated in crystalline form and was not labeled. The pattern of labeling and the order of quantitative recovery of radioactivity observed in this study were compatible with the concept that the entire side chain of biosynthetic coenzyme Q is constructed by the stepwise incorporation of C_5-units from mevalonic acid.

The biosynthesis of the side chain precursor and its reaction with an aromatic precursor are visualized through the mediation of intermediate allylic pyrophosphate esters (Fig. 4).[34–36] Mevalonic acid (**23**) is converted to the triphospho intermediate (**27**) in three steps. A concerted decarboxylation-dephosphorylation in (**27**) yields isopentenyl pyrophosphate (**28**); this compound is designated "active isoprene" and is the nucleophile component of polyisoprenoid biosynthesis. Isopentenyl pyrophosphate isomerizes to 3,3-dimethylallyl pyrophosphate (**29**), which is then alkylated at the oxygenated carbon atom by the nucleophile, isopentenyl pyrophosphate, to yield the allylic pyrophosphate ester (**30**, $n = 1$). Each subsequent alkylation of the allylic pyrophosphate (**30**) by isopentenyl pyrophosphate increases the chain length of (**30**) by one isoprenoid unit. The final condensation reaction in the biosynthesis of coenzyme Q is considered to be an electrophilic aromatic substitution on an as yet unknown dihydroquinone precursor (**31**) by the isoprenoid allylic pyrophosphate ester (**30**).[36] The intermediate condensation product (**32**) loses a proton and a shift of electrons occurs to yield the corresponding dihydrocoenzyme Q.

B. The Aromatic Ring

Administration of labeled lower homologs of the coenzyme Q group to rats, followed by chromatographic analysis of the coenzyme Q fraction of the liver, showed that the lower homologs of coenzyme Q are not converted to the higher homologs, but are either catabolized or excreted.[37]

34. F. Lynen, H. Eggerer, U. Henning, and I. Kessel, *Angew. Chem.*, *70*, 657 (1959).
35. F. Lynen, B. Agranoff, H. Eggerer, U. Henning, and E. M. Möslein, *Angew. Chem.*, *71*, 657 (1959).
36. F. Lynen, *J. Cellular Comp. Physiol.*, *54*, *Suppl. 1*, 33 (1959).
37. H. Rudney and T. Sugimura, in G. E. W. Wolstenholme and C. M. O'Connor, eds., *Ciba Foundation Symposium on Quinones in Electron Transport*, Churchill, London, 1961, p. 211.

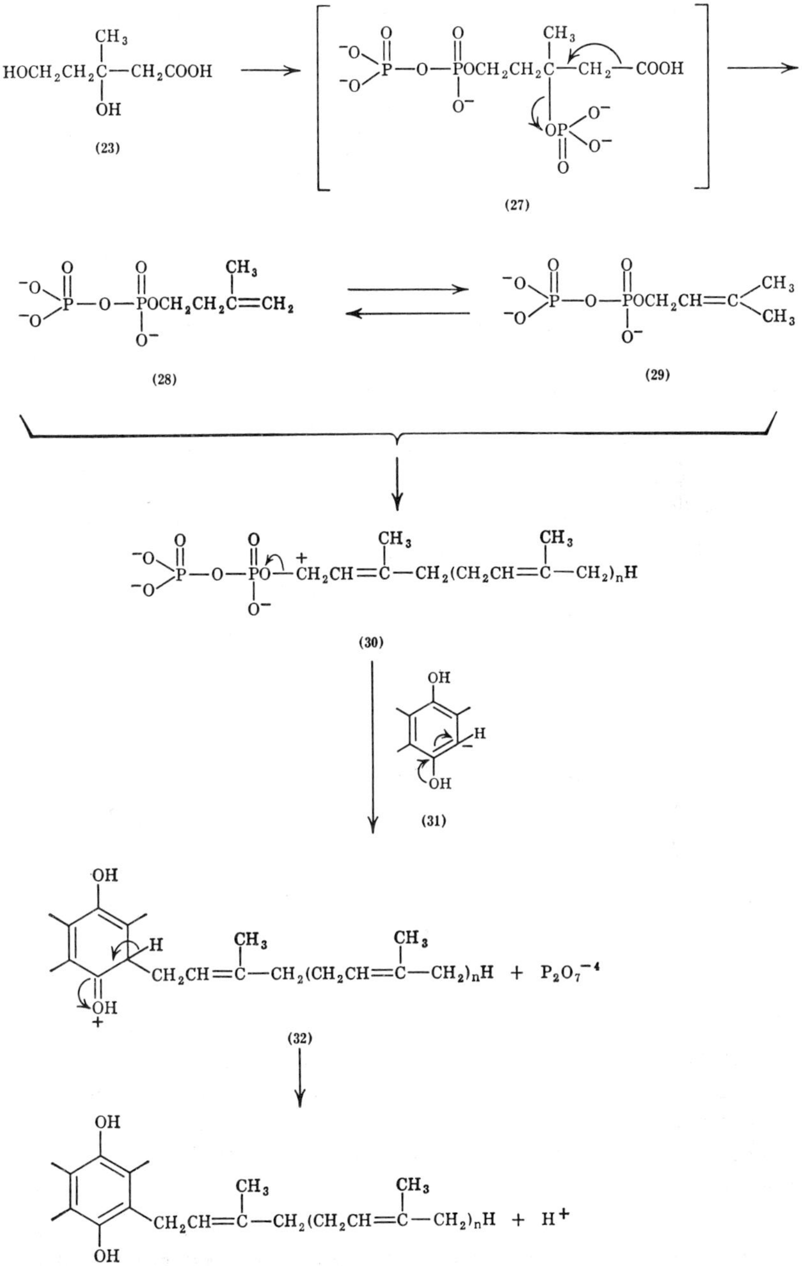

CH_3

$HOCH_2CH_2C-CH_2COOH$ $\longrightarrow$

OH

(23)

[O O CH_3

^{-}O P—O—$POCH_2CH_2C-CH_2-COOH$] $\longrightarrow$

^{-}O O^{-} O^{-}

OP

O^{-}

O]

(27)

O O CH_3

^{-}O P—O—$POCH_2CH_2C=CH_2$ $\rightleftarrows$ ^{-}O P—O—$POCH_2CH=C$ CH_3

^{-}O O^{-} ^{-}O O^{-} CH_3

(28) (29)

$\downarrow$

O O CH_3 CH_3

^{-}O P—O—PO—$\overset{+}{C}H_2CH=C-CH_2(CH_2CH=C-CH_2)_nH$

^{-}O O^{-}

(30)

$\downarrow$

OH

H

OH

(31)

OH

H CH_3 CH_3

$CH_2CH=C-CH_2(CH_2CH=C-CH_2)_nH + P_2O_7^{-4}$

OH

+

(32)

$\downarrow$

OH

CH_3 CH_3

$CH_2CH=C-CH_2(CH_2CH=C-CH_2)_nH + H^+$

OH

Fig. 4. Biosynthesis of coenzyme Q from mevalonate.[34–36]

Thus, all biosynthetic coenzymes Q appear to stem from the same aromatic precursor.

Some indication of the nature of the aromatic precursor in coenzyme Q biosynthesis was derived from studies with labeled formate.[37] When C^{14}-formate was injected into the rat intraperitoneally over a period of several days, the coenzyme Q_9 in the liver was radioactive. Methoxyl group analysis of the biosynthetically labeled coenzyme showed a substantial incorporation of radioactivity in these functional groups and demonstrated that formate participates directly in the biosynthesis through the one-carbon metabolic pool. *S*-Adenosyl methionine ("active methionine") is one of the mediators in one-carbon metabolism and participates as a methyl group donor in the *O*-methylation of catechol derivatives. Consequently, the observation on the direct incorporation of formate suggested the possible participation of a catechol-like precursor during coenzyme Q biosynthesis. Comparison of the rates of isotope incorporation in the biosynthesis of coenzyme Q from labeled formate and acetate revealed an initial lag in the biosynthesis from formate,[37] which was construed to suggest that the isoprenoid side chain precursor is condensed with the catechol-like precursor prior to the methylation reaction.

The biosynthesis of an aromatic compound is unknown in mammalian metabolism, so it was suggested that an aromatic dietary constituent such as phenylalanine (**33**) may serve as a precursor for the aromatic nucleus in the mammalian biosynthesis of coenzyme Q.[38] Support for this

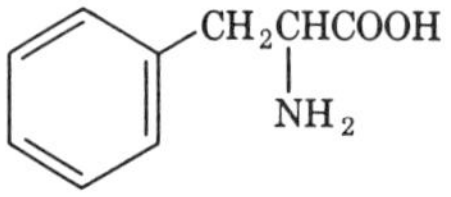

$CH_2CHCOOH$ / NH_2 (**33**)

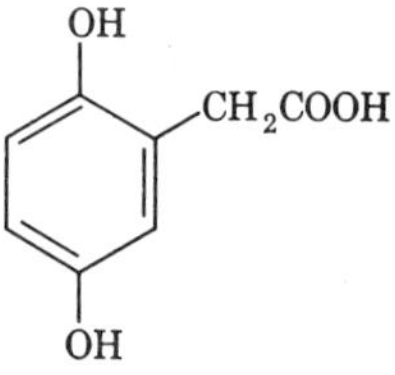

OH / CH_2COOH / OH (**34**)

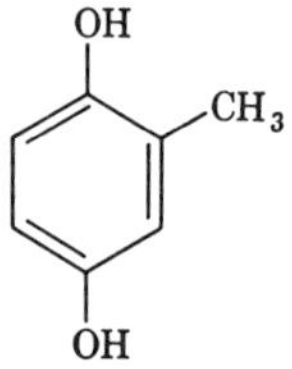

OH / CH_3 / OH (**35**)

possibility rested on the known biosynthetic pathway from phenylalanine to homogentisic acid (**34**); decarboxylation of the latter compound would yield 2-methyl-1,4-hydroquinone (**35**) which could be converted to an appropriate 2-methyl-1,4-benzoquinone precursor for biosynthesis. When uniformly labeled C^{14}-phenylalanine was administered to rats intraperitoneally, the coenzyme Q fraction from the liver was radioactive.[30]

38. R. E. Olson, H. Dialameh, and R. Bentley, in G. E. W. Wolstenholme and C. M. O'Connor, eds., *Ciba Foundation Symposium on Quinones in Electron Transport*, Churchill, London, 1961, p. 284.

However, this did not constitute evidence for the direct incorporation of isotope from phenylalanine since radioactivity could also be introduced as a result of side chain biosynthesis by way of the metabolic pathway—phenylalanine, acetoacetate, hydroxymethylglutarate, mevalonate, etc. In later experiments the coenzyme Q_9 biosynthesized from uniformly labeled phenylalanine was isolated and reductively acetylated.[39] Ozonolysis of this isotopically labeled intermediate, followed by oxidation with neutral potassium permanganate yielded isotopically labeled 3,6-diacetoxy-4,5-dimethoxy-2-methylphenylacetic acid and levulinaldehyde. Although the extent of incorporation of activity from uniformly labeled phenylalanine was low, it was predominantly in the aromatic moiety.

Another compound considered for the role of aromatic precursor in the biosynthesis of coenzyme Q is 2,3-dimethoxy-5-methyl-1,4-benzoquinone ("coenzyme Q_0"). In one investigation, a "uniformly labeled" sample of H^3-"coenzyme Q_0" was prepared by exposing "coenzyme Q_0" to tritium, and the labeled compound was administered to vitamin A-deficient rats.[29] The absence of radioactivity in the coenzyme Q fraction derived from the liver of these test animals appeared to constitute evidence that "coenzyme Q_0" is not a precursor for mammalian biosynthesis of the coenzyme Q group. "Randomly labeled" H^3-"coenzyme Q_0" prepared by exposure to tritium contains over 99% of the isotope in the 6-position.[40] Since a label at this position would be eliminated during the biosynthetic alkylation reaction, this labeled compound is not useful for such precursor studies.

In other studies, "coenzyme Q_0" was labeled with tritium in the 5-methyl substituent.[41,42] When this labeled intermediate was added to homogenates of the heart and liver from the chick and rat, tritium-labeled homologs of the coenzyme Q group were biosynthesized. On the basis of these enzymic studies, "coenzyme Q_0" can function as an aromatic precursor in a biosynthesis of members of the coenzyme Q group.

6. Ubichromenol(50)

A. Isolation

Two related substances provisionally designated SA and SC were isolated from the unsaponifiable fraction of liver of the vitamin A-deficient

39. R. Bentley, V. G. Ramsey, C. M. Springer, G. H. Dialameh, and R. E. Olson, *Biochem. Biophys. Res. Commun.*, *5*, 443 (1961).
40. A. F. Wagner, A. Lusi, and K. Folkers, *Arch. Biochem. Biophys.*, *101*, 316 (1963).
41. W. Stoffel and C. Martius, *Biochem. Z.*, *333*, 440 (1960).
42. H. G. Schiefer and C. Martius, *Biochem. Z.*, *333*, 454 (1960).

rat.[1] Both substances were present in the unsaponifiable fraction of liver from several mammalian species, but as relatively minor constituents. As shown in the preceding sections of this chapter, SA was identified as the forerunner of a group of naturally occurring benzoquinone derivatives which are designated as either the coenzyme Q or ubiquinone group. Progress toward elucidating the nature of the related substance SC was slower because of difficulty in obtaining a sufficient quantity of material for structural studies. The liver of the vitamin A-deficient rat and the kidney of the "normal human" yielded the substance, but even with these source materials, SC was obtained in a relatively minor yield from the unsaponifiable fraction.

Human kidney was chosen as the source material from which to obtain sufficient material for structural studies. To achieve this goal, about 100 lbs. of human renal tissue was saponified and extracted.[43] Cholesterol was separated from other components of the unsaponifiable fraction by precipitation, and the filtrate was further purified by chromatography on alumina. Selected fractions were subjected to a second chromatographic purification on alumina, and the fraction eluted with 10% ether in petroleum ether was further purified by chromatography on magnesia. The material eluted from the magnesia column by methylal was purified by crystallization from ethanol and yielded 153 mg. of a crystalline product that was eventually designated ubichromenol(50).[43]

B. Structure Determination

The structure of ubichromenol(50) was established as 2,5-dimethyl-7,8-dimethoxy-2-[{3-methyl-2-butenyl-*octakis*-(3-methyl-2-butenylene)}methyl] -3-chromen-6-ol (**36**) chiefly on the basis of spectral data.[43]

Elemental analysis of ubichromenol(50) showed that the compound has the same empirical composition as coenzyme Q_{10}. Molecular weight

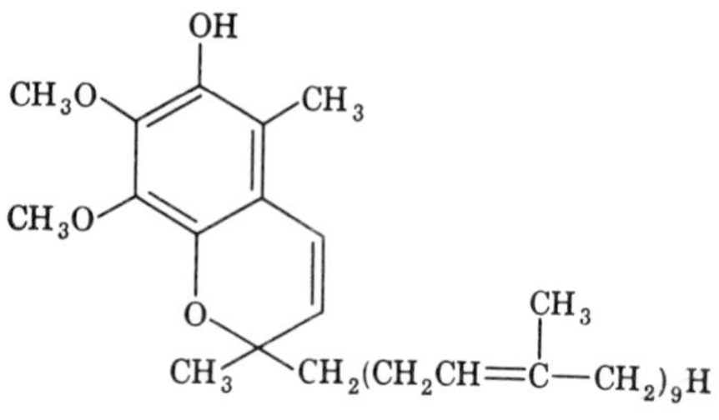

(**36**)

43. D. L. Laidman, R. A. Morton, J. Y. F. Paterson, and J. F. Pennock, *Chem. & Ind. (London)*, 1019 (1959); *Biochem. J.*, *74*, 541 (1960).

determinations were variable, but it was assumed that ubichromenol(50) was isomeric with ubiquinone(50).

The infrared absorption spectrum of ubichromenol(50) was characterized by absorption bands due to aromatic, hydroxyl, and unsaturated moieties. The intensity of absorption by ubichromenol(50) at 275 mμ and 283 mμ in the ultraviolet region of the spectrum was consistent with the presence of an aromatic ring and one double bond in conjugation with this ring. Hydrogenation studies indicated the presence of a large number of unsaturated centers in ubichromenol(50).

Two of the oxygen atoms of ubichromenol(50) were established in the form of methoxyl groups by analysis. One of the two remaining oxygen atoms was accounted for in an aromatic hydroxyl group by infrared and ultraviolet absorption spectroscopy. Ubichromenol(50) was converted to a monoacetate; the infrared absorption spectrum of this monoacetate was characterized by absorption due to an aromatic ester moiety and the absence of absorption associated with a hydroxyl function. The reversible shift of the ultraviolet absorption maximum of perhydro-ubichromenol(50) in the presence of alkali confirmed the aromatic nature of the hydroxyl function, and the presence of isosbestic points in a series of curves depicting the response of the ultraviolet absorption of the perhydro derivative to varying concentrations of base was cited as further evidence for the presence of only one hydroxyl group in ubichromenol(50).

The fourth oxygen atom of ubichromenol(50) was assigned as a substituent of the aromatic ring at the position *para* to the hydroxyl group on the basis of a maximum at 291 mμ in the ultraviolet absorption spectrum of ubichromenol(50) and an assumed close structural relationship between ubichromenol(50) and ubiquinone(50). The functional nature of the oxygen at this position was not established, although spectral data precluded its being a carbonyl or hydroxyl group.

The data summarized to this point suggested that ubichromenol(50) has a moiety consisting of an aromatic ring and one conjugated carbon-carbon double bond; the ring substituents include two methoxyl groups, a hydroxyl group, an oxygen atom at the position *para* to the hydroxyl group, and a polyunsaturated side chain. The nuclear magnetic resonance spectrum of ubichromenol(50) showed that in contrast to ubiquinone(50), the two methoxyl groups were not equivalent; in addition, nuclear magnetic resonance indicated the presence of nine isoprenoid units in the side chain and the presence of one hydrogen atom at each of two *ortho* carbon atoms of the ring system.

When the structure of ubichromenol(50) was formulated,[43] the ring system was designated as a chromenol. Confirmatory evidence for this

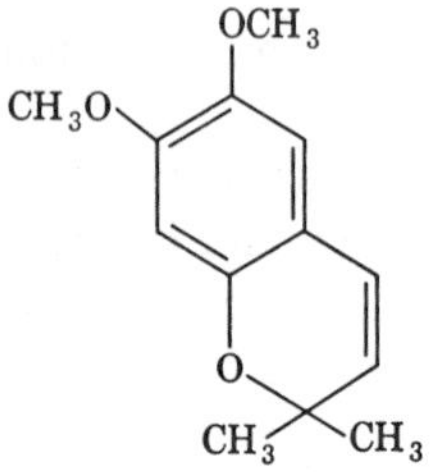

(37) 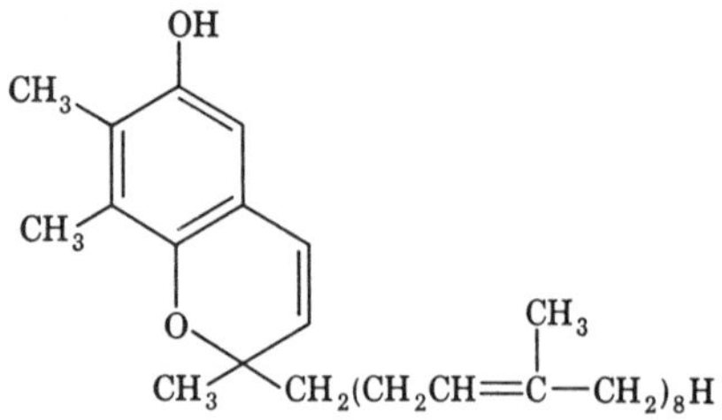 (38)

structure was obtained by comparing the spectral properties of ubichromenol(50) with those of the two known chromene derivatives ageratochromene (**37**)[44] and solanachromene (**38**),[45] which had been isolated from natural sources and structurally identified prior to the completion of the structural studies with ubichromenol(50).

C. Conversion of Ubiquinone(50) *to Ubichromenol*(50)

Ubiquinone(50) was converted to ubichromenol(50) by adsorption on alumina, followed by elution with acetone-10%hydrochloric acid.[46] Others studied the adsorption and elution of ubiquinone(50) on alumina columns and reported no conversion to the chromenol on elution with nonacidic solvents.[47] Furthermore, they suggested that the isoprenoid side chain was no longer intact in the chromenol that was obtained in low yield by the elution of adsorbed ubiquinone(50) from alumina with acidic solvents. A third group confirmed the earlier report and established the conversion of ubiquinone(50) (coenzyme Q_{10}) to ubichromenol(50) by adsorption on alumina, followed by elution with nonacidic solvents.[48] The nuclear magnetic resonance spectrum of the chromenol prepared in this manner was in accord with the accepted structure of ubichromenol(50).

D. Does Ubichromenol(50) *Occur in Naturę*

The conversion of ubiquinone(50) to ubichromenol(50) by chromatographic and alkaline treatment raised the question as to whether ubichromenol(50) is a naturally occurring substance or simply an artifact produced in the course of isolation.[46,48] Evidence to support the existence of

44. A. R. Alertsen, *Acta Chem. Scand.*, *9*, 1725 (1955).
45. R. L. Rowland, *J. Am. Chem. Soc.*, *80*, 6130 (1958).
46. J. Links, *Biochim. et Biophys. Acta*, *38*, 193 (1960).
47. J. Green, E. E. Edwin, A. T. Diplock, and D. McHale, *Biochem. Biophys. Res. Commun.*, *2*, 269 (1960).
48. C. H. Shunk, F. R. Koniuszy, E. L. Wong, N. R. Trenner, B. H. Arison, and K. Folkers, *Biochem. Biophys. Res. Commun.*, *3*, 228 (1960).

ubichromenol(50) as a natural component of the human kidney stemmed from the observation that the compound isolated from human kidney is optically active.[49] The compound prepared by the cyclization of ubiquinone(50) is racemic. Additional support for the natural occurrence of ubichromenol(50) was taken from data on yields observed in the conversion of ubiquinone(50) to ubichromenol(50) which appear to account for about 15% of the substance obtained from the human kidney.[50]

E. Synthesis of the 6-*Chromenols of the Coenzyme Q Group*

The 6-chromenol (**36**) was synthesized in good yield from coenzyme Q_{10} (**1**) by cyclization with sodium hydride (Fig. 5).[51] The cyclization reaction may be visualized as proceeding by the elimination of a proton from the 1-position of the isoprenoid side chain and the withdrawal of electrons to the carbonyl oxygen atom at the 4-position of the quinone moiety. The intermediate (**39**) is then stabilized by a shift of electrons and bond formation between the carbonyl oxygen atom at the 1-position of the quinone moiety and the carbon atom at the 3-position of the isoprenoid side chain to yield the oxyanion of the 6-chromenol (**40**). Protonation of this intermediate yields the chromencl (**36**) (ubichromenol(50)).

7. The 6-Chromanols of the Coenzyme Q Group

The 6-chromanols derived from the coenzyme Q group are markedly similar structurally to the tocopherols (Chapter XVIII). Of all the members, analogs, and derivatives of the coenzyme Q group, the 6-chromanols have provided to date the most provocative *in vivo* biological data bearing on a nutritional and metabolic role for the coenzyme Q group.

In early studies of coenzyme Q chemistry, reactions were studied which, on the basis of tocopherol chemistry, result in formation of a 6-chromanol moiety.[43,52] There was also evidence for secondary reactions leading to modification of the side chain by reduction or cyclization. The characterization of products was meager, and no firm structural conclusions

49. F. W. Hemming, R. A. Morton, and J. F. Pennock, *Biochem. J.*, *80*, 445 (1960).
50. F. W. Hemming, D. L. Laidman, R. A. Morton, and J. F. Pennock, *Biochem. Biophys. Res. Commun.*, *4*, 393 (1961).
51. B. O. Linn, C. H. Shunk, E. L. Wong, and K. Folkers, *J. Am. Chem. Soc.*, *85*, 239 (1963).
52. J. Bouman, E. C. Slater, H. Rudney, and J. Links, *Biochim. et Biophys. Acta*, *29*, 456 (1958).

CH_3O, CH_3O, O, O, CH_3, CH—H, CH, C, CH_3, CH_3, $CH_2(CH_2CH{=}C{-}CH_2)_9H$ **(1)** $\xrightarrow{NaH}$

O^-, CH_3O, CH_3O, O, CH_3, CH_3, CH_3, $CH_2(CH_2CH{=}C{-}CH_2)_9H$ **(39)** $\longrightarrow$

O^-, CH_3O, CH_3O, O, CH_3, CH_3, CH_3, $CH_2(CH_2CH{=}C{-}CH_2)_9H$ **(40)** $\xrightarrow{H^+}$

OH, CH_3O, CH_3O, O, CH_3, CH_3, CH_3, $CH_2(CH_2CH{=}C{-}CH_2)_9H$ **(36)**

Fig. 5. Conversion of coenzyme Q_{10} to ubichromenol by sodium hydride.[51]

could be made. In a detailed study of 6-chromanol synthesis from coenzyme Q_{10}, it was shown that treatment of coenzyme Q_{10} with excess stannous chloride in acetic acid resulted in the reduction of coenzyme Q_{10} to the corresponding hydroquinone, followed by cyclization to a 6-chromanol derivative.[53] However, other changes also took place since the nuclear magnetic resonance spectrum of the product showed that the isoprenoid side chain had been converted to a totally paraffinic structure. Since treatment of dihydrocoenzyme Q_{10} with stannic chloride also produced a product of similar nature, the side chain modification is a result of condensation rather than reduction of the isoprenoid side chain. The structure of the product of the over-all reaction has been depicted as (**41**). Evidence for the presence of less completely cyclized products was also obtained.

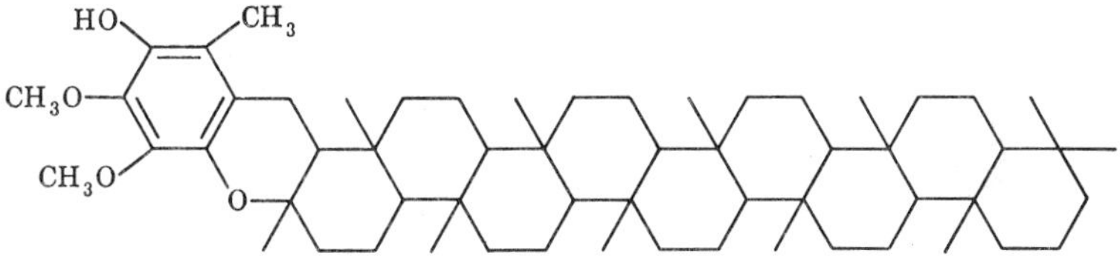

HO CH$_3$ CH$_3$O CH$_3$O O

(41)

Since early studies on the reductive cyclization of coenzyme Q_{10} to the corresponding 6-chromanol were complicated by the reactions of the isoprenoid side chain, hexahydrocoenzyme Q_4 was converted to the corresponding 6-chromanol, 7,8-dimethoxy-2,5-dimethyl-2-(4,8,12-trimethyltridecyl)-6-chromanol (**42**), by refluxing the quinone in acetic acid with

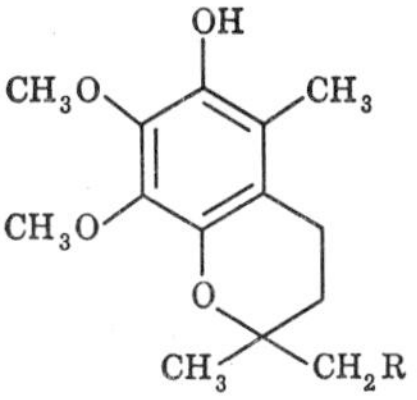

OH CH$_3$O CH$_3$ CH$_3$O O CH$_3$ CH$_2$R

$R{=}(CH_2CH_2\overset{CH_3}{\overset{|}{C}}HCH_2)_3H$

(42)

$R{=}(CH_2CH{=}\overset{CH_3}{\overset{|}{C}}{-}CH_2)_9H$

(43)

excess stannous chloride.[53] The reaction proceeded smoothly because the double bond of the phytyl side chain is properly located for the conversion to the 6-chromanol. Since there are no other centers of unsaturation in the isoprenoid side chain, other cyclization reactions are avoided. The chromanol (**42**) has served as a useful member of the coenzyme Q

53. C. H. Shunk, N. R. Trenner, C. H. Hoffman, D. E. Wolf, and K. Folkers, *Biochem. Biophys. Res. Commun.*, *2*, 427 (1960).

group in a variety of biological systems to elucidate the metabolic and nutritional role of the coenzyme Q group.

The 6-chromanol (**43**) of coenzyme Q_{10} has been synthesized from dihydrocoenzyme Q_{10}; the cyclization reaction was accomplished in acetic acid containing potassium bisulfate.[54]

8. Plastoquinone

The compound now known as plastoquinone was first isolated in pure form from alfalfa in 1946 and was described as a benzoquinone derivative melting at 48–49°.[55] About twelve years later a benzoquinone derivative tentatively designated "Q-254" was isolated from cauliflower and spinach mitochondria.[56] This product was identified as the same compound that was isolated twelve years earlier from alfalfa. Subsequent studies revealed that this quinone is widely distributed in chlorophyll-containing tissue.[57,58] The term plastoquinone was chosen to designate the compound in order to emphasize its localization in the plastid fraction of plant cells and to distinguish it from other members of the coenzyme Q group. In 1959 evidence was presented showing that plastoquinone functions in photosynthetic electron transport.[59] The wide distribution of plastoquinone in the plant kingdom, and the fact that it participates by an as yet unknown mechanism in the photochemical evolution of oxygen stimulated new interest in the nature of this new benzoquinone derivative.

The structure of plastoquinone was established as 2,3-dimethyl-5-[3-methyl-2-butenyl-*octakis*-(3-methyl-2-butenylene)]-1,4-benzoquinone (**44**)

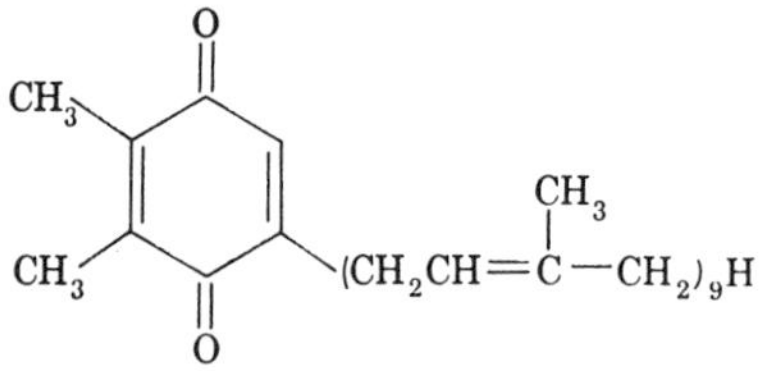

O, CH3, CH3, CH3, $(CH_2CH{=}C(CH_3){-}CH_2)_9H$, O

(44)

54. C. H. Hoffman, N. R. Trenner, D. E. Wolf, and K. Folkers, *J. Am. Chem. Soc.*, *82*, 4744 (1960).
55. M. Kofler, *Festschrift E. C. Barell*, Hoffman-LaRoche and Co. Ltd., Basle, 1946, p. 199.
56. F. L. Crane and R. L. Lester, *Plant Physiol.*, *33*, *Suppl. 7* (1958).
57. F. L. Crane, *Plant Physiol.*, *34*, 128 (1959).
58. R. L. Lester and F. L. Crane, *J. Biol. Chem.*, *234*, 2169 (1959).
59. N. I. Bishop, *Proc. Natl. Acad. Sci. U.S.*, *12*, 1696 (1959).

on the basis of nuclear magnetic resonance spectra and synthesis.[60,61] Preliminary evidence based on a color test with ethyl cyanoacetate (Craven's test) led to the erroneous assumption that plastoquinone was a fully substituted benzoquinone derivative.[55,62] Nuclear magnetic resonance studies, however, showed that plastoquinone was a trisubstituted benzoquinone with two adjacent methyl groups and a long isoprenoid side chain.[60] In the course of this investigation, 2,3-dimethyl-5-farnesylbenzoquinone was synthesized for comparative nuclear magnetic resonance studies. A critical quantitative comparison of the nuclear magnetic resonance spectra of plastoquinone and its side chain reduction product, 2,3-dimethyl-5-farnesylbenzoquinone and its side chain reduction product, and coenzyme Q_{10} led to the designation of plastoquinone as 2,3-dimethyl-5-[3-methyl-2-butenyl-*octakis*-(3-methyl-2-butenylene)]-1,4-benzoquinone. The molecular extinction coefficients of plastoquinone at 253 mμ and 261 mμ relative to those of 2,3-dimethyl-5-farnesylbenzoquinone were also in accord with the presence of a nine-isoprenoid unit side chain in plastoquinone.

Other structural studies suggested that the isoprenoid side chain of plastoquinone contained ten rather than nine isoprenoid units,[63,64] but the nine-isoprenoid unit side chain in plastoquinone was confirmed by the following synthesis.[61,65]

Solanesol, a polyisoprenol isolated from tobacco, was structurally identified as a polyisoprenol composed of nine isoprenoid units.[65] Early evidence had indicated that solanesol was composed of ten isoprenoid units, but the condensation of 2,3-dimethoxy-5-methylhydroquinone with solanesol yielded a product that was indistinguishable from coenzyme Q_9. On the basis of this observation and further structural investigation, solanesol was established as an isoprenol composed of nine rather than ten isoprenoid units. Condensation of 2,3-dimethylhydroquinone with solanesol in the presence of boron trifluoride etherate yielded 2,3-dimethyl-5-solanesyl-1,4-benzoquinone which was found to be identical with plastoquinone in respect to melting point, paper chromatography, ultraviolet, infrared, and nuclear magnetic resonance spectroscopy.[61]

60. N. R. Trenner, B. H. Arison, R. E. Erickson, C. H. Shunk, D. E. Wolf, and K. Folkers, *J. Am. Chem. Soc.*, *81*, 2026 (1959).
61. C. H. Shunk, R. E. Erickson, E. L. Wong, and K. Folkers, *J. Am. Chem. Soc.*, *81*, 5000 (1959).
62. F. L. Crane, *Plant Physiol.*, *34*, 546 (1959).
63. M. Kofler, A. Langemann, R. Rüegg, L. H. Chopard-dit-Jean, A. Rayroud, and O. Isler, *Helv. Chim. Acta*, *42*, 1283 (1959).
64. C. von Planta, E. Billeter, and M. Kofler, *Helv. Chim. Acta*, *42*, 1278 (1959).
65. R. E. Erickson, C. H. Shunk, N. R. Trenner, B. H. Arison, and K. Folkers, *J. Am. Chem. Soc.*, *81*, 4999 (1959).

9. Metabolic Studies

A. Oxidative Phosphorylation

Investigations to establish a role for coenzyme Q in the respiratory chain have dealt mainly with mitochondrial systems. A mitochondrion is a highly organized particle found in the cytoplasm of cells and has been depicted as an organization of interlocking enzymes, proteins, lipids, and other moieties that energetically couples the aerobic oxidation of certain substrates to the biosynthesis of adenosine triphosphate.[66] In the performance of this function, the mitochondrion has been visualized in terms of two segments:[66] (a) a group of dehydrogenation complexes, and (b) a particulate, structured segment known as the electron transport particle. The dehydrogenation complexes are associated with the electron transport particle and appear to be detachable from the latter by mechanical or chemical means.

In the mitochondrion, the reaction sequence of respiration proceeds from the dehydrogenation complexes through a DPN bridge to the electron transport particle; the latter is the mitochondrial fragment directly involved in coupled oxidative phosphorylation. The basic components of the electron transport chain in this particle consist of the two flavoproteins—succinic, and DPNH dehydrogenase, and the four hemoproteins—cytochrome *a*, *b*, c_1, and *c*. Coenzyme Q, nonheme iron, and copper are also present and participate in the interaction of the basic protein components with one another or in their interaction with molecular oxygen. The

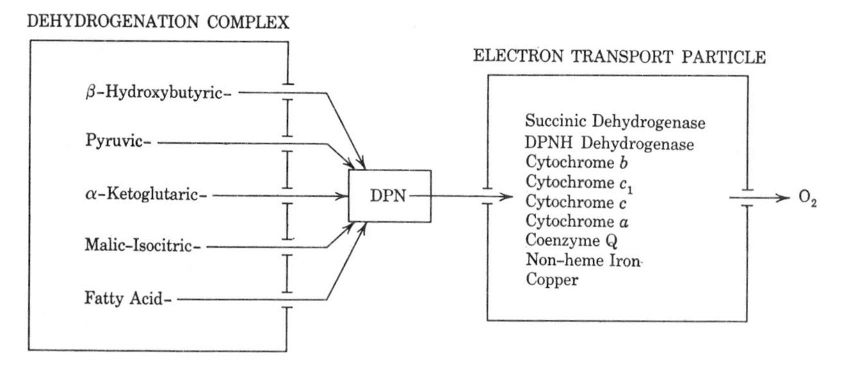

Fig. 6. Diagrammatic relationship between dehydrogenation complexes and electron transport particle in the mitochondrial unit.[66]

66. D. E. Green and T. Oda, *J. Biochem.* (*Japan*), *49*, 742 (1961).

relationship between the various dehydrogenating complexes and the electron transport particle in the mitochondrial unit has been depicted as in Fig. 6.[66]

Evidence that coenzyme Q may occupy a key position in the respiratory process of mitochondria consists of the following observations.

(a) Coenzyme Q_{10} is widely distributed in mitochondria derived from plant, animal, and microbial sources, and at a concentration of four to five times that of the individual cytochromes.[57,58]

(b) When mitochondria are extracted with acetone, they lose their capacity to oxidize succinate with molecular oxygen, but when coenzyme Q is added at catalytic levels, this capacity is restored.[67]

(c) The endogenous coenzyme Q of particles with an intact electron transport chain was reported to be oxidized and reduced at a rate compatible with the concept of coenzyme Q being a direct hydrogen carrier.[68] Later investigations indicate that the maximum rate of reduction of coenzyme Q_{10} cannot account for the rate of substrate oxidation by the enzyme.[69,70]

(d) Amytal, antimycin A, and cyanide were reported to disrupt the oxidation-reduction of endogenous coenzyme Q in a manner supporting a central position for coenzyme Q in the electron transport process.[71] Experimental re-examination of the effect of these inhibitors in mitochondrial systems shows that Amytal inhibits the reduction of coenzyme Q and that antimycin A and cyanide inhibit the oxidation of dihydrocoenzyme Q.[68,72]

One approach to establish the role and fix the position of coenzyme Q in the respiratory chain of mitochondria consisted of fractionating the electron transport component to yield subparticles or complexes. After the purification and characterization of the complexes, reconstitution of the electron transport system from its component parts was studied. The reconstitution procedure departs from the usual enzyme coupling techniques in that a water-soluble common intermediate is not used to establish contact between the components. Reconstitution is studied by mixing relatively concentrated solutions of the component particles; if reconstitution has been achieved, dilution of the reconstituted system

67. R. L. Lester and S. Fleischer, *Arch. Biochem. Biophys.*, *80*, 470 (1959).
68. D. E. Green, Y. Hatefi, and W. F. Fechner, *Biochem. Biophys. Res. Commun.*, *1*, 45 (1959).
69. E. R. Redfearn and A. M. Pumphrey, *Biochem. J.*, *76*, 64 (1960).
70. B. Chance and E. R. Redfearn, *Biochem. J.*, *80*, 632 (1961).
71. Y. Hatefi, R. L. Lester, F. L. Crane, and C. Widmer, *Biochim. et Biophys. Acta*, *31*, 490 (1959).
72. A. M. Pumphrey and E. R. Redfearn, *Biochem. J.*, 2*P* (1959).

should produce no tendency for dissociation, and the system should react as a functional entity. It has been assumed that the recombination of component particles takes place in a specific manner to yield a system with the structural and functional integrity of the parent system.

The segment of the mitochondrial respiratory chain catalyzing the reduction of cytochrome *c* by substrate has been fractionated under varying conditions to yield three distinct particles that have been designated DPNH-cytochrome *c* reductase,[73,74] succinic-cytochrome *c* reductase,[75] and succinic, DPNH-cytochrome *c* reductase.[76] These particles correspond to three possible fragments of the electron transport chain from succinate or DPNH to cytochrome *c*.

Further fractionation of the DPNH-cytochrome *c* reductase complex yielded a DPNH-coenzyme Q reductase and a dihydrocoenzyme Q-cytochrome *c* reductase.[77–79] The activity of DPNH-coenzyme Q reductase is inhibited by Amytal, Demerol, and *p*-chloromercuriphenylsulfonate, but not by antimycin A. The dihydrocoenzyme Q-cytochrome *c* reductase is inhibited by antimycin A, but not by Amytal.

Stepwise fractionation of the mitochondrial respiratory chain using another set of conditions yielded a succinic-coenzyme Q reductase complex of the succinic-cytochrome *c* reductase particle.[80]

From the three enzyme complexes—DPNH-coenzyme Q reductase, succinic-coenzyme Q reductase, and dihydrocoenzyme Q-cytochrome *c* reductase—it was considered possible to reconstitute the DPNH-cytochrome *c* reductase system, the succinic-cytochrome *c* reductase system, and the DPNH, succinic-cytochrome *c* reductase system by mixing the component enzyme complexes at high concentration. When this was done, the corresponding reconstituted systems were reported to be indistinguishable from the original systems which exist in mitochondria and derived particles.[77,81] Thus, the DPNH-cytochrome *c* reductase system was reconstituted from DPNH-coenzyme Q reductase and dihydrocoenzyme

73. Y. Hatefi, A. G. Haavik, and P. Jurtshuk, *Biochim. et Biophys. Acta*, *52*, 106 (1961).
74. Y. Hatefi, A. G. Haavik, and P. Jurtshuk, *Biochim. et Biophys. Acta*, *52*, 119 (1961).
75. D. E. Green and R. K. Burkhard, *Arch. Biochem. Biophys.*, *92*, 312 (1961).
76. M. Rabinowitz and B. de Bernard, *Biochim. et Biophys. Acta*, *26*, 22 (1957).
77. Y. Hatefi, A. G. Haavik, and D. E. Griffiths, *Biochem. Biophys. Res. Commun.*, *4*, 441 (1961).
78. Y. Hatefi, A. G. Haavik, and D. E. Griffiths, *J. Biol. Chem.*, *237*, 1676 (1962).
79. Y. Hatefi, A. G. Haavik, and D. E. Griffiths, *J. Biol. Chem.*, *237*, 1681 (1962).
80. D. M. Ziegler and K. A. Doeg, *Biochem. Biophys. Res. Commun.*, *1*, 344 (1959); *Arch. Biochem. Biophys.*, *97*, 41 (1962).
81. Y. Hatefi, A. G. Haavik, and D. E. Griffiths, *Biochem. Biophys. Res. Commun.*, *4*, 447 (1961).

Q-cytochrome *c* reductase. Similarly, the succinic-cytochrome *c* reductase system and DPNH, succinic-cytochrome *c* reductase system were reconstituted from their corresponding component enzyme complexes.

The electron transport system from substrate to oxygen operative in succinoxidase and DPNH oxidase may be divided into the following four enzyme complexes: DPNH-coenzyme Q reductase, succinic-coenzyme Q reductase, dihydrocoenzyme Q-cytochrome *c* reductase, and cytochrome *c* oxidase. The fourth complex, cytochrome *c* oxidase, was isolated earlier than the other three enzyme complexes.[82] More recently a cytochrome *c* oxidase of high specific activity and high spectral purity was isolated from beef heart mitochondria and characterized.[83] The constitution of enzyme complexes derivable from the terminal mitochondrial electron transport chain is summarized in Table II.

TABLE II

Enzyme Complex	Constituents
Succinic-coenzyme Q reductase	Succinate flavoprotein Nonheme iron Lipid Cytochrome *b*
DPNH-coenzyme Q reductase	DPNH flavoprotein Nonheme iron Lipid
Dihydrocoenzyme Q-cytochrome *c* reductase	Cytochrome *b* Cytochrome c_1 Nonheme iron Lipid
Cytochrome *c* oxidase	Cytochrome *a* Copper Lipid

On the basis of these data, coenzyme Q is considered to occupy a key position between the flavoproteins and the cytochromes in the respiratory system of mitochondria.[66] The reduction of endogenous coenzyme Q by succinate or DPNH and the oxidation of dihydrocoenzyme Q by oxygen was considered as evidence for the participation of coenzyme Q in the respiratory mechanism. The sensitivity of the oxidation of dihydrocoenzyme

82. B. de Bernard, *Biochim. et Biophys. Acta*, *23*, 510 (1957).
83. D. E. Griffiths and D. C. Wharton, *Biochem. Biophys. Res. Commun.*, *4*, 199 (1961).

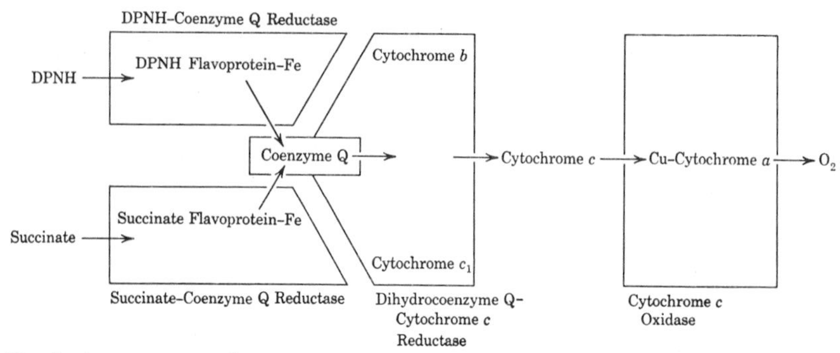

Fig. 7. Arrangement of component complexes of the mitochondrial electron transport chain.[66]

Q to antimycin A and the failure of antimycin A to inhibit the reduction of coenzyme Q was considered as evidence for placing the coenzyme between the flavoproteins and the cytochromes.[68,72] Other studies suggested that cytochrome *b* was not on the main pathway of electron transport, and coenzyme Q was placed between the flavoproteins and cytochrome c_1.[84] The arrangement between the four component complexes of the respiratory chain and coenzyme Q has been depicted in Fig. 7.[66]

Other investigators have studied the effect of coenzyme Q on the respiratory reactions of mitochondria or derived systems and have considered divergent interpretations.[85,86] For example, kinetic studies showed that the rate of reduction of endogenous coenzyme Q cannot account for the total substrate oxidized by the enzyme system.[69,70] It may be rationalized that since coenzyme Q is present in far higher concentration relative to other components of the respiratory chain, only a small percentage of the native quinone is required to achieve stoichiometry. Barring this point, the kinetic data constitute strong evidence that coenzyme Q does not mediate the reaction between flavoprotein and the cytochromes by way of the antimycin A-sensitive site. One may interpret the kinetic data as showing coenzyme Q to participate in a branch pathway between the flavoproteins and the antimycin A-sensitive site in the respiratory sequence.[85] In this sequence (Fig. 8), the flavoproteins are linked to the cytochromes by at least two pathways, one through coenzyme Q and the other through an unidentified antimycin A-sensitive factor. Additional

84. B. Chance, *J. Biol. Chem.*, *233*, 1223 (1958).
85. E. R. Redfearn, in G. E. W. Wolstenholme and C. M. O'Connor, eds., *Ciba Foundation Symposium on Quinones in Electron Transport*, Churchill, London, 1961, p. 346.
86. B. Chance, in G. E. W. Wolstenholme and C. M. O'Connor, eds., *Ciba Foundation Symposium on Quinones in Electron Transport*, Churchill, London, 1961, p. 327.

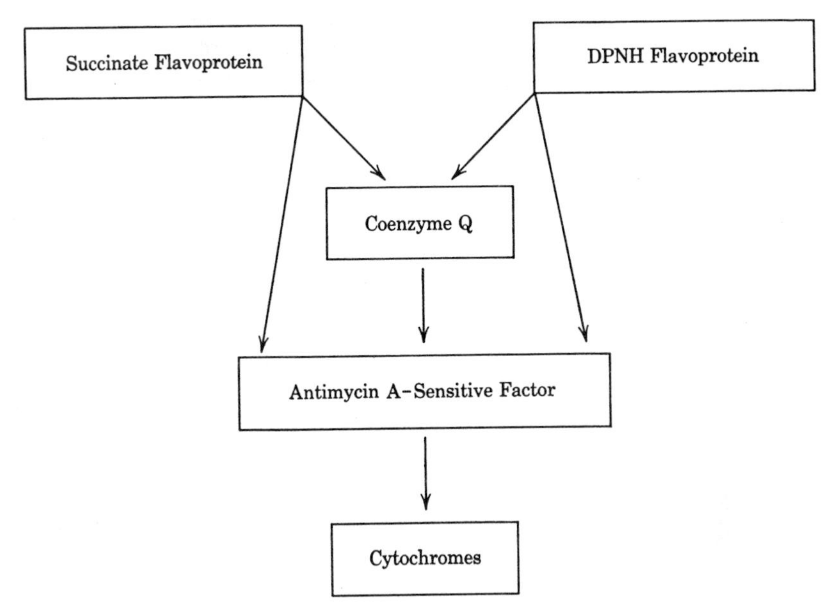

Fig. 8. Role of coenzyme Q in a branch pathway sequence of mitochondrial respiration.[85]

evidence for this concept rests on the partial inhibition of a DPNH-fumarate system by antimycin A.[85]

It has also been suggested that the respiratory reactions in fractionated and reconstituted mitochondrial systems are sufficiently altered from the reactions in the native particle, so a direct carry-over of observations from these systems to the sequence of electron transfer in the intact mitochondrion may be questionable.[86] To circumvent this uncertainty, spectrophotometric methods were devised to study the kinetics of oxidation and reduction and to establish the steady state concentrations of the respiratory pigments in intact mitochondria.[87] When this method was used with intact phosphorylating mitochondria, the kinetics of reduction showed that coenzyme Q does not function on the main pathway of electron transfer in the intact mitochondrion.[70] On the basis of similarity in the rates of reduction of DPN and coenzyme Q and a discrepancy between these reduction rates and the rate of reduction of oxygen, it was concluded that most of the endogenous coenzyme Q is on a branch path of the electron transport chain in the intact mitochondrion.

87. B. Chance and G. R. Williams, *Nature*, *176*, 250 (1955); *J. Biol. Chem.*, *217*, 409 (1955).

B. Other Metabolic Processes

Coenzyme Q_{10} is a natural component of the internal electron transport system of rabbit liver aldehyde oxidase.[88] This protein, which is found only in the soluble fraction of a rabbit liver homogenate, is apparently derived from the cytoplasm and is the first purified water-soluble enzyme in which a coenzyme Q functions as an integral part of the internal electron transport chain.

The hepatic oxidase in the supernatant fraction of a rabbit liver homogenate was purified 400-fold, and the purified enzyme was found to contain two molecules of flavine-adenine dinucleotide, eight atoms of iron, two atoms of molybdenum, and two molecules of coenzyme Q_{10} per molecule of protein. The presence of coenzyme Q_{10} was established by the following observations.

(a) A maximum is present at 275 mμ in the ultraviolet absorption spectrum of the enzyme.

(b) The enzyme is inhibited by Amytal and antimycin A, which were previously known to inhibit the reduction of coenzyme Q_{10} and the oxidation of dihydrocoenzyme Q_{10}, respectively, in mitochondrial electron transport.

(c) The enzyme is inhibited by Triton X-100, which is used for the dispersion of coenzyme Q_{10} in aqueous media.

(d) Coenzyme Q_{10} was identified chromatographically and spectrophotometrically in extracts from an aqueous solution or a lyophilized sample of the enzyme.

The purified enzyme catalyzes the oxidation of formaldehyde, acetaldehyde, salicylaldehyde, and pyridoxal and the hydroxylation of quinine, quinoline, and N^1-methylnicotinamide. Oxygen, cytochrome *c*, ferricyanide, methylene blue, 2,6-dichlorophenolindophenol, and phenazine methosulfate function as electron acceptors. In the absence of a conventional oxidizable substrate, phenazine methosulfate is oxidized by the hepatic oxidase;[89] the oxidation product is apparently 10-methylphenazin-3-one. This observation may signify the presence of a similar enzyme system in photophosphorylation systems since phenazine methosulfate is also oxidized by microbial preparations capable of photosynthesis.

The concentration of cytochromes and coenzyme Q is high in brown adipose tissue.[90] In the rat, the cytochrome *c* content of this tissue is as

88. K. V. Rajagopalan, I. Fridovich, and P. Handler, *Federation Proc.*, *20*, 42 (1961); *J. Biol. Chem.*, *237*, 922 (1962).
89. K. V. Rajagopalan and P. Handler, *Biochem. Biophys. Res. Commun.*, *8*, 43 (1962).
90. C. D. Joel and E. G. Ball, *Federation Proc.*, *19*, 32 (1960); *Biochemistry*, *1*, 281 (1962).

high as that reported for any tissue and is compatible with the high rate of oxygen consumption by this tissue; the molar concentration of coenzyme Q_9 in the same tissue is 6-fold that of cytochrome *c*. Brown adipose tissue is most abundant in hibernating animals and is a subject of current interest on the basis of its possible role in the hibernating animal, its preferential invasion by a variety of viruses, and the possibility that it functions as a site for the storage and multiplication of viruses.

10. Nutritional and Therapeutic Studies

A. In Animals

Dietary components such as whole soybean, Drackett protein, corn oil, and wheat germ oil contain significant quantities of coenzyme Q_{10}.[91] In view of this observation, it was suggested that certain early nutritional data be re-examined since such dietary components were used extensively in the animal studies.

Coenzyme Q_{10} did not prevent the gestation-resorption syndrome in the tocopherol-deficient rat. The 6-chromanol of hexahydrocoenzyme Q_4 prevented the gestation-resorption syndrome and permitted the birth of live young.[92]

The 6-chromanol of hexahydrocoenzyme Q_4 produced a significant response in the tocopherol-deficient Rhesus monkey being maintained on a special cooked diet for periods up to eighteen months (see Chapter XVIII).[93] Treatment of the anemic and dystrophic monkey with the 6-chromanol of hexahydrocoenzyme Q_4 produced an unequivocally favorable clinical response which was characterized by a prompt reticulocyte response followed by a consistent rise in hemoglobin. The excretion of creatine was sharply reduced, and the dystrophic symptoms improved noticeably within a few days. Such complete remission has not been observed previously without specific therapy with α-tocopherol. Consequently, the following questions arise.

(a) Are both tocopherol and the 6-chromanol of hexahydrocoenzyme Q_4 exhibiting a basic biological activity in a native biochemical sequence?

91. A. C. Page, Jr., P. H. Gale, F. Koniuszy, and K. Folkers, *Arch. Biochem. Biophys.*, *85*, 474 (1959).
92. J. L. Smith, H. N. Bhagavan, R. Bleiler Hill, S. Gaetani, P. B. Rama Rao, Q. E. Crider, B. C. Johnson, C. H. Shunk, A. F. Wagner, and K. Folkers, *Arch. Biochem. Biophys.*, *101*, 388 (1963).
93. J. S. Dinning, C. D. Fitch, C. H. Shunk, and K. Folkers, *J. Am. Chem. Soc.*, *84*, 2007 (1962).

(b) Is only one of the two compounds exhibiting a basic biological activity and the other substituting solely on the basis of similarity of structure?

(c) Does one compound simply protect the other because of its antioxidant properties?

Compounds of the coenzyme Q group are active in maintaining the motility of chicken sperm cells.[94] Of the compounds reported, the 6-chromanol of hexahydrocoenzyme Q_4 has shown impressive activity and with consistency.

B. In the Human

The liver, heart, spleen, kidney, pancreas, and adrenals of the human contain relatively high concentrations of coenzyme Q_{10}, and the total body content of coenzyme Q_{10} was estimated to be in the range of 0.5–1.5 g.[95]

Coenzyme Q_{10} was isolated from normal human urine,[96] and the coenzyme Q_{10} content of urine specimens from patients having diabetes mellitus and also for some of these cases atherosclerotic heart disease have been determined.[97] With diabetic patients, no apparent correlation could be made between the urinary excretion of coenzyme Q_{10} and the state of diabetic control, type of management, or insulin requirement.

Coenzyme Q_{10} is widely distributed in the plant and animal kingdom. Among the best sources of the compound are the heart, liver, and kidney of animals and the leaves and seeds of plants.

94. A. C. Page, Jr., M. C. Smith, P. H. Gale, D. Polin, and K. Folkers, *Biochem. Biophys. Res. Commun.*, *6*, 141 (1961).
95. P. H. Gale, F. R. Koniuszy, A. C. Page, Jr., K. Folkers, and H. Siegel, *Arch. Biochem. Biophys.*, *93*, 211 (1961).
96. F. R. Koniuszy, P. H. Gale, A. C. Page, Jr., and K. Folkers, *Arch. Biochem. Biophys.*, *87*, 298 (1960).
97. S. S. Bergen, F. R. Koniuszy, A. C. Page, Jr., and K. Folkers, *Arch. Biochem. Biophys.*, *95*, 348 (1961).

Author Index

C

G

H

L

M

Q

R

S

T

Y

Z

Subject Index

C

D

E

G

H

I

K

O

Q

R

S

W

X

Y

Z